# The Cell Cycle in Malignancy and Immunity

Proceedings of the Thirteenth Annual
Hanford Biology Symposium at 13th, Richland, Wash, 1973
Richland, Washington, October 1—3, 1973

Sponsored by
Battelle Pacific Northwest Laboratories
and
U. S. Atomic Energy Commission

James C. Hampton
Chairman

1975

Published by
Technical Information Center
Office of Public Affairs
U. S. Energy Research and Development Administration

Available as CONF-731005 for $13.60 from

National Technical Information Service
U. S. Department of Commerce
Springfield, Virginia 22161


International Standard Book Number 0-87079-016-6
Library of Congress Catalog Card Number 74-600181
ERDA Distribution Category UC-48

Printed in the United States of America
USERDA Technical Information Center, Oak Ridge, Tennessee

January 1975

# PREFACE

Many agents have been shown to induce tumors, or at least to be associated with tumor induction. As we learn to eliminate some of these agents from the environment, the incidence of tumors, particularly malignancies, should eventually begin to decrease. The more immediate need is the detection and treatment of cancer in the existing population, and it is to this problem that this symposium has addressed itself. Surgery, radiation, and chemotherapeutic agents are reasonably effective and along with immunotherapy hold much promise. Implicit in the concept of cancer control is an increased awareness and understanding of the biology of cancers if a more sound rationale for therapy is to be forthcoming. Tumor growth and treatment relate directly to the life cycles of tumor-cell populations and, as such, to points in the cell cycle where therapeutic agents, individually and in combination, can be most effective. The papers comprising this volume illustrate the kind of innovative approaches necessary to solve the problem and point the way to more effective treatment of a dreaded and deadly disease.

It is a pleasure to acknowledge the splendid contributions of the authors and participants and to offer special thanks to Judith A. Harrison, symposium secretary, to Glen Horstman and the local arrangements committee, and to W. F. Simpson, Technical Information Center, U. S. Atomic Energy Commission, Oak Ridge, Tennessee, who edited the papers and managed publication of the proceedings.

*J. C. Hampton*
Chairman

# CONTENTS

# MOLECULAR MANIFESTATIONS
# OF THE CELLULAR CLOCK

ROBERT R. KLEVECZ
Department of Cell Biology, Division of Biology, City of Hope National Medical
Center, Duarte, California

## ABSTRACT

Control by negative feedback is a common feature of many regulatory processes operating at different levels of organization in biological systems. An inherent property of such systems is a tendency for the components to oscillate. Cells can respond to the information stored in DNA through its transcription into RNA and translation into functional proteins. These macromolecules can in turn respond to the information inherent in a population of small molecules whose concentration changes with time. In all likelihood, timing of cell division and the occurrence of distinct cellular events is the end product of a large series of coupled oscillations in populations of large and small molecules.

## INTRODUCTION

If one could choose an ideal mammalian cell system, it would not be one in which the cells were growing at random and were therefore of mixed age and chemical composition. Interpretation of experimental results and the consequences of manipulation are greatly complicated when random cell populations are used since all processes and products are exponential functions and the concentration of any cellular component is an age-averaged value. Often in the past, synchrony studies and results from cell-cycle work have not been considered to apply to general questions of regulation in cells when, in fact, it can be argued that control processes can properly be studied only in biochemically uniform cell populations.

Early theories of cell division focused on mitosis, which is understandable in view of the inaccessibility of intermitosis to analysis by the techniques of the day. To the cytologists of the late 19*th* and early 20*th* centuries, the growth that went on between one cell division and the next was incidental to the regulatory event that occurred when the cell divided; to them it was a question of the

1

mechanism of mitosis rather than the timing of cellular events. Generally, early theories regarding the control of cell division were what we might term single-cause hypotheses[1] and involved a search for a division protein or trigger.[2] Such ideas now seem simplistic in view of the obvious coupling of many parallel pathways leading to cell division;[3] moreover, they attribute causal properties to events that may only be correlates of cell division. In the words of Erwin Bünning,[4] they "confuse the hands with the clock."

## FEEDBACK REPRESSION AND TEMPORAL ORDER IN THE CELL CYCLE

Separating the timing of cell-cycle events and cell division from the control of gene expression and differentiation is difficult. Progress through a single cell cycle represents a process of differentiation in the sense that there are a sequentially changing ensemble of proteins and a point or points at which the cell must review its environment and constituents and decide whether to enter another replicative round or to assume a nonreplicative state. Having committed itself to another round of DNA replication, it must then determine anew in the course of replicating its DNA which genes are to be transcribed and which are to remain quiescent. We shall consider how a cell such as fibroblast chooses among these alternatives.

According to the equations developed by Goodwin,[5,6] there are two possible states for any cellular component, oscillatory and nonoscillatory, and Rubin and Sitgreaves[7] have argued that the more complex an interacting dynamic system is, the more likely are its components to oscillate. Goodwin has pointed out[8] that, if cells maintained steady-state conditions and if their many components had constant specific activities through the cell cycle, then such cells would be homogeneous in time. A decision to divide could be made only on the basis of one of a limited number of general characteristics, such as surface-to-volume ratio, and could only provide a very coarse mechanism of control over cellular events.

Negative feedback is a common feature of many regulatory processes operating at different levels of organization in biological systems, and an inherent property of such systems is a tendency for the components to oscillate.[9] Macromolecules can respond to the information inherent in a population of ligands whose concentration changes with time,[10] but whether it is also necessary for the concentration of macromolecules to oscillate in order for the system to endure in an undamped fashion is not yet clear. It is attractive to speculate that, in the course of evolution, cells and organisms have exploited the oscillatory properties of negative feedback to develop an efficient timekeeping mechanism when timekeeping is important and have found the means to damp out such periodicities when they are injurious. Sizeable fluctuations in the concentration of certain key metabolites or macromolecules could then function as a switching signal. Given that periodicities in metabolic and macromolecular components can form the basis of an elegant timekeeping mechanism, is there in fact any evidence that such fluctuations do occur?

At the cellular level, the most common examples of periodicities are the circadian rhythms[11-13] although Chance, Estabrook, and Ghosh[14] have observed high-frequency oscillations in the level of reduced pyridine nucleotide in intact yeast cell suspensions.

## Oscillatory Repression of Enzymes in the Protista

In prokaryotes and in some unicellular eucaryotes, the genome is available for transcription at all points in the cell cycle.[15-18] On replication of a particular gene, there is a clear dosage effect expressed as a doubling in potential for enzyme synthesis.[19] In completely repressed and fully induced or derepressed genes, enzyme synthesis is continuous through the cycle. In normally growing cells subject to control by negative feedback, synthesis is autogenous, and enzymes are made periodically, often, but not rigorously, in register with their location and time of replication on the bacterial chromosome.[20,21] In its simplest form[19] the feedback repression model predicts that the concentration of end products or catabolites of particular genes will vary depending on the concentration of enzyme and that together the components of the system will oscillate out of phase. Support for this prediction has recently been provided by Molloy and Schmidt.[22] Goodwin[6] amplified this model by suggesting that periodic enzyme synthesis is entrained to DNA replication by a burst in messenger synthesis. Substance is given to this by Geiduschek,[23] who finds that transcription of T-4 late genes requires the presence of a replicating fork or nick to occur effectively. The coupling between DNA replication, transcription, and expression of gene products displays considerable inertia since autogenous peaks in enzyme synthesis occur throughout the cycle even though DNA replication is inhibited.[21]

A question immediately arises whether such simple feedback loops would all have the same dynamic properties and in particular if they would display maxima at one-generation intervals. Griffith[24] has argued that sustained oscillations of the sort envisaged originally, involving the interaction of the gene, one enzyme, and its metabolites, are unlikely and that only by introducing additional steps in the control circuit can such periodicities be generated.[24]

## Linear Reading in the Lower Eucaryotes

In *Saccharomyces cerevisiae* many enzymes display periodic behavior, and induction or repression may alter the amount of enzyme synthesized but not the time of synthesis.[25] Halvorson[26] has suggested that transcription of particular genes is restricted to limited portions of the cycle and occurs sequentially along each linkage unit. It is not restricted to S phase. Consequently entrainment of enzyme synthesis to DNA replication is not a tenable component of this model in its simplest form although multiple peaks in synthesis entrained to, but not directly dependent on, DNA replication can be envisioned. Unfortunately, this model is awkward when applied to mammalian systems. All the enzymes examined in our laboratory display multiple[27] peaks in activity. In particular, glucose-6 phosphate dehydrogenase (G6PD) activity in both Chinese hamster[28] and human diploid cells displays three peaks. A strict interpretation of the linear reading model would require three distinct genes for each of these enzymes, all residing in different replicating units. Although such an arrangement is not impossible to imagine, the rationale for maintaining this state is hard to develop. In addition, contradictory evidence exists, since G6PD, which displays three peaks in activity, exists as a single gene locus in mammals.[29] Moreover, many enzymes in V79 display two peaks in activity (Fig. 1) of somewhat reduced amplitude relative to Don C and WI-38, where three peaks in lactate dehydrogenase (LDH) activity are detectable (Figs. 2 and 3). It seems very unlikely that all enzymes in Don, Don C, and WI-38 cells would have the same number of loci and even more unlikely that such chromosome rearrangements and changes in morphology as have occurred in V79 could account for the simultaneous loss of one of each of the enzyme loci.

A more significant objection to linear reading in mammals is the fact that synthesis of new LDH occurs in an oscillatory fashion in the presence[30] of actinomycin D, indicating that controls other than, or in addition to, transcription are operative.

## PERIODIC GENE EXPRESSION IN MAMMALIAN CELLS

### Patterns of Marker Enzyme Activity

In attempting to define the conditions under which enzyme synthesis is periodic in mammalian cells and to assess the generality of oscillatory changes in activity, we need to examine a number of cell types and a variety of enzymes. Two major parameters will be presented for purposes of comparison: DNA synthetic rate as assayed by incorporation of tritiated thymidine and the activity of several enzymes involved in glucose metabolism. The rationale for using these enzymes as cell-cycle markers and general indicators of the mode of synthesis in the cell cycle can be elaborated as follows. Some proteins, such as histones, are more directly and intimately coupled to the replicative and division processes of the cell and may reasonably be expected to be synthesized in a restricted portion of the cell cycle[31] without revealing much regarding the general mode of enzyme regulation and timekeeping in eucaryotic cells. On the other hand, such proteins as LDH are only remotely connected with cell division and consequently, if synthesized in a periodic fashion, may tell us a great deal about the control mechanisms involved. In this section we will summarize our work comparing glycolytic, respiratory, catabolic, and biosynthetic enzyme activity patterns in heteroploid[32] G3, heteroploid Don, cloned aneuploid[27,33] V79, the uncloned parent[27] V79, pseudodiploid[28] Don C and diploid Don[32] Chinese hamster lines, and the human fibroblast WI-38 line.[34] This work was performed in our laboratory during the past 5 years. In each instance the results from other laboratories will be compared. Hopefully, a consistent description of enzyme activity patterns will emerge.

We chose as our model of a heteroploid cell the Chinese hamster lines G3 and heteroploid Don in which approximately 60% of the cells have the modal chromosome complement of 23. The remainder of the cells have between 19 and 46 chromosomes. The generation times in these cells are 14 and 11 hr, respectively. When synchronized by colcemid-enhanced mitotic selection, G3 displayed a more or less continuous increase in LDH content.[32] The DNA synthetic rate in these cells is a unimodal function with the maximum rate occurring between 5 and 9 hr. In other laboratories this pattern has been observed for several glycolytic enzymes[35] in KB cells in suspension, for pyroline-5 carboxylase[36] in HeLa, and for thymidine kinase and thymidine phosphokinase in HeLa cell monolayers.[37] However, with regard to the latter, Brent[38] recently repeated his earlier work and observed marginal intracyclic periodicities. Scharff and Robbins[39] reported this type of curve for the rate of protein and RNA synthesis in HeLa cells. In the following section we will discuss the effects of population heterogeneity on the detection of oscillations. The question that immediately occurs is whether this synthetic pattern is expressed by each member of the population or whether it represents the average of a variety of different patterns.

To test these alternatives, we cloned a second cell line, V79, which has since been widely used in synchrony studies. The cell line is extremely uniform, and greater than 95% of the cells have the same chromosome number. In V79, $^3$H−TdR incorporation is a unimodal function of time, but the rise and fall in rate of incorporation occurs sharply (Fig. 1). Adding a further complication to this story is the fact that DNA content assayed fluorometrically shows fairly sharp discontinuities,[40] more in keeping with the thymidine-incorporation pattern observed in WI-38.[34] A discussion of possible reasons for this has been presented elsewhere.[40] Glycolytic enzymes in the cloned line display a two-peaked pattern, with one maximum occurring in late $G_1$ or early S and a second maximum in late S or $G_2$. The decrease in glycolytic enzyme activity occurs in early S phase at the time when the DNA synthetic rate is increasing. This correlation has been noted previously in this cell for glycolytic enzymes[33] and microtubule protein[34] and in diploid Chinese hamster cells for glycolytic enzymes.[32] This two-peaked pattern has been observed for acid phosphatase[42] in L5178Y, for alkaline phosphatase and alkaline DNase in HeLa,[43] for thymidine kinase in L cells,[44] and for the total RNA synthesis rate in HeLa cells and L cells.[45,46] Not all enzymes display maximums at the same times, and not all proteins show two clear peaks in synthesis. Serine dehydratase (SD), a catabolic enzyme, is almost perfectly out of phase with the glycolytic

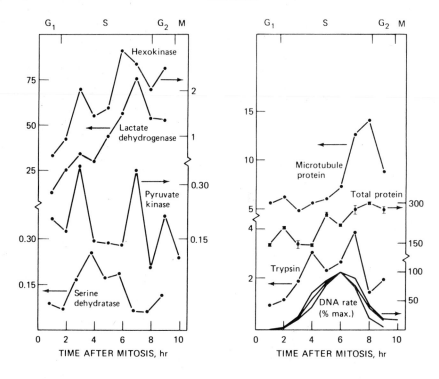

**Fig. 1  Enzyme activity patterns in the cloned aneuploid fibroblast V79. Cells were brought into a synchronous state by repeated selection and automated detachment and dispensing of mitotic cells from roller bottles.[33] Thymidine—methyl—[3]H (specific activity, 6.7 Ci/mmole or 50.3 Ci/mmole) labelling and acid extraction were performed on monolayers growing in scintillation vials as described previously.[40] Following synchronization, the cells were distributed into Falcon plastic flasks or glass scintillation vials; and enzyme activity,[28,33,71,72] microtubule colchicine-binding activity,[41] and total protein[65] were determined.**

enzymes, suggesting that intermediary metabolism may be temporally as well as spacially compartmentalized. A pattern similar to that of SD is also found for trypsin-like activity (Fig. 1). In the uncloned parent V79 line, we found that peaks in activity were much less distinct, demonstrating in the most direct way possible that detection of periodicities requires a homogeneous population. The V79-9 has been synchronized using the cell-cycle analyzer to detach mitotic cells, by colcemid-enhanced mitotic selection, and by high thymidine to arrest cells at the $G_1/S$ boundary. All three methods give identical results.

A more complex pattern was obtained originally using the pseudodiploid Don C[28] cell line that displays the same morphology and growth characteristics as the diploid parent. Distinct peaks in LDH activity occur at 3, 7, and 10 hr after mitosis (Fig. 2). Here, the results are presented as activity per culture and cells per culture for a cell cycle and a half following synchronization. The periodicity in LDH activity endures and can be detected into the second S phase, giving greater confidence that an endogenous process is involved as opposed to a perturbation resulting from the synchronization procedure. The two $G_1$- and S-phase activity peaks are separated by an interval equal to the generation time of the cells, and the peak activity per cell is similar in the first and second cycles. The activity pattern differs from that in V79 by having an additional mid-S phase peak. Similar patterns have been observed for total nuclear protein synthesis in CMP cells,[47] for $\kappa$-chain immunoglobulin synthesis in lymphoid cells,[48] and for thymidylate synthetase activity[49] in Don C.

Chinese hamster cells often acquire the ability of growing in culture indefinitely without undergoing an obvious phase III crisis. Consequently the distinction between an established cell line and one which has been grown in culture for some time but which is not yet significantly different from a primary explant is difficult to make. For this reason it seemed especially desirable to examine the cell cycle of the human-diploid-fibroblast line WI-38, which has become to many the model of a "normal" fibroblastic cell.

The LDH activity in WI-38 behaves in the expected manner and displays very distinct oscillations in activity (Fig. 3). There is a maximum in $G_1$ before any detectable DNA synthesis, a second maximum in mid-S phase just prior to the bulk of DNA synthesis, and a third that occurs as DNA synthesis is ceasing in late S or $G_2$.

The activities of three additional enzymes, G6PD, SD, and pyruvate kinase (PK), were observed as a function of cell-cycle position (Fig. 3). For PK four peaks are apparent, the first three occurring at 4, 9, and 13 to 14 hr. The fourth peak occurred at 16 hr. The bottom figure shows the average of two independent experiments with standard errors.

Pyruvate kinase gave a pattern in WI-38 similar to that found in V79 (Fig. 1), which has two very prominent peaks, one in late $G_1$ or early S and the second approximately at the $S-G_2$ boundary. However, the two smaller peaks during S in WI-38 are not observable in V79, perhaps owing to the shorter generation time and consequent loss of some temporal structure.

In V79 (Fig. 1) SDH activity roughly parallels DNA synthesis. This was also found to be true in WI-38. Figure 3 shows the cell-cycle pattern of SDH in the WI-38 cell cycle. Peaks are apparent at 5, 8 to 9, and 11 hr, with a smaller peak at 15 to 16 hr; all these occur within S phase.

The third enzyme, G6PD (Fig. 3), showed a strikingly different pattern from what would have been expected from the results using Chinese hamster cells. In Don C the enzyme has an easily detectable activity over the entire cell cycle.[28] However, in WI-38 there was a very prominent peak in $G_1$ and a decline to very low activity at early S, some activity around mid S, and very low activity over late S to $G_2$. However, this decrease may be partially artifactual since culture conditions were relatively more aerobic in roller bottles than in the culture flasks in which the cells were plated after mitotic selection.

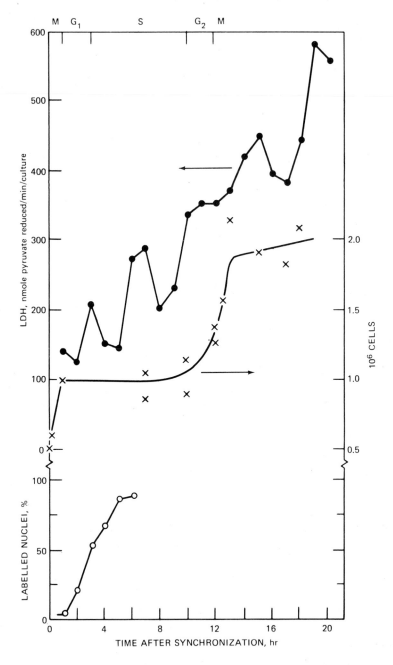

Fig. 2 Lactate dehydrogenase (LDH) activity pattern in Don C Chinese hamster cells. Cell cultures were prepared and LDH activity was assayed as described in the caption to Fig. 1.

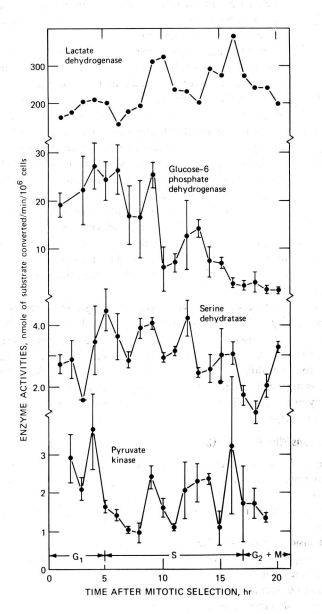

Fig. 3 Enzyme activity patterns in WI-38. Cell cultures were prepared and enzyme activities assayed as described in the caption to Fig. 1. The G6PD was assayed as described previously.[28]

Of the three enzymes reported here, two showed roughly the patterns of activity that would have been expected from previous work with other cell lines; only G6PD did not conform to expectations.

Observations made using Chinese hamster and WI-38 cells suggest that explanted cells with limited culture histories, such as WI-38, will display multiple intracyclic peaks in enzyme activity similar to those originally described for Don C. Established cell lines either show less distinct periodicities or a simpler pattern of fluctuations. In a previous paper[32] we emphasized the reciprocal relationship between maximum thymidine incorporation into DNA and maximum glycolytic enzyme activity and the fact that recently explanted diploid cells tended to display a greater temporal structure in their DNA synthetic pattern than did established and, particularly, heteroploid cell lines. On the basis of the published data from other laboratories, we were obliged to admit the possibility that some heteroploid cell lines would show more or less continuous increases in enzyme activity, cell protein, and cell volume. It was unclear, however, whether this pattern was intrinsic to individual cells in the population or was caused by heterogeneity in generation time and cycle substages within an apparently synchronous population. These ideas are summarized in Figs. 4a and 4b.

Mitchison[50] has codified enzyme activity changes in mammalian cells and suggested four possible patterns based on published results. Increasingly, observations in our own and other laboratories urge us toward the idea that most, if not all, enzymes display multiple (at least two) intracyclic maxima. Contrary to the codification suggested by Mitchison, we consider that periodic synthesis is a general characteristic of the higher eucaryotes and that turnover of many enzymes is of sufficient magnitude to generate an oscillatory or multiple peak activity pattern.

## Some Reasons Why Periodic Gene Expression May Not Be Detected

Ignoring obvious technical flaws, such as poor synchrony, there are a number of explanations that come to mind for discrepancies in the literature. These would include

1. Artifacts due to perturbation of the cells by the synchronization procedure.

2. Intrinsic differences in the mode of synthesis between cell types.

3. Heterogeneity of the cell population with regard to generation time or substage of the cycle (i.e., effects of heteroploidy on the length of S phase).

4. Effects of medium composition.

5. Effects of culturing methods.

6. Mental set of the investigator.

### Synchronization Artifacts

Intuitively, differences in synchronization procedure might seem the most reasonable explanation for the variations in reported results, but this explanation is not borne out at all by the literature. For each of the three major synchronization methods, simple mitotic selection, colcemid-enhanced mitotic selection, and S-phase arrest, at least one example of linear and periodic enzyme synthesis can be found. Blomquist, Gregg, and Tobey,[51] using simple mitotic selection, claim to have found a continuous increase in enzymes of glucose metabolism, whereas Klevecz and Kapp[27,33,34] found a periodic change in some of these same enzymes. Colcemid-enhanced mitotic selection of HTC cells by Martin, Tomkins, and Granner[52] gave what may be a continuous pattern of increase although the method of presenting the data (enzyme activity per milligram of protein rather than per cell) makes it difficult to say this with certainty (see Mitchison[50] for a discussion of denominators). This is not the pattern observed by others using the colcemid method.[28] The same variance in results is true of S-phase arrest. Littlefield[44] observed peaks in TK activity using

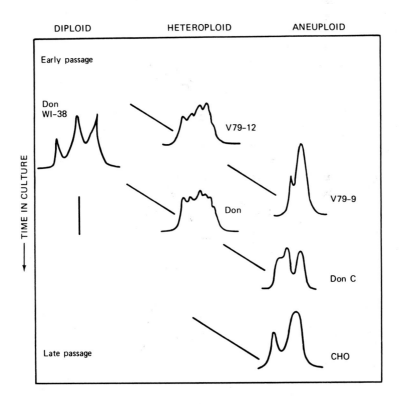

Fig. 4a  Schematic diagram of changes in the temporal structure of S phase as expressed by rates of thymidine incorporation into DNA showing proposed changes in incorporation as a function of time in culture and degree of population heterogeneity.

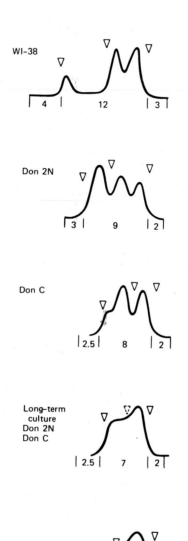

Fig. 4b Schematic diagram of changes in the temporal structure of S phase as expressed by rates of thymidine incorporation into DNA showing concurrent changes in peak LDH activity ($\nabla$) compared with altered DNA replication patterns as expressed in thymidine incorporation. Numbers indicate nominal duration of $G_1$ S, and $G_2$.

FUdR synchronized L cells, while Brent, Butler, and Crathorn[37] found a continuous increase in TK in synchronized HeLa.

## Intrinsic Differences

It now appears that there are intrinsic differences in the patterns of enzyme and DNA synthesis in different cell types.[32] Cloned aneuploid V79 cells display a unimodal rate curve for thymidine incorporation into DNA and two peaks in activity of marker glycolytic enzymes. Homogeneous diploid cells display considerably more temporal structure in their DNA synthesis rate curves and three peaks in activity of these same marker enzymes. The differences in enzyme activity patterns seem to be those of more and less complex periodicities rather than continuous as opposed to periodic increases.

## Population Heterogeneity

Population heterogeneity would seem to be the major reason why some workers have failed to observe sharp changes in activity or synthesis. A comparison of reported findings suggests that marginal periodicities are observed primarily when heteroploid cells are synchronized. Since considerable chromosome rearrangement occurs in these cells, the normal order of replication may be scrambled, and, in view of the rather close coordination which occurs between DNA replication and enzyme synthesis in diploid cells, may result in the loss of detectable periodicities. However, as a consequence of the findings in cloned aneuploid cells where periodicities occur but are less dramatic than those observed in diploid early passage cells, this effect would have to be considered a population artifact. The argument can be made that individual cells within a heteroploid population are displaying periodic maxima in various marker enzymes which are obscured by cell-cycle heterogeneity. Even in cases where fluctuations in enzyme activity have been noted in heteroploid cells,[43] they are considerably less distinct than those observed in homogeneous aneuploid and diploid lines. In the case cited above,[43] two peaks in activity and unimodal DNA synthesis curves were noted. To reiterate, a heteroploid line will be composed of individual cells whose synthetic patterns resemble the cloned aneuploid lines.

## Medium Composition

In prokaryotic cells basal and fully induced derepressed synthesis is linear, whereas autogenous synthesis is periodic. It is conceivable that some inadvertant difference in medium composition or culture conditions in different laboratories has lead to an analogous but uncontrolled situation in cultured mammalian cells in which enzyme synthesis is either basal or completely derepressed. Recently, Stambrook and Sisken[53] reported a linear increase in the rate of RNA synthesis in cells grown in calf serum and a stepwise increase in cells grown in fetal calf serum. It is also true, however, that continuous increases in RNA synthesis rates have been observed in medium with fetal calf serum[54] and periodic increases in medium with calf serum only.[45]

*Culture Conditions*

Most evidence for continuous synthesis comes from studies using suspension cultures of cells that in vivo grow as solid tissues. It may be that the reduced ratio of surface area to volume of cells in suspension leads to aberrant metabolism. Moreover, it is probably not the use of suspension cultures alone but rather the adaptation of solid tissue cells to this form of culture which is at fault. For example, Kapp and Okada[42] found fluctuations in acid phosphatase in the cell cycle of L5178Y mouse leukemia cells. One could argue that it alone among all the cell lines commonly used for synchrony studies should be grown in suspension since HTC, CHO, KB, and HeLa cells were all originally taken from solid tissues.

## CATABOLISM OF PROTEINS

Is there reason to believe that the lability of macromolecules is greater in rapidly dividing mammalian cells than was previously thought to be the case? Certainly the fluctuations in enzyme activity are suggestive of this, and, in at least two cases, immunoprecipitation and acrylamide electrophoresis have been used to demonstrate that the changes in activity reflect changes in the level of enzyme protein.[30,41] However, under most conditions the cell-culture system may be refractory to direct analysis of turnover. Time-dependent changes in the amount of a particular macromolecule in cells can only be observed in synchronous populations, since, in random exponentially growing cell cultures, all changes in macromolecular content are expressed as exponential functions. This fact, together with the propensity expressed by rapidly growing cells for reutilizing amino acids in protein synthesis, has hampered studies on the turnover of proteins and on the control of degradative processes in cells. In steady-state systems such as the liver where net protein synthesis is not a problem and where guanido-labelled arginine can be used to further avoid reutilization, the half-life values for many enzyme proteins can be measured by pulse-chase methods and have been shown to be short, the most notable example being ornithine decarboxylase, which has an 11-min half-life.[55]

The most common method for determining the rate of total protein catabolism involves administering labelled amino acids, chasing with the unlabelled analogue, and following the diminution of protein-bound radioactivity in some manner.[56,57] This approach underestimates the rate of protein degradation,[58,59] since destruction of previously labelled proteins contributes amino acids to the pool for resynthesis.[60] Chase experiments have validity only when a single protein is examined and when the labelling time is short compared to the majority of proteins.

As an alternative to chasing, Eagle and his coworkers[61] adjusted medium conditions so that there was no increase in cell number or cell protein and then determined "excess" amino-acid incorporation. This continuous-isotope-administration method is preferred for measuring total protein catabolism, but, as these authors recognized,[61] there is still reason to question whether the values obtained accurately assay the absolute rate of degradation since unlabelled amino acids may be recycled and obscure the true incorporation rate.[62-64] Furthermore, if degradation of particular proteins is cell-cycle dependent, as appears to be the case,[41] then interruption of progress through the cycle may affect the degradative process.

Protein-bound radioactivity from maximally labelled cell cultures decreases abruptly following the addition of medium containing unlabelled amino acids. Isotopically labelled amino acids appear briefly at increased concentrations in the acid-soluble fraction and are then reutilized in protein. The release of amino acids from cells occurs at a rate of only 1% per hour and must be limiting in measurements of protein catabolism, especially in estimates made by pulse-chase techniques.[65] Recently, Righetti, Little, and Wolf[66] induced ferritin in HeLa cells and demonstrated that the probability of reutilization, the probability that an amino acid derived from a peptide would be reincorporated into a peptide rather than being lost to the medium, was >0.9 for most amino acids.

Protein turnover is an aspect of cellular metabolism that is commonly considered to distinguish mammalian and other metazoan cells from bacteria.[67] In bacteria and other protista, the cell is the organism, and survival is often a matter of rapid proliferation. Adaptive increases in enzyme level can be diluted out by growth and repeated cell divisions. The limitations on growth in metazoan cells in vivo requires that adaptive increases in enzyme levels, in response to a transient environmental change, be reduced through destruction or inactivation of an enzyme. Dilution of the enzyme through repeated cell divisions in the absence of concomitant enzyme synthesis, which is the normal mechanism in bacteria,[68] is not a permitted strategy in mammalian systems.

Superficially, there would appear to be no good reason for essential and functional proteins to be degraded in the early part of the cell cycle, only to be resynthesized later on. Consequently it is essential that a plausible explanation of the role of protein catabolism in the development of the cell be made.

In organisms that cannot synthesize all the amino acids, biochemical mechanisms must be provided to anticipate amino-acid deprivation, at least in those cells which are likely to be called on to synthesize a constantly changing ensemble of proteins. The adaptive value accruing to an organism that maintains sufficient flux to draw on existing proteins as an amino-acid source when necessary may be great.

Our work with cells in synchrony would suggest that precisely timed, intermittent and rather sharp changes in a number of enzyme proteins may be an important component of the cellular clock. Very suggestive of this is the fact that changes in enzyme levels occur at specific portions of the cell cycle and are temporally coordinated with DNA replication. The additional energy expended in this process is the price a cell must pay to achieve orderly progress through the cell cycle as well as flexibility with regard to its differentiated state.

The most perplexing question remaining involves the mechanism of protein catabolism in mammals. Walter[69] suggested a number of years ago that hydrolysis of the peptide bond might occur by some mechanism that would conserve bond energy, possibly by the formation of activated amino acids. Modifying this argument somewhat are the observations of Brostrom and Jeffay[70] showing that adenosine triphosphate is necessary for maximal proteolysis.

The full significance of the altered expression of enzyme activity in established and tumor cell lines is elusive. It may be worth noting that during the course of embryogenesis there is an increase in the complexity of the DNA-synthetic pattern. We might consider that this process is reversed in culture or during transformation and that established tumor cell lines have fallen back to a relatively simpler and less differentiated state. In keeping with the idea is the fact that embryonic proteins are expressed in several types of cancer.

## ACKNOWLEDGMENTS

This work was made possible in part by support from the Drug and Cosmetics Industry Research Fund honoring Joseph H. Hecht and by grants HD-04699 and CA-10619 from the National Institutes of Health.

## REFERENCES

1. M. M. Swann, The Control of Cell Division: A Review. I. General Mechanisms, *Cancer Res.*, **17**: 727 (1957).

2. Y. Hotta and H. Stern, Molecular Facts of Mitotic Regulation. I. Synthesis of Thymidine Kinase, *Proc. Nat. Acad. Sci. U.S.A.*, **49**: 648 (1963).

3. D. Mazia, *The Cell. III. Meiosis and Mitosis*, J. Bracket and A. E. Mirsky (Eds.), Academic Press, Inc., New York, 1961.

4. E. Bunning, *The Physiological Clock*, Springer-Verlag, Berlin-Göttingen, 1964.

5. B. C. Goodwin, *Temporal Organization in Cells*, Academic Press, Inc., New York, 1963.

6. B. C. Goodwin, An Entertainment Model for Timed Enzyme Synthesis in Bacteria, *Nature*, **209**: 479 (1966).

7. H. Rubin and R. Sitgreaves, Technical Report 19A, Applied Mathematics and Statistics Laboratory, Stanford University, 1954.

8. B. C. Goodwin, Biological Control Processes and Time, *Ann. New York Acad. Sci.*, **138**: 748 (1967).

9. C. S. Pittendrigh, On Temporal Organization in Living Systems, *Harvey Lectures*, Series 56, p. 93, Academic Press, Inc., 1961.

10. J. Monod, P. Changeux, and F. Jacob, Allosteric Proteins and Cellular Control Systems, *J. Mol. Biol.*, **6**: 306 (1963).

11. J. W. Hastings and B. M. Sweeney, On the Mechanisms of Temperature Independence in a Biological Clock, *Proc. Nat. Acad. Sci. U.S.A.*, **43**: 804 (1957).

12. K. H. Nealson, A. Eberhard, and J. W. Hastings, Catabolite Repression of Bacterial Bioluminescence: Functional Implications, *Proc. Nat. Acad. Sci. U.S.A.*, **69**: 1073 (1972).

13. F. Strumwasser, A Circadian Rhythm of Activity and Its Endogenous Origin in a Neuron, *Fed. Proc.*, **22**: 220 (1963).

14. B. Chance, R. W. Estabrook, and A. Ghosh, Damped Sinusoidal Oscillations of Cytoplasmic Reduced Pyridine Nucleotide in Yeast Cells, *Proc. Nat. Acad. Sci. U.S.A.*, **51**: 1244 (1964).

15. C. Knutsen, Induction of Nitrite Reductase in Synchronized Cultures of Chlorella Pyrenoidosa, *Biochim. Biophys. Acta*, **103**: 495 (1965).

16. J. M. Mitchison and J. Creanor, Linear Synthesis of Sucrose and Phosphatase During the Cell Cycle of Schizosacharomyces, *J. Cell Sci.*, **5**: 373 (1969).

17. W. D. Donachie and M. Masters, in *The Cell Cycle: Gene Enzyme Interactions*, p. 37, G. M. Padilla, G. L. Whitson, and I. Cameron (Eds.), Academic Press, Inc., New York, 1969.

18. F. S. Baechtel, H. A. Hopkins, and R. R. Schmidt, Continuous Inducibility of Isocitrate Lyase During the Cell Cycle of the Eucaryote *Chlorella*, *Biochim. Biophys. Acta*, **217**: 216 (1970).

19. P. Kuempel, M. Masters, and A. B. Pardee, Bursts of Enzyme Synthesis in the Bacterial Duplication Cycle, *Biochem. Biophys. Res. Commun.*, **18**: 858 (1965).

20. M. Masters and A. B. Pardee, Sequence of Enzyme Synthesis and Gene Replication During the Cell Cycle of *Bacillus Subtilis*, *Proc. Nat. Acad. Sci. U.S.A.*, **54**: 64 (1965).

21. M. Masters and W. D. Donachie, Repression and the Control of Cyclic Enzyme Synthesis in *Bacillus Subtilis*, *Nature*, **209**: 476 (1966).

22. G. R. Molloy and R. R. Schmidt, Studies on the Regulation of Ribulose-1,5-Diphosphate Carboxylase Synthesis During the Cell Cycle of the Eucaryote *Chlorella*, *Biochem. Biophys. Res. Commun.*, **40**: 1125 (1970).

23. S. Riva, H. Cascine, and E. P. Geiduschek, Coupling of Late Transcription to Viral Replication in Bacteriophage T4 Development, *J. Mol. Biol.*, **54**: 85 (1970).

24. J. S. Griffith, Mathematics of Cellular Control Processes. I. Negative Feedback to One Gene, *J. Theoret. Biol.*, **20**: 202 (1968).

25. J. Gorman, P. Tauro, M. Laberge, and H. O. Halvorson, Timing of Enzyme Synthesis During Synchronous Division in Yeast, *Biochem. Biophys. Res. Commun.*, **15**: 43 (1964).

26. H. O. Halvorson, B. L. A. Carter, and P. Tauro, Synthesis of Enzymes During the Cell Cycle, *Advan. Microbial Physiol.*, **6**: 47 (1971).

27. L. N. Kapp and R. R. Klevecz, The Common Occurrence of Intracyclic Enzyme Oscillations in Cultured Mammalian Cells, *J. Cell Physiol.*, submitted.

28. R. R. Klevecz and F. H. Ruddle, Cyclic Changes in Synchronized Mammalian Cell Cultures, *Science*, **159**: 634 (1968).

29. K. H. Grzeschik, P. W. Allderdice, H. Grzeschik, J. M. Opitz, O. J. Miller, and M. Siniscalco, Cytological Mapping of Human X-Linked Genes by Use of Somatic Cell Hybrids Involving an X-Autosome Translocation, *Proc. Nat. Acad. Sci. U.S.A.*, **69**: 69 (1972).

30. R. R. Klevecz, Temporal Order in Mammalian Cells. 1. The Periodic Synthesis of Lactate Dehydrogenase in the Cell Cycle, *J. Cell Biol.*, **43**: 207 (1969).

31. T. W. Borun, M. D. Scharff, and E. Robbins, Rapidly Labeled, Polyribosome-Associated RNA Having the Properties of Histone Messenger, *Proc. Nat. Acad. Sci. U.S.A.*, **58**: 1977 (1967).

32. R. R. Klevecz, Temporal Coordination of DNA Replication With Enzyme Synthesis in Diploid and Heteroploid Cells, *Science*, **166**: 1536 (1969).

33. R. R. Klevecz, An Automated System for Cell Cycle Analysis, *Anal. Biochem.*, **49**: 407 (1972).

34. R. R. Klevecz and L. N. Kapp, Intermittent DNA Synthesis and Periodic Expression of Enzyme Activity in the Cell Cycle of WI-38, *J. Cell Biol.*, **58**: 564 (1973).

35. L. J. Bello, Studies on Gene Activity in Synchronized Cultures of Mammalian Cells, *Biochim. Biophys. Acta*, **179**: 204 (1969).

36. P. Volpe, Depression of Ornithine-δ-Transaminase Synchronized With the Life Cycle of HeLa Cells Cultivated in Suspension, *Biochem. Biophys. Res. Commun.*, **34**: 190 (1969).

37. T. P. Brent, J. A. V. Butler, and A. V. Crathorn, Variations in Phosphokinase Activities During the Cell Cycle in Synchronous Populations of HeLa Cells, *Nature*, **207**: 176 (1965).

38. T. P. Brent, Periodicity of DNA Synthetic Enzymes During the HeLa Cell Cycle, *Cell Tissue Kinet.*, **4**: 297 (1971).

39. M. D. Scharff and E. Robbins, Synthesis of Ribosomal RNA in Synchronized HeLa Cells, *Nature*, **208**: 464 (1965).

40. R. R. Klevecz, L. N. Kapp, and J. A. Remington, Intermittent Amplification and Catabolism of DNA and Its Correlation With Gene Expression, in *Control of Proliferation in Animal Cells*, B. Clarkson and R. Baserga (Eds.), Cold Spring Harbor Laboratory Press, Cold Spring Harbor, New York, 1974.

41. G. L. Forrest and R. R. Klevecz, Synthesis and Degradation of Microtubule Protein in Synchronized Chinese Hamster Cells, *J. Biol. Chem.*, **247**: 3147 (1972).

42. L. N. Kapp and S. Okada, Actinomycin D Induction of Acid Phosphatase in Synchronized L5178Y Mouse Leukemia Cells, *Exp. Cell Res.*, **72**: 465 (1972).

43. J. R. Churchill and G. P. Studzinski, Thymidine as Synchronizing Agent. III. Persistence of Cell Cycle Patterns of Phosphatase Activities and Elevation of Nuclease Activity During Inhibition of DNA Synthesis, *J. Cell. Physiol.*, **75**: 297 (1970).

44. J. W. Littlefield, The Periodic Synthesis of Thymidine Kinase in Mouse Fibroblasts, *Biochim. Biophys. Acta*, **114**: 398 (1966).

45. J. H. Kim and A. G. Perez, Ribonucleic Acid Synthesis in Synchronously Dividing Populations of HeLa Cells, *Nature*, **207**: 974 (1965).

46. J. M. Reiter and J. W. Littlefield, Nuclear RNA Synthesis in Partially Synchronized Mouse Fibroblasts, *Biochim. Biophys. Acta*, **80**: 562 (1964).

47. F. H. Kasten and F. F. Strasser, Amino Acid Incorporation Patterns During the Cell Cycle of Synchronized Human Tumor Cells, *Nat. Cancer Inst. Monogr.*, **23**: 353 (1966).

48. Y. Yagi, Mechanisms in the Expression of Cellular Phenotypes. Production of Immunoglobulin by Cells of Established Human Lymphocytoid Cell Lines, International Society for Cell Biology, Symposium, Vol. 9, H. A. Radykula (Ed.), Academic Press, Inc., 1970.

49. H. H. Conrad, Thymidylate Synthetase Activity in Cultured Mammalian Cells, *J. Biol. Chem.*, **246**: 1318 (1971).

50. J. M. Mitchison, *The Biology of the Cell Cycle*, Cambridge University Press, New York, 1971.

51. C. H. Blomquist, C. T. Gregg, and R. A. Tobey, Enzyme and Coenzyme Levels, Oxygen Uptake and Lactate Production in Synchronized Cultures of Chinese Hamster Cells, *Exp. Cell Res.*, **66**: 75 (1971).

52. D. Martin, G. M. Tomkins, and D. Granner, Synthesis and Induction of Tyrosine Aminotransferase in Synchronized Hepatoma Cells in Culture, *Proc. Nat. Acad. Sci. U.S.A.*, **62**: 248 (1969).

53. P. J. Stambrook and J. Sisken, Induced Changes in the Rates of Uridine-³H Incorporation into RNA During the G1 and S Periods of Synchronized Chinese Hamster Cells, *J. Cell Biol.*, **52**: 514 (1972).

54. M. D. Enger and R. A. Tobey, RNA Synthesis in Chinese Hamster Cells. II. Increase in Rate of RNA Synthesis During G1, *J. Cell Biol.*, **42**: 308 (1969).

55. S. H. Synder and D. H. Russell, Polyamine Synthesis in Rapidly Growing Tissues, *Fed. Proc.*, **29**: 1575 (1970).

56. D. W. King, K. G. Bensch, and R. B. Hill, State of Dynamic Equilibrium in Protein of Mammalian Cells, *Science*, **131**: 106 (1960).

57. G. M. Kolodny and P. R. Gross, Changes in Patterns of Protein Synthesis During the Mammalian Cell Cycle, *Exp. Cell Res.*, **56**: 117 (1969).

58. H. C. Jordan and P. A. Schmidt, Constant Protein Turnover in Mammalian Cells During Logarithmic Growth, *Biochem. Biophys. Res. Comm.*, **4**: 313 (1961).

59. R. T. Schimke, in *Current Topics in Cellular Regulation*, Vol. 1, p. 77, B. L. Horecker and E. R. Stadtman (Eds.), Academic Press, Inc., New York, 1969.

60. M. Rechcigl, in *Enzyme Synthesis and Degradation in Mammalian Systems*, M. Rechcigl (Ed.), University Park Press, Baltimore, 1971.

61. H. Eagle, K. A. Piez, R. Fleischman, and V. I. Oyana, Protein Turnover in Mammalian Cell Cultures, *J. Biol. Chem.*, **234**: 592 (1959).

62. R. B. Loftfield and A. Harris, Participation of Free Amino Acids in Protein Synthesis, *J. Biol. Chem.*, **219**: 151 (1956).

63. J. C. Gan and H. Jeffay, Origins and Metabolisms of the Intracellular Amino Acid Pools in Rat Liver and Muscle, *Biochim. Biophys. Acta*, **148**: 448 (1967).

64. A. L. Koch, The Evaluation of the Rates of Biological Processes from Tracer Kinetic Data, *J. Theor. Biol.*, **3**: 283 (1962).

65. R. R. Klevecz, Rapid Protein Catabolism in Mammalian Cells is Obscured by Reutilization of Amino Acids, *Biochem. Biophys. Res. Commun.*, **43**: 76 (1971).

66. P. Righetti, E. P. Little, and G. Wolf, Reutilization of Amino Acids in Protein Synthesis in HeLa Cells, *J. Biol. Chem.*, **246**: 5724 (1971).

67. D. S. Hogness, M. Cohn, and J. Monod, Studies on the Induced Synthesis of β-Galactosidase in *Escherichia coli*: The Kinetics and Mechanisms of Sulfur Incorporation, *Biochim. Biophys. Acta*, **16**: 99 (1955).

68. H. L. Segal, in *Regulatory Mechanisms for Protein Synthesis in Mammalian Cells*, p. 373, A. San Pietro (Ed.), Academic Press, Inc., 1968.

69. H. Walter, Protein Catabolism, *Nature*, **168**: 643 (1960).

70. C. O. Brostrom and H. Jeffay, Protein Catabolism in Rat Liver Homogenates, *J. Biol. Chem.*, **245**: 4001 (1970).

71. H. C. Pitot and N. Pries, The Automated Assay of Complete Enzyme Reaction Rates. I. Methods and Results, *Anal. Biochem.*, **9**: 454 (1964).

72. R. Schindler, A. Grieder, and U. Maurer, Studies of the Division Cycle of Mammalian Cells VI. DNA Polymerase Activities in Partially Synchronous Suspension Culture, *Exp. Cell Res.*, **71**: 218 (1972).

# CYCLIC-AMP-MEDIATED REPRESSION
# OF THE MITOTIC CELL CYCLE

ALBERT J. T. MILLIS, GARY FORREST, and DONALD A. PIOUS
Department of Pediatrics, University of Washington School of Medicine,
Seattle, Washington

## ABSTRACT

Cellular growth was examined in synchronous cultures of an established human lymphoid line to determine if cyclic AMP (adenosine $3',5'$ monophosphate) repressed specific points in the mitotic cell cycle. Examination of thymidine-synchronized cells revealed levels of endogenous cyclic AMP in S and M that were 20% of the $G_2$ level. In colcemid-synchronized cells cyclic AMP was high in $G_1$ when compared to the level in M. The activities of adenylate cyclase and cyclic-AMP-dependent phosphodiesterase were investigated to determine their roles in the regulation of cyclic-AMP periodicity. Both enzymes appeared to have a regulatory function.

Progression of the cells through S, $G_2$, and M was examined in detail by the addition of agents that increase intracellular levels of cyclic AMP. Continuous exposure to dibutyryl cyclic AMP, catecholamine hormones, or the phosphodiesterase inhibitor 1-methyl-3-isobutylxanthine (MIX) resulted in suppression of the mitotic wave. Cultures treated with either 1.0 mmolar dibutyryl cyclic AMP or 1.0 mmolar noradrenaline during S and subsequently suspended in untreated media produced a mitotic wave 2 to 3 hr earlier than similar cultures treated with either 5.0 mmolar MIX or 0.75 mmolar isopropylnoradrenaline during S. Examination of thymidine uptake and incorporation revealed that both MIX and isopropylnoradrenaline inhibited incorporation into DNA. Dibutyryl cyclic AMP and noradrenaline did not inhibit that process.

The nucleotide cyclic AMP (adenosine monophosphate) has been implicated in a wide variety of hormonal[1-3] and growth responses and thus represents a potential point of control in the regulation of cell growth. There are several reports suggesting that cyclic AMP has a direct association with the regulation of mammalian-cell growth. In mouse skin[4] and pathologic human skin,[5] an inverse relationship was shown to exist between the percent mitotic and the endogenous level of the cyclic nucleotide. The repression of cell growth by cyclic AMP was also demonstrated in cultured cells. In mouse fibroblasts high levels of cyclic AMP were associated with increased steady-state doubling times[6] with density-dependent inhibition of growth.[7] Serum and trypsin treatments decreased[6] levels of intracellular cyclic AMP and stimulated confluent monolayers of 3T3 to leave $G_1$ and undergo a wave of DNA synthesis.[8-10] In human diploid fibroblasts as well as 3T3 cells, treatment with $N^6$, $O^{2'}$-dibutyryl cyclic AMP (dbcAMP), or cyclic-AMP-inhibited serum stimulated DNA synthesis.[11]

The studies presented here were initiated to detect whether the phenomenon of cyclic-AMP repression of growth occurred continuously or at specific times during the cell cycle. Initial examination of synchronized cells revealed cell-cycle-related differences in the levels of intracellular cyclic AMP. Those differences may have resulted from the following:

1. Increased synthesis of cyclic AMP owing to activation of adenylate cyclase.

2. Increased degradation of cyclic AMP resulting from phosphodiesterase activation.

3. Uptake of cyclic AMP from the medium.

4. Excretion of cyclic AMP into the medium.

5. A shift in the equilibrium between protein-bound and unbound cyclic AMP.

Four of those mechanisms were examined. Finally, we report on investigations of agents that function to increase intracellular levels of cyclic AMP for their effects on mitosis, thymidine uptake, and DNA synthesis.

In these studies we used a clone of the human lymphoid line RPMI 8866 originally established from a patient with acute myelogenous leukemia. Cells were cultured in suspension in Eagle's MEM supplemented with 20% fetal bovine serum in a 5% $CO_2 - 95\%$ air environment in the presence of penicillin and streptomycin. Cultures were routinely examined for contamination by pleuro-pneumonia-like organisms (PPLO) and found to be negative. Experimental cells were drawn from a population growing exponentially at less than $6.5 \times 10^5$ cells/ml.

To effect a synchronizing block in S, we treated cultures for 18 hr with 2 mmolar thymidine, a modification of the method of Galavazi, Schenk, and Bootsma.[12] Figure 1 shows the patterns of DNA synthesis and the mitotic index in cultures released from such a synchronizing block. The mitotic wave reproducibly peaked at 6 to 7 hr after release from thymidine blockage. A second wave of mitosis occurred 25 to 26 hr after removal of thymidine, indicating a generation time of about 18 hr (data not shown). This was similar to a generation time of 18 to 20 hr evident in exponentially growing cultures and indicated that the timing of the cell cycle was not seriously affected by the thymidine treatment.

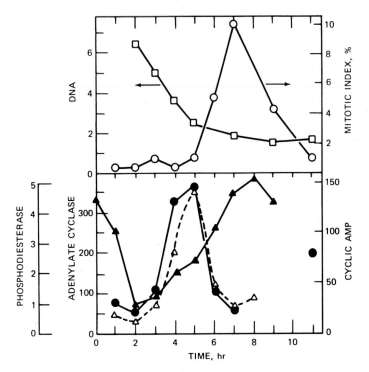

Fig. 1 Levels of cyclic AMP, adenylate cyclase activity, and phospho-diesterase activity in thymidine-synchronized cultures. Cells were released from the thymidine block at 0 hr, and the mitotic index (○), DNA synthesis (□), adenylate cyclase activity (△), phosphodiesterase activity (▲), and cyclic-AMP levels (●) were determined as described in Ref. 13. DNA synthesis is expressed as $10^3$ cpm/$10^5$ cells x 30 min; adenylate cyclase activity, as pmole cyclic AMP formed/mg protein/min; phosphodiesterase activity, as nmole cyclic AMP hydrolyzed/mg protein/min; and cyclic AMP, in levels per milligram of protein. [From A. J. T. Millis, G. Forrest, and D. A. Pious, Cyclic AMP Dependent Regulation of Mitosis in Human Cells, *Exp. Cell Res.*, 83: 335-343 (1974).]

## LEVELS OF CYCLIC AMP, ADENYLATE CYCLASE ACTIVITY, AND CYCLIC-AMP-DEPENDENT PHOSPHODIESTERASE ACTIVITY IN SYNCHRONIZED CELLS

Thymidine-synchronized cells were assayed for cyclic-AMP levels at intervals during the cell cycle (Fig. 1). Cyclic AMP was prepared from lymphoid cells as previously described[13-14] and assayed by a competitive binding method.[15] The level of the cyclic nucleotide was low during S and increased during $G_2$. Subsequently, the level decreased in late $G_2$ to a minimal value during mitosis. The level appeared to rise as the cells entered $G_1$. Because of the rapid decay of synchrony after the cells passed through mitosis, the $G_1$ levels of cyclic AMP were examined in more detail with cultures that had been synchronized with 0.02 μg of colcemid per milliliter for 18 hr (Fig. 2). Such cultures support the observation of low levels of cyclic AMP during M and present evidence for the existence of high levels during early $G_1$.

We examined the enzymes responsible for synthesis and degradation of cyclic AMP to see if enzymatic activity might account for the high levels of cyclic AMP in $G_2$ and its subsequent decrease in M. A schematic representation of the metabolism and utilization of cyclic AMP is shown in Fig. 3. The cyclic nucleotide was generated from ATP (adenosine triphosphate) via the membrane-bound adenylate—cyclase complex.[16] Degradation to 5' AMP occurred through the activity of the largely soluble cyclic-AMP-dependent phosphodiesterase.[17] The activities of both enzymes were determined, and the results are shown in Fig. 1.

Adenylate cyclase activity was measured in broken-cell preparations, stimulated by the addition of 10 mmolar NaF, using $C^{14}$-ATP as the substrate.[13] The radioactive products of the reaction were separated by paper chromatography, and the cyclic-AMP-containing spot was cut out and counted by liquid scintillation spectroscopy.[18] In cells from synchronized cultures, the pattern of enzymatic activity coincided with the levels of cyclic AMP during S,

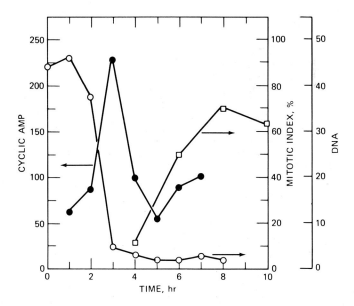

Fig. 2  Cyclic AMP in colcemid-synchronized cells. Release from the synchronizing block occurred at 0 hr. The mitotic index (○), DNA synthesis (□), and cyclic-AMP (●) levels were determined as described in Ref. 13. [From A. J. T. Millis, G. Forrest, and D. A. Pious, Cyclic AMP Dependent Regulation of Mitosis in Human Cells, *Exp. Cell Res.,* 83: 335-343 (1974).]

$G_2$, and M. This same parameter was examined, in less detail, with colcemid-synchronized cells (Table 1), and, in general, the results support each other.

Adenylate—cyclase activity has been reported to vary with the cell cycle in other systems. For example, in virally infected BHK cells, enzymatic activity has been shown[22] to be high during $G_1$ and to drop during S in association with the level of cyclic AMP. Our observations extend that relationship to $G_2$ and M. There is a conflicting report that in synchronized liver cells, adenylate cyclase activities are maximal during mitosis.[23] However, because the spread of time between each point is large, the high activity may actually be in early $G_1$.

The activity of phosphodiesterase during the cell cycle was also determined. The specific activity was high during S and decreased in early $G_2$. The activity then increased during late $G_2$ and reached a maximum value in M. Although the presence of increasing amounts of cyclic AMP in $G_2$ may have stimulated phosphodiesterase activity,[19] the overall pattern of activity indicated that phosphodiesterase plays a role in the regulation of the level of cyclic AMP.

The relative increases and decreases in enzymatic activities are consistent with the notion that both enzymes are involved in cyclic-AMP regulation. However, for technical reasons we were unable to produce evidence that shows a direct molar relationship between enzymatic activities and cyclic-AMP levels. This was due, in part, to the use of broken-cell preparations for the enzymatic

TABLE 1

ACTIVITIES OF ADENYLATE CYCLASE AND
PHOSPHODIESTERASE IN COLCEMID-
SYNCHRONIZED CELLS*

| | Enzymatic activity† | |
| Position in cell cycle | Adenylate cyclase | Phosphodiesterase |
| --- | --- | --- |
| Mitosis | | |
| Early | 69.8 | |
| Late | 2.4 | 7.1 |
| $G_1$ | | |
| Early | 165.6 | 4.0 |
| Late | | 9.5 |
| S | | |
| Early | | 8.1 |
| Late | | 6.2 |

*From A. J. T. Millis, G. Forrest, and D. A. Pious, Cyclic AMP Dependent Regulation of Mitosis in Human Cells, *Exp. Cell Res.,* **83:** 335-343 (1974).

†Units of enzymatic activity are shown in the caption to Fig. 1.

assays, the stimulation of adenylate cyclase with fluoride ion, and the phosphodiesterase assay of only the low Km binding site.

Oscillations in the levels of cyclic AMP during the cell cycle have been reported to occur in mouse,[20] hamster,[21] human,[14] and virally infected BHK cells.[22] However, the mechanism of regulation of the levels of the cyclic nucleotide is not known. As shown in Fig. 3, there are at least five mechanisms that could regulate the observed periodicity in the levels of the cyclic nucleotide. They include (1) activation of adenylate cyclase, (2) activation of phosphodiesterase, (3) uptake from the medium, (4) excretion into the medium, and (5) binding to specific proteins. It appears that the equilibrium levels of cyclic AMP may reflect some interplay of these mechanisms.

It is unlikely that cyclic-AMP levels are regulated either by uptake of the cyclic nucleotide from the culture media or by excretion into the media. There is considerable evidence that cell membranes are impermeable to cyclic AMP. The addition of high concentrations of cyclic AMP to media containing unsynchronized cells did not inhibit DNA synthesis, but the addition of dbcAMP did inhibit that process (Table 2). Although there is a report that cyclic AMP is excreted into the media by bacterial cells,[24] we do not detect an increase in cyclic AMP in media containing synchronized cells. The level in the media did not appear to oscillate as cells progressed through the cell cycle (Millis,

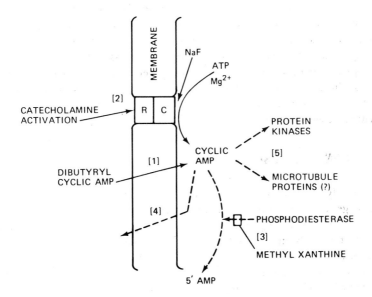

**Fig. 3 Metabolism of cyclic AMP. The symbol R represents the hormone receptor site and C the catalytic site of adenylate cyclase. Solid arrows show methods of increasing the cyclic-AMP pool, and broken arrows show methods of depleting the pool. The numerals are referred to in the text. Based on Ref. 37.**

**TABLE 2**

EFFECTS OF CYCLIC NUCLEOTIDES AND
CATECHOLAMINE HORMONES ON DNA SYNTHESIS
IN EXPONENTIALLY GROWING CULTURES*

| Material | Concentration, mmolar | Inhibition, % |
|---|---|---|
| Cyclic AMP | 0.5 | 0 |
| | 1.0 | 8 |
| | 5.0 | 11 |
| dbcAMP | 0.5 | 20 |
| | 1.0 | 64 |
| Noradrenaline | 0.5 | 12 |
| Adrenaline | 0.5 | 1 |
| Isopropylnoradrenaline | 0.5 | 97 |

*DNA was labelled and prepared for counting as described in Ref. 13.

manuscript in preparation). Therefore, it is doubtful that either uptake or excretion was responsible for the change in the levels of intracellular cyclic AMP.

Finally, the possibility exists that cyclic AMP levels, as assayed by our methods, do not include nucleotide that is bound to proteins or other macromolecules. We have not investigated that possibility and therefore are unable to comment on whether a transition between the bound and unbound state has influenced these observations. Nevertheless, it is conceivable that assayable levels decrease when cyclic AMP is bound and increase when the molecule is released into the soluble phase.

## REPRESSION OF MITOSIS

Previously we postulated that the level of intracellular cyclic AMP regulates the passage of cells through the cell cycle.[14] We examined in detail the progression of cells through the S, $G_2$, and M stages of the cell cycle by adding agents that have been shown to increase intracellular levels of cyclic AMP. Specifically, in regard to $G_2$, where cyclic-AMP levels are high (Fig. 1), we questioned whether the maintenance of continued high levels would prevent cells from entering mitosis. We used three independent methods of increasing the cyclic-AMP pool (Fig. 3): (1) addition of the cyclic-AMP analog dbcAMP to the media, (2) stimulation of adenylate cyclase activity by the addition of catecholamine hormones to the media, and (3) inhibition of phosphodiesterase activity by treatment with 1-methyl-3-isobutylxanthine (MIX). All these experiments were done with thymidine-synchronized cells.

Intracellular cyclic AMP was increased by the addition of 1.0 mmolar dbcAMP to cultures at the time of their removal from the synchronizing block. Figure 4 shows that such treatment inhibited the mitotic wave. When dbcAMP was washed from the cultures after 4 hr (present during late S and early $G_2$), the mitotic wave occurred more normally.

Figure 5 shows the effects on mitosis of treatment with either 0.75 mmolar isopropylnoradrenaline or 1.0 mmolar noradrenaline. Addition of either agent at 0 hr inhibited mitosis, but, when the hormones were washed from the cultures at the end of S, the mitotic wave was restored. The inhibition of phosphodiesterase with 5.0 mmolar MIX produced similar results. The mitotic wave was suppressed by the presence of MIX but restored when MIX was removed. When either isopropylnoradrenaline or MIX was added during $G_2$ to

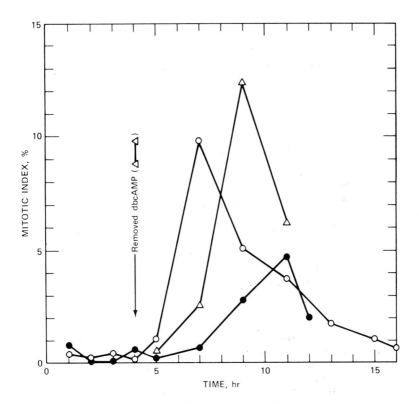

Fig. 4   An effect of exogenous dibutyryl cyclic AMP on the mitotic index of thymidine-synchronized cells. At 0 hr, 1.0 mmolar dbcAMP was added to two cultures (● and △); then, at 4 hr of incubation, it was washed from one culture (△). A parallel untreated culture is also shown (○). Mitotic indexes were determined as described in Ref. 13. From A. J. T. Millis, G. Forrest, and D. A. Pious, Cyclic AMP in Cultured Human Lymphoid Cells: Relationship to Mitosis, *Biochem. Biophys. Res. Commun.*, 49: 1645-1649 (1972).

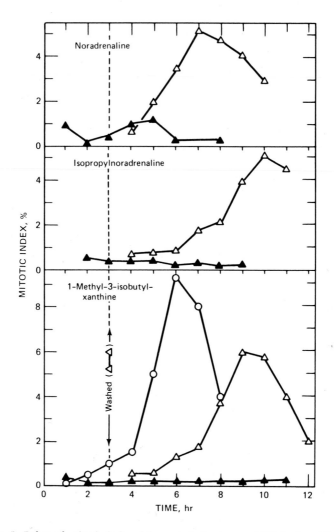

Fig. 5 Delay of mitosis induced by catecholamines or MIX in thymidine-synchronized cultures. The mitotic index of the control culture (○) is shown in the bottom panel. At 0 hr either 1.0 mmolar noradrenaline, 0.75 mmolar isopropylnoradrenaline, or 5 mmolar MIX was added to parallel cultures, and the resulting mitotic indexes (▲) are represented in the corresponding panels. Other cultures were similarly exposed to those agents at 0 hr but were washed and resuspended in fresh mediums at 3 hr. The mitotic indexes of those cultures are shown (△). [From A. J. T. Millis, G. Forrest, and D. A. Pious, Cyclic AMP Dependent Regulation of Mitosis in Human Cells, *Exp. Cell Res.*, 83: 335-343 (1974).]

cultures unexposed during S, mitosis was inhibited.[13] Table 3 shows that such treatment also elevated cyclic-AMP levels.

The specific mechanism through which cyclic AMP inhibited mitosis is not known. However, there is a large body of literature which has related cyclic AMP to activities that were also associated with microtubules. Possibly, the level of intracellular cyclic AMP affected the synthesis of microtubule protein or the assembly of the microtubules that compose the spindle apparatus. Under conditions where the action of cyclic AMP was determined, it was shown to involve activation of specific protein kinases, which then catalyzed the phosphorylation of other proteins. Cyclic AMP has been shown to phosphorylate isolated neurotubule subunits[25] and purified rat-brain microtubule protein.[26] In addition, Gillespie[27] has shown a biphasic effect of cyclic AMP on the equilibrium that exists between microtubules and microtubular subunits. It appeared from her data that low concentrations favored subunit formation. A hypothesis that fits the data presented here states that high levels of cyclic AMP during $G_2$ stimulated subunit formation and prevented the assembly of the microtubules of the spindle. The normal decrease in the level of cyclic AMP during late $G_2$ favored the microtubule formation, and mitosis occurred. In support of that notion, colchicine-binding experiments in synchronized cells have shown that the level of microtubule subunits was higher during late S and $G_2$ than during the rest of the cell cycle.[28]

## EFFECTS ON DNA SYNTHESIS

A variety of reports have implicated dbcAMP,[29-32] cyclic AMP,[29,30,32] and catecholamine hormones[29,33] in the inhibition of DNA synthesis. The

TABLE 3

STIMULATION OF CYCLIC AMP
DURING $G_2$

| Treatment | Cyclic AMP, pmole/mg protein | Mitotic, % |
|---|---|---|
| Control* | 40.2 | 5 |
| Isopropylnoradren-aline† | 80.0 | 0.3 |
| MIX† | 155.0 | 0.1 |

*Thymidine-synchronized culture, released from synchronizing block and the per cent mitotic determined at 6 hr.

†Cultures treated at 4 hr ($G_2$) with specified agent. The per cent mitotic and cyclic AMP levels were determined at 6 hr.

observations reported in the previous section suggested that in some cases an event preceding mitosis appeared to be affected when cyclic-AMP levels were high during S. A comparison of the recovery times of mitotic waves in cultures exposed to dbcAMP, noradrenaline, isopropylnoradrenaline, or MIX revealed two "classes" of recovery. The cultures treated with either dbcAMP or noradrenaline generated mitotic waves 2 to 3 hr earlier than did parallel cultures treated with either isopropylnoradrenaline or MIX. We postulated that the 2- to 3-hr delay might represent the time necessary to complete DNA synthesis.

Treatment with 1.0 mmolar dbcAMP did not inhibit DNA synthesis in thymidine-synchronized cultures (Table 4), although it did inhibit about 65% of the DNA synthesis in unsynchronized cultures (Table 2). In light of a report[9] that the addition of dbcAMP to cultures in $G_1$ inhibited DNA synthesis, it was likely that there existed a specific time during the cell cycle when dbcAMP could inhibit such synthesis. Once DNA synthesis was initiated, it was not inhibitable by dbcAMP.

The catecholamines noradrenaline and isopropylnoradrenaline reacted differently with respect to DNA synthesis. Noradrenaline inhibited neither thymidine uptake nor incorporation in synchronized cultures (Table 2). Hourly examination of DNA synthesis in a noradrenaline-treated culture (Fig. 6) revealed a pattern of pulse-labelled DNA synthesis similar to that of an untreated culture. However, isopropylnoradrenaline prevented the incorporation of thymidine into acid-insoluble product without inhibiting precursor uptake (Table 5).

**TABLE 4**

DNA SYNTHESIS IN THYMIDINE-
SYNCHRONIZED CELLS TREATED WITH
dbcAMP*†

| | DNA Synthesis, cpm/$10^5$ cells for 30 min | | | |
|---|---|---|---|---|
| | At 3 hr | At 4 hr | At 5 hr | At 7 hr |
| Control | 5115 | 3716 | 2716 | 1933 |
| 1 mmolar dbcAMP | 5740 | 4015 | 2800 | 2340 |
| Percent control‡ | 112 | 108 | 103 | 121 |

*From A. T. J. Millis, G. Forrest, and D. A. Pious, Cyclic AMP in Cultured Human Lymphoid Cells: Relationship to Mitosis, *Biochem. Biophys. Res. Commun.*, **49**: 1645-1649 (1972).

†DNA was labelled with $H^3$-labelled thymidine and analyzed as described in Ref. 13.

‡dbcAMP cpm/control cpm.

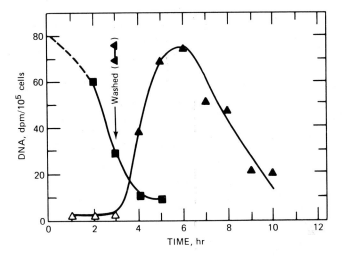

Fig. 6 DNA synthesis in cultures treated with either noradrenaline or 1-methyl-3-isobutylxanthine. At the time the synchronizing block was removed, cultures were exposed to either noradrenaline (■) or MIX (△). At the end of S phase, the MIX culture was washed and resuspended in untreated medium (▲). [From A. J. T. Millis, G. Forrest, and D. A. Pious, Cyclic AMP Dependent Regulation of Mitosis in Human Cells, *Exp. Cell Res.*, 83: 335-343 (1974).]

### TABLE 5

### EFFECTS OF CATECHOLAMINES AND MIX ON DNA SYNTHESIS IN SYNCHRONIZED CELLS*

|  | Thymidine uptake, dpm/$10^5$ cells | Thymidine incorporation, for 30 min |
|---|---|---|
| Control | 4300 | 56,000 |
| Noradrenaline | 3000 | 67,300 |
| Isopropylnor-adrenaline | 42,000 | 1,300 |
| Control | 11,200 | 40,600 |
| MIX | 1,400 | 190 |

*From A. J. T. Millis, G. Forrest, and D. A. Pious, Cyclic AMP Dependent Regulation of Mitosis in Human Cells, *Exp. Cell Res.*, **83**: 335-343 (1974).

When the catecholamine was washed from the cul⁻ıre after 3 hr, high levels of DNA synthesis occurred during the time period usually reserved for $G_2$ and M.

Our experiments showed MIX to inhibit both the uptake and the incorporation of thymidine (Table 5). This agent virtually inhibits DNA synthesis (Fig. 5). When MIX was washed from the culture at the end of S, a wave of DNA synthesis occurred. That wave of synthesis preceded the onset of mitosis (Fig. 4). It is clear from Table 6 that in unsynchronized cultures, the effects of MIX (elevation of cyclic AMP) were reversed within 30 min of the time that the cells were washed.

The mechanism through which cyclic AMP acts to inhibit DNA synthesis remains undetermined. It is likely that cyclic AMP affects membrane transport and can regulate DNA synthesis by preventing uptake of precursors.[34] This may be related in some way to its probable influence on microtubules.[35] However, the data in Table 5 indicate the possibility of another method of inhibition unrelated to precursor uptake.

The association of cyclic nucleotides with so many physiologic and metabolic processes leads to the question of how specificity is conferred in cyclic-AMP-mediated activities. There is evidence that some specificity occurred through binding to particular protein kinases[36] and by variations in the degree of sensitivity to adenylate cyclase activators.[37] The evidence presented here also suggests that various cellular activities are only receptive to cyclic-AMP regulation during specific times of the cell cycle. In addition, comparison of the effects of noradrenaline, isopropylnoradrenaline, dbcAMP, and MIX leads to the speculation that cyclic AMP may be present in separate subcellular pools and that a measure of specificity is conferred by changes in particular pool levels. The general effects of MIX and dbcAMP might result from increased cyclic AMP

TABLE 6

CHANGES IN CYCLIC-AMP LEVELS IN NONSYNCHRONOUS
CULTURES EXPOSED TO MIX

| Treatment* | Cyclic AMP, pmole/mg protein |
|---|---|
| Control (1) | 48.7 |
| MIX (1) | 193.7 |
| Control/chase (2) | 102.1 |
| MIX/chase (2) | 12.6 |

*1. Comparison of the level of cyclic AMP in 2.0 mmolar MIX-treated and untreated cultures. Exposure to MIX was for 30 min.

2. After treatment with 2.0 mmolar MIX for 30 min, cells were washed three times by centrifugation and resuspended in the original volume of fresh media; incubation was continued for 30 min more. Control cells were similarly washed, resuspended, and incubated.

in all pools. However, the differential effects of the two catecholamines on DNA synthesis might result from isopropylnoradrenaline activation of a cyclic-AMP pool regulating DNA synthesis and one regulating mitosis. Noradrenaline only activates the cyclic-AMP pool associated with mitosis. On the cellular level such compartmentalization might be the result of noradrenaline activation of plasma membrane receptor sites whereas isopropylnoradrenaline activates receptor sites on both plasma and nuclear membranes.[38]

## ACKNOWLEDGMENTS

We wish to express our appreciation to Searle Laboratories for providing the 1-methyl-3-isobutylxanthine. This investigation was supported by the U. S. National Institute of General Medical Sciences and the National Institute of Child Health and Development. Donald A. Pious is a recipient of a Career Research Development Award from the National Institutes of Health.

## REFERENCES

1. J. P. Jost and H. V. Rickenberg, Cyclic AMP, *Annu. Rev. Biochem.*, **40**: 741-775 (1971).
2. G. M. Tomkins and D. W. Martin, Hormones and Gene Expression, *Annu. Rev. Genet.*, **4**: 91-105 (1970).
3. I. Pastan and R. L. Perlman, Cyclic AMP in Metabolism, *Nature (London) New Biol.*, **229**: 5-7 (1971).
4. F. Marks and W. Grimm, Diurnal Fluctuation and $\beta$-Adrenergic Elevation of Cyclic AMP in Mouse Epidermis in vivo, *Nature (London) New Biol.*, **240**: 178-179 (1972).
5. J. J. Voorhees, E. A. Duell, and W. H. Kelsey, Dibutyryl Cyclic AMP Inhibition of Epidermal Cell Division, *Arch. Dermatol.*, **105**: 384-386 (1972).
6. J. R. Sheppard, Difference in the Cyclic Adenosine 3',5'-Monophosphate Levels in Normal and Transformed Cells, *Nature (London) New Biol.*, **236**: 14-16 (1972).
7. J. Otten, G. S. Johnson, and I. Pastan, Cyclic AMP Levels in Fibroblasts: Relationship to Growth Rate and Contact Inhibition of Growth, *Biochem. Biophys. Res. Commun.*, **44**: 1192-1198 (1971).
8. G. T. Todaro, G. K. Lazar, and H. Green, The Initiation of Cell Division in a Contact-Inhibited Mammalian Cell Line, *J. Cell. Comp. Physiol.*, **66**: 325-334 (1965).
9. M. C. Willingham, G. S. Johnson, and I. Pastan, Control of DNA Synthesis and Mitosis in 3T3 Cells by Cyclic AMP, *Biochem. Biophys. Res. Commun.*, **48**: 743-748 (1972).
10. K. Nilansen and H. Green, Reversible Arrest of Growth in $G_1$ of an Established Fibroblast Line (3T3), *Exp. Cell Res.*, **40**: 166-168 (1965).
11. J. E. Froehlich and L. Rachmeler, Effect of Cyclic AMP on Cell Proliferation, *Exp. Cell Res.*, **55**: 19-31 (1972).
12. G. Galavazi, H. Schenk, and D. Bootsma, Synchronization of Mammalian Cells in vitro by Inhibition of DNA Synthesis, *Exp. Cell Res.*, **41**: 428-437 (1966).
13. A. J. T. Millis, G. Forrest, and D. A. Pious, Cyclic AMP Dependent Regulation of Mitosis in Human Cells, *Exp. Cell Res.*, **83**: 335-343 (1974).
14. A. J. T. Millis, G. Forrest, and D. A. Pious, Cyclic AMP in Cultured Human Lymphoid Cells: Relationship to Mitosis, *Biochem. Biophys. Res. Commun.*, **49**: 1645-1649 (1972).

15. A. Gilman, A Protein Binding Assay for Adenosine 3′,5′-Cyclic Monophosphate, *Proc. Nat. Acad. Sci. U.S.A.*, **67**: 305-312 (1970).

16. P. R. Davoren and E. W. Sutherland, The Cellular Location of Adenyl Cyclase in the Pigeon Erythrocyte, *J. Biol. Chem.*, **238**: 3016-3023 (1963).

17. L. A. Menahan, K. D. Hepp, and O. Wieland, Liver 3′,5′-Nucleotide Phosphodiesterase and Its Activity in Rat Livers Perfused with Insulin, *Eur. J. Biochem.*, **8**: 435-443 (1969).

18. G. J. S. Rao, M. Del Monte, and H. L. Nadler, Adenyl Cyclase Activity in Cultivated Human Skin Fibroblasts, *Nature (London) New Biol.*, **232**: 253-255 (1971).

19. M. D'Armiento, G. S. Johnson, and I. Pastan, Regulation of Adenosine 3′,5′-Cyclic Monophosphate Phosphodiesterase Activity in Fibroblasts by Intracellular Concentrations of Cyclic Adenosine Monophosphate, *Proc. Nat. Acad. Sci. U.S.A.*, **69**: 459-462 (1972).

20. M. M. Burger, B. M. Bombik, B. McL. Breckenridge, and J. R. Sheppard, Growth Control and Cyclic Alterations of Cyclic AMP in the Cell Cycle, *Nature (London) New Biol.*, **239**: 161-163 (1972).

21. J. R. Sheppard and D. M. Prescott, Cyclic AMP Levels in Synchronized Mammalian Cells, *Exp. Cell Res.*, **75**: 293-296 (1972).

22. K. Raska, Cyclic AMP in $G_1$-Arrested BHK 21 Cells Infected with Adenovirus Type 12, *Biochem. Biophys. Res. Commun.*, **50**: 35-41 (1973).

23. M. H. Makman and M. I. Klein, Expression of Adenylate Cyclase, Catecholamine Receptor, and Cyclic Adenosine Monophosphate-Dependent Protein Kinase in Synchronized Culture of Chang's Liver Cells, *Proc. Nat. Acad. Sci. U.S.A.*, **69**: 456-458 (1972).

24. R. S. Makman and E. W. Sutherland, Adenosine 3′,5′-Phosphate in *Escherichia coli*, *J. Biol. Chem.*, **240**: 1309-1314 (1965).

25. D. B. P. Goodman, H. Rasmussen, F. DiBella, and C. E. Guthrow, Adenosine 3′,5′-Cyclic Monophosphate Stimulated Phosphorylation of Isolated Neurotubule Subunits, *Proc. Nat. Acad. Sci. U.S.A.*, **67**: 652-659 (1970).

26. A. W. Murray and M. Froscio, Cyclic Adenosine 3′,5′-Monophosphate and Microtubule Function: Specific Interaction of the Phosphorylated Protein Subunits with a Soluble Brain Component, *Biochem. Biophys. Res. Commun.*, **44**: 1089-1095 (1971).

27. E. Gillespie, Colchicine Binding in Tissue Slices, *J. Cell Biol.*, **50**: 544-549 (1971).

28. G. Forrest and R. R. Klevecz, Synthesis and Degradation of Microtubule Protein in Synchronized Chinese Hamster Cells, *J. Biol. Chem.*, **247**: 3147-3152 (1972).

29. L. D. Johnson and C. W. Abell, The Effects of Isoproterenol and Cyclic AMP on PHA-Stimulated Lymphocytes from Patients with Chronic Lymphocytic Leukemia, *Cancer Res.*, **30**: 2718-2723 (1970).

30. D. R. Webb, D. P. Sites, J. D. Perlman, D. Luong, and H. H. Fudenberg, Lymphocyte Activation: The Dualistic Effect of cAMP, *Biophys. Res. Commun.*, **53**: 1002-1008 (1973).

31. R. W. Teel, Inhibition of DNA Synthesis in Hamster Cheek Pouch Tissue in Organ Culture by Dibutyryl Cyclic AMP and a Homologous Extract, *Biochem. Biophys. Res. Commun.*, **47**: 1010-1014 (1972).

32. R. Hirschhorn, J. Grossman, and G. Weissman, Effect of Cyclic AMP and Theophilline on Lymphocyte Transformation, *Proc. Soc. Exp. Biol. Med.*, **133**: 1361-1365 (1970).

33. J. W. Smith, A. L. Steiner, and C. W. Parker, Human Lymphocyte Metabolism. Effects of Cyclic and Non-Cyclic Nucleotides on Stimulation by PHA, *J. Clin. Invest.*, **50**: 442-448 (1971).

34. R. Kram, P. Marmont, and G. M. Tomkins, Pleiotypic Control by Adenosine 3′,5′-Cyclic Monophosphate: A Model for Growth in Animal Cells, *Proc. Nat. Acad. Sci. U.S.A.*, **70**: 1432-1436 (1973).

35. R. Kram and G. M. Tomkins, Pleiotypic Control by cAMP: Interaction with cGMP and Possible Role of Microtubules, *Proc. Nat. Acad. Sci. U.S.A.*, **70**: 1659-1663 (1973).
36. J. F. Kuo and P. Greengard, Cyclic Nucleotide-Dependent Protein Kinases. IV. Widespread Occurrence of Adenosine 3′,5′-Monophosphate-Dependent Protein Kinase in Various Tissues and Phyla of the Animal Kingdom, *Proc. Nat. Acad. Sci. U.S.A.*, **64**: 1349-1355 (1969).
37. G. A. Robison, R. W. Butcher, and E. W. Sutherland, Adenyl Cyclase As an Adrenergic Receptor, *Ann. N. Y. Acad. Sci.*, **139**: 703-723 (1967).
38. E. W. Sutherland and G. A. Robison, The Role of Cyclic 3′,5′-AMP in Response to Catecholamines and Other Hormones, *Pharmacol. Rev.*, **18**: 145-161 (1966).
39. H. J. Wedner, B. J. Hoffer, F. E. Bloom, and C. W. Parker, Catecholamine Stimulation of Cyclic AMP in the Nucleus of Human Peripheral Lymphocytes, *Fed. Proc.*, **32**: 744, Abstract (1973).

# SERINE DEHYDRATASE ACTIVITY
# AND CATABOLITE REPRESSION
# IN SYNCHRONOUS CHO CELLS

LEON N. KAPP, JOHN A. REMINGTON, and ROBERT R. KLEVECZ
Department of Cell Biology, Division of Biology, City of Hope National Medical Center,
Duarte, California

## ABSTRACT

Serine dehydratase activity in Chinese hamster ovary (CHO) cells changes in response to dibutyryl cyclic AMP (adenosine monophosphate) and glucose levels in the medium. Dibutyryl cyclic AMP plus theophylline induces enzyme activity to 250% of that of the controls. Glucose-free medium elevated enzyme activities to 230% of that of the controls, whereas high glucose concentrations caused a depression of enzyme activity to approximately 40% of normal. Cycloheximide blocked low glucose induction completely, indicating that this rise in activity is probably due to de novo serine dehydratase synthesis. Although glucose-free medium and dibutyryl cyclic AMP each independently induced serine dehydratase, a combined treatment with both of these resulted in limited enzyme induction of about 130 to 150% of control levels.

Synchronized cells were treated at hourly intervals of the cell cycle for 1 hr. Glucose-free medium was found to induce enzyme activity at $G_1$, mid S, and late S to $G_2$. Dibutyryl cyclic AMP plus theophylline added to glucose-free medium inhibited almost all induction. However, dibutyryl cyclic AMP plus theophylline in normal medium (3 mg/ml glucose) was able to induce enzyme activity at 10 to 11 hr of cell cycle and had little, if any, effect at other times. High glucose content (30 mg/ml) repressed most enzyme activity at almost all points of the cell cycle. However dibutyryl cyclic AMP plus theophylline in the medium apparently prevented enzyme repression at 5 hr ($G_1$ –S boundary) and 12 to 14 hr (late S to $G_2$) and prevented complete repression at 6 to 10 hr (mid S). Thus, the exact response of the cells to dibutyryl cyclic AMP depends strongly on the glucose levels in the medium, and, in addition, the synchronized-cell studies also suggest that the response has a strong cell-cycle dependency.

Mammalian cells in tissue culture are being used as a model system to study the regulation of enzyme activity. One advantage of tissue culture over most other systems is the existence of techniques for obtaining large populations of synchronized cells, which make it possible to investigate the role of the cell cycle in regulating enzyme activities.

Enzyme activity and enzyme protein synthesis of tyrosine aminotransferase in hepatoma tissue-culture cells[1] and alkaline phosphatase in HeLa cells[2] are elevated by glucocorticoids and steroid hormones, and an effort has been made to discover the steps involved in enzyme induction. Several workers have reported the induction of serine dehydratase and other enzymes by cyclic AMP or dibutyryl cyclic AMP in rat liver and in cultured mammalian cells.[3-7] In addition, Jost, Khairallah, and Pitot,[8] Mendelson, Grossman, and Boctor,[9] and Wimhurst and Manchester[10] have shown that serine dehydratase in rat liver and rat diaphragm is induced by low levels of glucose and can be repressed by high levels of glucose, and Jost, Khairallah, and Pitot[8] have compared this to catabolite repression in bacteria. However, one parameter of enzyme regulation that has been studied in little detail is the role of the cell cycle. Most enzymes examined show some variance over the cell cycle,[11-15] and actinomycin D induction of acid phosphatase[16] and dibutyryl cyclic AMP (adenosine monophosphate) induction of serine dehydratase[12] are both strongly dependent on the cell cycle, with enzyme induction occurring only at restricted times in the cell cycle.

In the work reported here, low-glucose-concentration induction and high-glucose-concentration repression of serine dehydratase activity and the effects of dibutyryl cyclic AMP on this phenomenon have been observed over the cell cycle. It is not clear whether this effect is strictly analogous to catabolite repression in bacteria. However, the effects of high and low glucose concentrations on enzyme activity do depend on the cell-cycle position, and these effects are modified by dibutyryl cyclic AMP. In addition, these modifying effects of dibutyryl cyclic AMP also depend strongly on the cell cycle. In view of the results shown here, it is possible that, if one studies glucose regulation of enzyme activity in a random population of cells, particularly in vivo, the results could vary depending on the cell-cycle distribution or points of arrest of the cells in the tissue.

## MATERIALS AND METHODS

The Chinese hamster ovary (CHO) cells used were those described by Tjio and Puck.[17] Cells were grown in monolayer cultures in McCoy's 5a medium supplemented with 20% fetal calf serum. The generation time was about 14 hr. Synchronous populations of cells were collected by the automatic synchrony apparatus described by Klevecz[18] and Klevecz and Kapp.[19] Cells were grown in roller bottles, which rotated at 0.5 rpm to maintain the cells. At hourly intervals the speed of the rollers was increased to 100 rpm for 5 min; this increased speed detached the mitotic cells, which were then pumped into a series of scintillation vials. At the end of 14 hr, the machine had provided a series of 14 cultures, each of which was separated from the others by 1 hr of the cell cycle.

Cells for all experiments were grown in scintillation vials as described previously.[14] For enzyme assays the medium was removed from a scintillation vial, 0.5 ml of Tris [tris(hydroxymethyl)-aminomethane] buffer (0.01$M$, pH 7.5) was added, and the vial was sonicated for 30 sec in an external sonifier. Fifty microliters of this sonicate containing approximately $10^5$ cells was used to assay for serine dehydratase activity (EC 4.2.1.13). Assay mixtures contained 1.4 × $10^{-4}M$ NADH, 1 unit/ml lactic dehydrogenase, and 0.1$M$ L-serine in 0.1$M$ Tris HCl, pH 8.4. After the sonicate was added to the assay mixture, the decrease in absorbance at 340 nm was followed at 37°C with a spectrophotometer.[20] Enzyme activities were calculated as activity per cell.

Incorporation of $^3$H—methyl—thymidine ($^3$H—TdR, 6.0 Ci/mmole) into DNA of cells grown in scintillation vials (30-min exposure, 2 $\mu$Ci $^3$H—TdR/ml) was determined as described previously.[19] Over 400 cells were counted in each sample to determine the mitotic index.

Normal McCoy's 5a medium contains 3 mg glucose/ml. For concentrations less than this, McCoy's 5a medium was made up according to the formula except that no glucose was added. High-glucose-content medium consisted of McCoy's 5a medium supplemented with the appropriate amount of glucose. Cycloheximide was used at a concentration of 100 $\mu$g/ml. Dibutyryl cyclic AMP was used at a concentration of 0.1 mmolar and theophylline at 1 mmolar. All these were dissolved in the appropriate medium immediately before use.

## RESULTS

In the experiments described, the cells were plated approximately 12 to 15 hr before the experiment and grown in normal medium. At zero time the medium was removed and replaced with new medium with the appropriate glucose concentration. To test the effect of glucose levels on serine dehydratase activity, we replaced normal medium with medium containing 0, 1, 3, 15, 30, and 50 mg glucose/ml. The cells were incubated for 2 hr, and enzyme activity was assayed. The results are shown in Fig. 1. Low glucose content (0.1 mg/ml) elevated enzyme activities, and the extent of induction was inversely proportional to the glucose concentration. In glucose-free medium induction was usually about 200% of the controls. In contrast, high glucose levels (15, 30, and 50 mg/ml) caused a reduction in enzyme activity. Such enzyme repression by glucose has been reported for serine dehydratase[8] and tyrosine aminotransferase,[9] and, in addition, glucose has been shown to block induction of threonine dehydratase and ornithine transaminase.[21] These phenomena have been compared to catabolite repression in bacteria.[8]

Figure 2 shows the time course of the effects of several treatments on serine dehydratase activities. Dibutyryl cyclic AMP plus theophylline or testosterone has been reported to induce serine dehydratase activity (Refs. 4, 5, 7, and 12); Fig. 2 shows the effects of dibutyryl cyclic AMP plus testosterone on serine

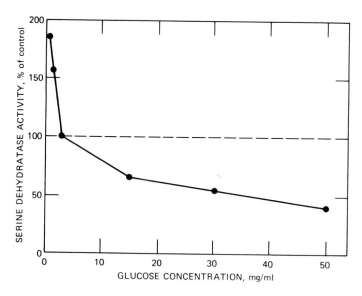

Fig. 1  Effect of glucose concentration on serine dehydratase activity in log phase cells.

dehydratase. Enzyme induction was approximately 250% of controls at 3 hr. Glucose-free medium had a very similar effect on enzyme activity, and the time course of induction appears very similar under both conditions, although maximum induction in the presence of glucose-free medium was about 230% of the controls or slightly less than the cyclic nucleotide induction. Since the two enzyme activity curves appeared to be very similar, glucose-free medium was supplemented with dibutyryl cyclic AMP plus theophylline to determine if the two effects on serine dehydratase were additive. These results are also shown in Fig. 2 and were surprising in that the combined treatment of the cells resulted in enzyme induction of approximately 150% of controls, or less than half of the activity increase due to either a low glucose concentration or dibutyryl cyclic AMP alone.

To determine if glucose-free-medium induction of enzyme activity was due to de novo protein synthesis, we next incubated cells with glucose-free medium and with glucose-free medium with 100 μg cycloheximide/ml (Fig. 3). When cells were incubated with cycloheximide, induction was blocked completely, indicating that the increase in enzyme activity in this case was probably due to new protein synthesis. Similar conclusions have also been found for serine dehydratase induction by dibutyryl cyclic AMP by several workers using immunoprecipitation techniques.[4],[8]

Thus, either glucose-free medium or dibutyryl cyclic AMP was able to elevate enzyme activity alone although the combination of the two resulted in less than half the induction produced by either one alone. In addition, induction

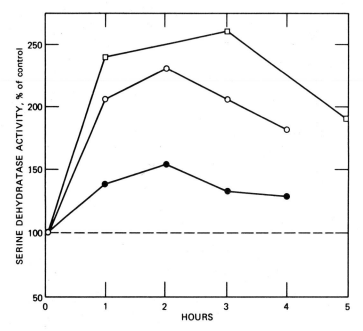

Fig. 2 Effect of dibutyryl cyclic AMP, glucose-free medium, and dibutyryl cyclic AMP plus glucose-free medium. ○, glucose-free medium. □, normal medium with dibutyryl cyclic AMP plus testosterone. ●, glucose-free medium plus dibutyryl cyclic AMP plus theophylline.

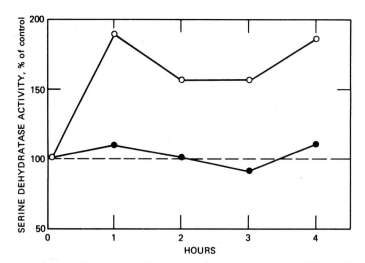

Fig. 3 Effect of cycloheximide (100 μg/ml) on glucose-free-medium induction of serine dehydratase. ○, glucose-free medium; ●, glucose-free medium plus 100 μg cycloheximide/ml.

appears to be due to de novo protein synthesis. Since cyclic AMP levels do show variations during the cell cycle[22-24] and since dibutyryl cyclic AMP induction of serine dehydratase is cell-cycle dependent,[12] enzyme induction under these various conditions (low and high glucose concentrations with and without dibutyryl cyclic AMP plus theophylline) was examined in synchronous cultures.

Figure 4 shows some parameters of the CHO cell cycle. The generation time is 14 hr with the peak mitotic index at 14 hr. DNA synthesis as determined by

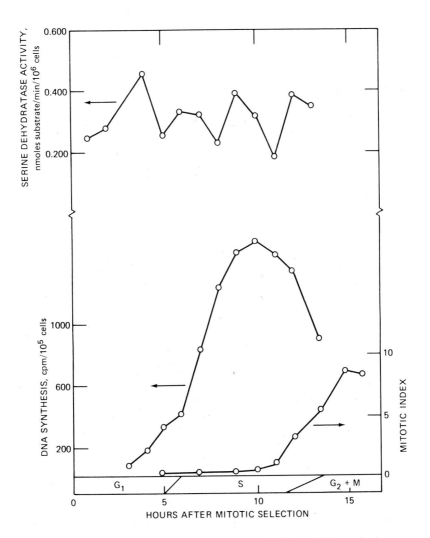

Fig. 4   Cell-cycle parameters of CHO cells. Mitotic index, DNA synthesis as determined by ³H—TdR incorporation, and serine dehydratase activity are shown for a control population.

[3]H—thymidine incorporation begins at approximately the 5th hour after mitosis and lasts until the 12th or 13th hour. Serine dehydratase activity shows four peaks and appears to oscillate through the cell cycle with maximums occurring at 4, 6 to 7, 9, and 11 hr into the cell cycle. Synchronous cell populations were obtained using the automatic synchrony apparatus of Klevecz,[18,19] which selects mitotic cells from roller-bottle surfaces by increasing the roller speed from 0.5 to 100 rpm. Thus, mitotic cells are selected without the use of drugs, lowered temperatures, or centrifugation.

To examine the effects of high and low glucose concentrations and dibutyryl cyclic AMP on enzyme activities in synchronous cells, we used the following procedure. Synchronous populations of cells were selected by automatic synchrony apparatus. At each hour of the cell cycle, samples were taken, and the normal medium was removed and replaced with normal medium (3 mg glucose/ml), high-glucose-content medium (30 mg glucose/ml), or glucose-free medium with or without dibutyryl cyclic AMP plus theophylline. The cells were incubated in the appropriate medium for 1 hr; then enzyme activity was assayed. The results are shown in Fig. 5 as percent of control. Control cells were incubated in fresh normal medium for the same 1-hr period.

The effect of glucose-free medium on serine dehydratase activity in synchronous cells is shown in Fig. 5. There appear to be three peaks of enzyme induction: $G_1$ (1 to 5 hr), mid S (6 to 8 hr), and $S-G_2$ boundary (12 to 13 hr); little or no effect was observed at the points between these peaks ($G_1-S$ boundary and late S). When dibutyryl cyclic AMP and theophylline were added to the glucose-free medium, most of the enzyme induction was prevented. There appears to be some induction at the first hour of the cell cycle and also during the 12th to 13th hours (to 130% of controls). A noticeable feature of this curve is the degree of parallelism between it and the curve for glucose-free medium alone. The patterns of the two are very similar, but the cyclic nucleotide appears primarily to have depressed the amplitude of enzyme activity.

The effect of dibutyryl cyclic AMP plus theophylline in the presence of normal glucose levels is also shown in Fig. 5. Under these conditions there appears to be little effect on enzyme activity except at the 9th to 11th hours of the cell cycle, where enzyme activity was induced to 250% of controls. This is in excellent agreement with the results reported for serine dehydratase induction by dibutyryl cyclic AMP plus testosterone in colcemid synchronized CHO cells.[12] Thus, dibutyryl cyclic AMP appears to have identical effects in the presence of theophylline or of testosterone. A comparison of the curves in Fig. 5 shows that the single peak of enzyme induction in normal medium plus cyclic nucleotide occurs at the 10th to 11th hours of the cell cycle and that at this time glucose-free medium has no effect on enzyme activity.

Since high glucose concentrations repressed enzyme activity in log phase cells, this was also examined in synchronous cells. Figure 6 shows that high-glucose-content medium (30 mg/ml) reduced enzyme activity throughout

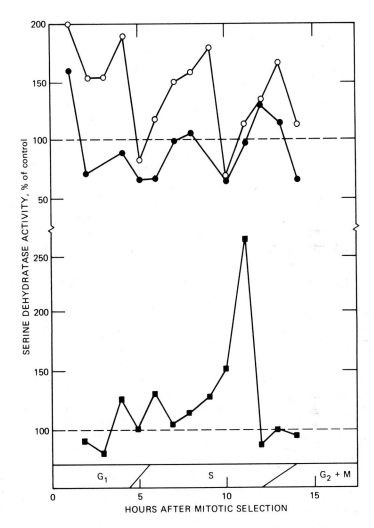

Fig. 5 Effect of glucose-free medium and dibutyryl cyclic AMP plus theophylline on serine dehydratase activity in synchronous CHO cells. ○, glucose-free medium. ●, glucose-free medium with dibutyryl cyclic AMP plus theophylline. ■, normal medium (3 mg glucose/ml) plus dibutyryl cyclic AMP plus theophylline.

the cell cycle. At hours 1 to 7, enzyme activity was below the levels necessary to be accurately measured by the assay as used here (approximately 0.01 nmole of substrate used per minute per $10^6$ cells). There appear to be two small peaks of enzyme activity at 4 hr (mid S) and 6 to 9 hr (latter half of S). When dibutyryl cyclic AMP was present in this medium, it appeared to prevent the complete

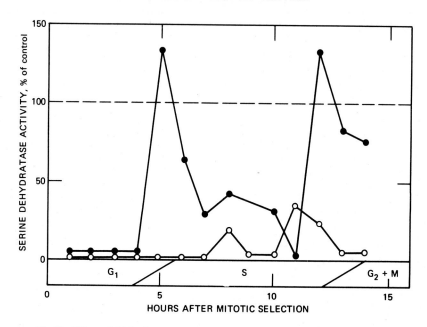

**Fig. 6** **Effect of high glucose and dibutyryl cyclic AMP plus theophylline on serine dehydratase activity in synchronous CHO cells.** ○, 30 mg glucose/ml. ●, 30 mg glucose/ml plus dibutyryl cyclic AMP plus theophylline.

repression of enzyme activity from approximately 4 hr to the end of the cell cycle. In addition, it seemed to prevent any repression of activity at the 5*th* hour (corresponding to a time of the cell cycle when glucose-free medium has no inducing effect) and again at the 12*th* to 14*th* hours (which may correspond to the dibutyryl cyclic AMP induction peak in normal medium and to another minimum in the induction curve due to glucose-free medium).

In view of these data, it appears that the effects of dibutyryl cyclic AMP plus theophylline depend on the level of glucose in the medium and also that the relationship between these two factors may vary as a function of the cell cycle.

## DISCUSSION

In bacteria a number of enzymes appear to be regulated by catabolite repression. Enzymes responsible for the catabolism of carbon compounds can be repressed by their ultimate products or related compounds. These ultimate products of catabolism, i.e., catabolites, are molecules such as ATP (adenosine triphosphate) which serve as energy donors or building blocks for biosynthetic reactions. Since each catabolic pathway leads eventually to the same final products, the metabolism of one carbon compound would produce catabolites that could cause the repression of enzymes responsible for the degradation of other carbon compounds,[25] e.g., the repression of serine dehydratase by glucose. Perlman and Pastan[26] have shown that this repression operates via cyclic AMP and can be overcome by exogenous cyclic AMP in the medium. Nealson, Eberhard, and Hastings[27] have reported similar results for the synthesis of the bioluminescent system of a marine bacterium, and similar results have been reported in mammalian systems. Peraino and Pitot[21] found that glucose could prevent induction of threonine dehydratase and ornithine transaminase in rat liver in vivo, and Yuweiller, Wetterberg, and Geller[28] showed that glucose lowered the basal level and extent of induction of tyrosine aminotransferase and tryptophan oxygenase in rat liver. Mendelson, Grossman, and Boctor[9] observed similar effects on tyrosine aminotransferase in hepatoma tissue-culture cells. They also found that glucose-free medium supplemented with excess L-tyrosine caused a two- to threefold increase in tyrosine aminotransferase activity from 48 to 72 hr after the cells had been transferred to this medium. The induction could be blocked by restoring glucose to the medium. The extent of induction was very similar to that reported here for serine dehydratase, although here the serine dehydratase induction was far more rapid and essentially complete 1 to 2 hr after the cells had been initially exposed to glucose-free medium. In further studies with the same system Grossman, Boctor, and Masuda[3] found that dibutyryl cyclic AMP also stimulated tyrosine aminotransferase activity in normal medium supplemented with excess L-tyrosine. Both inductive effects (glucose-free medium and dibutyryl cyclic AMP) could be prevented by cycloheximide and actinomycin D, which implies that the regulatory events occurred at transcriptional and translational levels and involved de novo protein synthesis. In addition, the induction caused by dibutyryl cyclic AMP in glucose-free medium was not additive, which suggests that the increased enzyme synthesis in both cases occurred via the same mechanism. The data shown here indicate that, although dibutyryl cyclic AMP and glucose-free medium have similar induction effects, there is a marked decrease of enzyme induction when they are used together.

Although in bacterial systems the effect of glucose does seem to be mediated via cyclic AMP,[26,27] this may or may not be true of mammalian systems. Jost, Hsie, and Rickenberg[5] found that serine dehydratase formation in rat liver was stimulated by cyclic AMP, epinephrine, and glucagon and that inhibition of enzyme formation by glucose could be overcome by cyclic AMP or dibutyryl cyclic AMP. Thus they feel, as do Grossman, Boctor, and Masuda,[3] that the glucose effect is mediated via cyclic AMP. Sudilovski et al.[29] show that serine dehydratase and tyrosine aminotransferase activity are inducible by glucagon and that such induction is repressed by glucose. However, although glucose does block enzyme induction, it has no effect on the hepatic cyclic AMP increase due to glucagon. Thus these investigators conclude that, unlike catabolite repression in bacteria, glucose repression in mammalian liver operates independently of the intracellular cyclic AMP concentration.

Additional evidence that glucose repression may operate independently of cyclic AMP levels comes from Buschiazzo, Exton, and Park,[30] who conclude that glucose increases glycogen synthesis and is responsible for the conversion of glycogen synthetase to the active form and of glycogen phosphorylase to the inactive form and that these effects are independent of changes in the levels of hormones or cyclic AMP. Wimhurst and Manchester,[10] in observing the response of serine dehydratase and other enzymes in isolated perfused rat liver, reached a similar conclusion. Finally, it has also been reported that glucose could affect phosphorylase phosphatase directly in rat diaphragm[31] and glycogen synthetase and phosphorylase activities in rat liver in the absence of any detectable changes of cyclic AMP levels.[32]

In summary, there is work supporting both the view that glucose repression operates via cyclic AMP as in microorganisms and the opposite view that glucose operates independently of hormone or cyclic AMP levels.

In the work reported here glucose-free-medium induction of, and high-glucose-content repression of, serine dehydratase activity in CHO cells in tissue culture were observed. Glucose repression has been mentioned often, and glucose-free induction of enzyme activity has been reported for tyrosine aminotransferase in hepatoma tissue-culture cells[9] and for serine dehydratase in isolated perfused liver of starved rats.[10] Serine dehydratase activity can be induced by dibutyryl cyclic AMP but is also strongly dependent on the cell cycle.[12] Similarly, glucose-free-medium induction of serine dehydratase was also found to be cell-cycle dependent (Fig. 5). Enzyme activity was inducible in $G_1$ (1 to 4 hr), mid S (6 to 9 hr), and late $S-G_2$ (12 to 13 hr). Dibutyryl cyclic AMP in glucose-free medium inhibited or eliminated almost all such induction. However, in normal medium dibutyryl cyclic AMP induction occurred at 10 to 11 hr in the cell cycle, a time when glucose-free medium failed to have any inductive effect on enzyme activity, suggesting the possibility that there may be two independent mechanisms operating during glucose modulation of enzyme activity. Just which one is expressed would depend on the position of the cell in the cell cycle and on the glucose concentration. Next, high-glucose-content repression of enzyme activity was seen to be strongest during the first 7 hr of the cell cycle but operated at all points of the cell cycle (Fig. 6). When dibutyryl cyclic AMP plus theophylline was present along with high glucose, enzyme activity was not completely repressed from the 5*th* hour to the end of the cell cycle. However, at the 5*th* hour and the 12*th* to 14*th* hours of the cell cycle, the presence of the cyclic nucleotide completely prevented any enzyme repression. At these times its effect appears very much like catabolite repression in bacteria. It can also be noted that the 5*th* hour corresponds to a time when glucose-free medium has no inductive effect on enzyme activity and that the 12*th* hour may also correspond to the peak of dibutyryl cyclic AMP induction in normal medium.

Thus, studies on synchronous cells may shed additional light on enzyme regulation and the glucose effect in mammalian cells. It has been shown that some inducible enzymes are only inducible at specific times during the cell cycle: actinomycin D inducible acid phosphatase in L5178Y cells[16] and dibutyryl cyclic AMP inducible serine dehydratase in CHO cells.[12] The work reported here shows that (1) glucose-free-medium induction of serine dehydratase is also cell-cycle dependent, (2) dibutyryl cyclic AMP protection of glucose-repressed serine dehydratase activity (catabolite repression as described in bacteria) is cell-cycle dependent, and (3) these two effects may be independent and may occur during mutually exclusive periods of the cell cycle. These findings could account for some of the conflicting reports concerning the glucose effect on serine dehydratase and other enzymes since the mechanism observed would depend very strongly on the system used; e.g., if the cells were all arrested in one portion of the cell cycle, one type of result would be seen. The $G_2$ cells could display cyclic AMP mediated glucose repression, whereas $G_1$ cells would appear to regulate enzyme activities independently of cyclic AMP levels. This assumes that the capacity to express a cell-cycle effect endures in arrested cells. If a sufficiently large fraction of the cells were cycling, the results could be indeterminate or would depend on the age distribution of the cycling cells.

Finally, two other points are apparent from these results: (1) there is some interaction between glucose-free induction and dibutyryl cyclic AMP induction since the combination of the two abolishes most of the enzyme induction due to either one alone. The relationship of these two inductive mechanisms is unclear from the work reported here. (2) Although the effect of dibutyryl cyclic AMP on enzyme activity is strongly cell-cycle dependent, the exact cell-cycle pattern of enzyme induction caused by the cyclic nucleotide also depends very strongly on the level of glucose in which the cells have been growing.

## ACKNOWLEDGMENTS

This work was supported by grants HD-04699 and CA-10619 from the National Institutes of Health.

## REFERENCES

1. G. M. Tomkins, T. D. Gelehrter, D. Granner, D. Martin, H. H. Samuels, and E. B. Thompson, Control of Specific Gene Expression in Higher Organisms, *Science,* **166**: 1474-1480 (1969).
2. M. Griffin and R. Ber, Cell Cycle Events in the Hydrocortisone Regulation of Alkaline Phosphatase in HeLa S3 Cells, *J. Cell Biol.,* **40**: 297-304 (1969).
3. A. Grossman, A. Boctor, and Y. Masuda, Induction of Tyrosine Aminotransferase with $N^6,O^2$-Dibutyryl Adenosine 3'-5'-Monophosphate in Rat Hepatoma Cells Grown in Culture, *Eur. J. Biochem.,* **24**: 149-155 (1971).
4. J. P. Jost, A. Hsie, S. D. Hughes, and L. Ryan, Role of Cyclic Adenosine 3',5'-Monophosphate in the Induction of Hepatic Enzymes. I. Kinetics of the Induction

of Rat Liver Serine Dehydratase by Cyclic Adenosine 3′,5′-Monophosphate, *J. Biol. Chem.*, **245**: 351-357 (1970).

5. J. P. Jost, A. Hsie, and H. U. Rickenberg, Regulation of the Synthesis of Rat Liver Serine Dehydratase by Adenosine 3′,5′-Cyclic Monophosphate, *Biochem. Biophys. Res. Commun.*, **34**: 748-754 (1969).

6. H. Koyama, R. Kato, and T. Ono, Induction of Alkaline Phosphatase by Cyclic AMP or its Dibutyryl Derivative in a Hybrid Line Between Mouse and Chinese Hamster in Culture, *Biochem. Biophys. Res. Commun.*, **46**: 305-311 (1972).

7. W. D. Wicks, F. T. Kenney, and K. Lee, Induction of Hepatic Enzyme Synthesis in Vivo by Adenosine 3′,5′-Monophosphate, *J. Biol. Chem.*, **244**: 6008-1013 (1969).

8. J. P. Jost, E. A. Khairallah, and H. C. Pitot, Studies on Induction and Repression of Enzymes in Rat Liver, *J. Biol. Chem.*, **243**: 3057-3066 (1968).

9. D. Mendelson, A. Grossman, and A. Boctor, D-Glucose Suppression of Tyrosine Aminotransferase in Rat Hepatoma Cells Grown in Tissue Culture, *Eur. J. Biochem.*, **24**: 140-148 (1971).

10. J. M. Wimhurst and K. L. Manchester, Induction and Suppression of the Key Enzymes of Glycolysis and Gluconeogenesis in Isolated Perfused Rat Liver in Response to Glucose, Fructose and Lactate, *Biochem. J.*, **134**: 143-156 (1973).

11. L. N. Kapp and S. Okada, Factors Affecting Acid Phosphatase Activity in Exponential and Synchronized L5178Y Mouse Leukemia Cells, *Exp. Cell Res.*, **72**: 465-472 (1972).

12. L. N. Kapp, J. A. Remington, and R. R. Klevecz, Induction of Serine Dehydratase Activity by Cyclic AMP is Restricted to S Phase in Synchronized CHO Cells, *Biochem. Biophys. Res. Commun.*, **52**: 1206-1212 (1973).

13. R. R. Klevecz, Temporal Order in Mammalian Cells. I. The Periodic Synthesis of Lactate Dehydrogenase in the Cell Cycle, *J. Cell Biol.*, **43**: 207-219 (1969).

14. R. R. Klevecz and F. H. Ruddle, Cyclic Changes in Enzyme Activity in Synchronized Mammalian Cell Cultures, *Science*, **159**: 634-636 (1968).

15. E. Stubblefield and S. Murphree, Synchronized Mammalian Cell Cultures. II. Thymidine Kinase Activity in Colcemid Synchronized Fibroblasts, *Exp. Cell Res.*, **48**: 652-656 (1967).

16. L. N. Kapp and S. Okada, Actinomycin D Induction of Acid Phosphatase Activity in Synchronized L5178Y Mouse Leukemia Cells, *Exp. Cell Res.*, **72**: 473-479 (1972).

17. J. H. Tjio and T. T. Puck, Genetics of Somatic Mammalian Cells. II. Chromosomal Constitution of Cells in Tissue Culture, *J. Exp. Med.*, **108**: 259-268 (1958).

18. R. R. Klevecz, An Automated System for Cell Cycle Analysis, *Anal. Biochem.*, **49**: 407-415 (1972).

19. R. R. Klevecz and L. N. Kapp, Intermittent DNA Synthesis and Periodic Expression of Enzyme Activity in the Cell Cycle of WI-38, *J. Cell Biol.*, **58**: 564-573 (1973).

20. H. C. Pitot and N. Pries, The Automated Assay of Complete Enzyme Reaction Rates. I. Methods and Results, *Anal. Biochem.*, **9**: 454-466 (1964).

21. C. Peraino and H. C. Pitot, Studies on the Induction and Repression of Enzymes in Rat Liver, *J. Biol. Chem.*, **239**: 4308-4313.

22. M. M. Burger, B. M. Bombik, B. M. Breckenridge, and J. R. Sheppard, Growth Control and Cyclic Alterations of Cyclic AMP in the Cell Cycle, *Nature (London) New Biol.*, **239**: 161-163 (1972).

23. J. R. Sheppard and D. M. Prescott, Cyclic AMP Levels in Synchronized Mammalian Cells, *Exp. Cell Res.*, **75**: 293-296 (1972).

24. C. E. Zeilig, R. A. Johnson, D. L. Friedman, and E. W. Sutherland, Cyclic AMP Concentrations in Synchronized HeLa Cells, *J. Cell Biol.*, **55**: 296a (1972).

25. B. Magasanik, Glucose Effects: Inducer Exclusion and Repression, in *The Lactose Operon*, pp. 189-219, J. R. Beckwith and D. Zipper (Eds.), Cold Spring Harbor Laboratory, New York, 1970.

26. R. L. Perlman and I. Pastan, Regulation of β-Galactosidase Synthesis in E. coli by Cyclic Adenosine 3',5'-Monophosphate, *J. Biol. Chem.*, **243**: 5420-5427 (1968).

27. K. H. Nealson, A. Eberhard, and J. W. Hastings, Catabolite Repression of Bacterial Bioluminescence: Functional Implications, *Proc. Nat. Acad Sci. U. S. A.*, **69**: 1073-1076 (1972).

28. A. Yuwciller, L. Wetterberg, and E. Geller, Alterations in Induction of Tyrosine Aminotransferase and Tryptophan Oxygenase by Glucose Pretreatment, *Biochim. Biophys. Acta*, **208**: 428-433 (1970).

29. O. Sudilovski, A. Pestana, P. Hinderaker, and H. C. Pitot, Cyclic Adenosine 3',5'-Monophosphate During Glucose Repression in the Rat Liver, *Science*, **174**: 142-144 (1971).

30. H. Buschiazzo, J. H. Exton, and C. R. Park, Effects of Glucose on Glycogen Synthetase, Phosphorylase, and Glycogen Deposition in the Perfused Rat Liver, *Proc. Nat. Acad. Sci. U. S. A.*, **65**: 383-387 (1970).

31. P. A. Holmes and T. E. Manosour, Glucose as a Regulator of Glycogen Phosphorylase in Rat Diaphragm. II. Effects of Glucose and Related Compounds on Phosphorylase Phosphatase, *Biochim. Biophys. Acta*, **156**: 275-284 (1968).

32. W. Glinsman, G. Pauk, and E. Hern, Control of Rat Liver Glycogen Synthetase and Phosphorylase Activities by Glucose, *Biochem. Biophys. Res. Commun.*, **39**: 774-782 (1970).

# ACCUMULATION OF POLYAMINES AFTER STIMULATION OF CELLULAR PROLIFERATION IN HUMAN DIPLOID FIBROBLASTS

OLLE HEBY,[*1] LAURENCE J. MARTON,[*1] LUCIANO ZARDI,[†]
DIANE H. RUSSELL,[*2] and RENATO BASERGA[†]
*Laboratory of Pharmacology, Baltimore Cancer Research Center,
National Cancer Institute, National Institutes of Health, Baltimore, Maryland, and
†Department of Pathology and Fels Research Institute,
Temple University School of Medicine, Philadelphia, Pennsylvania.

## ABSTRACT

Confluent monolayers of WI-38 human diploid fibroblasts can be stimulated to synthesize DNA and divide by replacement of the exhausted medium with fresh medium containing 10% fetal calf serum. Several biochemical changes have been shown to occur during the prereplicative phase, which lasts about 12 to 15 hr. In this investigation the cellular content of the polyamines putrescine, spermidine, and spermine was studied at various intervals after the nutritional change. Spermine was the quantitatively dominating polyamine in WI-38 fibroblasts. In unstimulated cells spermine content was 4 times that of spermidine and 18 times that of putrescine. Upon stimulation a sixfold increase in putrescine content was observed. The accumulation of putrescine preceded the onset of DNA synthesis and coincided with peak of synthesis of ribosomal RNA. The magnitude of putrescine accumulation depended on the percentage of cells that were stimulated to proliferate. Putrescine stimulates the first step in spermidine synthesis, the decarboxylation of S-adenosyl-L-methionine, and is a precursor of spermidine, which is in turn a precursor of spermine. Accordingly, the cellular content of spermidine and spermine increased subsequently to that of putrescine. However, within 1 hr after stimulation, there was an increase in spermidine content, followed by a gradual decrease. During the remainder of the prereplicative phase, the spermidine content was within the same range as that of unstimulated cells. The activity of putrescine-activated S-adenosyl-L-methionine decarboxylase showed a similar pattern, i.e., an increase within 2 hr, a depression at about 8 hr, and an increase during the period of DNA synthesis. The early stimulation of spermidine synthesis coincides with the increased synthesis of nonhistone chromosomal proteins, the marked rise

---

[1] Present address: Brain Tumor Research Center, Department of Neurological Surgery, University of California Medical Center, San Francisco, Calif.
[2] Present address: Department of Pharmacology, Arizona Medical Center, University of Arizona, Tucson, Ariz.

in chromatin template activity for RNA synthesis, and the increased incorporation of [3]H—uridine into the RNA of whole cells, which have been previously shown to occur within the first few hours after stimulation.

Cells of the adult animal can be divided with respect to DNA synthesis and cell division into three categories: (1) continuously dividing cells that repeatedly traverse the cell cycle; (2) nondividing cells that have left the cell cycle and are destined to die without dividing again; and (3) quiescent cells that have left the cell cycle and do not synthesize DNA or divide unless stimulated to do so by an appropriate stimulus.[1] The molecular events that precede the onset of DNA synthesis and cell division have been discussed in several reviews dealing both with continuously dividing cells[2,3] and cells stimulated to synthesize DNA and divide from a quiescent state.[4,5] Among the biochemical events that occur after stimulation is the synthesis of polyamines, i.e., putrescine, spermidine, and spermine. The synthesis of these amines involves four enzymes: L-ornithine decarboxylase,[6] S-adenosyl-L-methionine decarboxylase,[7] spermidine synthase[8,9] and spermine synthase[8-10] (Fig. 1). There is some evidence, however, that the last three enzymes may form a multienzyme complex in vivo.[11]

Elevated activities of the enzymes in the polyamine biosynthetic pathway and subsequent accumulation of the polyamines have been observed in several

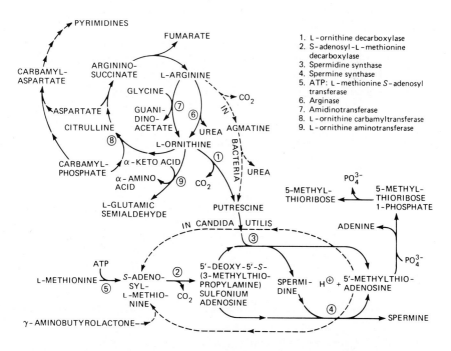

Fig. 1 Biosynthesis of the polyamines putrescine, spermidine, and spermine.

models of stimulated growth, both in vitro (Table 1) and in vivo (Table 2). In many of those models of stimulated growth, e.g., phytohemagglutinin-stimulated lymphocytes, regenerating liver, and estrogen-stimulated uterus, the changes in polyamine metabolism may be related to hypertrophy of the cells rather than to preparation for DNA synthesis and division.

The experiments described in this paper were designed (1) to give some information on the metabolism of polyamines in a model of stimulated growth in which the changes observed cannot be related to tissue hypertrophy but can be related more directly to DNA synthesis and cell division and (2) to determine whether there is a positive quantitative correlation between increasing cellular polyamine content and increasing percentage of cells stimulated to synthesize DNA and divide from a quiescent state.

Changing the medium stimulates confluent monolayers of WI-38 human diploid fibroblasts to initiate DNA synthesis and cell division.[31] Biochemical events that pertain to DNA synthesis and cell division in stimulated WI-38 cells have been studied in detail.[31-37] Consequently, changes in polyamine metabolism can be related to the sequence of biochemical events occurring in WI-38 cells stimulated to proliferate. Further, the degree of stimulation, i.e., the percentage of cells that are stimulated to proliferate, can be altered by varying the composition of the stimulating medium.[38] Thus, the possible correlation between cellular polyamine content and degree of stimulation can be examined.

To determine the content of putrescine, spermidine, and spermine in WI-38 human diploid fibroblasts at various intervals after stimulation, we used a method developed by Seiler and Wiechmann,[39] which is sensitive enough to make possible a quantitative analysis of the polyamines in a confluent monolayer of WI-38 cells grown in one Falcon flask, i.e., approximately $2 \times 10^6$ cells. This method allows an accurate determination of putrescine in spite of its low cellular concentration and adequately separates putrescine from compounds that interfere with its quantitative determination.[40,41]

TABLE 1

POLYAMINE METABOLISM IN MAMMALIAN IN VITRO MODELS
OF STIMULATED GROWTH

| Target cells | Stimulus | Assays* | References |
|---|---|---|---|
| Hepatoma cells (rat) | Change of medium | D | Hogan[12] |
| Lymphocytes (human) | Phytohemagglutinin | D–E | Kay and Lindsay[13] |
| Lymphocytes (human) | Phytohemagglutinin | A–C | Graziano et al.[14] |
| Lymphocytes (bovine) | Concanavalin A | A–E | Fillingame and Morris[15] |
| Lymphocytes (human) | Allogeneic lymphocytes | A–C | Marton et al.[16] |

*Assay of putrescine (A), spermidine (B), and spermine (C) concentration and L-ornithine decarboxylase (D) and S-adenosyl-L-methionine decarboxylase (E) activity.

TABLE 2

POLYAMINE METABOLISM IN MAMMALIAN IN VIVO MODELS
OF STIMULATED GROWTH

| Target tissue | Stimulus | Assays* | References |
|---|---|---|---|
| Liver (rat) | Partial hepatectomy | A–C | Jänne[17] |
| Liver (rat) | Partial hepatectomy | A, D–E | Höltta and Jänne [18] |
| Liver (rat) | Partial hepatectomy | D–G | Hannonen et al.[19] |
| Liver (mouse) | Partial hepatectomy | A–C | Heby and Lewan[20] |
| Liver (mouse) | Partial hepatectomy | A–E | Russell and McVicker[21] |
| Liver (rat) | Thioacetamide | B–D | Fausto[22] |
| Liver (hypophy-sectomized rat) | Growth hormone | A–C | Jänne[17] |
| Liver (hypophy-sectomized rat) | Hydrocortisone | D | Richman et al.[23] |
| Skin (mouse) | Epidermal growth factor | D | Stastny and Cohen[24] |
| Prostate (orchiectomized rat) | Testosterone | A–E | Pegg et al.[25] |
| Uterus (ovariectomized rat) | Estradiol—17β | A–E | Russell and Taylor[26] |
| Ovary (rats in proestrus) | Luteinizing hormone Human chorionic gonadotropin | D | Kobayashi et al.[27] |
| Kidney (rat) | Unilateral nephrectomy | A–D | Brandt et al.[28] |
| Mammary gland (rat) | Lactation | A–E | Russell and McVicker[29] |
| Adrenals (hypophy-sectomized rat) | Adrenocorticotropin | D | Levine et al.[30] |

*Assay of putrescine (A), spermidine (B), and spermine (C) concentration and L-ornithine decarboxylase (D), S-adenosyl-L-methionine decarboxylase (E), spermidine synthase (F), and spermine synthase (G) activity.

# MATERIALS AND METHODS

## Cell Culture

The WI-38 human diploid fibroblasts[42] were grown in roller vessels in Eagle's basal medium supplemented with 10% fetal calf serum, streptomycin (50 μg/ml) and 2 mmolar glutamine. Between the 24th and 28th generations, the cells were transferred for the actual experiments to (1) 1-liter Blake bottles containing 75 ml of medium or (2) plastic Falcon flasks containing 25 ml of medium. The culture medium was changed 24 hr after plating, and the experiments were performed 7 days later when the monolayers were confluent and when a Blake bottle contained approximately $7 \times 10^6$ cells and a Falcon flask approximately $2 \times 10^6$ cells. At 7 days after plating, confluent monolayers of WI-38 cells showed a very low rate of DNA synthesis and mitosis, with 0.1 to 0.5% of the cells being labelled by a 20 to 25 hr exposure to $^3$H—thymidine.[33]

When WI-38 cells had reached confluence, they were stimulated to proliferate by replacing the conditioned medium with fresh medium containing 10% fetal calf serum. Under these conditions 60 to 80% of the quiescent cells were stimulated to synthesize DNA and divide. In some experiments 10% fetal calf serum was added to the conditioned medium, or the conditioned medium was replaced with fresh medium containing only 0.3% fetal calf serum. Under these latter conditions 30 to 40% and 0 to 5%, respectively, of the quiescent cells were stimulated to proliferate. Following stimulation, the individual cultures were arrested at specified times (see Figs. 2 to 4, Tables 3 to 5) by washing the cells twice with 20 ml (Blake bottle) or 10 ml (Falcon flask) of ice-cold phosphate-buffered saline (PBS).[43] The cells were subsequently harvested from the culture flasks in 15 ml of PBS (Blake bottle) or 10 ml of PBS (Falcon flask) by scraping with a rubber policeman and collected in a refrigerated centrifuge at 2000 G at 0°C for 5 min. Since L-ornithine decarboxylase is not stable in a frozen state, the cells were immediately assayed for the activities of the polyamine biosynthetic enzymes. Cells to be used for polyamine assays, however, were kept frozen until analysis.

## Preparation of Cell Extracts for Polyamine Determination

Cellular pellets from Falcon-flask cultures were thawed and sonicated for 1 min with an ultrasonic cell disrupter equipped with a 4.5-in. probe in 400 $\mu$l of 0.2$M$ HClO$_4$ at 0 to 2°C. The homogenates were centrifuged at 1000 G for 15 min, and the supernatant was used for polyamine determination.

## Quantitative Polyamine Analysis

A method developed by Seiler and Wiechmann[39,40] was used for the analyses. The details of the method as applied have been described elsewhere by Heby et al.[44] Briefly, 200 $\mu$l of the cell extracts were dansylated by the addition of 400 $\mu$l of 1-dimethylamino-naphthalene-5-sulfonyl chloride (DANS-Cl) (30 mg/ml aceton) and 100 $\mu$l of a saturated Na$_2$CO$_3$ solution. After 16 hr in the dark at room temperature, 100 $\mu$l of proline (150 mg/ml) was added to remove the excess DANS-Cl by conversion to DANS-proline. After 30 min the DANS-amides were extracted into 500 $\mu$l of benzene. The benzene layer was evaporated to dryness and the residue was dissolved in $\frac{1}{10}$ of its original volume of benzene. Aliquots (5 to 20 $\mu$l) of the benzene extracts were applied to thin-layer chromatography (TLC) plates, and di-DANS-putrescine, tri-DANS-spermidine, and tetra-DANS-spermine were separated by development of the TLC plates in ethyl acetate/cyclohexane (2:3,v/v). These conditions allowed an adequate separation of di-DANS-putrescine from DANS—NH$_2$. The plates were sprayed with triethanolamine/propan-2-ol (1:4,v/v) and desiccated for

16 hr in the dark at room temperature to enhance and stabilize the fluorescence of the DANS-derivatives. After equilibration of the TLC plates at atmospheric pressure for 1 to 2 hr, the fluorescence intensities of the dansylated polyamines were measured with a spectrophotofluorometer equipped with a TLC scanner and recorder (excitation wavelength, 365 nm; emission wavelength, 500 nm).

## Preparation of Cell Extracts for Enzymatic Assays

All procedures were carried out at 0 to 2°C. Cellular pellets from Blake bottle cultures were homogenized immediately after collection for 1 min with an ultrasonic cell disrupter equipped with a 4.5-in. probe in 250 $\mu$l of 0.05$M$ sodium–potassium phosphate buffer, pH 7.2, containing 1.0 mmolar dithiothreitol. The supernatant fraction obtained after 20 min centrifugation at 20,000 G was used for the estimation of enzyme activities.

## Assay of L-Ornithine Decarboxylase Activity

The activity of L-ornithine decarboxylase (L-ornithine carboxy-lyase EC4.1.1.17) was determined by measuring the release of $^{14}CO_2$ from DL-ornithine-1-$^{14}C$ monohydrochloride as previously described.[45] Incubation was carried out in 15-ml centrifuge tubes. Reaction mixtures consisted of 75 $\mu$l of cell extract, added to 4 nmoles of pyridoxal 5-phosphate and 1 $\mu$Ci of DL-ornithine-1-$^{14}C$ monohydrochloride (specific activity 11.9 mCi/mmole) in 0.05$M$ sodium–potassium phosphate buffer, pH 7.2, containing 1.0 mmolar dithiothreitol, to make a total volume of 200 $\mu$l. Radioactivity was assayed with a liquid scintillation spectrometer at an efficiency of 90% (for $^{14}C$). All values were corrected against a "boiled enzyme" assay.

## Assay of S-Adenosyl-L-Methionine Decarboxylase Activity

Enzyme activity was determined by measuring the release of $^{14}CO_2$ from S-adenosyl-L-methionine-carboxyl-$^{14}C$ as described by Pegg and Williams–Ashman.[46] Putrescine dihydrochloride is added as an activator of S-adenosyl-L-methionine[7] and as an acceptor for the propylamine moiety, derived from 5'-deoxy-5'-S-(3-methylthiopropylamine) sulfonium adenosine ("decarboxylated S-adenosyl-L-methionine").[46]

Reaction mixtures consisted of 75 $\mu$l of cell extract added to 4 nmoles of pyridoxal 5-phosphate, 0.5 $\mu$moles of putrescine dihydrochloride, and 0.2 $\mu$Ci of S-adenosyl-L-methionine-carboxyl-$^{14}C$ (specific activity 7.3 mCi/mmole) in 0.05$M$ sodium–potassium phosphate buffer, pH 7.2, containing 1.0 mmolar dithiothreitol, to make a total volume of 200 $\mu$l. Incubations were carried out as previously described,[45] and radioactivity was measured as previously described for the assay of L-ornithine decarboxylase. All values were corrected against a "boiled enzyme" assay.

## Incorporation of $^3$H—Thymidine into DNA

For these experiments WI-38 cells were grown in Falcon flasks as described. At 19 hr after change of medium, the cells were pulse-labelled with $^3$H—thymidine (thymidine-methyl-$^3$H, specific activity 6.7 Ci/mmole) (5 $\mu$Ci/ml in balanced salt solution) for 30 min to determine the incorporation of $^3$H—thymidine into DNA. Unstimulated confluent monolayer cells were also pulse-labelled. The incorporation was stopped by washing the cells with ice-cold PBS containing an excess of unlabelled thymidine. The amount of $^3$H—thymidine incorporated into DNA was measured in a liquid scintillation spectrometer using the Triton—toluene scintillation cocktail[47] at an efficiency of 30% for $^3$H.

## Chemicals

Information regarding the commercially available chemicals used in these experiments may be obtained by writing the author.

## RESULTS

### Stimulation of Cell Proliferation

Seven days after plating, confluent monolayers of WI-38 cells show a very low rate of $^3$H—thymidine incorporation into DNA, and very few mitoses are seen.[31] Practically all the cells are in the G$_0$ phase of the cell cycle.[38]

Replacement of the exhausted medium with fresh medium containing 10% fetal calf serum stimulates the cells to synthesize DNA and divide.[31] The incorporation of $^3$H—thymidine into DNA begins to increase at 12 hr and reaches a peak between 15 and 21 hr after stimulation.[31,32] The cells start dividing 24 hr after stimulation, and the cumulative mitotic index reaches a peak at 27 to 33 hr.[31,32]

The percentage of cells that are stimulated to proliferate varies with the batch of fetal calf serum and with the age (number of generations) of the culture.[33] Cultures older than 30 generations showed poor stimulation and were not used routinely.

To study the degree of stimulation in the actual experiments, we measured the $^3$H—thymidine incorporation at 19 hr (maximal rate of incorporation) after change of medium. Table 3 shows the rates of $^3$H—thymidine incorporation into DNA after the addition of media of various composition. Fresh medium supplemented with 10% fetal calf serum induced maximal stimulation, 10% fetal calf serum added directly to the conditioned medium resulted in half maximal stimulation, and fresh medium supplemented with 0.3% fetal calf serum caused only a minimal stimulation of DNA synthesis.

## Polyamine Content in Confluent Monolayers of WI-38 Human Diploid Fibroblasts After Change of Medium

Figures 2 to 4 show the changes in polyamine content that occurred in WI-38 cells after stimulation with fresh medium supplemented with 10% fetal calf serum. Spermine was the quantitatively dominating polyamine, and in unstimulated WI-38 cells the cellular content was 3.9 and 18.2 times that of spermidine and putrescine, respectively.

By 6 hr after stimulation, the cellular putrescine content was significantly increased, and by 19 hr it was 5.5 times that of unstimulated WI-38 cells (Fig. 2). A marked decrease in the putrescine content occurred 24 hr after stimulation, followed by an increase over the subsequent 24 hr.

Very shortly after stimulation there was a sudden increase in the cellular spermidine content. It was already evident within 30 to 60 min after stimulation; the content was 50% higher than in unstimulated cells (Fig. 3). Subsequently, however, the spermidine content decreased, and, during the remainder of the prereplicative phase, it was similar to that of unstimulated

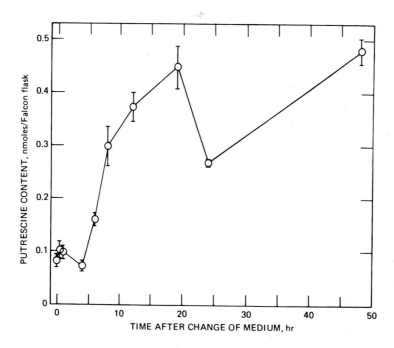

Fig. 2 Putrescine content in confluent monolayers of WI-38 human diploid fibroblasts after change of medium. Fresh medium supplemented with 10% fetal calf serum was added at time 0. One Falcon flask contains approximately $2 \times 10^6$ cells. Means ± S.E.M. of 3 to 6 Falcon-flask cultures.

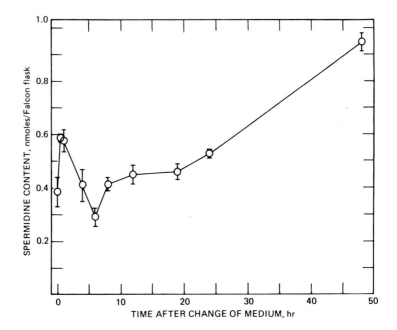

Fig. 3 Spermidine content in confluent monolayers of WI-38 human diploid fibroblasts after change of medium. Fresh medium supplemented with 10% fetal calf serum was added at time 0. One Falcon flask contains approximately $2 \times 10^6$ cells. Means ± S.E.M. of 3 to 6 Falcon-flask cultures.

WI-38 cells. At 24 hr after stimulation, the spermidine content started to increase, and spermidine accumulated over the next 24 hr.

The cellular spermine content was relatively constant during the prereplicative phase (Fig. 4). It seemed that spermine accumulation was initiated approximately 24 hr after stimulation, i.e., after DNA synthesis, and by 48 hr the increase was almost two times that of unstimulated cells.

At 48 hr after stimulation, i.e., when the cells have traversed the cell cycle once, the cellular content of putrescine, spermidine, and spermine was 5.9, 2.4, and 1.8 times that of unstimulated WI-38 cells, respectively.

## Polyamine Content in Confluent Monolayers of WI-38 Human Diploid Fibroblasts After Various Degrees of Stimulation

Table 3 shows the content of putrescine, spermidine, and spermine in confluent monolayers of WI-38 fibroblasts 1, 8, and 19 hr after various degrees of stimulation.

When 10% fetal calf serum in fresh medium is added to monolayers, 60 to 80% of the cells are stimulated to proliferate, and, 19 hr after change of

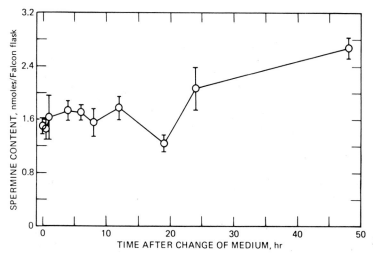

Fig. 4 Spermine content in confluent monolayers of WI-38 human diploid fibroblasts after change of medium. Fresh medium supplemented with 10% fetal calf serum was added at time 0. One Falcon flask contains approximately $2 \times 10^6$ cells. Means ± S.E.M. of 3 to 6 Falcon-flask cultures.

TABLE 3

POLYAMINE CONTENT IN CONFLUENT MONOLAYERS OF WI-38 HUMAN
DIPLOID FIBROBLASTS AFTER VARIOUS DEGREES OF STIMULATION

| Experimental conditions | Time after stimulation, hr | $^3$H—thymidine incorporation into DNA, cpm/Falcon flask* | Polyamine content, pmoles/Falcon flask* | | |
|---|---|---|---|---|---|
| | | | Putrescine | Spermidine | Spermine |
| Unstimulated cells | 0 | 2,600 ± 417 | 86 ± 13 | 502 ± 11 | 1,508 ± 130 |
| Cells stimulated by | 1 | | 61 ± 10 | 520 ± 28 | 1,588 ± 47 |
| the addition of fresh | 8 | | 89 ± 6 | 538 ± 21 | 1,564 ± 92 |
| medium containing 0.3% | 19 | 6,122 ± 1,979 | 53 ± 11 | 483 ± 22 | 1,487 ± 65 |
| fetal calf serum | | | | | |
| Cells stimulated by | 1 | | 73 ± 6 | 533 ± 61 | 1,458 ± 86 |
| the addition of 10% | 8 | | 156 ± 8 | 503 ± 28 | 1,363 ± 41 |
| fetal calf serum to | 19 | 39,516 ± 2,219 | 263 ± 14 | 523 ± 43 | 1,418 ± 114 |
| the conditioned medium | | | | | |
| Cells stimulated by | 1 | | 120 ± 11 | 558 ± 27 | 1,449 ± 132 |
| the addition of fresh | 8 | | 236 ± 27 | 388 ± 23 | 1,113 ± 77 |
| medium containing 10% | 19 | 80,246 ± 9,863 | 448 ± 41 | 460 ± 29 | 1,238 ± 134 |
| fetal calf serum | | | | | |

*One Falcon flask contains approximately $2 \times 10^6$ cells. Means ± S.E.M. of three Falcon-flask cultures.

medium, the cellular putrescine content was 5.2 times that of unstimulated cells. When 10% fetal calf serum is added directly to the old conditioned medium, only 30 to 40% of the cells are stimulated, and the putrescine content at 19 hr was 3.1 times that of unstimulated cells. When 0.3% fetal calf serum in fresh medium is added to monolayers, only a few cells are stimulated, and at 19 hr no increase in the putrescine content was observed.

The changes in cellular content of spermidine (and spermine) that occurred in cells stimulated maximally were negligible when the cells were stimulated to a lesser extent.

It seems that the increase in putrescine content during the prereplicative phase is directly related to stimulation of DNA synthesis since its magnitude is dependent on the fraction of cells that is stimulated to proliferate.

### Stimulation of the Activities of the Polyamine Biosynthetic Enzymes in Confluent Monolayers of WI-38 Human Diploid Fibroblasts After Change of Medium

In a preliminary study (Table 4), the L-ornithine decarboxylase activity in unstimulated WI-38 fibroblasts was found to be low. However, 6 hr after change of medium, concomitant with the increase in putrescine content, a 7.2-fold increase in the activity of the enzyme was observed.

The activity of the putrescine-activated $S$-adenosyl-L-methionine decarboxylase, which reflects spermidine synthesis, followed a pattern similar to that of the cellular content of spermidine (Table 5).

TABLE 4

PRELIMINARY DATA ON PUTRESCINE
SYNTHESIS IN CONFLUENT MONOLAYERS OF
WI-38 HUMAN DIPLOID FIBROBLASTS
AFTER STIMULATION

| Time after change of medium,* hr | L-Ornithine decarboxylase activity,† pmoles $^{14}CO_2$/30 min/Blake bottle‡ |
|:---:|:---:|
| 0 | 60 |
| 1 | 81 |
| 2 | 70 |
| 4 | 87 |
| 6 | 431 |

*Fresh medium supplemented with 10% fetal calf serum was added at time 0.
†Means of two Blake-bottle cultures. (Each separate 0 to 6 hr series showed the same pattern of changes.)
‡One Blake bottle contains approximately 7 x 10⁶ cells.

TABLE 5

PRELIMINARY DATA ON SPERMIDINE
SYNTHESIS IN CONFLUENT MONOLAYERS OF
WI-38 HUMAN DIPLOID FIBROBLASTS
AFTER STIMULATION

| Time after change of medium,* hr | Putrescine-activated S-adenosyl-L-methionine decarboxylase activity,† pmoles of $^{14}CO_2$ /30 min/Blake bottle‡ |
|---|---|
| 0 | 24 |
| 2 | 92 |
| 4 | 79 |
| 8 | 52 |
| 19 | 89 |

*Fresh medium supplemented with 10% fetal calf serum was added at time 0.

†Means of two Blake-bottle cultures. (Each separate 0 to 19 hr series showed the same pattern of changes.)

‡One Blake bottle contains approximately 7 x 10⁶ cells.

## DISCUSSION

The biochemical events that follow the stimulation of DNA synthesis and division of confluent monolayers of WI-38 human diploid fibroblasts have been described in detail.[31-38] Within the first 1 to 3 hr after stimulation there is a marked rise in chromatin template activity,[33] an increased incorporation of ³H—uridine into the RNA of whole cells,[33] an increased synthesis of nonhistone chromosomal proteins,[32] etc.

In spite of the very early increase of L-ornithine decarboxylase activity that has been observed as a response to stimulation of cellular proliferation in several other experimental systems (for references see Tables 1 and 2), no change was observed in the activity of this enzyme in WI-38 cells within the first few hours, nor did the putrescine content change during this time period.

Höltta and Jänne[18] and Gaza, Short, and Lieberman[48] recently showed that the increase in putrescine synthesis in regenerating rat liver was biphasic. The time between partial hepatectomy and occurrence of the first peak was not related to the age of the animal; it was 4 hr in all age groups.[18] The time between operation and occurrence of the second peak, however, was related to the age of the animals; i.e., the older the animal the later the occurrence of the peak of putrescine synthesis.[18] Previously, Bucher, Swaffield, and DiTroia[49] had observed a correlation between length of the prereplicative phase in regenerating liver and age of the animal; i.e., the older the animal the later the occurrence of the peak of DNA synthesis. Therefore, our conclusion from combining these results is that only the second peak of putrescine synthesis is likely to be related to DNA synthesis. The first peak is probably related to other events, e.g., events involved in tissue hypertrophy. Actually, it has been shown that agents that do not stimulate hepatic DNA synthesis and division cause a large increase in L-ornithine decarboxylase activity within 4 hr after treatment.[50] Contrary to the long duration of the increase in L-ornithine decarboxylase activity after partial hepatectomy, only a brief increase in enzyme activity, with a peak within 4 hr, was produced by these agents even after extended duration of treatment.

When comparing the results of these studies on the regenerating rat liver[18,49,50] with those obtained using WI-38 human diploid fibroblasts stimulated to proliferate by nutritional changes, we found that putrescine synthesis in WI-38 cells was increased at a time of the prereplicative phase which corresponds to the time of occurrence of the second peak of putrescine synthesis in regenerating liver. Because of this fact and because the magnitude of putrescine accumulation was related to the fraction of WI-38 cells stimulated to synthesize DNA, we believe it very likely that there is a connection between increase in putrescine content of the cells and subsequent replication of their DNA. No peak in putrescine synthesis corresponding in time to that of the first peak in regenerating liver was observed in WI-38 cells following stimulation. This fact may be explained by the lack of a hypertrophic response to the stimulus in WI-38 cells, and it further corroborates the hypothesis that only the second peak of putrescine synthesis in regenerating liver is related to DNA synthesis.

The increase in putrescine synthesis in stimulated WI-38 cells preceded the onset of DNA synthesis and coincided with the increased rate of ribosomal RNA synthesis.[51] Only those nutritional changes which stimulated cellular proliferation caused an increased synthesis of ribosomal RNA and putrescine. Our results are in accordance with those of Kay and Cooke[52] and Kay and Lindsay,[13] showing a correlation between increases in L-ornithine decarboxylase activity and ribosomal RNA synthesis in phytohemagglutinin-stimulated lymphocytes. Furthermore, their studies showed that low concentrations of actinomycin D, which specifically inhibited ribosomal RNA synthesis, inhibited the increase in L-ornithine decarboxylase activity more than the increase in the overall rate of protein synthesis.

The decrease in putrescine content of the WI-38 cells which occurred between 19 and 24 hr after the nutritional change is probably caused by the increased synthesis of spermidine and spermine which started at this time. A transient increase in the cellular spermidine content occurred as early as 30 to 60 min after the change of medium. It seems that this early increase in cellular spermidine content is due to synthesis rather than uptake of spermidine from the medium, since the activity of putrescine-activated S-adenosyl-L-methionine decarboxylase, the enzyme that catalyzes spermidine formation, parallelled the changes in spermidine content. Fetal calf serum and therefore the culture medium contained putrescine as well as spermidine. These exogenous polyamines, however, did not seem to enter the WI-38 cells to any appreciable extent, even after stimulation, as determined after the addition of $^{14}$C-labelled polyamines to the culture medium and subsequent determination of the amount of incorporation into washed cells (data not shown). Exogenous spermidine did not affect the cellular proliferation when added to the culture medium instead of fetal calf serum in a concentration equal to that in fresh medium supplemented with 10% fetal calf serum. The effect of the addition of spermidine on $^3$H—thymidine incorporation into DNA of WI-38 cells was evaluated 19 hr after the addition of polyamine-supplemented medium. Pohjanpelto and Raina[53] have identified a growth factor in conditioned medium of human fibroblast cultures as putrescine. However, cellular proliferation was stimulated only within a strikingly small concentration range, and growth stimulation was not expressed until 2 to 3 days after the addition of putrescine.

## ACKNOWLEDGMENT

This work was supported in part by U. S. Public Health Service grants CA-08373 and CA-12923 from the National Cancer Institute, National Institutes of Health.

## REFERENCES

1. R. Baserga, Biochemistry of the Cell Cycle: A Review, *Cell Tissue Kinet.*, **1**: 167-191 (1968).
2. G. C. Mueller, Biochemical Perspectives of the $G_1$ and S Intervals in the Replication Cycle of Animal Cells: A Study in the Control of Cell Growth, in *The Cell Cycle and Cancer*, R. Baserga (Ed.), pp. 269-308, Marcel Dekker, Inc., New York, 1971.
3. R. A. Tobey, D. F. Petersen, and E. C. Anderson, Biochemistry of $G_2$ and Mitosis, in *The Cell Cycle and Cancer*, R. Baserga (Ed.), pp. 309-353, Marcel Dekker, Inc., New York, 1971.
4. R. Baserga, Control of DNA Synthesis in Mammalian Cells, *Miami Winter Symposia 2*, pp. 447-461, North Holland Publishing Company, Amsterdam, 1970.
5. H. L. Cooper, Biochemical Alterations Accompanying Initiation of Growth in Resting Cells, in *The Cell Cycle and Cancer*, R. Baserga (Ed.), pp. 197-226, Marcell Dekker, Inc., New York, 1971.
6. A. E. Pegg and H. G. Williams-Ashman, Biosynthesis of Putrescine in the Prostate Gland of the Rat, *Biochem. J.*, **108**: 533-539 (1968).
7. A. E. Pegg and H. G. Williams-Ashman, Stimulation of the Decarboxylation of S-adenosylmethionine by Putrescine in Mammalian Tissues, *Biochem. Biophys. Res. Commun.*, **30**: 76-82 (1968).
8. J. Jänne and H. G. Williams-Ashman, Dissociation of Putrescine-Activated Decarboxylation of S-adenosyl-L-methionine from the Enzymic Synthesis of Spermidine and Spermine by Purified Prostatic Enzyme Preparations, *Biochem. Biophys. Res. Commun.*, **42**: 222-229 (1971).
9. A. Raina and P. Hannonen, Separation of Enzyme Activities Catalyzing Spermidine and Spermine Synthesis in Rat Brain, *FEBS (Fed. Eur. Biochem. Soc.) Lett.*, **16**: 1-4 (1971).

10. P. Hannonen, J. Jänne, and A. Raina, Partial Purification and Characterization of Spermine Synthase from Rat Brain, *Biochim. Biophys. Acta,* **289:** 225-231 (1972).

11. M. J. Feldman, C. C. Levy, and D. H. Russell, The Purification of S-adenosyl-L-methionine Decarboxylase from Rat Liver: Inability to Separate Decarboxylation from Spermidine Synthesis, *Biochem. Biophys. Res. Commun.,* **44:** 675-681 (1971).

12. B. L. M. Hogan, Effect of Growth Conditions on the Ornithine Decarboxylase Activity of Rat Hepatoma Cells, *Biochem. Biophys. Res. Commun.,* **45:** 301-307 (1971).

13. J. E. Kay and V. J. Lindsay, Polyamine Synthesis During Lymphocyte Activation. Induction of Ornithine Decarboxylase and S-adenosyl Methionine Decarboxylase, *Exp. Cell Res.,* **77:** 428-436 (1973).

14. K. D. Graziano, L. J. Marton, and M. R. Mardiney, Jr., The Correlation of PHA Induced Polyamine Changes in Human Lymphocytes with Tritiated Thymidine Incorporation, submitted for publication.

15. R. H. Fillingame and D. R. Morris, Accumulation of Polyamines and Its Inhibition by Methyl Glyoxal Bis-(Guanylhydrazone) During Lymphocyte Transformation, in *Polyamines in Normal and Neoplastic Growth,* D. H. Russell (Ed.), pp. 249-260, Raven Press, New York, 1973.

16. L. J. Marton, K. D. Graziano, M. R. Mardiney, Jr., and D. H. Russell, Specific Increases in Polyamines in Mixed Lymphocyte Reactions, in *Polyamines in Normal and Neoplastic Growth,* D. H. Russell (Ed.), pp. 215-219, Raven Press, New York, 1973.

17. J. Jänne, Studies on the Biosynthetic Pathway of Polyamines in Rat Liver, *Acta Physiol. Scand., Suppl.,* **300:** 1-71 (1967).

18. E. Höltta and J. Jänne, Ornithine Decarboxylase Activity and the Accumulation of Putrescine at Early Stages of Liver Regeneration, *FEBS (Fed. Eur. Biochem. Soc.) Lett.,* **23:** 117-121 (1972).

19. P. Hannonen, A. Raina, and J. Jänne, Polyamine Synthesis in the Regenerating Rat Liver; Stimulation of S-adenosylmethionine Decarboxylase, and Spermidine and Spermine Synthases After Partial Hepatectomy, *Biochim. Biophys. Acta,* **273:** 84-90 (1972).

20. O. Heby and L. Lewan, Putrescine and Polyamines in Relation to Nucleic Acids in Mouse Liver After Partial Hepatectomy, *Virchows Arch., B.,* **8:** 58-66 (1971).

21. D. H. Russell and T. A. McVicker, Polyamine Metabolism in Mouse Liver After Partial Hepatectomy, *Biochim. Biophys. Acta,* **244:** 85-93 (1971).

22. N. Fausto, RNA and Amine Synthesis in the Liver of Rats Given Injections of Thioacetamide, *Cancer Res.,* **30:** 1947-1952 (1970).

23. R. A. Richman, L. E. Underwood, J. J. Van Wyk, and S. J. Voina, Synergistic Effect of Cortisol and Growth Hormone on Hepatic Ornithine Decarboxylase Activity, *Proc. Soc. Exp. Biol. Med.,* **138:** 880-884 (1971).

24. M. Stastny and S. Cohen, Epidermal Growth Factor. IV. The Induction of Ornithine Decarboxylase, *Biochim. Biophys. Acta,* **204:** 578-589 (1970).

25. A. E. Pegg, D. H. Lockwood, and H. G. Williams-Ashman, Concentrations of Putrescine and Polyamines and Their Enzymic Synthesis During Androgen-Induced Prostatic Growth, *Biochem. J.,* **117:** 17-31 (1970).

26. D. H. Russell and R. L. Taylor, Polyamine Synthesis and Accumulation in the Castrated Rat Uterus After Estradiol-17$\beta$ Stimulation, *Endocrinology,* **88:** 1397-1403 (1971).

27. Y. Kobayashi, J. Kupelian, and D. V. Maudsley, Ornithine Decarboxylase Stimulation in Rat Ovary by Luteinizing Hormone, *Science,* **172:** 379-380 (1971).

28. J. T. Brandt, D. A. Pierce, and N. Fausto, Ornithine Decarboxylase Activity and Polyamine Synthesis During Kidney Hypertrophy, *Biochim. Biophys. Acta,* **279:** 184-193 (1972).

29. D. H. Russell and T. A. McVicker, Polyamine Biogenesis in the Rat Mammary Gland During Pregnancy and Lactation, *Biochem. J.,* **130:** 71-76 (1972).

30. J. H. Levine, W. E. Nicholson, G. W. Liddle, and D. N. Orth, Stimulation of Adrenal Ornithine Decarboxylase by Adrenocorticotropin and Growth Hormone, *Endocrinology*, **92**: 1089-1095 (1973).

31. F. Wiebel and R. Baserga, Early Alterations in Amino Acid Pools and Protein Synthesis of Diploid Fibroblasts Stimulated to Synthesize DNA by Addition of Serum, *J. Cell Physiol.*, **74**: 191-202 (1969).

32. G. Rovera and R. Baserga, Early Changes in the Synthesis of Acidic Nuclear Proteins in Human Diploid Fibroblasts Stimulated to Synthesize DNA by Changing the Medium, *J. Cell Physiol.*, **77**: 201-211 (1971).

33. J. Farber, G. Rovera, and R. Baserga, Template Activity of Chromatin During Stimulation of Cellular Proliferation in Human Diploid Fibroblasts, *Biochem. J.*, **122**: 189-195 (1971).

34. G. Rovera, J. Farber, and R. Baserga, Gene Activation in WI-38 Fibroblasts Stimulated to Proliferate: Requirement for Protein Synthesis, *Proc. Nat. Acad. Sci. U.S.A.*, **68**: 1725-1729 (1971).

35. R. Baserga, G. Rovera, and J. Farber, Control of Cellular Proliferation in Human Diploid Fibroblasts, *In Vitro*, **7**: 80-87 (1971).

36. A. Tsuboi and R. Baserga, Synthesis of Nuclear Acidic Proteins in Density-Inhibited Fibroblasts Stimulated to Proliferate, *J. Cell Physiol.*, **80**: 107-117 (1972).

37. G. Stein, S. Chaudhuri, and R. Baserga, Gene Activation in WI-38 Fibroblasts Stimulated to Proliferate, Role of Non-Histone Chromosomal Proteins, *J. Biol. Chem.*, **247**: 3918-3922 (1972).

38. G. Rovera and R. Baserga, Effect of Nutritional Changes on Chromatin Template Activity and Non-Histone Chromosomal Protein Synthesis in WI-38 and 3T6 Cells, *Exp. Cell Res.*, **78**: 118-126 (1973).

39. N. Seiler and M. Wiechmann, Die Mikrobestimmung von Spermin und Spermidin als 1-Dimethylamino-naphthalin-5-sulfonsäure-Derivate, *Hoppe-Seyler's Z. Physiol. Chem.*, **348**: 1285-1290 (1967).

40. N. Seiler and M. Wiechmann, TLC Analysis of Amines as Their DANS-Derivatives in *Progress in Thin-Layer Chromatography and Related Methods*, A. Neiderwieser and G. Pataki (Eds.), Vol. 1, pp. 94-144, Ann Arbor—Humphrey Science Publishers, Ann Arbor, Michigan, 1970.

41. N. Seiler, Use of the Dansyl Reaction in Biochemical Analysis, *Methods Biochem. Anal.*, **18**: 259-337 (1970).

42. L. Hayflick and P. S. Moorhead, The Serial Cultivation of Human Diploid Cell Strains, *Exp. Cell Res.*, **25**: 585-621 (1961).

43. D. J. Merchant, R. H. Kahn, and W. H. Murphy, *Handbook of Cell and Organ Culture*, p. 217, Burgess Publishing Co., Minneapolis 1964.

44. O. Heby, G. P. Sarna, L. J. Marton, M. Omine, S. Perry, and D. H. Russell, Polyamine Content of AKR Leukemic Cells in Relation to the Cell Cycle, *Cancer Res.*, **33**: 2959-2964 (1973).

45. O. Heby and D. H. Russell, Depression of Polyamine Synthesis in L1210 Leukemic Mice During Treatment with a Potent Antileukemic Agent, 5-Azacytidine, *Cancer Res.*, **33**: 159-165 (1973).

46. A. E. Pegg and H. G. Williams-Ashman, On the Role of S-adenosyl-L-methionine in the Biosynthesis of Spermidine by Rat Prostate, *J. Biol. Chem.*, **244**: 682-693 (1969).

47. M. S. Patterson and R. C. Greene, Measurement of Low-Energy Beta Emitters in Aqueous Solution by Liquid Scintillation Counting of Emulsions, *Anal. Chem.*, **37**: 854-857 (1965).

48. D. J. Gaza, J. Short, and I. Lieberman, On the Possibility that the Prereplicative Increases in Ornithine Decarboxylase Activity Are Related to DNA Synthesis in Liver, *FEBS (Fed. Eur. Biochem. Soc.) Lett.*, **32**: 251-253 (1973).

49. N. L. R. Bucher, M. N. Swaffield, and J. F. DiTroia, Influence of Age upon Incorporation of Thymidine-2-$^{14}$C into DNA of Regenerating Rat Liver, *Cancer Res.*, **24**: 509-512 (1964).

50. T. R. Schrock, N. J. Oakman, and N. L. R. Bucher, Ornithine Decarboxylase Activity in Relation to Growth of Rat Liver. Effects of Partial Hepatectomy, Hypertonic Infusions, Celite Injection or Other Stressful Procedures, *Biochim. Biophys. Acta*, **204**: 564-577 (1970).

51. L. Zardi and R. Baserga, Ribosomal RNA Synthesis in WI-38 Cells Stimulated to Proliferate, *Exp. Mol. Pathol.*, **20**: 69-77 (1974).

52. J. E. Kay and A. Cooke, Ornithine Decarboxylase and Ribosomal RNA Synthesis During the Stimulation of Lymphocytes by Phytohaemagglutinin, *FEBS (Fed. Eur. Biochem. Soc.) Lett.*, **16**: 9-12 (1971).

53. P. Pohjanpelto and A. Raina, Identification of a Growth Factor Produced by Human Fibroblasts in Vitro as Putrescine, *Nature (London) New Biol.*, **235**: 247-249 (1972).

# MICROTUBULE PROTEIN IN RELATION TO THE CELL CYCLE IN REGENERATING RAT LIVER

NANCY L. R. BUCHER and PATRICIA BERKLEY

John Collins Warren Laboratories, Massachusetts General Hospital,
Boston, Massachusetts

## ABSTRACT

Rat liver induced to regenerate by partial hepatectomy affords an in vivo experimental model for investigating microtubule proteins during the transition from the normal state of arrested growth ($G_1$ or $G_0$) to one of active proliferation as the cells, in partial synchrony, reengage in the cellular life cycle. As determined by the rate of incorporation of labelled amino acids, with due allowance for changes in size and specific activity of intracellular pools, the rate of tubulin synthesis starts to increase at about the time DNA replication gets under way. It reaches a maximum of two to three times the normal rate, approximately coincident with the peak of mitotic activity, then falls to lower levels. Associated with the rise in biosynthetic rate is an approximate doubling of the soluble tubulin content as determined by $^3$H—colchicine binding activity; this declines more slowly than the rate of synthesis, suggesting relative molecular stability.

Regenerating rat liver affords an experimental model for investigating specific biochemical steps taken by mammalian cells in vivo as they prepare for mitosis. The hepatocytes of adult rats are known to be arrested in a prolonged $G_1$ (or $G_0$) phase under normal conditions but are readily induced to reenter the cell cycle. Excision of the two main lobes of the liver, which comprise approximately 68% of the whole organ, is a well-tolerated and highly reproducible procedure with essentially no mortality; the growth process that it initiates, although almost universally termed "regeneration," actually is a compensatory hyperplasia of the residual lobes, with no regrowth of the missing parts. The liver deficit sets in motion a series of biochemical and morphological changes in the liver remnant, including, after a lapse of about 14 hr, a partially synchronized burst of DNA synthesis followed 6 to 8 hr later by a similar burst of mitosis. The proliferative activity continues at progressively lower levels for 1 to 2 weeks, until the original organ mass is restored.[1]

Many aspects of the transition from arrested growth to cell division have been intensively studied in a variety of mammalian systems—particularly the events surrounding DNA replication and the biosynthesis of various RNAs and enzymes involved in the proliferative process. However, although a few partially discrepant results have been reported from synchronized cell lines in cultures,[2,3] there is little or no information concerning synthesis of the components of cellular structures by which mitosis is effected in mammalian cells under in vivo conditions. As an initial step in this direction we have undertaken a study of microtubule proteins (tubulins) in rat liver during the early and most active period of regeneration.

To estimate the amount of tubulin present, we employed a [3]H—colchicine-binding assay[4,5] on the assumption, supported by numerous reports, that colchicine binds stoichiometrically to tubulin with a high degree of specificity.[6-9] At intervals after partial hepatectomy or a sham operation, livers were excised, homogenized, and centrifuged at 100,000 G. The supernatants were incubated with [3]H—colchicine, and the protein-bound [3]H—colchicine was separated by means of Sephadex G-100 columns and assayed for radioactivity.[4,5]

Franke[10] reported that centrifugation of rat liver homogenates for 2 hr at 100,000 G results in sedimentation of as much as 77% of the colchicine binding activity, and our findings are similar. It appears that a major fraction of the binding sites of liver are associated with the particulate matter and resist solubilizing. Franke has proposed that the particulate binding sites in liver may function as "nucleation centers" for microtubule assembly or as reserves of tubulin subunits that can be mobilized for rearrangement into microtubules and related structures.[10] On the other hand, as suggested by Wilson for the chick brain, activity associated with the particulate fraction may be merely an entrapment of soluble tubulins.[11]

Our initial investigation is focused on the tubulins that appear in the 100,000-G supernatant, i.e., those which are solubilized under the usual experimental conditions.

Following partial hepatectomy, the various components of the liver do not increase in parallel; rather, their concentrations change at quite different rates. Accordingly, we determined the colchicine-binding activity per unit of 100,000-G supernatant protein (i.e., "soluble" protein) and, for comparison, the activity per unit of hepatic DNA (Fig. 1). Both curves express tubulin concentration relative to some other hepatic constituent; for this purpose DNA and protein are probably the most satisfactory reference standards in that they tend to reflect the amount of functional hepatic tissue. On the other hand, liver weight has less relevance in this regard because it is significantly affected by the presence of inert storage materials, such as glycogen and lipid, which fluctuate considerably during this early period of rapid growth. About 18 hr after partial hepatectomy, soluble tubulin concentration begins to rise fairly sharply; it nearly doubles by 36 hr and decreases slowly thereafter (Fig. 1).

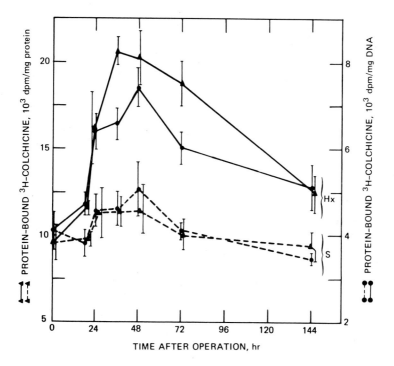

Fig. 1   Soluble ³H—colchicine-binding activity in livers of partially hepatectomized and sham-hepatectomized control rats. ▲, disintegrations per minute in
protein-bound ³H—colchicine per milligram of protein in 100,000-G supernatant. ●, disintegrations per minute in protein-bound ³H—colchicine per
milligram of DNA, i.e., DNA in the homogenate from which the 100,000-G
supernatant for incubation with the ³H—colchicine was derived. DNA is used
here as an index of the relative amount of functional liver tissue, comparable
to disintegrations per minute in protein-bound ³H—colchicine per average liver
cell. Hx, partially hepatectomized rats. S, sham-hepatectomized control rats.

In view of the large proportion of colchicine-binding protein that is
associated with the hepatic particulate fraction, the question arises as to whether
this fraction supplies the extra soluble tubulins that appear during regeneration,
or whether they accrue, at least partially, through enhanced de novo synthesis or
through diminished rate of elimination. To evaluate the rate of tubulin synthesis,
we investigated the incorporation of labelled amino acids in vivo at intervals
after partial hepatectomy. At either 10 min or 3 hr, respectively, after
intravenous injection of ³H—valine or ³H—leucine, the livers were quickly
perfused with ice-cold homogenizing medium to remove blood and to block
further incorporation. They were rapidly excised, homogenized in medium
containing sucrose, magnesium chloride, dithiothreitol, and GTP (guanosine
5'-triphosphate), in Tris[tris(hydroxymethyl)-aminomethane] —HCl buffer at pH

6.8, and centrifuged at 100,000 G. Tubulin was precipitated from the supernatant by addition of vinblastine sulfate.[8,12,13]

Electrophoresis of the material in the vinblastine precipitate on either alkaline urea[14] or sodium dodecyl sulfate (SDS)[15] polyacrylamide gels, followed by scanning the gels at 280 nm or staining with Coomassie Blue, showed a major component with the molecular weight and other characteristics of tubulin. Its identity was further supported by coelectrophoresis with known tubulin from calf brain,* which showed that the tubulin bands from the two sources coincided.

TABLE 1

COMPARISON OF SPECIFIC ACTIVITIES OF
TUBULIN DETERMINED IN ELUATES FROM SDS
AND UREA POLYACRYLAMIDE GELS

| | Specific activity, dpm/$\mu$g protein | | |
|---|---|---|---|
| Sample No. | Electrophoresis | | Isoelectric focusing |
| | SDS gel | Urea gel | Urea gel |
| 1 | 13.5 | | 13.5 |
| 2 | 8.25 | 8.60 | |
| 3 | 59.1 | 53.4 | |

The tubulin bands, localized with the aid of a gel scanner, were cut out, minced, and eluted by shaking at 37°C in appropriate buffers.[15,16] The eluates were assayed for radioactivity in a liquid scintillation spectrometer and for protein content by absorbancy at 280 nm. The results were expressed as tubulin specific activity (disintegrations per minute per microgram of tubulin).

Tubulin specific activities, determined on portions of the same sample by electrophoresis on urea gels or on SDS gels or by isoelectric focusing on urea gels,[17] were compared and found to be in good agreement (Table 1). Since separations by the three methods depend on different physical properties of proteins, we concluded that acceptable radiochemical purity could be achieved by vinblastine precipitation of the tubulin from 100,000-G supernatants of liver homogenates, followed by electrophoresis on 8$M$ urea gels; this procedure was accordingly adopted for subsequent routine assays.

We found significant increases in tubulin labelling as regeneration got under way; 10-min incorporation of $^3$H—valine and 3-hr incorporation of $^3$H—leucine yielded closely similar results (Fig. 2). To find whether this enhanced rate of labelling was a mere reflection of changes in the specific activity of the precursor amino acid pools, we examined in detail the valine pool,

---

*Kindly provided by D. Michael Young.

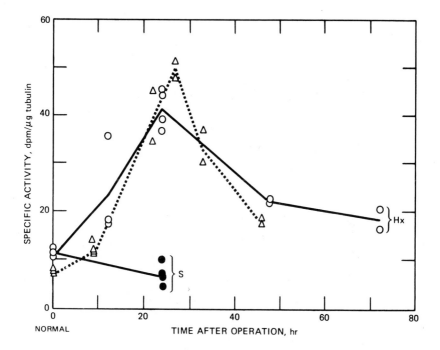

Fig. 2   Rate of incorporation of $^3$H amino acids into soluble liver tubulin at intervals after partial hepatectomy (Hx) or sham operation (S). Δ, specific activity of tubulin 3 hr after intravenous injection of 200 μCi of $^3$H—leucine (15,000 μCi/μmole). Each point is derived from the combined livers of two rats. ○, specific activity of tubulin 10 min after intravenous injection of 400 μCi of $^3$H—valine (6700 μCi/μmole). Each point is from a single rat. All rats were partially hepatectomized except those at zero time, which were intact normal rats, and those represented by solid circles (●), which were control rats injected with valine 24 hr after a sham operation.

using a slight modification of the procedure of Regier and Kafatos[18] in which $^3$H—amino acids are extracted and then reacted quantitatively with $^{14}$C—fluoro-dinitrobenzene and the resulting dinitrophenyl-amino acids are purified by two-dimensional thin-layer chromatography on silica gel plates. From the ratio of $^3$H to $^{14}$C in the valine spot, which is readily isolated, the specific activity of the valine can be calculated. If, instead of in vivo labelling with $^3$H—valine, we add a known amount of $^3$H—valine to a nonlabelled liver homogenate and process the mixture by the same routine, the actual valine content of the liver can be determined. From these studies we found that the rate of labelling of the valine pool followed quite a different course from that of tubulin; whereas tubulin specific activity was greatest at around 24 to 27 hr, valine specific activity rose to 2.5 times normal at 10 hr and fell to only 1.4 times normal by 24 hr. A cause of this decline was enlargement of the valine pool, which nearly doubled in size by 24 hr and remained at about 1.5 times normal for the next 2 days.

If it is assumed that the intracellular amino acid pools behave as if homogeneous, as indicated by Henshaw et al.[19] for rat liver in vivo, it is possible, by means of calculations based on the specific activity of the whole hepatic valine pool and the specific activity of the [3]H—valine-labelled tubulin, to express the rate of tubulin synthesis in absolute terms, as micromoles of valine incorporated per milligram of tubulin per 10 min. If, however, the amino acid pools are compartmented, as many reports based largely on in vitro systems indicate,[20-23] so that the precursor pool from which proteins are synthesized and the whole amino acid pool have different specific activities, such a calculation may be valid only under the particular experimental conditions employed by Henshaw. Since our experiments along these lines are still incomplete, it seems justifiable to present only a preliminary version of such a calculation, i.e., on a relative basis, by comparing apparent rates of synthesis in regenerating relative to normal livers (Fig. 3, curve 1).

An alternative means of evaluating the rate of tubulin synthesis is to consider the specific activity of the tubulin relative to the average specific activity of other liver proteins on the assumption that, although the labelling of individual proteins may fluctuate independently, their average specific activity will reflect significant changes in the specific activity of that compartment of the precursor pool from which tubulin as well as the other proteins are being synthesized. In Fig. 3 the specific activity of tubulin relative to other proteins of the soluble fraction (curve 2) and relative to whole liver proteins (curve 3) is plotted after being normalized for comparison with the rate of synthesis calculated as described in the preceding paragraph (curve 1). All three curves represent relative rates of tubulin synthesis adjusted by various means for changes in precursor specific activity. There is general agreement, except that curve 1, calculated from [3]H—valine specific activity, differs in not returning to normal by 48 hr; the reasons for the discrepancy are at present unclear.

Soluble tubulin appears to turn over slowly; in normal livers the rate of labelling is only about 25% of that of the total proteins and 50% of that of the soluble proteins.

The findings are summarized in Fig. 4, which also includes a curve showing the rate of DNA synthesis as determined by incorporation of [3]H—thymidine under the same experimental conditions. The rate of tubulin synthesis starts to increase at about the time DNA replication gets under way. It reaches a maximum of between 2 to 3 times the normal rate at a time approximately coinciding with the peak of mitotic activity, which parallels replication approximately 6 to 8 hr later.[24] The synthesis then drops to lower levels in conformity with the diminishing growth rate. Coincident with the rise in synthetic rate is an approximate doubling of the soluble tubulin content, which remains elevated for a prolonged period, diminishing slowly. This relatively slower decline, in conjunction with the low rates of incorporation of amino acids

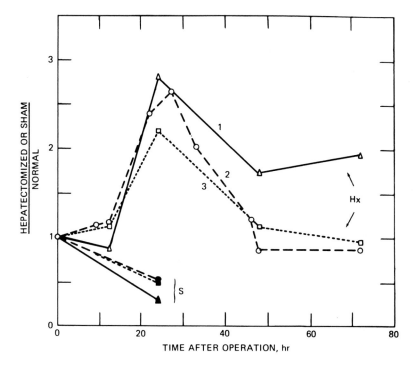

Fig. 3 Relative rates of tubulin synthesis at intervals after partial hepatectomy (Hx) or sham operation (S). Data for Fig. 3 have been compensated for changes in specific activity of the amino acid precursor pools and normalized. Curve 1, apparent $\mu$moles of valine incorporated per micromole of tubulin. Curve 2, specific activity of tubulin relative to protein of 100,000-G supernatant (dpm/$\mu$g soluble tubulin)/(dpm/$\mu$g soluble protein), following 10-min incorporation of $^3$H—valine, or 3-hr incorporation of $^3$H—leucine. Curve 3, specific activity of tubulin relative to whole-liver protein (dpm/$\mu$g tubulin)/(dpm/whole-liver protein), following 10-min incorporation of $^3$H—valine. Solid symbols are sham-hepatectomized control values.

into tubulin in comparison with other proteins, suggests that the soluble tubulin is relatively stable and not rapidly catabolized, at least during hepatic regeneration.

## ACKNOWLEDGMENTS

This work was supported by grant CA02146-17 from the National Institutes of Health and grant ACS 1425-C-1 from the Massachusetts Division of the American Cancer Society. This is publication No. 1459 of the Cancer Commission of Harvard University.

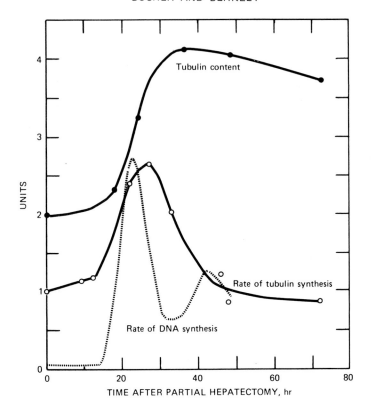

Fig. 4   Relation of hepatic tubulin content and rate of synthesis to the initial peak of DNA synthesis. Tubulin content: 1 unit = 5000 dpm in protein-bound $^3$H—colchicine per milligram of protein. Tubulin synthesis: 1 unit = ratio of 1.0 for the rate in hepatectomized rats to the rate in normal rats. DNA synthesis: 1 unit = 2000 dpm/10 $\mu$g DNA.

## REFERENCES

1. N. L. R. Bucher and R. A. Malt, *Regeneration of Liver and Kidney*, pp. 1-159, Little, Brown and Company, Boston, 1971.
2. E. Robbins and M. Shelanski, Synthesis of a Colchicine-Binding Protein During the HeLa Cell Life Cycle, *J. Cell Biol.*, 43: 371-373 (1969).
3. G. L. Forrest and R. P. Klevecz, Synthesis and Degradation of Microtubule Protein in Synchronized Chinese Hamster Cells, *J. Biol. Chem.*, 247(10): 3147-3152 (1972).
4. G. G. Borisy and E. W. Taylor, The Mechanism of Action of Colchicine. Binding of Colchicine—$^3$H to Cellular Protein, *J. Cell Biol.*, 34(2): 525-533 (1967).
5. R. C. Weisenberg, G. G. Borisy, and E. W. Taylor, The Colchicine-Binding Protein of Mammalian Brain and Its Relation to Microtubules, *Biochemistry*, 7(12): 4466-4479 (1968).
6. L. Wilson, Properties of Colchicine Binding Protein from Chick Embryo Brain, Interactions with Vinca Alkaloids and Podophyllotoxin, *Biochemistry*, 9(25): 4999-5007 (1970).

7. R. C. Weisenberg and S. N. Timasheff, Aggregation of Microtubule Subunit Protein. Effects of Divalent Cations, Colchicine and Vinblastine, *Biochemistry*, 9(21): 4110-4116 (1970).

8. J. B. Olmsted, K. Carlson, R. Klebe, F. Ruddle, and J. Rosenbaum, Isolation of Microtubule Protein from Cultured Mouse Neuroblastoma Cells, *Proc. Nat. Acad. Sci. U.S.A.*, 65(1): 129-136 (1970).

9. G. G. Borisy, Rapid Method for Quantitative Determination of Microtubule Protein Using DEAE-Cellulose Filters, *Anal. Biochem.*, 50(2): 373-385 (1972).

10. J. Stadler and W. W. Franke, Colchicine-Binding Proteins in Chromatin and Membranes, *Nature (London) New Biol.*, 237: 237-238 (1972).

11. J. R. Bamburg, E. M. Shooter, and L. Wilson, Developmental Changes in Microtubule Protein of Chick Brain, *Biochemistry*, 12(8): 1476-1482 (1973).

12. R. Marantz, M. Ventilla, and M. Shelanski, Vinblastine-Induced Precipitation of Microtubule Protein, *Science*, 165: 498-499 (1969).

13. R. A. Raff, G. Greenhouse, K. W. Gross, and P. R. Gross, Synthesis and Storage of Microtubule Proteins by Sea Urchin Embryos, *J. Cell Biol.*, 50(2): 516-527 (1971).

14. B. J. Davis, Disc Electrophoresis-II. Method and Application to Human Serum Proteins, *Ann. N.Y. Acad. Sci.*, 121: 404-427 (1964).

15. K. Weber and M. Osborn, The Reliability of Molecular Weight Determinations by Dodecyl Sulfate-Polyacrylamide Gel Electrophoresis, *J. Biol. Chem.*, 244(16): 4406-4412 (1969).

16. J. Bryan and L. Wilson, Are Cytoplasmic Microtubules Heteropolymers? *Proc. Nat. Acad. Sci. U.S.A.*, 68(8): 1762-1766 (1971).

17. C. W. Wrigley, Gel Electrofocusing, *Methods in Enzymology*, Vol. 22, pp. 559-564, Academic Press, Inc., New York, 1971.

18. J. C. Regier and F. C. Kafatos, Microtechnique for Determining the Specific Activity of Radioactive Intracellular Leucine and Applications to in Vivo Studies of Protein Synthesis, *J. Biol. Chem.*, 246(21): 6480-6488 (1971).

19. E. C. Henshaw, C. A. Hirsch, B. E. Morton, and H. H. Hiatt, Control of Protein Synthesis in Mammalian Tissues Through Changes in Ribosome Activity, *J. Biol. Chem.*, 246(2): 436-446 (1971).

20. D. M. Kipnis, E. Reiss, and E. Helmreich, Functional Heterogeneity of the Intracellular Amino Acid Pool in Mammalian Cells, *Biochim. Biophys. Acta*, 51: 519-524 (1961).

21. D. Garfinkel and A. Lajtha, A Metabolic Inhomogeneity of Glycine in Vivo, *J. Biol. Chem.*, 238(7): 2429-2434 (1963).

22. R. C. Hider, E. B. Fern, and D. R. London, Relationship Between Intracellular Amino Acids and Protein Synthesis in the Extensor Digitorum Longus Muscle of Rats, *Biochem. J.*, 114: 171-178 (1969).

23. G. E. Mortimore, K. H. Woodside, and J. E. Henry, Compartmentation of Free Valine and Its Relation to Protein Turnover in Perfused Rat Liver, *J. Biol. Chem.*, 247(9): 2776-2784 (1972).

24. J. W. Grisham, Morphologic Study of Deoxyribonucleic Acid Synthesis and Cell Proliferation in Regenerating Rat Liver: Autoradiography with Thymidine-H$^3$, *Cancer Res.*, 22: 842-849 (1962).

# MITOTIC CONTROL IN THE BODY

IVAN L. CAMERON
Department of Anatomy, The University of Texas Health Science Center at San
Antonio, San Antonio, Texas

## ABSTRACT

These studies indicate that there are different levels of mitotic control operating throughout
the body: (1) general controls that affect all proliferative cell populations of the
body, (2) controls that affect specific organs, tissues, or cell populations, and (3) controls
that act between cells of the same population. Examples of these are given. Evidence is
presented to show that it is possible to simultaneously stimulate cell proliferation in some
tissues and inhibit cell proliferation in other cell populations. The conclusion is that both
general and specific levels of mitotic control can operate simultaneously in the body. It is
necessary to postulate that some cell types have specific receptor sites or thresholds of
activation in order to explain specific mitotic controls. Evidence that specific receptor
sites do exist on the plasma membrane, in the cytoplasm, and in the nucleus is presented.

From the work reported in this paper on superficial corneal wounds and from the work
of others on wounds to the skin, to the lens, and to post confluent monolayers of cells in
culture, it can be concluded that a lowered level of cell-to-cell contact is the most tenable
explanation for the local stimulation of cell proliferation in these cell populations. It is not
necessary to postulate a diffusion gradient of cellular products (stimulatory or inhibitory
substances) to explain such local control of cell proliferation. In the same regard
tumorigenesity of cell lines has been related to the failure of tumor cells to form cell-to-cell
contact.

Adaptation to a changing environment is a fundamental property of all living
things. In the adult mammal such adaptation often involves a change in the rate
of new-cell production. Although a few cell populations of the adult body, such
as neurons and cardiac-muscle cells, are not capable of cell proliferation, they are
capable of other forms of cellular adaptation.

This paper deals exclusively with the control of cell proliferation in those
cell populations which retain the power of mitosis.

The literature and our studies at the Health Science Center indicate that
there are different levels of mitotic control which operate in the body:

(1) general controls that affect all proliferating cell populations of the body, (2) specific controls that affect specific organ, tissue, or cell populations, and (3) local controls that act between cells of the same cell population. Examples of each level of mitotic control are given. An example and an explanation are given of how different levels of mitotic controls can operate simultaneously.

## GENERAL MITOTIC CONTROLS THAT AFFECT ALL PROLIFERATIVE CELL POPULATIONS OF THE BODY

A fair amount of work suggests that mitotic activity can be regulated by starving and refeeding animals. The stimulation of mitotic activity by refeeding was first reported by Morpurgo in 1889.[1] Leduc[2] showed that mitosis in the liver of young mice disappeared during prolonged fasting and reappeared upon feeding. However, a meal of gelatin (a biologically poor protein) did not revive mitotic activity.[3] Overton[4] found that mitotic activity following starvation and refeeding was related to the duration of starvation as well as to the amount of food refed.

For a while there was a controversy in the literature concerning the effects of starvation on mitotic activity in different renewal cell populations of the body. Bullough[5] and others[6-8] showed that fasting depresses and that refeeding stimulates mitotic activity in stratified epithelial populations. On the other hand, Blair and Hooper[9] presented evidence that starved rats showed no significant change in the mitotic activity in the duodenal crypts. They concluded that mitotic activity was not altered by fasting and refeeding, at least not in the duodenal crypts. More recently it has been shown that refeeding of starved chickens stimulates mitotic activity in stratified epithelium as well as in the duodenal crypts.[10] The differences in the findings of Blair and Hooper[9] and of Cameron and Cleffmann[10] are perhaps best accounted for by differences in the severity of starvation. Although careful studies of the general effects of inanition on a number of different cell populations are still needed, mitotic activity seems to be generally responsive to severe and general nutritional changes in the body.

Diurnal rhythm of mitotic activity may also be cited as a phenomenon that brings about changes in cell proliferation throughout the cell populations of the body. Although diurnal fluctuations in mitotic activity have been reported for many cell populations in the body (see Sigdestad et al.[11,12] and Sigdestad, this volume), several reported studies failed to demonstrate such fluctuations in the rapidly proliferating intestinal crypts.[13-15] The more recent studies by Sigdestad et al.[11,12] now make it clear that the intestinal crypts do indeed demonstrate diurnal fluctuations of mitotic activity. The purpose of this paper is not to assess the specific factors that might control such diurnal fluctuations throughout the body but simply to recognize that such general control does exist.

It now appears that there is an age-dependent decrease in the mitotic rate of cell proliferation in mammals.[16,17] Figure 1 illustrates cell proliferation in four

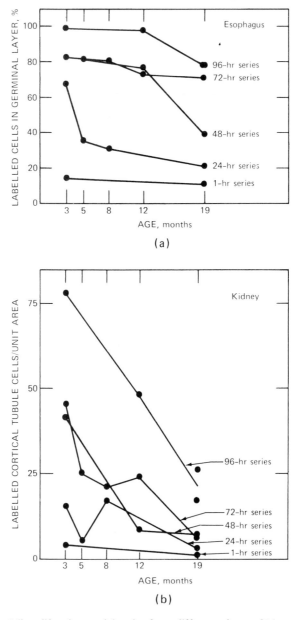

Fig. 1  Cell-proliferation activity in four different tissues [(a) esophagus, (b) kidney, (c) ear epidermis, and (d) tongue] of the mouse as determined by microscopic analysis of radioautographs. Mice of different ages got repeated injections of $^3$H—thymidine over periods of time ranging from 1 to 96 hr. [From I. L. Cameron, Cell Proliferation and Renewal in Aging Mice, *J. Gerontol.*, 27: 162 (1972).]

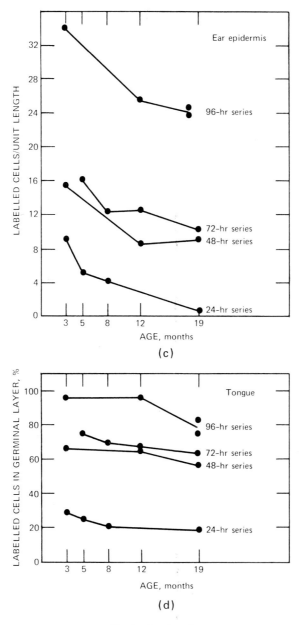

Fig. 1 Continued.

cell populations of mice as a function of age. The mice in each age group were given a series of injections of tritiated thymidine (three per day) to label cells in preparation for cell reproduction. Adult nongrowing mice in the various age groups were killed after being on the isotope for 1, 2, 3, and 4 days. Histological sections of tissues were prepared for radioautography and microscopic analysis. Through this experimental approach essentially all the reproducing cells become labelled, and with time there is an accumulative increase in the number of labelled cells. This technique is therefore cumulative and magnifies even small differences that may exist in rates of cell proliferation. The data show an age-dependent decline in rate of cell proliferation in all cell populations examined, even in slowly proliferating cell populations. The cause of the age change is not discussed, only the fact that aging is a general control factor affecting the cell-proliferation rate throughout all tissues of the body.

Other factors that appear to demonstrate systemic control of cell proliferation may include somatotrophic (growth) hormone,[18] thyroid hormone, body-temperature variations, and general conditions that control the *milieu interieux* of the entire body.

In conclusion, there appear to be general mitotic control factors that affect all proliferative cell populations of the body.

## MITOTIC CONTROLS THAT AFFECT SPECIFIC ORGAN, TISSUE, OR CELL POPULATIONS OF THE BODY

Table 1 lists examples of factors that have been cited as causing mitotic stimulation to cell populations of specific tissues in the body. The list is not intended to be exhaustive of possible examples. The specific mitogenic factor is listed opposite the specific target cell population that is affected.

To state that a factor is a specific mitogen that affects a specific tissue or organ cell system implies that other proliferating cell systems in the body are not responding to the mitogenic factor. All too often workers have dealt solely with the specific target tissues and have assumed that nontarget tissues are not responding.

Regeneration of the liver following partial hepatectomy is commonly cited as an example of a specific factor or condition that stimulates mitosis in the remaining portion of the liver. In fact, Paschkis et al.,[19] Vinogradova,[20] and Rucci, Satta, and Tota[21] all claim that partial hepatectomy also stimulates mitosis in the corneal epithelium. Virolainen,[22] however, could not detect an increase in mitotic indexes in the corneal epithelium, but he did find a decrease in proliferative activity in the orbital gland of rats. Thus far, the specificity of the mitotic response in the liver has not been conclusively established. Recent work[23,24] indicates the existence of a mitotic inhibitor of hepatic origin called "the hepatic chalone," which specifically inhibits cell proliferation in liver cells but not in other cell populations, such as in the kidney, the lung, the heart, the

**TABLE 1**

LEVELS OF MITOTIC CONTROL

| Some examples of mitogenic factors | Tissue-cell population affected |
|---|---|
| General factors | |
|   Nutrition | |
|   Age | |
|   Diurnal rhythm | All cells capable of |
|   Nontarget hormones: | cell proliferation |
|     Growth hormone | |
|     Thyroxin | |
| Specific factors | |
|   Bacterial endotoxin | Endothelium and reticuloendothelial system |
|   Antigen | Peripheral lymphatic tissues |
|   Compensatory organ regeneration: | |
|     Unilateral nephrectomy or excess folic acid | Kidney |
|     Partial hepatectomy or carbon tetrachloride | Liver |
|     Unilateral salivary gland removal or denervation | Parotid gland |
|   Target hormones: | |
|     Estradiol | Uterus and other female secondary sex tissues |
|     Testosterone | Seminiferous epithelium and male secondary sex tissues |
|     Tissue-specific hormones (may be same as compensatory organ regeneration), stimulants or promoters, inhibitors or chalone(s) | Skin, liver, kidney, etc. |
|   Poietins: | |
|     Erythropoietin or anoxia | Erythroblasts |
|     Thrombopoietin or antiplatelet serum | Megakaryocytes |
|     Granulopoietin | Granulocytes |
|     Tumor-angiogenesis factor[61] | Local endothelium of vessels |
| Local factors | |
|   Loss of contact inhibition | Lens, cornea, skin, etc. |
|   Local wound hormones | |

intestine, or the tongue epithelium. This hepatic chalone may very well prove to be a specific mitotic factor controlling the liver.

We have reinvestigated the question of a specific mitogenic factor operating after unilateral nephrectomy.[25] Following unilateral nephrectomy, the rate of cell proliferation was stimulated in eight kidney-cell populations sampled in the remaining kidney (Fig. 2 and Table 2). In contrast, the rate of cell proliferation of several extrarenal cell populations, including cell populations in the heart,

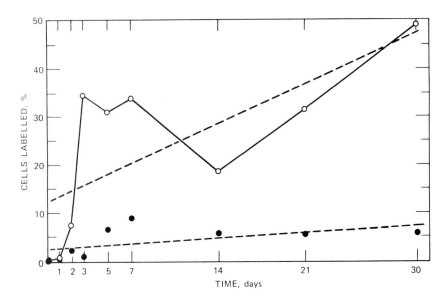

Fig. 2    Percentage of labelled cell nuclei in the distal tubule cells of the kidney
vs time on ³H–thymidine in the drinking water. Each point represents one
mouse. o, mice nephrectomized unilaterally at zero time. ●, untreated control
mice. The dashed curves represent the calculated least-squares linear-regression
fit. [From  L. E.  Tingle and I. L.  Cameron, Cell Proliferation Response in
Several Tissues Following Combined Unilateral Nephrectomy and High Salt
Diet in Mice, *Tex. Rep. Biol. Med.*, 31: 537 (1973).]

liver, and ear, showed no significant increase. This finding suggests that unilateral
nephrectomy initiates a specific or preferential stimulus to cell proliferation in
most if not all of the cell populations in the remaining kidney.

Perhaps the most commonly cited example of a specific mitogenic factor is
the female sex hormone, estradiol. This hormone is assumed to be a specific
stimulus to the uterus and to the female secondary sex tissues. Figure 3 shows
the tritiated thymidine labelling index of the littoral cells obtained from
radioautographs of the mouse liver following administration of endotoxin and of
estradiol.[26] The isotope was given 1 hr before the mice were killed. Although
the stimulation of reticuloendothelial cell proliferation by endotoxin is expected
as a specific response to endotoxins, the figure reveals that estradiol also
stimulates mitotic activity of the same littoral-cell population. Thus the
assumption that estradiol is a specific mitogenic agent for female sex tissues is
not entirely warranted by the findings.

It seems safe to conclude that there are mitogenic factors that have at least
preferential mitogenic effects on specific cell populations in the body.
Specificity of mitotic response has often been assumed without experimental

**TABLE 2**

STATISTICAL COMPARISON OF RATES OF CELL PROLIFERATION
(INCREASE IN PERCENT OF $^3$H–THYMIDINE LABELLED
NUCLEI) IN RENAL AND EXTRARENAL CELL POPULATIONS OF
MICE FOLLOWING UNILATERAL NEPHRECTOMY*

| Cell population | Experimental linear slope | Control linear slope | Significance† |
|---|---|---|---|
| Kidney | | | |
| Total cortical tubule | 0.98 | 0.22 | $p < 0.001$ |
| Proximal tubule | 0.92 | 0.25 | $p < 0.001$ |
| Distal tubule | 1.1 | 0.16 | $p < 0.001$ |
| Interstitial | 0.72 | 0.44 | $p < 0.10$ |
| Glomerular tuft | 0.87 | 0.31 | $p < 0.001$ |
| Macula densa | 0.25 | 0.11 | $p < 0.01$ |
| Parietal layer of | | | |
| Bowman's capsule | 1.8 | 0.92 | $p < 0.05$ |
| Arterial media | 0.77 | 0.05 | $p < 0.001$ |
| Juxtaglomerular | 0.59 | 0.18 | $p < 0.05$ |
| Heart | | | |
| Capillary endothelium | 0.79 | 0.75 | N.S. |
| Connective tissue | 0.41 | 0.84 | $p < 0.01$ |
| Ear | | | |
| Ear epidermis | 3.4 | 3.6 | N.S. |
| Liver | | | |
| Hepatocytes | 0.03 | 0.04 | N.S. |
| Littoral | 1.1 | 1.5 | N.S. |

*The slope of the least-squares linear regression is related to the rate of cell proliferation (larger numbers indicate faster rates).

†As determined by Student's t test. N.S., not significant; $p < 0.05$, probably significant; $p < 0.01$, definitely significant; and $p < 0.001$, highly significant.

verification. Clearly, better designed experiments and additional observations of specific mitogenic factors are needed.

# SIMULTANEOUS STIMULATION
# AND INHIBITION OF CELL PROLIFERATION
# (Report of a Tumor–Host Interaction Study)

A fast growing transplantable tumor (hepatoma) affects cell proliferation in several host tissues of the mouse.[27] We investigated the effects of a transplanted hepatoma on cell proliferation in various cell populations of the host liver, spleen, kidney, ear, and tongue of male and female A/J mice. Figures 4, 5, and 6 summarize much of the data from our study.

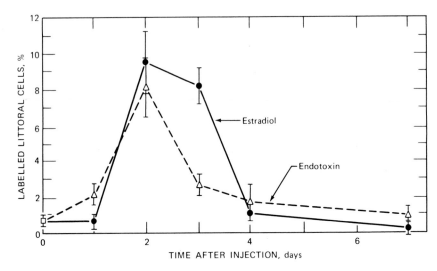

Fig. 3   The $^3$H−thymidine radioautographic labelling index of littoral cells in the mouse liver as a function of time after injection of estradiol or endotoxin. The $^3$H−thymidine was given 1 hr before killing. Zero point in time represents normal untreated mice. [From L. S. Kelly and E. L. Dobson, Evidence Concerning the Origin of Liver Microphages, Brit. J. Exp. Path., 52: 88 (1971).]

A week after young mice were inoculated with the hepatoma, they were injected with tritiated thymidine three times during the last 24-hr period before being killed. The mice were then weighed and killed and their organs were removed for study. The presence of the tumor slowed the growth rate of the tumor-bearing mice compared to the control mice. Both biochemical and radioautographic procedures were used to quantitate the effects of the tumor on whole-organ DNA content and DNA synthesis and to define the particular cell populations in those organs which were primarily affected by the tumor. Increases greater than twofold in DNA content and DNA synthesis (as indicated by $^3$H−labelled thymidine incorporation into DNA) were observed in the spleens of tumor-bearing mice; these observations support those of other investigators. Increases in DNA content and synthesis also were observed in the livers of tumor-bearing animals. Radioautographic analysis shows an increase in the percentage of labelled hepatocytes and nonhepatocytes (including sinusoidal lining and Kupffer cells) in these livers. An increase in labelled leukocytes was also observed in the tissue spaces of the livers of tumor-bearing animals. The kidneys of the tumor-bearing animals showed a substantial increase in DNA synthesis, owing primarily to an increase in the turnover rate of the endothelial cells. A new finding in this study was that some cell populations (such as the ear epidermis and the ventral tongue epithelium) decrease in proliferation and

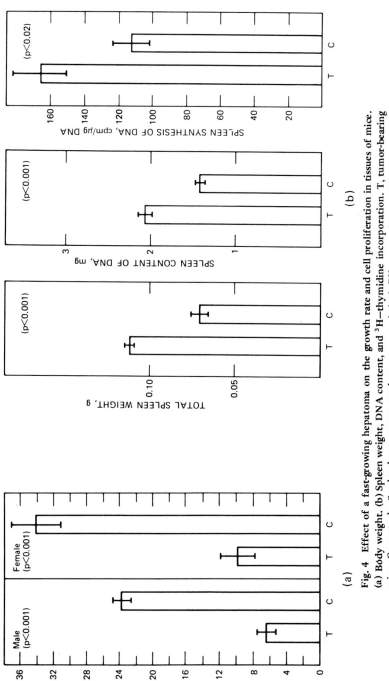

Fig. 4 Effect of a fast-growing hepatoma on the growth rate and cell proliferation in tissues of mice. (a) Body weight. (b) Spleen weight, DNA content, and ³H–thymidine incorporation. T, tumor-bearing mice; C, controls. Student's t test was used to assess statistical differences. [From W. W. Morgan and I. L. Cameron, Effect of Fast-Growing Transplantable Hepatoma on Cell Proliferation in Host Tissue of the Mouse, *Cancer Res.,* 33: 442-443 (1973).]

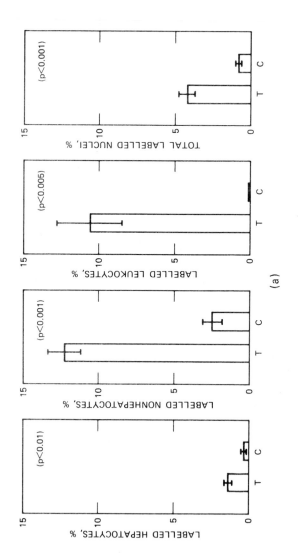

(a)

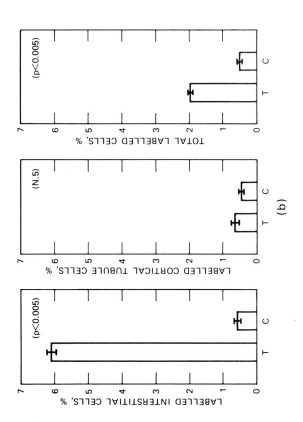

Fig. 5 Effect of a fast-growing hepatoma on $^3$H–thymidine incorporation in the liver (a) and kidney (b) of mice. T, tumor-bearing mice; C, controls. Student's t test was used to assess statistical differences. [From W. W. Morgan and I. L. Cameron, Effect of Fast-Growing Transplantable Hepatoma on Cell Proliferation in Host Tissue of the Mouse, *Cancer Res.*, 33: 444, 447 (1973).]

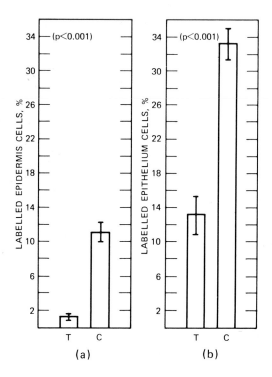

Fig. 6  Effect of a fast-growing hepatoma on $^3$H—thymidine incorporation in
the epidermis of the ear (a) and the ventral epithelium of the tongue (b). T,
tumor-bearing mice; C, controls. Student's t test was used to assess statistical
differences. [From W. W. Morgan and I. L. Cameron, Effect of Fast-Growing
Transplantable Hepatoma on Cell Proliferation in Host Tissue of the Mouse,
*Cancer Res.*, 33: 447 (1973).]

turnover in tumor-bearing animals at the same time that other cell populations in
other tissues increase their proliferative activity. The results of this study show
that the effects of the tumor on the host are complex and that they seem to be
the result of at least three primary factors.

The first is an immunological response of the host to the transplanted
hepatoma. The increase in spleen weight and cell proliferation probably is due
exclusively to an attempt of the host to repel the foreign tissue. The increased
proliferation of the host sinusoidal lining and Kupffer cell populations in the
liver may also be an effort of the host to engulf the debris and toxic materials
released by the tumor. In addition, the increased turnover rate of the endothelial
cell population in the kidneys of tumor-bearing animals may reflect a response
of these cells to toxic material secreted by the tumor. A similar stimulation of
endothelial-cell proliferation was reported by Gaynor[28] after the injection of
endotoxin into rabbits.

The second factor probably reflects either a systemic reduction of nutritional precursors or a release of systemic growth-retarding factors by the hepatoma.[29] In this study the effect of this second factor is clearly demonstrated by the depression of cell renewal in the tongue and ear epithelium and by the general retardation in body growth. This observation is of particular interest, inasmuch as this decrease in cell proliferation in the skin and oral epithelium was observed at the same time that the liver, kidney, and spleen demonstrated increased cell proliferation.

The third factor is reflected by the increase in cell proliferation in the hepatocyte-cell population of the livers of the tumor-bearing animals. One possible explanation for the increased liver-cell proliferation is that the hepatoma may secrete a growth factor that is specific for the liver. Other investigators[30,31] who have studied hepatoma-bearing animals report similar results. Possibly there is a homology of the growth-stimulating factor secreted by the hepatoma with the stimulatory factor that Fisher, Szuch, and Fisher[32] report is involved in initiating liver compensatory hypertrophy after partial hepatectomy. It seems somewhat doubtful that such a liver growth factor is produced only by hepatomas, inasmuch as other types of tumors also stimulate liver growth or regeneration.[31,33-37]

To explain how it is possible to increase mitotic activity in some cell populations of the body and at the same time decrease mitotic activity in other cell populations, one must postulate that two mitotic control factors are operating at the same time. For example, in the tumor—host response, it is suggested that the tumor-bearing animal has a systemic reduction of nutrition while the antigenic nature of the tumor has stimulated the immune system (lymphopoiesis) in the host. The specific response to antigens requires that some lymphocytes contain specific receptor sites. For lymphocytes these receptor sites may be specific antibodies located at the cell surface. In this way the antigen-triggered lymphocytes are stimulated to proliferate.

Other examples of specific receptor sites or thresholds of activation can be cited. For instance, $10^{-9}$ moles of a hormone once bound to a specific receptor site on a target-cell membrane can trigger an adjacent enzyme (adenyl cyclase), which then produces $10^{-3}$ moles of cyclic AMP (Ref. 38). The cyclic AMP in turn activates various intracellular reactions. The important point is that one molecule of a given hormone can activate the production of a million molecules of cyclic AMP. This represents a million-fold amplification process! Thus, a particular cell population that bears a specific receptor site can be signaled by a specific factor which in turn can have its signal amplified many fold.

Spelsberg[39] and others have demonstrated that there are also specific hormone receptors in the cytosol and specific acceptors in the nucleus of target cells which enable the target cell to undergo an alteration of gene transcription which often results in a stimulus to cell proliferation in a specific target tissue.

## LOCAL MITOTIC CONTROLS THAT ACT BETWEEN CELLS OF THE SAME POPULATION

Wounds 1 mm or more in size which penetrate into the dermis of the skin or into the stroma of the cornea of the eye both result in a healing response (see reviews by Arey,[40] McMinn,[41] and Maibach and Rovee[42]). In the skin the vascularized dermis is involved in the repair process, and in the cornea a nonvascularized stroma is involved in the repair process. The reepithelialization response of the stratified squamous epithelium is our primary concern here, and this response appears to be very similar in both the skin and the cornea.

In both types of wounds, there is an early movement of cells at the edge of the wound into the wound area. The basal layer of cells actively migrates into the wound gap. The reepithelialization is rapid, and small wounds are covered within a day. A number of reports indicate that there is little or no proliferative activity in the wound area during the reepithelialization process.[43,44] In fact, the proliferative activity is far below normal near the wound edge; however, higher proliferative activity does occur later in epithelial cells located some distance from the wound edge. Thus there is a zone of inhibited cell proliferation immediately surrounding the wound edge and extending outward to at least 100 epithelial cells. Beyond this zone of inhibition, there is a small band or zone of increased proliferative activity which later moves with time like a wave toward the wound center.

In both the skin and the cornea, those epithelial cells which cover over the surface of small wounds are filled with glycogen.[45,46] Glycogen is not normally present in the epithelial cells of nonwounded skin or cornea; it accumulates in the epidermal cells prior to their movement into the wound area. It has been postulated that the accumulation of glycogen in these cells may in some way be related to the repair of the mucopolysaccharide components associated with the cell surface and the replacement of the disrupted basal lamina. The basal cells may not be able to enter into cell reproduction unless they are in contact with an intact basal lamina.

That mitotic activity is diminished during the migration phase of wound healing has led to the conclusion that the basal cells cannot divide while they are moving.[41,42] In fact, others have demonstrated that migration and mitosis can be separated by appropriate inhibitors and that the two cell processes are therefore independent and perhaps incompatible. It has even been suggested that the independence of mitosis and cell migration implies the existence of special metabolic requirements for cell migration.[46,47] This point will be returned to later.

There are two common explanations of the abnormally high mitotic activity adjacent to epithelial wounds. The first explanation is that a mitotic stimulant is released by the damaged tissue adjacent to the wound,[48] and the second explanation proposes that a mitotic inhibitor is decreased in the area of the wound.[47] In the latter case the decrease in the mitotic inhibitor substance may be due to decreased production of the substance by the damaged cells and/or to a diffusing away of the inhibitor into the wound cavity. Before choosing between one or the other of these two alternatives and excluding some other explanation, let us review information on superficial wounds to the skin and to the cornea.

Superficial wounds that involve only the epithelial layers have been subjected to some study. Small pinpricks (30 $\mu$m in diameter) were observed to be rapidly closed in 3 hr by pseudopodal-type movements, and there was no apparent multiplication of adjacent cells.[49] In small superficial burns produced by a cautery needle, no zone of cessation of DNA synthesis was found around the burned area, and adjacent basal cells underwent incorporation of tritiated thymidine between 8 and 24 hr.[44] In larger burns (approximately 1.5 mm wide) which are confined solely to the epithelium, a relative decrease in mitotic figures in the cornea of the injured eye as compared to a normal control eye was noted at 6 hr. After 12 hr a general increase in mitotic activity was seen, which frequently corresponded to the time reepithelialization was complete.[50] Unfortunately, these observations failed to include comments on the locations where the increased and decreased levels of mitotic activity were detected. In a related study on tongue epithelium, cauterization of the upper two to three layers of squamous cells was followed by a rapid increase in tritiated thymidine incorporation in the basal cells immediately below the wound. No changes away from the wound area were seen.[51]

The evidence indicates that different mechanisms of epithelial involvement in wound repair exist between superficial wounds and those which penetrate into the stroma or the dermis. This might naturally be expected since in superficial wounds the basement lamina is preserved and an inflammatory reaction does not occur. It is well known that superficial wounds heal with complete recovery, but wounds that penetrate into the stroma leave permanent scar tissue after healing. In a study on corneal lesions in rabbits produced by the infrared beam of the carbon dioxide laser, a sharp demarcation was recorded in the level of damaging radiation between burns where rapid complete recovery was seen and those which left scar tissue.[52] Since the heat energy was applied in a very short interval (55 msec), the burns, produced by a temporary change in the surface temperature, were confined to the actual exposure area. A repeatable level of irradiation was defined in which an opacity could be observed in the epithelial layers followed by rapid epithelial sloughing and complete healing in 24 to 48 hr. This level of irradiation could be exceeded by a factor of about 2 without any observable change in the results. Further increases always incurred permanent scarring, implying that the physical barrier of the basement lamina between the epithelium and the stroma had been destroyed.

The use of the carbon dioxide laser in producing corneal wounds has an obvious advantage in studies of the migration and proliferation patterns during healing. At short time exposures there is a range of irradiation levels that produce a burn of precise geometry encompassing the overlying epithelium but sparing the basement lamina and corneal stroma. Higher irradiation levels can penetrate into the stroma yet preserve the uniformity and geometry of the burn as long as the burn area remains large compared to the depth of penetration. This last condition, plus the requirement for short time exposures, is necessary to minimize the effects of heat conduction away from the desired burn area. Repeatability of selected burns in rabbits can be attained with high accuracy at the same irradiation levels. An investigation by Fine et al.[53] of long time exposures with the carbon dioxide laser revealed irregular burn characteristics and wound healing which were definitely unpredictable with respect to geometry and penetration.

This capacity for reproducibility and geometric precision in superficial corneal wound production has been used by Lehmiller[54] to study the interrelationships between cell migration, glycogen content, cell proliferation, and cell-population density in the basal layer of cells. Most of the following is taken from Lehmiller's report of this project.

Superficial wounds were produced in the rabbit corneal epithelium by a 2-mm circular beam from a carbon dioxide laser. In most cases tritiated thymidine was applied topically to the eye once every 6 hr after the wounding. A number of rabbits were examined at each of the following time periods: 4, 6, 12, 18, 24, 30, and 36 hr. Two other wounded rabbits received the tritiated thymidine only at 24 hr. All animals were killed 30 min after the last isotope administration. Radioautographs of histological sections were prepared, and the proliferative activity and cell-population density of the basal-cell layer were recorded. Figure 7 illustrates some of the data dealing with basal-cell migration, population density, and proliferative activity of individual wounds.

The data show that the rate of epithelialization of the 2-mm-diameter wounds is extremely rapid although there was a fair amount of individual variation. Burns observed at 6 and 12 hr after exposure were easily identified by the persistent mass of necrotic tissue or by a denuded area. By 18 hr several eyes had complete coverage of one or more layers of cells over the entire wound, and, in 2 out of 8 cases, no burns could be found under the dissecting scope or detected in serial sections of the original area. This apparent complete healing was even more pronounced at 24 hr when more than 50% (7 of 12) of the burns were not discernible. At 30 hr 75% (3 of 4) were completely healed, and at 36 hr 100% (4 of 4) were healed.

High percentages of basal cells labelled with tritiated thymidine are seen to be associated with the leading portion of migrating cells in both the recently repopulated area and in regions near the original wound edge (Fig. 7). These proliferative levels were considerably higher than the background averages obtained at 2.5 mm from the wound center, and they were demonstrable at all time periods analyzed. Many of the profiles shown in Fig. 7 are characterized by peaks or spikes of proliferation which are quite localized and accentuated. Pronounced proliferative activity always occurred between 4 to 10 intervals behind either the leading migratory edge or the burn center in cases of complete repopulation. The degree of proliferation in the migratory repopulation areas increased disproportionately at later times after wounding, as can be seen in the profile of the rabbit given a single tritiated thymidine application 24 hr after burning.

Migrating basal cells at the leading edge were generally very small and flattened with dense nuclei. Behind the migrating edge there was often a group of bunched cells with slightly larger dimensions; these cells had round to oval-shaped nuclei and were generally cuboidal. Then followed huge basal cells with large pale nuclei. The position of these huge basal cells on the graphs is correlated with the very high and broad proliferative peak observed from 4 to 10 intervals behind the leading edge. Continuing outward, the basal-cell size gradually became normal, the columnar shape was resumed, and the population density increased to the point of complete normalcy in morphology at about 2 mm from the wound center.

The number of labelled cells found above the basal layer increased with sampling time as would be expected. Very few were seen in the eyes examined at 6 hr, whereas it was common to find labelled cells in the third and fourth layers at 24 to 30 hr. Occasionally at 12 hr and frequently at later times, labelled cells were observed in the second and third layer of cells several intervals behind the leading edge in areas of rapid migration. Labelled cells in the nearby regions outside the original wound edge could often be seen making the transition out of the basal layer with accentuated cellular deformation in the direction of cell migration toward the wound.

Although extensive periodic acid-Schiff (PAS) staining was conducted throughout the experiment, no PAS-positive material was observed in any epithelial cells even though the adjacent basement membrane was PAS-positive. The glycogen-filled epithelial cells that are usually seen covering the penetrating wounds were not present. The necrotic mass of dead cells gave a moderately strong PAS-positive reaction of somewhat greater intensity than the stroma collagen, and Descemet's membrane gave the normal intense PAS-staining reaction. The continuous integrity of the basement lamina beneath migratory cells in the original burn area would be verified in all cases. No indication of stromal disturbance was found.

The high levels of proliferative activity recorded in the migrating cell masses is in obvious contradiction to the wound-healing phenomenon found in the penetrating wounds. The DNA synthesis by the basal cells was actually enhanced in and near the wound area as contrasted to remote regions, and no zones of inhibition or decreased activity were noted. The prevailing opinion that cell migration during epithelial wound healing is not compatible with proliferation can no longer be considered a valid assumption.

A clue to the difference in proliferative activity may be the observed absence of glycogen accumulation in the migrating cells of this experiment. It is well documented that there is a mucopolysaccharide component associated with the cell membrane and basement lamina. The appearance of glycogen-filled cells in

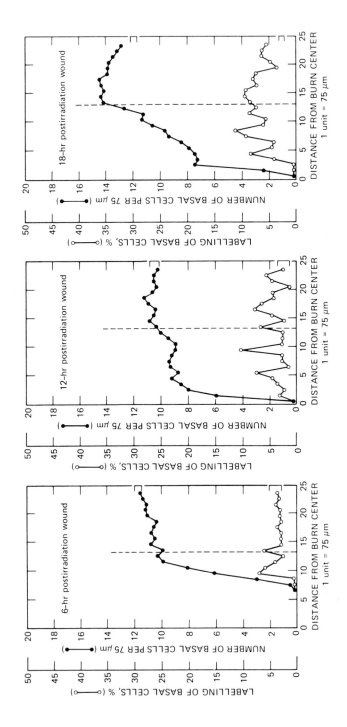

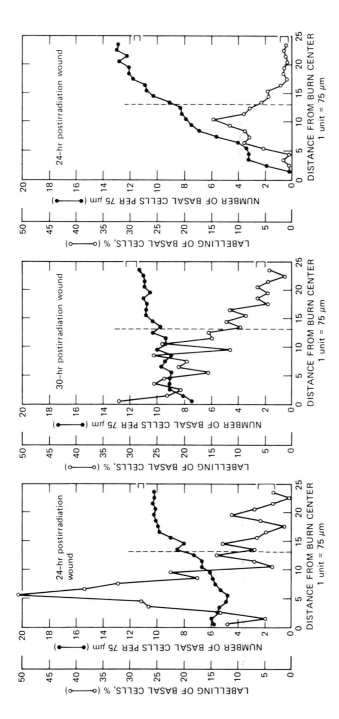

Fig. 7 Analysis of cell proliferation, migration, and population density at times during the repair of a 2-mm superficial corneal wound produced with a carbon dioxide laser. The analysis is made from radioautographs of corneas that were repeatedly exposed to $^3$H-thymidine during the healing response. The last 24-hr sample was exposed to $^3$H-thymidine only once 30 min before the cornea was fixed. - - - -, edge of the wounded area. The brackets on the right of the profiles indicate the range of values at 2.5 mm from the center of the wound.

penetrating wounds, where the basal lamina has been totally destroyed, may be due to the use of glucose as a precursor in the regeneration of the basement lamina. Restoration as well as preservation of such basement membranes may be quite demanding in deeper wounds where the inflammatory reaction is in progress. The concept that basal cells would be inhibited from entering the proliferation cycle without the presence of an intact basement lamina is quite reasonable. It is interesting to note that Fine et al.[53] reported electron-microscopic findings of glycogen-like particles near the basement membranes of basal cells, both intracellular and extracellular, in a wound-healing area.

A depression in the basal-cell population density is seen in almost all cases slightly behind the leading migratory edge or adjacent to the wound center if the eye has completely recovered. The coincidence of this trough in basal-cell population density and a very high peak of cell proliferation is unanimous and strongly suggests that gradients in basal-cell density may greatly influence proliferative activity. The stimulus for cells to undergo proliferation probably represents a broad summation of physical, chemical, and metabolic factors. However, the concept of decrease in cell-population density and the loosening of close cell-to-cell contacts as an overall regulatory mechanism for stimulation of cell populations in living tissues is quite sound from a general physiologic viewpoint. In areas where the basal-cell density has been thinned out, proliferative activity should be enhanced. Conversely, multiplication and growth to higher density cell populations would allow closer cell-to-cell contact and retard cell reproduction.

Other evidence supporting the importance of cell-population density in the control of proliferative activity can be seen in the work of Harding and Srinivasan,[55,56] who have shown that a small injury (000- to 0-gauge needle insertion) into the anterior epithelium of the rabbit lens produces a propagated wave of proliferative activity which advances outward from the site of injury as a concentric ring, quite analogous to the waves produced when a stone is tossed into a quiet pool of water. The single-layered epithelium shows a wave of cells in DNA synthesis which is followed by a wave of mitosis. With increase in time the first propagated wave of proliferative activity is often followed by a second wave of DNA synthesis and mitosis. DNA synthesis is first seen near the wound center at 14 hr after the injury, and mitotic figures are first seen by 24 hr. The second wave of proliferative activity starts at the wound center between 24 and 48 hr after injury.

Using the pictures published by Harding and Srinivasan,[55,56] I have reanalyzed their data to determine the population density in relation to waves of DNA synthesis and mitosis in the cells in the single-layered epithelium. Five of their photomicrographs were analyzed. The results from three of the photomicrographs are shown in Fig. 8. This figure shows the analysis of 48-hr-old wounds. In each of these three cases, tritiated thymidine was given 2 hr before the lens was fixed and prepared for enface radioautography. The total number of cells per 100 $\mu m^2$ and the number of labelled cells per 100 $\mu m^2$ are both plotted

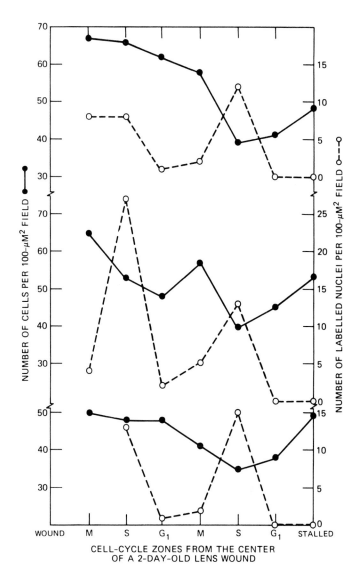

Fig. 8 Analysis of cell proliferation and cell-population density in a 48-hr-old wound to the lens epithelium of a rabbit. The lens was exposed to ³H—thymidine just before being fixed, and whole (enface) radioautographs were prepared. The analysis was made of three photomicrographs of radioautographs published by Harding and Srinivasan.[55,56] Cell-cycle zones are determined by the appearance of DNA-synthesizing cells and mitotic figures.

as a function of the cell-cycle zones which radiate from the wound center to the zone of stalled cells away from the wound. Cell-cycle zones were determined from the appearance of DNA synthesizing cells and from division figures in the radioautographs.

In each case the cell-population density of stalled cells (shown on the right side of the figure) is relatively high, but then the population density decreases in the $G_1$ zone and decreases even more in the zone of cells which are engaged in DNA synthesis (the S zone). Cells in the zone of mitosis show an increase in population density. This increase in population density is presumably due in part to the production of two daughter cells from one mother cell. The population density remains relatively high from this first zone of mitosis toward the wound center. Because the actual size or area of the wound is so small, it is difficult to think that the decrease in cell density seen in the broad outermost $G_1$ and S zones is due to the migration of cells toward the wound center. How then can the decreased density be accounted for in the outermost $G_1$ and S zones?

Figure 9 shows one explanation of the results and suggests a mechanism to explain the control of cell proliferation in the case of the wounded lens. This figure suggests that, soon after the wound is made, those cells which are adjacent to the wound move apart, which tends to loosen or break numerous cell-to-cell contacts in this zone. With time this zone of loosened cell contacts is propagated considerable distances from the wound center. To explain the decrease in cell-population density at later times (48-hr) and distances from the wound, we postulate that cells in the innermost $G_1$, S, and M zones must become quite tall and columnar in shape, which creates some space for the outermost $G_1$- and S-zone cells to decrease their population density. Histological cross sections through the wound center should validate this prediction.

It is felt that the breaking of cell-to-cell contacts in the lowered cell-density zones is the simplest and most tenable explanation to account for the stimulation of cell proliferation in local wounds. As cell proliferation increases, the population density increases; and new cell-to-cell contacts are formed, which slows the proliferative activity of the cells and causes a feedback control mechanism.

Actually the idea of contact inhibition of cell division is borrowed from the tissue-culture studies of Abercrombie[57] and others as reviewed by Martz and Steinberg.[58] Interest in what causes contact inhibition of cell proliferation has been stimulated by the studies of Loewenstein and coworkers,[59] which show that molecules as large as 50,000 mol. wt. can pass between normal cells by means of tight junctions. It is an established fact that cancer cells often fail to demonstrate the contact inhibition of cell proliferation which is seen in normal cells, and in this regard Loenwenstein and others have also shown that cancer cells are not able to communicate between one another in the same way as do normal cells.

Recently Burton and Canham[60] developed a model that can be used to explain the stimulation of cell proliferation when contact between normal cells

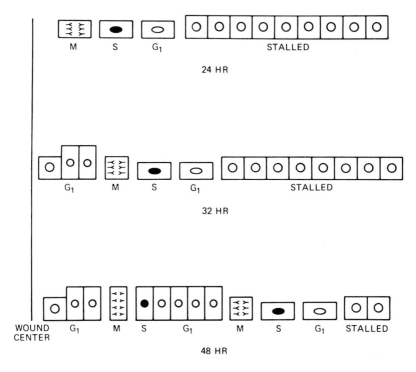

Fig. 9 Simulation of the progression of a wave of cell proliferation after a small wound to the lens epithelium. The wound center is at the left of the figure. The drawing gives one possible explanation for the results in Fig. 8.

is reduced, as may be postulated in the case of local wounds. Figure 10 is a drawing to explain their model of control of cell proliferation. The first assumption is that there is a continued rise and fall of a division-promoting substance in cells capable of cell proliferation. A group of cells not in close communication will show random cell proliferation of individual cells as the division-promoting substance reaches the threshold of activation in individual cells. If, however, the population of cells is in direct communication, it could exchange a division-promoting factor between one another in such a manner that the substance cannot reach a threshold of activation in any of the individual cells. Two other causes for uncontrolled cell proliferation could be brought about by excessive production of the division-promoting substance and by synchronization of groups of cells by some external induction process.

It seems that the anterior epithelium of the wounded lens presents an excellent opportunity to study the possible disruption and reestablishment of tight junctions by both ultrastructural observations or by intercellular communication studies (i.e., electrocoupling or microinjection studies), and the system

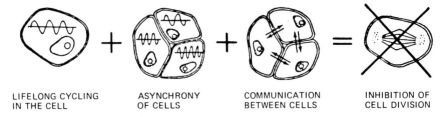

| LIFELONG CYCLING | ASYNCHRONY | COMMUNICATION | INHIBITION OF |
| IN THE CELL | OF CELLS | BETWEEN CELLS | CELL DIVISION |

Fig. 10  A logical explanation of the theory of contact inhibition of cell proliferation. A constant cycling in the cellular level of a division-promoting substance is implied by the first drawing. An exchange of the division-promoting substance between cells in an asynchronous cell population will keep the threshold of the substance below the threshold of mitotic activation. [From A. C. Burton and P. B. Canham, the Behavior of Coupled Biochemical Oscillators as a Model of Contact Inhibition of Cellular Division, *J. Theor. Biol.*, 39: 555 (1973).]

therefore presents an opportunity to test Burton and Canham's theory.[60] At this point there seems to be no compelling reason to postulate the production of an extracellular wound hormone or substance, be it stimulatory or inhibitory in nature, to explain the local control of mitotic activity.

In conclusion it is clear that control of cell proliferation within the body can occur at several levels and that these different levels of mitogenic control can operate simultaneously.

## ACKNOWLEDGMENTS

The work reported in this paper was supported in part by the Morrison Trust and by grant GB-31580 from the National Science Foundation.

## REFERENCES

1. B. Morpurgo, Sur Las Processus Physiologique de Neoformation Cellulaire Durant L'inanition Aigue de L'organisme, *Arch. Ital. Biol.*, 11: 118-133 (1889).
2. E. H. Leduc, The Effect of Fasting and Refeeding and of Changes in Dietary Protein Level on Mitosis in the Liver of the Mouse, *Anat. Rec.*, 99: 586 (1947).
3. E. H. Leduc, Mitotic Activity in the Liver of the Mouse During Inanition Followed by Refeeding with Different Levels of Protein, *Amer. J. Anat.*, 84: 397-429 (1949).
4. J. Overton, Mitotic Responses in Amphibian Epidermis to Feeding and Grafting, *J. Exp. Zool.*, 130: 433-483 (1956).
5. W. S. Bullough, The Effect of a Restricted Diet on Mitotic Activity in the Mouse, *Brit. J. Cancer*, 3: 275-282 (1949).
6. W. S. Bullough, Mitotic Activity in the Adult Male Mouse *Mus musculus L.* The Diurnal Cycles and Their Relation to Working and Sleeping, *Proc. Roy. Soc. (London), Ser. B*, 135: 212-232 (1948).

7. W. S. Bullough and E. B. Laurence, Stress and Adrenaline in Relation to the Diurnal Cycle of Epidermal Mitotic Activity in Adult Male Mice, *Proc. Roy. Soc. (London), Ser. B,* **154**: 540-556 (1961).

8. R. Vasama, The Diurnal Rhythm of Mitotic Activity in the Corneal Epithelium of Mice, *Ann. Univ. Turk. Ser., A1,* **29**: 11-80 (1961).

9. M. Blair and C. S. Hooper, The Effect of Starvation on the Rate of Renewal of the Epithelium in the Small Intestine, *Anat. Rec.,* **127**: 267 (1957).

10. I. L. Cameron and G. Cleffmann, Initiation of Mitosis in Relation to the Cell Cycle Following Feeding of Starved Chickens, *J. Cell Biol.,* **21**: 169-174 (1964).

11. C. P. Sigdestad, J. Bauman, and S. W. Lesher, Diurnal Fluctuations in the Number of Cells in Mitosis and DNA Synthesis in the Jejunum of the Mouse, *Exp. Cell Res.,* **58**: 159-162 (1969).

12. C. P. Sigdestad and S. Lesher, Further Studies on the Circadian Rhythm in the Proliferative Activity of Mouse Intestinal Epithelium, *Experientia,* **26**: 1321-1322 (1970).

13. H. Klein and H. Geisel, Zum Nachwees eines 24—Studenrhythmus der Mitosen bei Ratte und Maus, *Klin. Wochenschr.,* **25**: 662-663 (1947).

14. C. P. Leblond and C. E. Stevens, The Constant Renewal of the Intestinal Epithelium in the Albino Rat, *Anat. Rec.,* **100**: 357-378 (1948).

15. C. Pilgrim, W. Erb, and W. Mauer, Diurnal Fluctuations in the Number of DNA Synthesizing Nuclei in Various Mouse Tissues, *Nature,* **199**: 863 (1963).

16. D. E. Buetow, Cellular Content and Cellular Proliferation Changes in the Tissues and Organs of the Aging Mammal, *Cellular and Molecular Renewal in the Mammalian Body,* I. L. Cameron and J. D. Thrasher (Eds.), pp. 87-106, Academic Press, Inc., New York, 1971.

17. I. L. Cameron, Cell Proliferation and Renewal in Aging Mice, *J. Gerontol.,* **27**: 162-172 (1972).

18. P. Nettesheim and W. Oehlert, Die Wirkung des Wachstumshormons auf die Desoxyribonukleinsäure-Synthese in den Wechselgeweben der Weißen Maus, *Beitr. Pathol. Anat. Allg. Pathol.,* **126**: 395-412 (1962).

19. K. E. Paschkis, J. Goddard, A. Cantarow, and S. Adibi, Stimulation of Growth by Partial Hepatectomy, *Proc. Soc. Exp. Biol. Med.,* **101**: 184-186 (1959).

20. G. A. Vinogradova, The Effect of Reparative Regeneration of the Liver on the Mitotic Activity of the Corneal and Epidermal Epithelium in Mice, *Bull. Exp. Biol. Med. (USSR) Eng. Transl.,* **50**: 105-108 (1960).

21. F. S. Rucci, U. Satta, and G. Tota, Attivita Mitotica Corneale in Corso di Epatectomie Paryiali Atipiche Repetute, *Boll. Soc. Ital. Biol. Sper.,* **40**: 1183-1186 (1964).

22. M. Virolainen, Humoral Factors in Liver Cell Proliferation, in *Control of Cellular Growth in Adult Organisms,* H. Teir and T. Rytömaa (Eds.), pp. 232-249, Academic Press, Inc., New York, 1967.

23. A. Simard, L. Corneille, Y. Deschamps, and W. G. Verly, Inhibition of DNA Synthesis and Mitosis in Regenerating Liver by Hepatic Chalone, *J. Cell. Biol.,* **59**: 317a (1973).

24. R. A. Menzies and J. M. Kerrigan, Effect of Rat Liver Chalone of Chick Embryo Cell Division, *J. Cell Biol.,* **59**: 224a (1973).

25. L. E. Tingle and I. L. Cameron, Cell Proliferation Response in Several Tissues Following Combined Unilateral Nephrectomy and High Salt Diet in Mice, *Tex. Rep. Biol. Med.,* **31**: 537-549 (1973).

26. L. S. Kelly and E. L. Dobson, Evidence Concerning the Origin of Liver Macrophages, *Brit. J. Exp. Pathol.,* **52**: 88-99 (1971).

27. W. W. Morgan and I. L. Cameron, Effect of Fast-Growing Transplantable Hepatoma on Cell Proliferation in Host Tissue of the Mouse, *Cancer Res.,* **33**: 441-448 (1973).

28. E. Gaynor, Increased Mitotic Activity in Rabbit Endothelium After Endotoxin, *Lab. Invest.*, **24**: 318-320 (1971).

29. W. D. DeWys, A Quantitative Model for the Study of the Growth and Treatment of a Tumor and Its Metastases with Correlation Between Proliferative State and Sensitivity to Cyclophosphamide, *Cancer Res.*, **32**: 367-373 (1972).

30. B. Barbiroli, V. R. Potter, and H. P. Morris, DNA Synthesis in Morris Hepatoma 9618A and in Host Liver Following Partial Hepatectomy in Rats Adapted to Controlled Feeding Schedules, *Cancer Res.*, **32**: 7-10 (1972).

31. R. A. Malmgren, Observations on a Liver Mitotic Stimulant Present in Tumor Tissue, *Cancer Res.*, **16**: 232-236 (1956).

32. B. Fisher, P. Szuch, and E. R. Fisher, Evaluation of a Humoral Factor in Liver Regeneration Utilizing Liver Transplants. *Cancer Res.*, **31**: 322-331 (1971).

33. R. Baserga and W. E. Kisieleski, Cell Proliferation in Tumor-Bearing Mice, *Arch. Pathol.*, **72**: 24-30 (1961).

34. G. L. Rosene, Alteration of Tumor Cell and Hepatic Parenchymal Cell Mitotic Rates in Tumor-Injected Partially Hepatectomized Mice, *Cancer Res.*, **28**: 1469-1477 (1968).

35. A. G. Stewart and R. W. Begg, Systemic Effects of Tumors in Force-Fed Rats. II. Effect on the Weight of Carcass, Adrenals, Thymus, Liver and Spleen, *Cancer Res.*, **13**: 556-559 (1953).

36. A. Theologides and G. R. Zaki, Mitotic Index in the Regenerating Liver of Tumor-Bearing Mice, *Cancer Res.*, **29**: 1913-1915 (1969).

37. E. H. Yeakel, Increased Weight of the Liver in Wistar Albino Rats with Induced and Transplanted Tumors, *Cancer Res.*, **8**: 392-396 (1948).

38. D. F. H. Wallach, *The Plasma Membrane: Dynamic Perspectives, Genetics and Pathology,* Springer-Verlag, New York, 1972.

39. T. C. Spelsberg, The Role of Nuclear Acidic Proteins in Binding Steroid Hormones, in *Acidic Proteins of the Nucleus,* I. L. Cameron and J. R. Jeter, Jr. (Eds.), Academic Press, Inc., New York, in press.

40. L. B. Arey, Wound Healing, *Physiol. Rev.*, **16**: 327-406 (1936).

41. R. M. H. McMinn, *Tissue Repair,* Academic Press, Inc., New York, 1969.

42. H. I. Maibach and D. T. Rovee, *Epidermal Wound Healing,* Year Book Medical Publishers, Inc., Chicago, 1972.

43. L. B. Arey and W. M. Covode, The Method of Repair in Epithelial Wounds of the Cornea, *Anat. Rec.*, **86**(1): 75-86 (1943).

44. C. Hanna, Proliferation and Migration of Epithelial Cells, *Amer. J. Opthalmol.*, **61**(1): 55-63 (1966).

45. J. H. Dunnington and G. K. Smelser, Incorporation of $S^{35}$ in Healing Wounds in Normal and Devitalized Corneas, *Arch. Opthalmol. (Chicago)*, **60**: 116-129 (1958).

46. J. Raekallio and E. Levonen, Histochemical Demonstration of Transglucosylases and Glycogen in the "Lag" Phase of Wound Healing, *Exp. Mol. Pathol.*, **2**: 69-73 (1963).

47. W. S. Bullough and E. B. Laurence, The Control of Epidermal Mitotic Activity in the Mouse, *Proc. Roy. Soc. (London), Ser. B,* **151**: 517-536 (1960).

48. M. Abercrombie, Localized Formation of New Tissue in an Adult Mammal, *Symp. Soc. Exp. Biol.*, **11**: 235-254 (1957).

49. W. Buschke, J. S. Friedenwald, and W. Fleischmann, Studies on the Mitotic Activity of the Corneal Epithelium, *Bull. Johns Hopkins Hosp.*, **73**: 143-167 (1943).

50. G. K. Smelser and V. Ozanics, Effect of Chemotherapeutic Agents on Cell Division and Healing of Corneal Burns and Abrasions in the Rat, *Amer. J. Opthalmol.*, **27**: 1063-1072 (1944).

51. P. Block, I. Seiter, and W. Oehlert, Autoradiographic Studies of the Initial Cellular Response to Injury, *Exp. Cell Res.*, **30**: 311-321 (1963).

52. A. Vassiliadis et al., Investigations of Laser Damage to Ocular Tissues, Final Report, SRI Project 6680, Sanford Research Institute, Menlo Park, Calif., 1968.

53. B. S. Fine, S. Fine, L. Feigen, and D. MacKeen, Corneal Injury Threshold to Carbon Dioxide Laser Irradiation, *Amer. J. Opthalmol.,* **66:** 1-15 (1968).

54. D. J. Lehmiller, Cell Migration and Proliferation During Repair of Superficial Corneal Wounds Produced by a Carbon Dioxide Laser, SAM-TR 29 (AD-713831), School of Aerospace Medicine, Brooks Air Force Base, 1970.

55. C. V. Harding and B. D. Srinivasan, Stimulation of DNA Synthesis and Mitosis by Injury, *Ann. N. Y. Acad. Sci.,* **90:** 610-613 (1960).

56. C. V. Harding and B. D. Srinivasan, A Propagated Stimulation of DNA Synthesis and Cell Division, *Exp. Cell Res.,* **25:** 326-340 (1961).

57. M. Abercrombie, Contact Inhibition: The Phenomenon and Its Biological Implications, National Cancer Institute Monograph 26, pp. 249-264 (1966).

58. E. Martz and M. S. Steinberg, The Role of Cell—Cell Contact in "Contact" Inhibition of Cell Division: A Review and New Evidence, *J. Cell. Physiol.,* **79:** 189-210 (1972).

59. W. R. Loewenstein, Communication Through Cell Junctions, Implications in Growth Control and Differentiation, in *Emergence of Order in Developing Systems,* M. Locke (Ed.), pp. 151, Academic Press, Inc., New York, 1968.

60. A. C. Burton and P. B. Canham, The Behaviour of Coupled Biochemical Oscillators as a Model of Contact Inhibition of Cellular Division, *J. Theor. Biol.,* **39:** 555-580 (1973).

61. T. Cavallo, R. Sade, J. Folkman, and R. S. Cotran, Tumor Angiogenesis: Rapid Induction of Endothelial Mitoses Demonstrated by Autoradiography, *J. Cell Biol.,* **54:** 408-420 (1972).

# CIRCADIAN RHYTHM
# IN THE CELLULAR KINETICS
# OF THE MOUSE INTESTINAL EPITHELIUM

CURTIS P. SIGDESTAD,* S. LESHER,† and RALPH M. SCOTT*
*Radiation Center, University of Louisville School of Medicine, Louisville, Kentucky,
and †Cell and Radiation Biology Laboratory, Allegheny General Hospital,
Pittsburgh, Pennsylvania

## ABSTRACT

Circadian rhythms have been described for many tissues. Attempts to demonstrate a daily rhythm in the intestine have not yielded consistent results. In this attempt the number of $^3$H–TdR labelled nuclei (LN) and the number of mitotic figures (MF) per crypt as a function of time of day were determined. A peak and a nadir were found in both parameters at 0300 and 1500, respectively. At the peak proliferation the LN and the MF per crypt were $85 \pm 3.0$ and $4.9 \pm 0.3$, and at the nadir they were $47.4 \pm 1.5$ and $2.2 \pm 0.2$. A similar experiment in mice on a reversed light cycle for 35 days resulted in a complete reversal of the daily rhythm in LN per crypt, MF per crypt and disintegrations per minute per crypt. Further, the generation time for crypt cells was determined at the peak and the nadir of cell proliferation. A cell-cycle time of 13.1 hr was found in mice at 1500, and 11.1 hr was obtained when the percent labelled mitosis was started at 0300. From these results the number of proliferative cells per crypt was found to be 114 and 82 at 0300 and 1500, and the cell-production rate per crypt was 10 and 6 cells per hour, respectively. Possible mechanisms of the rhythmic cell proliferation in the intestine are discussed.

The killing of cells, either normal or malignant, often depends on the cell kinetic parameters of the tissues involved. If the kinetics of the tumor or normal tissue vary as a function of time of day, one might expect that treatment effects will vary in a similar fashion. For example, anticancer drugs are cytotoxic not only to neoplastic cells but also in varying degrees to normal cells. If a rhythmicity exists in either the normal or the malignant cells, the drug of choice or dose scheduling could be adjusted to enhance the survival of normal cells and the killing of malignant cells.

Most investigations have not yielded clear circadian patterns in the cellular proliferation of neoplastic tissue in mouse and man.[1-7] However, Echave Llanos[8] did show a circadian rhythm in mitotic activity of both slow and fast growing hepatomas. Normal tissues, however, have demonstrated clear rhythmicity in proliferative activity. Circadian rhythms have been described in such tissues as epidermis,[9] cornea,[10,11] lens epithelium,[12] oral epithelium,[13] and esophagus.[14]

Attempts to demonstrate a rhythm in the intestinal epithelium have not yielded consistent results. Klein and Geisel,[15] Bullough,[16] and Alov[17] showed slight and variable rhythms, but Leblond and Stevens,[18] and Pilgrim, Erb, and Mauer[19] could not show similar results. The purpose of this investigation was to reexamine this problem, using the crypt-assay technique. Much of the data presented have been published elsewhere.[20-23]

## MATERIALS AND METHODS

### Animals

Male C57B1 140- to 150-day-old mice were used throughout the investigation. They were maintained on sterilized commercial feed and tap water ad libitum. The animal rooms were maintained at a constant temperature and humidity and on a strict 12-hr light (0600 to 1800) and 12-hr dark (1800 to 0600) cycle.

### Labelled-Nuclei and Mitotic-Figure Determination

At 3-hr intervals throughout the day, 3 mice were injected intraperitoneally with 50 $\mu$Ci of tritiated thymidine ($^3$H—TdR, 0.36 Ci/mmole) and sacrificed by cervical dislocation 30 min later. Cold Carnoy's solution was injected into the jejunum just below the ligament of Treitz. A segment was removed for the determination of the number of mitotic figures (MF) and labelled nuclei (LN) per crypt, using crypt-squash and autoradiographic techniques described by Wimber et al.[24]

The amount of tritiated thymidine taken up by each crypt was determined by liquid scintillator counting. Fifty crypts were pipetted into liquid scintillation vials containing 0.5 ml of Soluene, and allowed to stand at room temperatures for 30 min; then 10 ml of scintillation solution (5.0 g of PPO and 0.2 g of OMPOPOP in 1000 ml of toluene) was added. The vials were counted in a liquid scintillation spectrometer operated at 5°C; quench correction was made with an automatic activity analyzer. Disintegrations per minute (dpm) per labelled nucleus was determined by relating the liquid scintillation data with LN obtained from autoradiographs of crypt squashes.

### Photoreversal of the Circadian Rhythm

Mice were adapted to a reversed light cycle for 35 days (lights on from 1800 to 0600 and lights off from 0600 to 1800). At 6-hr intervals throughout the day, 3 mice were injected with $^3$H—TdR and sacrificed 30 min later. The LN per crypt, MF per crypt, and disintegrations per minute (dpm) per crypt were determined as described.

## Cell-Cycle Time

The percent labelled mitosis (PLM) method of Quastler and Sherman[25] and of Painter and Drew[26] was used to determine the cell-cycle time and the times of its various stages. Briefly, at 1500 (nadir of cell proliferation) and at 0300 (peak), mice were injected intraperitoneally with 50 $\mu$Ci of tritiated thymidine, and at short intervals thereafter either 2 or 3 mice were sacrificed by cervical luxation. Tissues were taken from 2 cm distal to the ligament of Treitz, slit longitudinally, and fixed in a mixture of absolute ethanol and acetic acid (3:1) for 48 hr. The tissues were then dehydrated, embedded in paraffin, sectioned (3 $\mu$m), placed on glass slides, and stained with Feulgen reagent. Autoradiographs were prepared by dipping the slides in the dark into NTB-2 (Kodak) liquid emulsion diluted 1:1 with distilled water at 45°C and storing them in lighttight boxes with a desiccant at 5°C for 14 days. Kodak D-19 developer (1.5 min), acid stop, and Kodak fixer (5 min) were used to process the slides.

The number of proliferative cells per milligram of intestine was determined for the peak and the nadir of cell proliferation using the method of Hagemann, Sigdestad, and Lesher.[27] This technique is characterized by the following formulas:

$$\frac{dpm/mg}{dpm/crypt} = \frac{crypts}{mg} \tag{1}$$

$$\frac{LN/crypt}{T_S T/_{GT}} = \frac{proliferative\ cells}{crypt} \tag{2}$$

$$\left| \frac{LN/crypt}{T_S/T_{GT}} \times \frac{dpm/mg}{dpm/crypt} = \frac{proliferative\ cells}{mg} \tag{3}$$

$$\frac{Proliferative\ cells/crypt\ (mg)}{T_{GT}} = \frac{cells/crypt\ (mg)}{hr} \tag{4}$$

where $T_S$ is DNA synthesis time and $T_{GT}$ is generation time.

## RESULTS

### Labelled Nuclei and Mitotic Figures per Crypt

Fluctuations in the number of mitotic figures and the number of cells synthesizing DNA per crypt are shown in Fig. 1. The LN/crypt nearly doubles between 1500 and 0300. The MF/crypt more than doubles in the same time

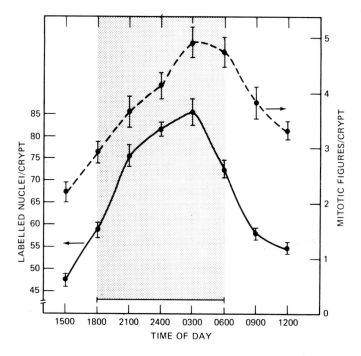

Fig. 1  Number of labelled nuclei (——) and number of mitotic figures
(— — —) per crypt as a function of time of day. Mean ± S.E. Shaded and light
areas represent the dark and light cycles. [From C. P. Sigdestad, J. Bauman,
and S. Lesher, Diurnal Fluctuations in the Number of Cells in Mitosis and
DNA Synthesis in the Jejunum of the Mouse, *Exp. Cell Res.*, 58: 160 (1969).]

period. Of the times of day tested, the peak of mitotic activity is seen at the
same time (0300) as the peak in the number of cells synthesizing DNA. The
nadir of these parameters also occurs at the same time of day (1500). There is an
indication, however, that the peak in the number of cells synthesizing DNA may
precede the peak seen in mitotic figures. This is suggested by the fact that there
is a decline in the number of S cells while the number of M cells remains
essentially unchanged. Therefore, the increase seen in mitotic figures may be a
reflection of the diurnal variation in the number of cells in S at some time
earlier.

Figure 2 shows the results of the liquid scintillation experiments. The
dpm/crypt varies as does the LN/crypt, the peak being seen between 2400 and
0300. On the other hand, Fig. 2 shows that there is no similar variation
throughout the day in the dpm/LN. This suggests no daily variation in the rate
of DNA synthesis.

Because the results suggested that there may be a lag between the peaks of
LN/crypt and MF/crypt, further experiments were designed at closer time

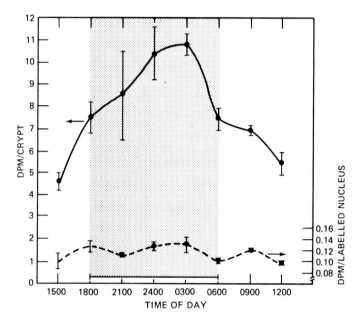

Fig. 2. Incorporation of $^3$H—TdR per crypt (——) and per labelled nucleus (— — —) as a function of time of day. Shaded and light areas represent the dark and light cycles. Mean ± S.E. [From C. P. Sigdestad, J. Bauman, and S. Lesher, Diurnal Fluctuations in the Number of Cells in Mitosis and DNA Synthesis in the Jejunum of the Mouse, *Exp. Cell Res.*, 58: 161 (1969).]

intervals to better resolve the peaks. These results are shown in Figs. 3 to 5. The peak in MF/crypt (Fig. 3) occurs at 0200 rather than at 0300 as seen in the previous figures. The absolute height of the curve is higher, which may represent animal variation. Between 0300 and 0500 there appears to be some fine structure to which no significance is attached. The LN/crypt (Fig. 4) and the dpm/crypt (Fig. 5) show similar peaks at 0200. There appears to be no lag between peaks in LN/crypt and MF/crypt. This indicates that the stimulus for increased cell proliferation in the night hours probably acts on both $G_1$ and $G_2$ cells simultaneously.

## Photoreversal

The reversal of the light—dark cycle (on at 1800 and off at 0600) in the animal rooms for 35 days resulted in a complete reversal of the rhythmic fluctuations in the parameters tested. Figures 6 to 8 show the results. Six-hour sampling intervals are not tight enough to give a precise curve shape; however, sufficient information is obtained to detect the reversal. In another experiment (data not shown), the 1500 point was tested with only 8 days of reversed light cycle. The results showed a 12-hr shift similar to the data presented.

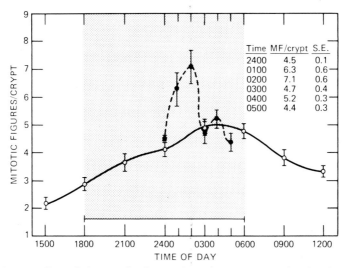

Fig. 3. Daily variation (●), in the number of MF/crypt. ○, data in Fig. 1. Shaded area represents the dark cycle in the animal rooms. [From C. P. Sigdestad and S. Lesher, Further Studies on the Circadian Rhythm in the Proliferative Activity of Mouse Intestinal Epithelium, *Experientia*, 26: 1322 (1970).]

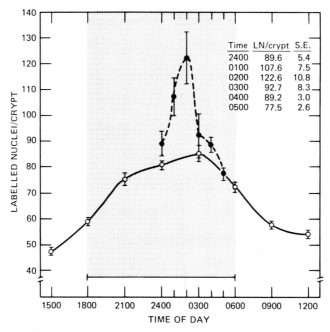

Fig. 4. Variation (●) in the number of cells synthesizing DNA (S cells) as a function of time of day. ○, data in Fig. 1. Shaded area represents the dark cycle in the animal rooms. [From C. P. Sigdestad and S. Lesher, Further Studies on the Circadian Rhythm in the Proliferative Activity of Mouse Intestinal Epithelium, *Experientia*, 26: 1322 (1970).]

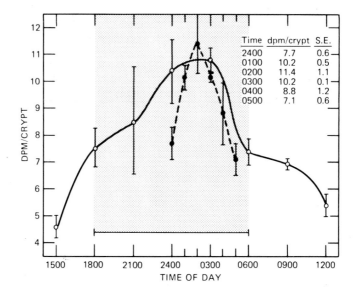

Fig. 5. Diurnal fluctuation (●) in dpm/crypt. ○, data in Fig. 2. Shaded area represents the dark cycle in the animal rooms. [From C. P. Sigdestad and S. Lesher, Further Studies on the Circadian Rhythm in the Proliferative Activity of Mouse Intestinal Epithelium, *Experientia*, **26**: 1322 (1970).]

## Cell-Cycle Time

The cell-cycle time was determined by the PLM method of Quastler and Sherman[25] and Painter and Drew.[26] The pulse label was given at 0300 in one group of mice and at 1500 in a second group. Mice were then sacrificed at close intervals, and the PLM was determined. The results are shown in Figs. 9 and 10 and in Table 1. The cell-cycle time is reduced by 2 hr just by starting the PLM at 0300 or 1500 (the peak and nadir of LN/crypt). The difference between the curves is primarily due to a shortening of the $G_1$ phase of the cell cycle. Little significance is attributed to the difference in DNA synthesis time owing to the relatively large error in the first descending arm of the curve started at 1500.

From such data it is possible to calculate the number of proliferative cells on a crypt and a milligram basis. Table 2 presents data on LN/crypt and MF/crypt at the two times of day at which the PLM curves were started. The number of cells synthesizing DNA per crypt divided by the fraction of the generation time occupied by S results in the proliferative cells per crypt. These values are 114 and 82 for the times 0800 and 1500, respectively (Table 3).

With the method of Hagemann, Sigdestad, and Lesher,[27] the number of crypts per milligram of intestine can be determined. Briefly, the method involves the injection of $^3H-TdR$ into mice, sacrifice of the mice 30 min later, and

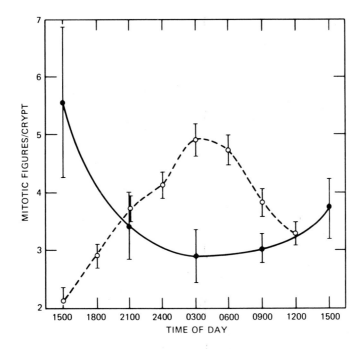

Fig. 6  Daily variation in the number of cells in mitosis. ○, data from Fig. 1 with normal light cycle (on 0600 to 1800). ●, results obtained with light cycle reversed for 35 days (on 1800 to 0600). [From C. P. Sigdestad and S. Lesher, Photoreversal of the Circadian Rhythm in the Proliferative Activity of the Mouse Small Intestine, *J. Cell Physiol.*, **78**: 122 (1971).]

TABLE 1

SALIENT CELL-CYCLE PARAMETERS*

| Stage | Time of intestinal cell-cycle parameters, hr | |
| --- | --- | --- |
| | At 0300 | At 1500 |
| $T_{GT}$ | 11.1 | 13.1 |
| $T_M$ | 1.1 | 0.9 |
| $T_{G_1}$ | 1.1 | 3.8 |
| $T_S$ | 8.3 | 7.6 |
| $T_{G_2}$ | 0.75 | 0.75 |

*[From C. P. Sigdestad and S. Lesher, Circadian Rhythm in the Cell Cycle Time of the Mouse Intestinal Epithelium, *J. Interdiscipl. Cycle Res.*, **3**: 41 (1972).]

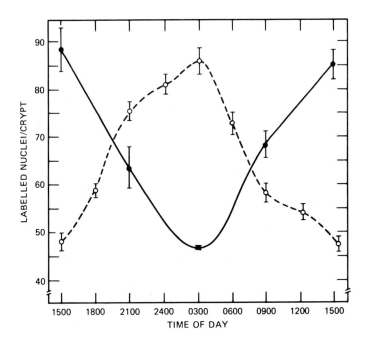

Fig 7.  Daily variation in the number of cells synthesizing DNA (LN/crypt). ○, data from Fig. 1 with normal light cycle. ●, results obtained with light cycle reversed for 35 days (on 1800 to 0600). [From C. P. Sigdestad and S. Lesher, Photoreversal of the Circadian Rhythm in the Proliferative Activity of the Mouse Small Intestine, *J. Cell Physiol.*, **78**: 123 (1971).]

TABLE 2

CELLS IN MITOSIS OR DNA SYNTHESIS PER CRYPT*

| Time | LN/crypt ±S.E. | MF/crypt ±S.E. | GT, hr | $T_S$, hr | $T_S/T_{GT}$ |
|------|------|------|------|------|------|
| 0300 | 85.5 ± 3.0 | 4.9 ± 0.3 | 11.1 | 8.3 | 0.7477 |
| 1500 | 47.4 ± 1.5 | 2.2 ± 0.2 | 13.1 | 7.6 | 0.5801 |

*[From C. P. Sigdestad and S. Lesher, Circadian Rhythm in the Cell Cycle Time of the Mouse Intestinal Epithelium, *J. Interdiscipl. Cycle Res.*, **3**: 42 (1972).]

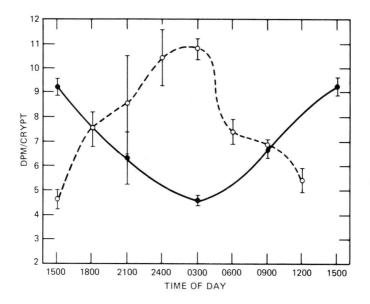

Fig. 8. The dpm/crypt as a function of time of day in mice on normal (– – –) and reversed (———) light cycles. [From C. P. Sigdestad and S. Lesher, Photoreversal of the Circadian Rhythm in the Proliferative Activity of the Mouse Small Intestine, *J. Cell Physiol.*, **78**: 123 (1971).]

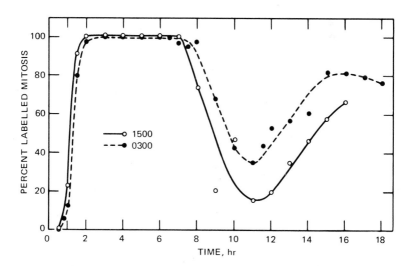

Fig. 9. The PLM curves for C57/B1-6J mouse intestinal epithelium. The curves were begun at either 1500 (○) or 0300 (●). [From C. P. Sigdestad and S. Lesher, Circadian Rhythm in the Cell Cycle Time of the Mouse Intestinal Epithelium, *J. Interdiscipl. Cycle Res.*, **3**: 40 (1972).]

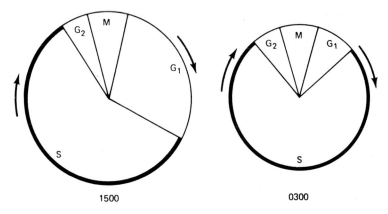

Fig. 10. A schematic drawing of the cell cycle in mouse intestinal epithelium. The PLM curves were started at 1500 or 0300. [From C. P. Sigdestad and S. Lesher, Circadian Rhythm in the Cell Cycle Time of the Mouse Intestinal Epithelium, *J. Interdiscipl. Cycle Res.*, 3: 41 (1972).]

TABLE 3

DATA FROM TABLES 1 AND 2, QUANTITATED*

| Time | Prolif. cells/crypt | Prolif. cells/mg | Production rate/ crypt, cells/hr | $G_1$ cells/ crypt | $G_2$ cells/ crypt | S cells/ crypt | M cells/ crypt |
|------|------|------|------|------|------|------|------|
| 0300 | 114 | $1.02 \times 10^5$ | 10 | 11 | 8 | 86 | 4.9 |
| 1500 | 82 | $7.3 \times 10^4$ | 6 | 24 | 5 | 47 | 2.2 |

*[From C. P. Sigdestad and S. Lesher, Circadian Rhythm in the Cell Cycle Time of the Mouse Intestinal Epithelium, *J. Interdiscipl. Cycle Res.*, 3: 42 (1972).]

determination of dpm/mg intestine and dpm/crypt by liquid scintillation counting. The quotient of these two values results in crypts/mg intestine. The number of proliferative cells/crypt multiplied by crypt/mg results in proliferative cells/mg intestine. The values obtained were $1.02 \times 10^5$ and $7.3 \times 10^4$ proliferative cells/mg at 0300 and 1500 respectively (Table 3). This amounts to about a 40% increase in proliferative cells at the two times of day separated by 12 hr.

## DISCUSSION

The study of biological rhythms in the proliferative activity of tissue is of extreme importance because of the implications it may have in developing concepts concerning control mechanisms of cell divisions. The number of $^3H-TdR$ labelled nuclei per intestinal crypt has been shown to nearly double (47 to 85 LN/crypt) during a 24-hr cycle. The peak in cell proliferation was seen at 0200, and the nadir was observed at about 1500. The MF/crypt showed a similar magnitude of difference, rising from 2.2 to 4.9 MF/crypt. The peaks noted in S and M phases of the cell cycle occurred simultaneously and suggested that the mechanism involved in the increased cell proliferation in the gut acted on both S and M compartments. These results were inconsistent with those of Brown and Berry[28] obtained in the cheek-pouch epithelium, which demonstrated a lag of approximately $0.5T_S + T_{G2} + 0.5T_M$ hr. The lag suggested the mechanism of this rhythm is a partial synchronization of late $G_1$ for early S phase cells, later seen as a peak in the mitotic stage of the cell cycle. These latter results confirmed the earlier data of Pilgrim, Erb, and Mauer,[19] who showed the same effect in various mouse tissues.

Using grain counts, Pilgrim, Erb, and Mauer[19] showed no daily rhythm in DNA synthesis rate. We were able to substantiate these results in the gut using dpm/LN method (see Fig. 2).

Reversal of the light cycles in the animal rooms for 35 days prior to analysis completely reversed the circadian rhythm of cells in mitosis and DNA synthesis. The nadir in proliferation (1500) was tested after only 8 days of reversed light and was also found to be reversed.

It was also demonstrated that with a normal light cycle the generation time started at 0300 was 2 hr shorter than it would have been if started at 1500. The stage of the cell cycle most affected was $G_1$. The differences in cell-cycle times are extremely difficult to evaluate statistically. Lesher and others found that, even with computer modeling of cell-cycle parameters from normal mouse intestinal epithelium, no improvement of the precision could be obtained. Perhaps the largest difference in cell-generation times was reported by Lesher and coworkers, who found a replication time of 7 hr 3 days after 1000 R of whole-body X-irradiation. That the time of day could shorten the cell-cycle time by 2 hr seems significant to us.

With cell-cycle data of the type reported here and results previously reported,[27] it was possible to calculate the number of proliferative cells on a per crypt and intestinal weight basis. These cells showed a 40% increase from the nadir to the peak of cellular proliferation.

From the information we have to date, no clear mechanism controlling cell proliferation in the intestinal epithelium can be postulated. It is, however, interesting to speculate from the numerous reported findings on factors that affect the histology, cell kinetics, or physiological function of the gut. Some examples of these stimuli are lactation,[29] thyrotoxicosis,[30] intermittent starvation,[31] alloxan diabetes,[32] bulk feeding,[33] intestinal resection,[34] acetyphenylhydrazine injection,[35] germ-free conditions,[36] and fasting.[37] These stimuli either alter the amount of solids ingested or are toxic to villous cells. The question arises whether or not the circadian rhythm in the intestine could be due to a daily feeding cycle rather than a light—dark cycle. The attrition of villous cells during the feeding hours could signal the proliferative compartments in the crypts. The results of such a stimulus could increase the number of mitotic figures and the number of cells synthesizing DNA in the crypt, perhaps by a hormonal mechanism similar to the one proposed by Loran and Carbone.[38] This hypothesis is consistent with the results of Alov,[17] who showed that access to food either in the day or in the night can stimulate mitotic activity.

It is probable, however, that feeding is not the entire answer because we (unpublished data) repeated the circadian rhythm curve (LN/crypt vs. time of day) in mice who either had access to food in the daylight hours or in the dark hours. The curve obtained for dark-fed mice was not different from that reported here for mice fed ad libitum. In the day-fed mice, however, the curve was somewhat altered but not reversed.

It is apparent from these studies that there is no simple answer to the question of the mechanism of daily fluctuations in the proliferative activity of the gut. Further study is required to obtain some of these answers.

## ACKNOWLEDGMENTS

The authors acknowledge the expert technical assistance of U. Kopp, Pamela Reducka, and Lois Cecil; we also thank Anne Howell for typing the manuscript. The work was supported in part by grants 1P02 CA 10438-02 and S TO1 CA 05184-03 from the National Cancer Institute, U. S. Public Health Service, and contract DADA 17-72-C-2038, U. S. Army Medical Research and Development Command. We also acknowledge the support of the Department of Radiology, University of Louisville School of Medicine.

## REFERENCES

1. W. B. Dublen, R. V. Gregg, and A. C. Broders, Mitosis in Specimens Removed During Day and Night from Carcinoma of Large Intestine, *Arch. Pathol.,* **30**: 893-899 (1940).
2. C. M. Blumenfeld, Studies of Normal and of Abnormal Mitotic Activity. II. Rate and Periodicity of the Mitotic Activity of Experimental Epidermoid Carcinoma in Mice, *Arch. Pathol.,* **35**: 667-673 (1943).
3. F. D. Bertalanffy and C. McAskell, Rate of Cell Division of Malignant Mouse Melanoma B16, *J. Nat. Cancer Inst.,* **32**: 535-544 (1964).
4. F. D. Bertalanffy and C. Lau, Rates of Cell Division of Transplantable Malignant Rat Tumors, *Cancer Res.,* **22**: 627-631 (1962).
5. F. D. Bertalanffy, Mitotic Rate of Spontaneous Mammary Gland Adenocarcinoma in C3H/HeJ Mice, *Nature,* **198**: 496-498 (1963).
6. A. Voutilainen, Über die 24-stunden-Rhythmik der Mitosenfrequenz in malignen Tumoren, *Acta Pathol. Microbiol. Scand., Suppl.,* **99**: 7-104 (1953).

7. E. Tahti, Studies of the Effect of X-Irradiation on 24-Hour Variations in the Mitotic Activity in Human Malignant Tumors, *Acta Pathol. Microbiol. Scand., Suppl.,* **117**: 1-61 (1956).

8. J. M. Echave Llanos and R. E. Nash, Mitotic Circadian Rhythm in a Fast Growing and Slow Growing Hepatoma, Mitotic Rhythm in Hypatomas, *J. Nat. Cancer Inst.,* **44**: 581-586 (1970).

9. W. S. Bullough, The Control of Mitotic Activity in Adult Mammalian Tissues, *Biol. Rev.,* **37**: 307-342 (1962).

10. M. T. Gololobova, Changes in Mitotic Activity of Rats Depending on the Time of Day, *Bull. Exp. Biol. Med. (USSR) (Engl. Transl.),* **46**: 118-122 (1958).

11. Raimo Vasama and Ritva Vasama, On the Diurnal Cycle of Mitotic Activity in the Corneal Epithelium of Mice, *Acta Anat.,* **33**: 230-237 (1958).

12. L. von Sallman, P. Grimes, and N. McElvain, Aspects of Mitotic Activity in Relation to Cell Proliferation in the Lens Epithelium, *Exp. Eye Res.,* **1**: 449-456 (1962).

13. J. R. Trott and S. L. Gorenstein, Mitotic Rates in the Oral and Gingival Epithelium of the Rat, *Arch. Oral Biol.,* **8**: 425-434 (1963).

14. V. N. Dobrokhotov and A. G. Kurdyumova, 24-Hour Periodicity of Mitotic Activity of the Epithelium in the Esophagus of Albino Rats, *Bull. Exp. Biol. Med. (USSR) (Engl. Transl.),* **53**: 81-84 (1962).

15. H. Klein and H. Geisel, Zum Nachweis eines 24-Stundenrhythmus der Mitosen bei Ratte und Maus, *Klin. Wochensch.,* **25**: 662-663 (1947).

16. W. S. Bullough, Mitotic Activity in the Adult Male Mouse, Mus musculus L., the Diurnal Cycles and Their Relation to Waking and Sleeping, *Proc. Roy. Soc. (London), Ser. B,* **135**: 212-231 (1948).

17. I. A. Alov, Daily Rhythm of Mitosis and Relationship Between Cell Work and Cell Division, *Fed. Proc., Transl. Suppl.,* **22**: T357-T362 (1963).

18. C. P. Leblond and C. E. Stevens, The Constant Renewal of the Intestinal Epithelium in the Albino Rat, *Anat. Rec.,* **100**: 357-377 (1948).

19. C. Pilgrim, W. Erb, and W. Mauer, Diurnal Fluctuations in the Numbers of DNA Synthesizing Nuclei in Various Mouse Tissues, *Nature,* **199**: 863 (1963).

20. C. P. Sigdestad, J. Bauman, and S. Lesher, Diurnal Fluctuation in the Number of Cells in Mitosis and DNA Synthesis in the Jejunum of the Mouse, *Exp. Cell Res.,* **58**: 159-162 (1969).

21. C. P. Sigdestad and S. Lesher, Further Studies on the Circadian Rhythm in the Proliferative Activity of Mouse Intestinal Epithelium, *Experientia,* **26**: 1321-1322 (1970).

22. C. P. Sigdestad and S. Lesher, Photoreversal of the Circadian Rhythm in the Proliferative Activity of the Mouse Small Intestine, *J. Cell Physiol.,* **78**: 121-126 (1971).

23. C. P. Sigdestad and S. Lesher, Circadian Rhythm in the Cell Cycle Time of the Mouse Intestinal Epithelium, *J. Interdiscipl. Cycle Res.,* **3**: 39-46 (1972).

24. R. E. Wimber, H. Quastler, O. L. Stein, and D. R. Wimber, Analysis of Tritium Incorporation into Individual Cells by Autoradiography of Squash Preparations, *J. Biophys. Biochem. Cytol.,* **8**: 327-331 (1960).

25. H. Quastler and F. G. Sherman, Cell Population Kinetics in the Intestinal Epithelium of the Mouse, *Exp. Cell Res.,* **17**: 420-438 (1959).

26. R. B. Painter and R. M. Drew, Studies on DNA Metabolism in Human Cancer Cell Cultures (HeLa). I. The Temporal Relationships of DNA Synthesis to Mitosis and Turnover Time, *Lab. Invest.,* **8**: 278 (1959).

27. R. F. Hagemann, C. P. Sigdestad, and S. Lesher, A Method for Quantitation of Proliferative Intestinal Mucosal Cells on a Weight Basis; Some Values for C57BL/6, *Cell Tissue Kinet.,* **3**: 21-26 (1970).

28. J. M. Brown and R. J. Berry, The Relationship Between Diurnal Variation of the Number of Cells in Mitosis and of the Number of Cells Synthesizing DNA in the Cheek Pouch, *Cell Tissue Kinet.*, **1**: 23-33 (1968).

29. A. B. Cairnie and R. E. Bentley, Cell Proliferation Studies in the Intestinal Epithelium of the Rat-Hyperplasia During Lactation, *Exp. Cell Res.*, **46**: 428-440 (1967).

30. R. J. Levine and D. H. Smyth, The Effect of the Thyroid Gland on Intestinal Absorption of Hexoses, *J. Physiol. (London)*, **169**: 755-769 (1963).

31. P. Fabry and V. Kujalova, Enhanced Growth of the Small Intestine in Rats as a Result of Adaption to Intermittent Starvation, *Acta Anat.*, **43**: 264-271 (1960).

32. E. L. Jervis and R. J. Levine, Anatomic Adaption of the Alimentary Tract of the Rat to the Hyperphagia of Chronic Alloxan Diabetes, *Nature*, **210**: 391-393 (1966).

33. R. H. Dowling, E. O. Riecken, J. W. Laws, and C. C. Booth, The Intestinal Response to High Bulk Feeding in the Rat, *Clin. Sci.*, **32**: 1-9 (1967).

34. M. R. Loran and T. T. Crocker, Population Dynamics of Intestinal Epithelia in the Rat Two Months After Partial Resection of the Ileum, *J. Cell Biol.*, **19**: 285-292 (1963).

35. M. E. Conrad, L. R. Weintraub, and W. H. Crosby, The Effect of Acetylphenylhydrazine upon Epithelial Turnover in the Small Intestine, *Amer. J. Dig. Dis.*, **10** (New Series): 43-46 (1965).

36. S. Lesher, H. Walberg, and G. A. Sacher, Generation Cycle in the Duodenal Crypt Cells of Germ-Free and Conventional Mice, *Nature*, **202**: 884-886 (1964).

37. J. P. A. McManus and K. J. Isselbacher, Effect of Fasting Versus Feeding on the Rat Small Intestine: Morphological, Biochemical and Functional Differences, *Gastroenterology*, **59**: 214-221 (1970).

38. M. R. Loran and J. V. Carbone, The Humoral Effect of Intestinal Resection on Cellular Proliferation and Maturation in Parabiotic Rats, in *Gastrointestinal Radiation Injury*, M. F. Sullivan (Ed.), Excerpta Medica Foundation, Princeton, N. J., 127-141 (1968).

# DNA POLYMERASE ENZYMES IN NORMAL AND NEOPLASTIC GROWTH

JEN-FU CHIU,*[1] CATHERINE CRADDOCK,* H. P. MORRIS,† and L. S. HNILICA*

*Department of Biochemistry, M. D. Anderson Hospital and Tumor Institute, Houston, Texas, and †Department of Biochemistry, Howard University, Washington, D. C.

## ABSTRACT

The activities of nuclear DNA polymerases were investigated in normal and neoplastic growth. A high-molecular-weight 6-8 S bound form DNA polymerase activity was found in fetal and neonatal livers of rats and in several Morris hepatomas. The 6-8 S DNA-polymerase activity of the Morris hepatomas could be directly correlated to their degree of differentiation and growth rates. However, there was only marginal activity detectable in the nuclei of regenerating rat liver. The activities of nuclear DNA polymerase enzymes were also investigated in rats maintained on a hepatocarcinogenic diet [N,N-dimethyl-p-(m-tolylazo)aniline, or 3′-MDAB]. The 6-8 S bound form DNA polymerase activity appeared in the liver about 2 weeks after the introduction of 3′-MDAB, increased considerably, and reached a prominent maximum between 30 to 40 days of the diet. After 40 days this DNA polymerase activity decreased gradually. No similar enzyme could be detected in control rats or in rats maintained on a diet of a noncarcinogenic hepatotoxin α-napthylisothiocyanate (α-NIT). The 6-8 S nuclear DNA polymerase of rats fed with 3′-MDAB for 32 days was purified and characterized.

Among the principal macromolecular events obligatory to growth and cellular proliferation is the replication of nuclear DNA. Perhaps one of the most outstanding features of malignant cells is their capability of perpetual division, out of control by the host. The elucidation of regulatory mechanisms concerning the DNA synthesis in living cells both normal and abnormal may be essential for the understanding and control of neoplastic growth.

Of the numerous studies concerning the control of DNA synthesis in normal and neoplastic cells, only a few deal with the changes in distribution of several DNA polymerase activities in normal livers and during hepatocarcinogenesis.[1-3] It has been shown[4-8] that mammalian DNA polymerases can be separated into

---

[1] Recipient of a Rosalie B. Hite postdoctoral fellowship.

several fractions by differentiating their localization, molecular weight, and enzymatic properties. One of these enzymes (3-4 S) is found in the nucleus, and other enzymes (6-8 S) are prevalent in the cytoplasmic fractions.[1,9-12] Although the DNA polymerase activity of the whole-cell extract from rat liver is very low,[13,14] isolated nuclei contain a much more active enzyme that has a relatively low molecular weight and is present in a tightly bound form.[14] According to the recent reports, the activity of this bound form of nuclear DNA polymerase increases considerably in rat-liver nuclei after partial hepatectomy[3,15] and during azo-dye carcinogenesis.[16]

We report here that a high-molecular-weight (6-8 S) DNA polymerase appears as a bound enzyme in the liver nuclei of rats fed a diet containing N,N-dimethyl-p-(m-tolylazo)aniline (3'-MDAB). The activity of this nuclear 6-8 S DNA polymerase is consistently correlated to the growth rate of Morris hepatoma. Its activity is also very high in other neoplasms and in young embryos. In adolescent animals, hormone-stimulated proliferating normal tissues, and regenerating liver, this enzymatic activity is very low or absent.

# MATERIALS AND METHODS

## Materials

Labelled [3]H−dCTP (30 Ci/mmole) and unlabelled deoxyribonucleotide triphosphates were used in the DNA polymerase assay. The poly A·poly U, poly (A-U), poly d(A-T), calf thymus DNA (high molecular weight), dithiothreitol, N,N-dimethyl-p-(m-tolylazo)aniline (3'-MDAB), and a non-carcinogenic hepatotoxin α-naphthylisothiocyanate (α-NIT) were purchased commercially. All other reagents were analytical grade and were obtained from commercial supplies.

## Animals

Hepatoma 7777 and hepatoma 7800 were transplanted into male Buffalo rats at Howard University, Washington, D. C. Normal male Fisher rats (120 to 150 g initial weight) were maintained on Wayne Laboratory meal supplemented with 10% corn oil. This control diet was mixed either with 0.06% 3'-MDAB or 0.05% α-NIT. Both chemicals were dissolved in corn oil and allowed to soak into meal pellets, replacing the 10% corn oil given to the control groups. Each experimental point on the graphs represents 3 to 4 animals. The α-NIT control was selected because it produces bile-duct cell proliferation similar to that caused by the 3'-MDAB carcinogen.[17]

Male albino rats (Sprague−Dawley) fed ad libitum and weighing between 150 to 200 g were subjected to partial hepatectomy under ether anesthesia.[18] No livers were removed in the sham-operated animals. All operations were performed between 0900 and 1100.

The liver nuclei were isolated by the method of Chauveau, Moule, and Rouiller.[19] The tightly bound DNA polymerase was solubilized with 0.2$M$ phosphate buffer,[14] pH 7.4. For sucrose density gradient centrifugation, the sample was carefully layered over a sucrose gradient (5 to 20% wt./vol.) in cellulose nitrate tubes[20] and centrifuged at 37,000 rpm at 0°C for 16 hr. After centrifugation the bottom of each tube was punctured, and 0.2-ml fractions were collected. Each fraction was assayed for DNA polymerase activity. The DNA polymerases were partially purified by the procedure described in Ref. 4 for normal rat liver. The purification involves ammonium sulfate fractionation and DEAE-cellulose (diethylaminoethyl cellulose) column chromatography. The DNA polymerase activity was assayed as described in Ref. 21. Incubation was at 37° for 30 min. The standard incubation mixture (0.4 ml) contained: 20 $\mu$mole Tris—HCl buffer, pH 7.4, 2 $\mu$moles MgCl$_2$, 2 $\mu$moles dithiothreitol, 20 $\mu$moles each of dATP (deoxyadenosine 5'-triphosphate), dGTP (deoxyguanosine 5'-triphosphate), and dCTP (deoxycytidine-5'-triphosphate) with 128 pmole of $^3$H—TTP (thymidine-5'-triphosphate, 15.7 Ci/mmole), and 2 $\mu$g of calf thymus DNA.

## RESULTS

### Nuclear DNA Polymerases in Developing Rat Liver

There are many similarities between the biochemical and metabolic properties of embryonal and neoplastic cells. The embryonic growth leads, however, to a differentiated and highly organized form of life, whereas the cancerous cells perpetuate only their own kind, frequently at a quite rapid pace. To investigate the character of DNA-replicating enzymes, we began a study of the changes of DNA polymerase enzymes during embryonic and neonatal development of rat liver.

Nuclear DNA polymerases of embryonal, 2-week-old, and adult rat livers were analyzed by sucrose gradient centrifugation. As shown in Fig. 1, there are two DNA polymerase activities in the nuclei of the embryonal and 2-week-old rat liver. One activity is associated with high-molecular-weight (6-8 S) particles, and the other is a low-molecular-weight (3-4 S) enzyme. Only the low-molecular-weight DNA polymerase is present in the nuclei of the adult-rat liver, but both the low- and high-molecular-weight DNA polymerase activities are present in the fetal- or neonatal-rat livers. All enzymatic activities shown in Fig. 1 were correlated to the protein content of the individual fractions. The protein assays were based on the procedure by Lowry et al.[22]

### Nuclear DNA Polymerases in Morris Hepatomas

Although the activities and distributions of DNA polymerases have been studied in many Morris hepatomas,[2,23,24] the character of the nuclear-bound

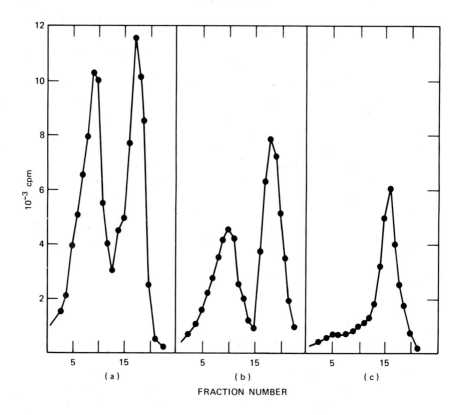

Fig. 1  Sucrose density gradient centrifugation of DNA polymerases in (a) embryonal (2.5 to 2.7 cm), (b) 2-week-old, and (c) adult-rat livers. The bottom of the gradient is to the left.

form of the DNA polymerase has not been described. Figure 2 compares the nuclear-bound DNA polymerase activities in rapid-growth-rate and intermediate-growth-rate Morris hepatomas with those of normal adult-rat liver. Hepatoma 7777, a poorly differentiated, rapidly growing tumor contained highly active bound 6-8 S nuclear DNA polymerase enzymes. On the other hand, hepatoma 7800, a well-differentiated hepatocellular carcinoma with an intermediate growth rate, contained only a relatively low DNA polymerase activity in the 6-8 S region. Both these hepatomas exhibited biochemical characteristics of fetal-rat liver, and the well differentiated 7800 hepatoma still retained some of the normal adult-liver character.

## DNA Polymerases in Regenerating Rat Liver

As shown in Fig. 1, the nuclei of the adult-rat liver contain only the low-molecular-weight DNA polymerase, and its activity is much lower than in the fetus or in 2-week-old rats. Studies on the Morris hepatoma tumors 7777 and

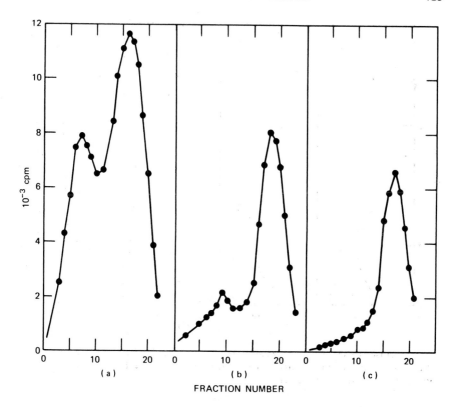

Fig. 2  Sucrose density gradient centrifugation of DNA polymerases in (a) Morris hepatoma 7777, (b) Morris hepatoma 7800, and (c) normal adult-rat livers. The bottom of the gradient is to the left.

7800 (Fig. 2) indicate that only rapidly proliferating tissues contain the bound 6-8 S nuclear DNA polymerase. To determine whether this bound 6-8 S DNA polymerase activity is typical of embryonic and neoplastic growth, we induced cell proliferation by partial hepatectomy in adult rats. Results of the sucrose density gradient centrifugation shown in Fig. 3 demonstrate that most of the low-molecular-weight (3-4 S) DNA polymerase activity is present in the sham-operated and hepatectomized rats. There is also some marginal activity in the 6-8 S DNA polymerase region appearing after the partial hepatectomy; it is very low compared to that of the fetal liver and hepatomas.

## Nuclear DNA Polymerases During Azo-Dye Hepatocarcinogenesis

To further investigate the nature of the differences in nuclear DNA polymerase patterns between normal and cancerous tissues, we began a study using the livers of animals fed with a hepatocarcinogenic diet containing

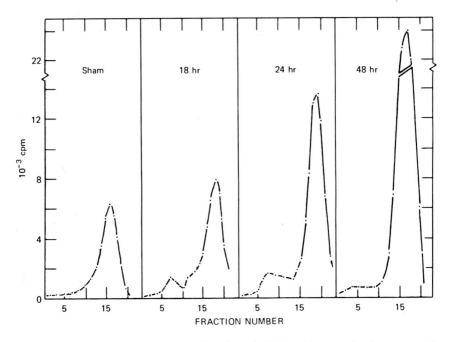

Fig. 3  Sucrose density gradient centrifugation of DNA polymerases in sham operated (24 hr after operation) and hepatectomized (18, 24, and 48 hr after hepatectomy) rats. The bottom of the gradient is to the left.

3'-MDAB. The morphological and histological effects of this carcinogen on rat liver have been well documented.[25] Various studies have demonstrated altered enzymatic mechanisms in livers of rats maintained on hepatoma-inducing diets.[26-31] The experiments reported here were performed over a 4-month period of feeding with 3'-MDAB. Toward the end of this period, many animals developed large hepatomas. A noncarcinogenic hepatotoxin α-NIT was also used as a second control group. The α-NIT produces bile-duct cell proliferation similar to that caused by the 3'-MDAB carcinogen.[17]

The sucrose density gradient sedimentation patterns shown in Fig. 4 demonstrate that only the low-molecular-weight 3-4 S DNA polymerase activity can be detected in the controls and in the animals fed with a diet containing α-NIT. The high-molecular-weight 6-8 S enzyme appears prominently only in rats fed the 3'-MDAB diet for 24 days, peaks around 32 days, decreases rapidly, and disappears after 72 days of this diet.

## Purification and Characterization of Nuclear DNA Polymerases

The 6-8 S bound form of the DNA polymerase, detectable only in the livers of rats exposed to 3'-MDAB diet, in fetal liver and in hepatomas was further

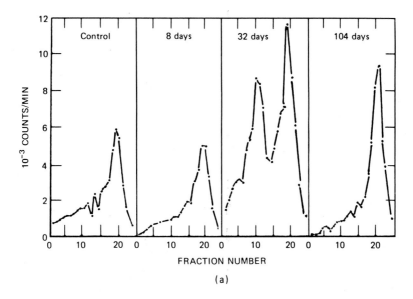

(a)

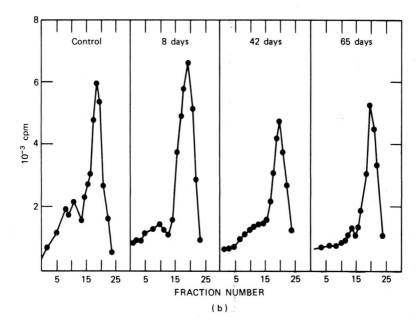

(b)

Fig. 4 Sucrose density gradient centrifugation of DNA polymerases in livers of (a) control rats and rats fed a diet containing 3'-MDAB for 8, 32, and 104 days and (b) control rats and rats fed a diet containing α-NIT for 8, 42, and 65 days. The bottom of the gradient is to the left.

characterized. The phosphate buffer extract of nuclei from livers of rats fed with diets containing 3'-MDAB for 32 days was used for purification and characterization of this enzyme (DABp). This extract was first subjected to ammonium sulfate fractionation by saturating the solution first to 0.25 to 0.45 saturation and then to 0.45 to 0.7 saturation. Both ammonium sulfate fractions were dissolved in $0.01M$ phosphate buffer, pH 7.4, containing 2 mmoles 2-mercaptoethanol and 5% glycerol and dialyzed against 4 liters of this buffer. The dialyzed enzymes were applied to a DEAE-cellulose column (1.3 X 20 cm) previously equilibrated with the same buffer. The DABp1 enzyme was recovered

TABLE 1

TEMPLATE SPECIFICITY OF DNA POLYMERASES IN LIVERS OF
RATS FED A DIET CONTAINING 3'-MDAB*

| Sample | Enzyme activity, cpm | | | | |
|---|---|---|---|---|---|
|  | Poly dAT | Poly AU | Poly A·poly U | Native DNA | Heated DNA |
| DABp1 | 3513 | 3102 | 3069 | 3839 | 4571 |
| DABp2 | 3602 | 242 | 252 | 6409 | 1618 |

*The activities of partially purified DNA polymerases DABp1 and DABp2 were compared using natural and synthetic templates. The conditions of incubation are described in the Methods section.

from the ammonium sulfate fraction 0.25 to 0.45 saturation and was eluted from the DEAE-cellulose column with KCl concentrations between 0.2 to $0.3M$. The second enzyme, DABp2, was obtained from the ammonium sulfate fraction 0.45 to 0.7 saturation and was eluted from the DEAE-cellulose column with $0.1M$ KCl. The sucrose density gradient centrifugation profiles of these two enzymes separated by DEAE-cellulose chromatography are essentially identical to the positions of corresponding enzymes in the sedimentation patterns of the original unpurified nuclear extracts (Fig. 5).

A comparison of the properties of the partially purified DNA polymerases DABp1 and DABp2 using natural and synthetic templates is shown in Table 1. The DABp2 enzyme has virtually no activity with the poly AU and poly A·poly U templates. On the other hand, the DABp1 enzyme very efficiently catalyzes the incorporation of $^3$H—TTP into the acid insoluble polymer using poly AU and poly A·poly U as templates. The incorporation of $^3$H—TTP increased slightly when denatured DNA was used as a template for the DABp1 enzyme. The partially purified enzyme DABp2 preferred native DNA very strongly over denatured DNA as a template.

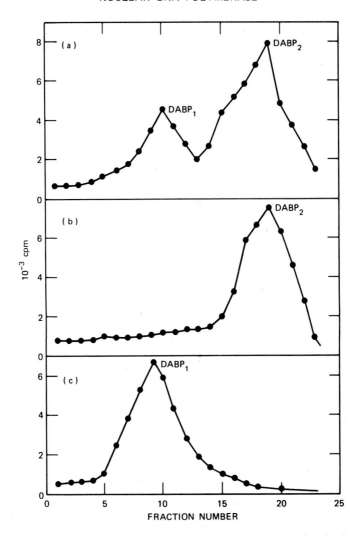

Fig. 5 Sucrose density gradient centrifugation of an extract of nuclei from livers of rats fed with 3′-MDAB for 32 days. (a) Before purification. (b) and (c) after purification.

The DABp1 and DABp2 enzymes also differed in their $Mg^{2+}$ ion requirements, DABp2 having a maximum activity in about 10 mmoles of $MgCl_2$ as compared with the 15 to 25 mmoles of $MgCl_2$ necessary for the maximum activity of DABp1 (Fig. 6). These two enzymatic activities also differed in their responses to monovalent-ion concentrations. The DABp2 activity increased about 200% in the presence of 30 mmoles of KCl, whereas the DABp1 enzyme was stimulated only about 50% (Fig. 7).

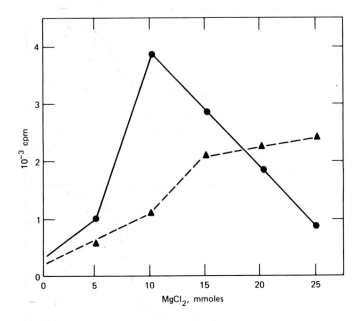

Fig. 6  The effect of $MgCl_2$ on the partially purified nuclear DNA polymerase activities. The assay conditions are described in the Methods section, except for the varied amounts of $MgCl_2$ indicated. ▲, DNA polymerase DABp1. ●, DNA polymerase DABp2.

## DISCUSSION

Chang and Bollum[32] suggested that only the low-molecular-weight (3.3 S) DNA polymerase is associated with the nucleus. More recently, the presence of two DNA polymerase enzymes was reported in the neoplastic cell nuclei.[16,24,33] Our results show that only the 3-4 S DNA polymerase can be detected in the nuclei of nonproliferating cells such as adult liver. However, both the 3-4 S and 6-8 S DNA polymerase activities can be found in the nuclei of embryonic liver, hepatomas, or in the livers of rats maintained on a diet containing 3'-MDAB. The activity of the 6-8 S DNA polymerase enzyme is very low, although detectable, in the nuclei of regenerating rat liver. This activity is related closely to the tissue growth rate.

The properties of 6-8 S nuclear DNA polymerase resemble very closely those of the reverse transcriptase, which was reported to be present in azo-dye carcinogenic livers[34] and in myeloma cells MOPC-21.[35] Baril et al.[24] demonstrated the presence of two DNA polymerase activities in proliferating liver nuclei; one was a high-molecular-weight activity, and the other was a low-molecular-weight activity. Both these activities were reported to be DNA-dependent DNA polymerases. Persico, Nicholson, and Gottlieb,[35] on the

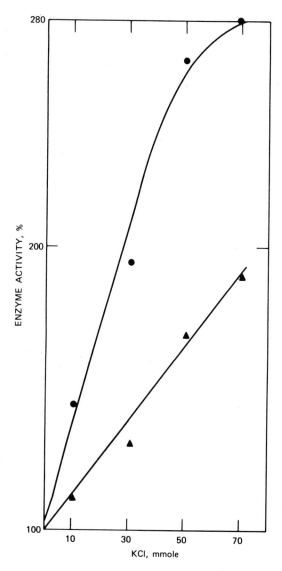

Fig. 7 The effect of KCl on the partially purified nuclear DNA polymerases. The assay conditions are described in the Methods section, except for the varied amounts of KCl indicated. ▲, DNA polymerase DABp1. ●, DNA polymerase DABp2.

other hand, detected two 6-8 S DNA polymerases in myeloma MOPC-21; one was a DNA-dependent DNA polymerase, and the other was an RNA-dependent DNA polymerase. Obviously, further characterization of the nuclear DNA polymerase enzymes is necessary to resolve these controversies.

Our studies on DNA polymerases from normal and neoplastic tissues are in good agreement with the data published by other investigators[36-40] in showing that certain embryonal genes normally inactive in adult liver are reactivated in hepatomas. There is a correlation between the extent of differentiation of the hepatoma and its content of 6-8 S nuclear DNA polymerase (Fig. 2).

The nuclear 6-8 S DNA polymerase activity first appears and markedly increases between the 24th and 40th day of 3'-MDAB feeding. This, together with the data of Price et al.,[25] who reported a considerable increase of mitotic activity between the 24th and 32nd day, supports Farber's proposal[41] that a cellular proliferative period (formation of hyperplastic nodules) is essential for the establishment of irreversible hepatomas. The appearance of a special DNA replicative enzyme, the 6-8 S DNA polymerase, may be an important part of the transformational process leading to the cancerous growth.

## ACKNOWLEDGMENTS

The research reported in this paper was supported by contract E-72-3269 with the National Cancer Institute, National Institutes of Health; U. S. Public Health Service grants CA 07746 and CA 10729; and The Robert A. Welch Foundation grant G-138. The animals involved in the research were maintained in facilities fully accredited by the American Association for Accreditation of Laboratory Animal Care.

## REFERENCES

1. E. Baril and J. Laszlo, *Advan. Enzyme Regul.*, **9**: 183 (1971).
2. P. Ove, O. E. Brown, and J. Laszlo, *Cancer Res.*, **29**: 1562 (1969).
3. J. F. Chiu and L. S. Hnilica, *Proc. Amer. Ass. Cancer Res.*, **14**: 74 (1973).
4. J. F. Chiu and S. C. Sung, *Biochim. Biophys. Acta*, **246**: 44 (1971).
5. P. G. Wallace, D. R. Hewish, M. M. Venning, and L. A. Burgoyne, *Biochem. J.*, **125**: 47 (1971).
6. L. M. S. Chang and F. J. Bollum, *J. Biol. Chem.*, **246**: 5835 (1971).
7. A. Weissbach, A. Schlabach, B. Friedlender, and A. Bolden, *Nature (London) New Biol.*, **231**: 167 (1971).
8. E. F. Baril, O. E. Brown, M. D. Jenkins, and J. Laszlo, *Biochemistry*, **10**: 1981 (1971).
9. J. F. Chiu and S. C. Sung, *J. Neurochem.*, **20**: 617 (1973).
10. G. S. Probst and R. R. Meyer, *Biochem. Biophys. Res. Commun.*, **50**: 111 (1971).
11. H. Berger, Jr., and R. C. C. Huang, *J. Biol. Chem.*, **246**: 7275 (1971).
12. J. F. Chiu and S. C. Sung, *Biochim. Biophys. Acta*, **262**: 397 (1972).
13. F. J. Bollum and V. R. Potter, *J. Biol. Chem.*, **233**: 478 (1958).
14. J. F. Chiu and S. C. Sung, *Biochim. Biophys. Res. Commun.*, **46**: 1830 (1972).
15. W. E. Lynch and I. Lieberman, *Biochem. Biophys. Res. Commun.*, **52**: 843 (1973).
16. J. F. Chiu, C. Craddock, and L. S. Hnilica, *FEBS (Feb. Eur. Biochem. Soc.) Lett.*, **36**: 235 (1973).
17. F. Capizzo and R. J. Roberts, *Toxicol. Appl. Pharmacol.*, **19**: 176 (1971).
18. G. M. Higgins and R. M. Anderson, *Arch. Pathol.*, **12**: 186 (1931).

19. J. Chauveau, V. Moule, and C. Rouiller, *Exp. Cell Res.*, **11**: 317 (1956).
20. R. G. Martin and B. N. Ames, *J. Biol. Chem.*, **236**: 1372 (1961).
21. J. F. Chiu and S. C. Sung, *Nature (London) New Biol.*, **239**: 176 (1972).
22. O. H. Lowry, N. J. Rosebrough, A. L. Farr, and R. J. Randall, *J. Biol. Chem.*, **193**: 265 (1951).
23. P. Ove, J. Laszlo, M. D. Jenkins, and H. P. Morris, *Cancer Res.*, **29**: 1557 (1969).
24. E. F. Baril, M. D. Jenkins, O. E. Brown, J. Laszlo, and H. P. Morris, *Cancer Res.*, **33**: 1187 (1973).
25. J. M. Price, J. W. Harman, E. C. Miller, and J. A. Miller, *Cancer Res.*, **12**: 192 (1952).
26. S. Fiala and W. Glinsman, *Neoplasma*, **10**: 83 (1963).
27. A. A. Hadjiolov and M. D. Dabeva, *Experientia*, **17**: 452 (1961).
28. D. E. Kizer, *J. Nat. Cancer Inst.*, **27**: 1503 (1961).
29. L. A. Poirier and H. C. Pitot, *Cancer Res.*, **29**: 475 (1969).
30. L. A. Poirier and H. C. Pitot, *Cancer Res.*, **30**: 1974 (1970).
31. N. B. Furlong and A. J. Thomann, *Proc. Soc. Exp. Biol. Med.*, **115**: 541 (1964).
32. L. S. M. Chang and F. J. Bollum, *Biochemistry*, **11**: 1264 (1972).
33. A. Weissbach, A. Schlabach, B. Fridlender, and A. Bolden, *Nature (London) New Biol.*, **231**: 167 (1971).
34. D. C. Ward, K. C. Humphryes, and I. B. Weinstein, *Nature*, **237**: 499 (1972).
35. F. J. Persico, D. E. Nicholson, and A. A. Gottlieb, *Cancer Res.*, **33**: 1210 (1973).
36. V. R. Potter, *Can. Cancer Conf.*, **8**: 9 (1969).
37. P. Dustin, Jr., *Cell Tissue Kinet.*, **5**: 519 (1972).
38. P. R. Walker and V. R. Potter, *Advan. Enzyme Regul.*, **10**: 339 (1972).
39. R. Kraes, G. M. Williams, and J. H. Weisburger, *Cancer Res.*, **33**: 613 (1973).
40. P. Gold and S. O. Freedman, *J. Exp. Med.*, **121**: 439 (1965).
41. E. Farber, *Cancer Res.*, **28**: 1210 (1968).

# EXPRESSION OF DIFFERENTIATED FUNCTIONS IN NEUROBLASTOMA CELL CULTURE

KEDAR N. PRASAD and SURENDRA KUMAR
Department of Radiology, University of Colorado Medical Center, Denver, Colorado

## ABSTRACT

Adenosine $3',5'$-cyclic monophosphate (cAMP) induced irreversibly many differentiated functions in mouse neuroblastoma cells in culture. These functions included formation of long neurites, increase in size of soma and nucleus associated with an elevation of total RNA and protein contents, increase in the levels of tyrosine hydroxylase, choline acetyltransferase (ChA) and acetylcholinesterase (AChE), inhibition of cell division, increase in sensitivity of adenylate cyclase (AC) to catecholamines, and loss of tumorigenicity. Most of the differentiated cells accumulated in the $G_1$ phase of the cell cycle. Further studies using X ray and serum-free medium indicate that the expression of differentiated phenotype can also occur in the $G_2$ phase of the cell cycle. Cells treated with sodium butyrate also accumulated in the $G_1$ phase but did not express their differentiated phenotype. The cAMP-induced differentiated neuroblastoma cells have an elevated level of AC, cAMP, and cAMP phosphodiesterase (PDE). Therefore a working hypothesis is proposed that the levels of AC, cAMP, and PDE and the sensitivity of AC to dopamine and norepinephrine increase during differentiation of mouse neuroblastoma cells in culture; the reverse, therefore, may be true during malignant transformation of nerve cells. Preliminary data indicate that cAMP may be involved in the differentiation of human neuroblastoma cells in culture. In neuroblastoma cells some of the differentiated functions can be induced by agents that may or may not elevate the intracellular level of cAMP. On the basis of several observations, the following conclusions have been reached:

    1. Certain differentiated functions, such as neurite formation and elevation of ChA and AChE, can be expressed without any change in the cAMP level.

    2. Neurite formation and an elevation of neural enzymes are independently regulated, since one can be expressed in the absence of the other.

    3. Neurite formation is also independent of increased sensitivity of adenylate cyclase to catecholamines, since one can be expressed in the absence of the other.

    4. An elevation of cAMP may not allow the expression of differentiated phenotype if the subsequent steps are not activated or if they are impaired.

The factors that induce and regulate the expression of differentiated functions in nerve cells are poorly understood. Recently we obtained some pertinent information on the problem using mouse neuroblastoma cell culture as an experimental model. Although the neuroblastoma cell culture may not be a perfect model for a study of neural differentiation, it has provided new information that appears to be pertinent at least in some aspects of neural differentiation. We have shown that adenosine $3',5'$-cyclic monophosphate (cAMP) induces irreversibly many differentiated functions in mouse neuroblastoma cells in culture. These include formation of long neurites,[1-3] increase in the size of soma and nucleus associated with an elevation of total RNA and protein content,[4] increase in the levels of tyrosine hydroxylase (TH),[5,6] choline acetyltransferase (ChA),[7] and acetylcholinesterase (AChE),[8,9] inhibition of cell division,[1-3] loss of tumorigenicity,[10] and increased sensitivity of adenylate cyclase (AC) to catecholamines.[11] Some of these differentiated functions can be induced by agents that may or may not elevate the intracellular level of cAMP. For example, serum-free medium (SFM) induces neurite formation[12] and increases AChE,[13] but it does not increase the level of TH,[5,13] ChA,[7] or AC.[11] The sensitivity of AC to catecholamine also does not change in the SFM-treated cell.[11] 5-Bromodeoxyuridine (5-BrdU) also induces neurite formation[14] and increases[15] the activities of TH and ChA. Serum-free medium and 5-BrdU elevate the cAMP level about twofold.[16] X ray and 6-thioguanine do not change the cAMP level[16] but induce neurite formation[17,18] and increase the level of ChA;[7,18] however, they do not increase TH activity.[5,18] Sodium butyrate does not induce neurite formation[1] but increases the levels of cAMP[16] and adenylate cyclase[11] without affecting the cAMP phosphodiesterase (PDE) activity.[19] In addition, the sensitivity of AC to catecholamines[11] and the levels of TH[5] and ChA[7] markedly increase in NB cells treated with sodium butyrate. Vinblastine sulfate and cytochalasin B, which are known to block the assembly of microtubules and microfilaments, respectively, do not decrease[20] the prostaglandin $(PG)E_1$-stimulated cAMP level; however, they completely block $PGE_1$-induced axon formation.[2] On the basis of these observations, the following conclusions have been reached:

1. Certain differentiated functions, such as neurite formation and elevation of ChA and AChE, can be expressed without any change in cAMP level.

2. Neurite formation and an elevation of neural enzymes are independently regulated, since one can be expressed in the absence of the other.

3. Neurite formation is also independent of increased sensitivity of adenylate cyclase to catecholamines, since one can be expressed in the absence of the other.

4. An elevation of cAMP may not allow the expression of differentiated phenotype if the subsequent steps are not activated or if they are imparied.

## FEATURES OF NEUROBLASTOMA CELLS

The procedures for culturing and maintaining mouse neuroblastoma (NB) cells have been previously described.[8] These cells have a relatively high rate of glycolysis.[21] They contain demonstrable levels[22,23] of TH, ChA, AChE, and catechol-*o*-methyltransferase (COMT)[24,25] but lack tryptophan hydroxylase.[22,26] Mouse NB tumors have 5*th* band of muscle lactate dehydrogenase,[27] which is absent from the brain. Four types of clone[22] have been isolated from mouse NB tumor. These include (1) clone with TH but no ChA, (2) clone with ChA but no TH, (3) clone with neither TH nor ChA, and (4) clone with both TH and ChA. The first three types of clone[26] have also been isolated by other investigators. Cells from all these clones have a doubling time of about 18 to 24 hr, show spontaneous morphological differentiation varying from 1 to 15%, and produce malignant tumors when injected subcutaneously into male A/J mice.

## MORPHOLOGICAL DIFFERENTIATION AND CYCLIC AMP

Analogs of cAMP, $PGE_1$, and PDE inhibitors induced morphological differentiation as shown by the formation of long neurites and by an increase in the size of nucleus and soma [Fig. 1(B and C)]. Some cells that did not form long neurites increased in size of soma and nucleus. Table 1 shows the relative potency of various agents in causing morphological differentiation. The $PGE_1$ and PDE inhibitors and 8-benzylthio cAMP were more effective than $N^6O_2'$-dibutyryl adenosine $3',5'$-cyclic monophosphate (dbcAMP). For a period of 4 days, no significant cell death occurred after these treatments. The viability of attached cells as determined by the uptake of supravital strain (trypan blue in 1% saline) was similar to that of control cells (90 to 95%).

The number of morphologically differentiated cells after $PGE_1$ treatment is time and concentration dependent.[2] A significant increase in the number of differentiated cells was noted 24 hr after treatment (Fig. 2), and cell division continued up to the third day (Fig. 3). This indicates that the inhibition of cell division temporally follows the induction of morphological differentiation and thus may be secondary to the neurite formation. The kinetics of morphological differentiation and growth after treatment with dbcAMP[1] or PDE inhibitors[3] were similar to those after $PGE_1$ treatment.

Cyclic AMP, $5'$-AMP, theophylline, some 8-substituted analogs of cAMP (8-hydroxyethylthio-, 8-amino-, 8-hydroxyethylamino- and 8-methylamino-cAMP), adenosine triphosphate, adenosine diphosphate, and sodium butyrate inhibited cell growth without causing morphological differentiation. These data indicate that the inhibition of cell division need not necessarily produce the expression of morphological differentiation; however, certain differentiated functions[5,7,8,11] can be expressed after the inhibition of cell division.

Like cAMP, guanosine $3',5'$-cyclic monophosphate (cGMP) is also present in mammalian cells.[28] Therefore, the effects of cGMP on neuroblastoma cell culture were examined. Cyclic GMP inhibited cell division without causing morphological differentiation.

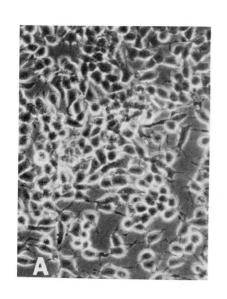

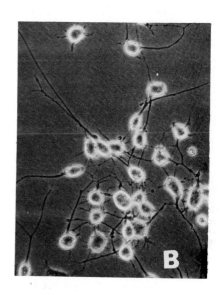

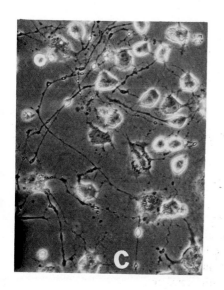

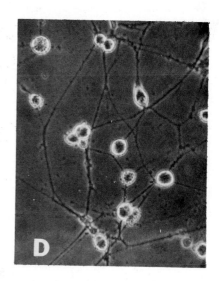

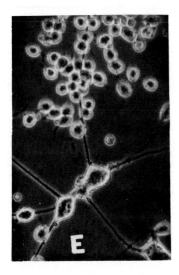
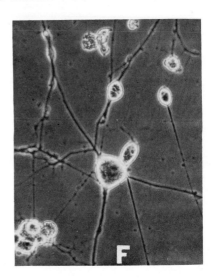

Fig. 1  Phase contrast photomicrographs of mouse neuroblastoma cells
[$NBA_{2(1)}$ clone] in culture. Cells (50,000) were plated in Falcon plastic
dishes (60 mm), and $PGE_1$ (10 μg/ml) and R020-1724 (200 μg/ml) were
added separately 24 hr later. The medium and drug were changed 3, 5, 8, and
11 days after treatment. The control culture (A) shows that cells grow in
clumps and some of them have short cytoplasmic processes. The
R020-1724-treated (B) and $PGE_1$-treated culture (C) 4 days after treatment
show the formation of long neurites. The $PGE_1$-treated culture 14 days after
treatment (D) shows that the remaining cells maintain their differentiated
phenotype. The R020-1724-treated culture 14 days after treatment (E) shows
that a few cells are dividing in the presence of drug. The R020-1724-treated
culture from which the drug was removed 3 days after treatment (F) (the
photomicrograph was taken 8 days later) shows that many cells maintain their
differentiated phenotype.[46] (98x.)

# IRREVERSIBILITY OF GROWTH INHIBITION AND
# MORPHOLOGICAL DIFFERENTIATION

The morphological differentiation and inhibition of growth induced by
dbcAMP, $PGE_1$, or R020-1724 for the most part were irreversible,[1-3] provided
the drug was present in the medium for at least 3 to 4 days. Three days after
treatment with R020-1724 or $PGE_1$, when the differentiated cells were removed
from dishes using Viokase solution and replated in separate dishes, cells attached
and formed long neurites within 24 hr even though no drug was present during
this period. The number of morphologically differentiated cells in the newly
plated dishes was similar to the number in dishes from which the drug had not
been removed. This indicates that the cellular factors which control the
expression of differentiated phenotype remain functional after subculturing.

**TABLE 1**

## EFFECT OF VARIOUS CYCLIC AMP AGENTS ON MOUSE NEUROBLASTOMA CELLS IN CULTURE[1-3]

| Treatment* | Differentiated cells, % of total ± S.D. |
|---|---|
| Control | 9.0 ± 2.0 |
| Monobutyryl cAMP (0.5 mmolar) | 47 ± 5.0 |
| dbcAMP (0.5 mmolar) | 51.0 ± 4.8 |
| 8-benzylthio cAMP (400 μg/ml) | 66.0 ± 4.5 |
| PGE$_1$ (10 μg/ml) | 72.0 ± 5.0 |
| RO20-1724 (200 μg/ml) | 71.0 ± 5.4 |
| Papaverine (25 μg/ml) | 79.0 ± 2.5 |

*For quantitating the number of differentiated cells, 50,000 cells were plated in Falcon plastic dishes (60 mm) and treated with a drug 24 hr after plating. The morphologically differentiated cells (cytoplasmic processes were greater than 50 μm long) were scored 3 days after treatment. At least 300 cells were counted. The number of differentiated cells is expressed as percent of total cells. Each value represents an average of six to eight samples.

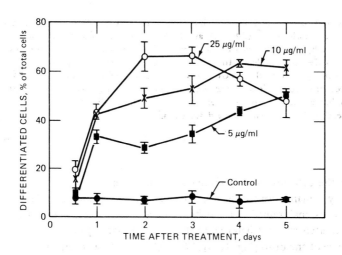

Fig. 2 Formation of morphologic differentiated cells as a function of time and PGE$_1$ concentration. Cells (50,000) were plated in Falcon plastic dishes (60 mm), and various concentrations of PGE$_1$ were added 24 hr later. A total of 300 to 500 cells were counted, and the number of morphologic differentiated cells was expressed as percent of total cells. Each value represents an average of 8 samples. Bars at each point represent standard deviation.[2]

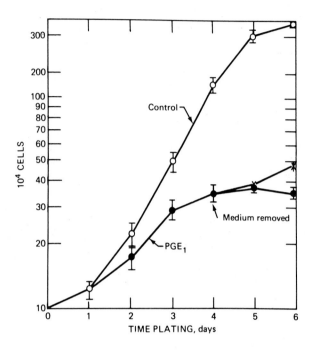

Fig. 3  Growth curve of neuroblastoma cells in vitro. Cells were plated in Falcon plastic dishes (60 mm), and $PGE_1$ (10 μg/ml) was added 24 hr later. The $PGE_1$ was removed from one group of dishes, and fresh growth medium was added 3 days later. In another group of dishes, fresh growth medium containing 10 μg/ml of $PGE_1$ was replaced at the same time. The growth medium in control dishes was also changed. The cell number was counted in a Coulter counter. Each point represents an average of five or six samples. Bars at each point represent standard deviation.[2]

When the cultures were maintained in the presence of R020-1724 or $PGE_1$ for 14 days, many dead cells were floating in the medium, but most of the attached cells maintained their differentiated phenotype [Fig. 1(D)]. At this time the treated cultures had two to three clones that appeared to be dividing in the presence of the drug [Fig. 1(E)]. When R020-1724 was removed 3 days after treatment and the culture was examined 8 days later, many cells maintained their differentiated phenotype [Fig. 1(F)], indicating further the irreversibility of neurite formation. The dbcAMP also induces an irreversible neurite formation in human neuroblasts.[29] These findings are in contrast to the observations made on nonnerve cells in which cAMP effects are reversible at all times soon after the removal of the drug.[30-33]

## REQUIREMENTS FOR THE EXPRESSION OF DIFFERENTIATED PHENOTYPE

Vinblastine sulfate (interferes with the assembly of microtubules), cyto-chalasin B (interferes with the assembly of microfilaments), and cycloheximide (inhibits protein synthesis) completely blocked the axon formation induced by cAMP, whereas actinomycin D (inhibits RNA synthesis) did not. Thus the expression of differentiated phenotype[1-3] requires at least the assembly of microtubules and microfilaments and the synthesis of new protein but does not require new RNA synthesis. Since the inhibitors used in this study are known to affect other cellular parameters in addition to those mentioned here, a different interpretation of these data cannot be excluded at the present time.

## SENSITIVITY OF NEUROBLASTOMA CLONES TO CYCLIC AMP

Cells of most clones were sensitive to cAMP in causing morphological differentiation. Also, some clones, irrespective of their neuronal cell type, were sensitive to $PGE_1$ but not to R020-1724 and vice versa.[22] The clone that was insensitive to R020-1724 was also unresponsive to dbcAMP.

## TUMORIGENICITY OF DIFFERENTIATED CELLS

Control cells when injected subcutaneously produced tumors in all A/J mice, whereas the tumorigenicity of differentiated cells (4 days after treatment) was either partially or completely abolished.[10] Uncloned cells were used since they were more nearly duplicate to in vivo condition. Since some cells were responsive to $PGE_1$ but not to PDE inhibitor and vice versa, $PGE_1$ was combined with R020-1724 to maximize the effect on differentiation. Indeed, cells treated in this manner lost completely a prime feature of malignancy, their tumorigenicity (Table 2).

## LEVELS OF TH, ChA, AChE, AND COMT ACTIVITIES IN DIFFERENTIATED CELLS

Tyrosine hydroxylase,[5] a rate-limiting enzyme in the biosynthesis of catecholamines was markedly increased (Table 3) by some analogs of cAMP and papaverine. The morphologically differentiated neuroblastoma cells induced by X ray,[17] SFM,[12] and cytosine arabinoside[13] showed no change in TH activity.[5,13] Sodium butyrate, which inhibits cell division without causing morphological differentiation,[1] increased the TH activity[5] and cAMP level.[16] These data suggest that morphological differentiation and TH activity are independently regulated and that cAMP may be involved in the regulation of TH

TABLE 2

## INCIDENCE OF TUMORS AFTER SUBCUTANEOUS INJECTION OF CONTROL AND DIFFERENTIATED NEUROBLASTOMA CELLS*

| Treatment† | Number of animals | Incidence of tumors, % of total |
|---|---|---|
| Control cell treated with or without solvent | 30 | 100 |
| dbcAMP (0.5 mmolar) | 15 | 50 |
| R020-1724 (200 µg/ml) | 15 | 40 |
| 8-benzylthio cAMP (400 µg/ml) | 15 | 60 |
| PGE$_1$ (10 µg/ml) | 15 | 25 |
| PGE$_1$ + dbcAMP | 15 | 0 |
| PGE$_1$ + 8-benzylthio cAMP | 15 | 0 |
| PGE$_1$ + R020-1724 | 16 | 0 |

*From K. N. Prasad, Cyclic AMP-Induced Differentiated Mouse Neuroblastoma Cells Lose Tumourgenic Characteristics, Cytobios, 6: 163 (1972).

†Cells ($10^5$) were plated in Falcon plastic dishes (60 mm) and treated with drugs 24 hr later. After 4 days of incubation, the control and differentiated cells (0.25 x $10^6$) were injected subcutaneously into male A/J mice (6 to 8 weeks old). Cell viability[10] in the control and drug-treated cultures was 90 to 95%.

TABLE 3

## TYROSINE HYDROXYLASE (TH) ACTIVITY AND DIFFERENTIATION OF MOUSE NEUROBLASTOMA CELLS IN CULTURE*

| Treatment† | TH, pmole product/30 min/$10^6$ cells ± S.D. |
|---|---|
| Control, log phase | 15.1 ± 1.9 |
| Control, confluent phase | 11.2 ± 0.7 |
| SFM | 17.3 ± 0.4 |
| dbcAMP (0.25 mmolar) | 473 ± 17 |
| 8-methylthio cAMP (0.3 mmolar) | 587 ± 9 |
| Papaverine (0.13 mmolar) | 977 ± 46 |
| Sodium butyrate (0.5 mmolar) | 300 ± 12 |

*From J. C. Waymire, N. Weiner, and K. N. Prasad, Regulation of Tyrosine Hydroxylase Activity in Cultured Mouse Neuroblastoma Cells. Elevations Induced by Analogs of Adenosine 3',5'-Cyclic Monophosphate, Proc. Nat. Acad. Sci. U.S.A., 69: 2241 (1972).

†The NBP$_2$ clone, which has both tyrosine hydroxylase (TH) and choline acetyltransferase (ChA), was used in this study. Neuroblastoma cells (0.5 x $10^6$) were treated with X rays 24 hr later. Each value represents an average of at least four samples.

activity. Our hypothesis that cAMP may be involved in the regulation of TH activity has been confirmed by recent studies on the TH level of mouse adrenal gland[34] and mouse NB cells in culture.[6]

The ChA, which synthesizes acetylcholine, was markedly increased in differentiated cells induced by cAMP and was also increased after X-irradiation and after treatment with 5'-AMP and sodium butyrate (Table 4). The maximal increase in the ChA level coincided with the cessation of cell division.[7] These data indicate that the levels of ChA and morphological differentiation are independently regulated and that cAMP is not necessarily involved in the regulation of ChA. Data[8] on AChE suggest a similar mode of regulation. Cyclic AMP is also not involved in the regulation of COMT, because the enzyme activity in cAMP-induced differentiated cells does not change.[24]

## CHANGES IN NUCLEIC ACID AND PROTEIN CONTENTS IN DIFFERENTIATED CELLS

Since the size of soma and of nucleus increases during cAMP-induced differentiation of NB cells, changes in the total content of nucleic acid and

TABLE 4

EFFECT OF VARIOUS AGENTS ON CHOLINE
ACETYLTRANSFERASE (ChA) LEVEL OF
NEUROBLASTOMA CELLS*

| Treatment† | ChA activity, pmole/15 min/10⁶ cells ± S.D. |
|---|---|
| Control (exponential) | 260 ± 35 |
| Control (confluent) | 300 ± 34 |
| dbcAMP (0.5 mmolar) | 1300 ± 72 |
| PGE₁ (10 µg/ml) | 880 ± 100 |
| R020-1724 (200 µg/ml) | 1280 ± 160 |
| 5'-AMP (0.25 mmolar) | 1320 ± 80 |
| Butyric acid (0.5 mmolar) | 760 ± 100 |
| X ray (600 rads) | 1640 ± 144 |

*From K. N. Prasad and B. Mandal, Choline Acetyltransferase Level in Cyclic AMP and X-Ray Induced Cells in Culture, *Cytobios*, **8**: 75(1973).

†Neuroblastoma cells (0.5 × 10⁶) were plated in Falcon plastic flasks (75 cm²), and each drug was added 24 hr later. Fresh growth medium and drug were added 2 days after drug treatment, and the ChA was analyzed 3 days after treatment. Each value represents an average of five to six samples.

protein were investigated 3 days after treatment. Table 5 shows that the total DNA of differentiated cells markedly decreased, indicating that most of the cells accumulated in the $G_1$ phase of the cell cycle.[4] The total RNA and protein increased about two- to threefold. This finding is consistent with the previous observation on the differentiation of mammalian neurons.

It is generally presumed that the blocking of cells in the $G_1$ phase allows the expression of differentiated phenotype. This does not appear to be the case in mouse neuroblastoma cells, because cells treated with sodium butyrate are blocked in the $G_1$ phase of the cell cycle[4] but no expression of morphological differentiation occurs;[1] however, the expression of several biochemical differentiated functions[5,7,8,11] does occur under this condition. In addition to cAMP, other agents, such as SFM,[12] 6-thioguanine,[15] X ray,[7,17] and 5-BrdU,[14,15] also induce some differentiated functions; therefore the total nucleic acid and protein contents were measured. Table 6 shows that the DNA content of cells treated with SFM and 6-thioguanine did not significantly change, indicating that the relative distribution of differentiated cells throughout the cell cycle may be similar to that of controls. It has been generally presumed that cells accumulate in the $G_1$ phase of the cell cycle when SFM is added. This does not appear to be the case in this neuroblastoma clone. The cells treated with 5-BrdU had about one-third the DNA[16] of control cells, indicating that most of the cells treated with 5-BrdU accumulate in the $G_1$ phase of the cell cycle. It should be pointed out that the DNA content per cell was less than that expected if the diploid cells were arrested in the $G_1$ phase; however, the neuroblastoma cells are

TABLE 5

TOTAL DNA, RNA, AND PROTEIN CONTENTS IN CYCLIC
AMP-INDUCED DIFFERENTIATED MOUSE NEUROBLASTOMA
CELLS IN CULTURE*

| Treatment† | Cell content, pg/cell ± S.D. | | |
| --- | --- | --- | --- |
| | DNA | RNA | Protein |
| Control | 13.3 ± 1.5 | 15.3 ± 1.0 | 500 ± 29 |
| dbcAMP (0.5 mmolar) | 6.6 ± 0.6 | 33.6 ± 2.5 | 1580 ± 122 |
| PGE₁ (10 μg/ml) | 6.0 ± 1.6 | 24.4 ± 1.9 | 870 ± 47 |
| R020-1724 (200 μg/ml) | 6.7 ± 1.2 | 33 ± 1.8 | 1016 ± 54 |
| Na butyrate (0.5 mmolar) | 5.3 ± 1.0 | 31.2 ± 3.9 | 1479 ± 111 |

*From K. N. Prasad, S. Kumar, K. Gilmer, and A. Vernadakis, Cyclic AMP-Induced Differentiated Neuroblastoma Cells: Changes in Total Nucleic Acid and Protein Contents, *Biochem. Biophys. Res. Commun.*, **50**: 973 (1973).

†Cells (0.5 x 10⁶) were plated in large Falcon plastic flasks (75 cm²) and drugs were added separately 24 hr later. The total nucleic acid and protein contents were assayed 3 days after treatment. Each value represents an average of four to six samples.

TABLE 6

TOTAL DNA, RNA, AND PROTEIN CONTENTS IN
DIFFERENTIATED MOUSE NEUROBLASTOMA CELLS IN
CULTURE INDUCED BY NONCYCLIC AMP AGENTS*

| | Cell content, pg/cell ± S.D. | | |
|---|---|---|---|
| Treatment† | DNA | RNA | Protein |
| Control | 19.8 ± 2.7 | 26 ± 1.3 | 152 ± 13 |
| SFM | 23.8 ± 2.3 | 65 ± 9.0 | 180 ± 12 |
| 6-thioguanine (0.5 μmolar) | 25.4 ± 3.5 | 79 ± 12.0 | 346 ± 7.0 |
| 5-BrdU (5 μmolar) | 7 ± 1.5 | 50 ± 3.4 | 343 ± 34 |
| X ray (1200 rads) | 62 ± 13.8 | 153 ± 27.0 | 768 ± 39 |

*From K. N. Prasad, K. Gilmer, and S. Kumar, Morphologically "Differentiated" Mouse Neuroblastoma Cells Induced by Non-Cyclic AMP Agents: Levels of Cyclic AMP, Nucleic Acid and Protein, *Proc. Soc. Exp. Biol. Med.*, **143**: 168 (1973).

†Cells (0.5 to 1 x 10[6]) were plated in large Falcon plastic flasks; drugs and X ray were given separately 24 hr later. The total DNA, RNA, and protein contents were analyzed 3 days after treatment. Each value represents an average of five to eight samples.

aneuploids,[26] and therefore the DNA value in each phase of the cycle may not be comparable to diploid cells.

The X-ray-induced differentiated cells had a DNA content threefold higher than that of controls. This value was much higher than that expected if all cells were accumulated in the $G_2$ phase. Since the formation of polyploid cells is a well-established response of irradiated mammalian cell culture, it is suggested that the expression of differentiated phenotype can occur in polyploid cells as well as in $G_2$ cells. Although most of mammalian neurons are diploid, some mammalian neurons, such as Purkinje cells, have tetraploid DNA contents.[35]

## CHANGES IN ADENYLATE CYCLASE ACTIVITY AND INCREASE IN SENSITIVITY OF ADENYLATE CYCLASE TO CATECHOLAMINES IN DIFFERENTIATED CELLS

Figure 4 shows the effect of various concentrations of dopamine (DA) and norepinephrine (NE) on AC activity in homogenates of control and differentiated NB cells in culture. Adenylate cyclase activity was stimulated by low concentrations of DA. In control cells a half-maximal increase in enzyme activity was achieved with about 0.8 μmolar DA; however, a concentration of about 200 μmolar NE was required to give a similar increase in enzyme activity. In differentiated cells a half-maximal increase in enzyme activity was achieved with about 0.91 μmolar DA; however, only 16 μmolar NE was required for a similar

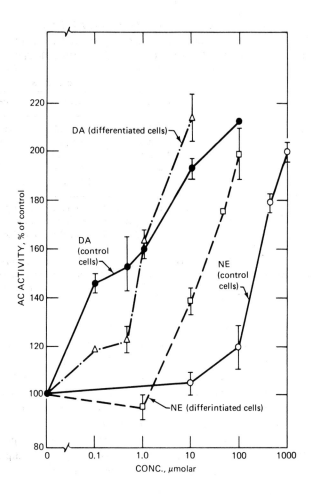

Fig. 4 Changes in AC activity in homogenates of control and differentiated mouse neuroblastoma (NB) cells after treatment with dopamine (DA) and norepinephrine (NE). An inhibitor of cAMP phosphodiesterase, R020-1724, was used to induce differentiation in NB cells in culture. Cells ($0.5 \times 10^6$) were plated in large Falcon plastic flasks ($75 \text{ cm}^2$), and R020-1724 (200 μg/ml) was added 24 hr later. Controls were treated with an equivalent volume of solvent. The drug and medium were changed 2 days after treatment, and the AC activity in homogenate of NB cells was measured 3 days after treatment. The basal activities of AC in control ($15 \pm 1.4$ pmole/mg/min) and differentiated ($21 \pm 1$ pmole/mg protein/min) cells were considered 100% control values, and the AC values of treated cells were expressed as percent of control. Each value represents an average of 8 to 12 samples. The bar at each point represents standard deviation.[11]

increase in enzyme activity. Dopamine and NE produced a maximal stimulation on enzyme activity to about the same level in both control and differentiated cells; however, in differentiated cells the effective concentration needed was about 10 times less than that required in control cells. In differentiated cells a higher concentration of DA (100 $\mu$molar) and NE (500 $\mu$molar) changed AC activity to 180 ± 11% and 62 ± 6% of control, respectively. A low concentration of isoproterenol stimulated the AC activity in control cells, but in differentiated cells even a high concentration of drug failed to do so. Acetylcholine did not stimulate the AC activity in control or differentiated cells (Table 7).

Table 8 shows that the basal activities of AC in differentiated NB cells induced by $PGE_1$ and R020-1724 increased by about 40% of control. In $PGE_1$-induced differentiated cells, $PGE_1$ stimulated the enzyme activity to a greater extent than did NaF; however, in R020-1724-induced differentiated cells, as well as in control cells, both $PGE_1$ and NaF increased the AC activity to about the same level.

Apomorphine, which is known to mimic the effect of DA in the caudate nucleus,[39,40] also increased the AC activity (Table 7). Haloperidol, which specifically blocks the dopamine "receptor", inhibited DA-stimulated AC activity; however, it did not significantly affect NE-stimulated enzyme activity

TABLE 7

EFFECT OF VARIOUS AGENTS ON ADENYLATE CYCLASE (AC)
ACTIVITY IN HOMOGENATES OF CONTROL AND DIFFERENTIATED
NEUROBLASTOMA CELLS*

| Status of cells | Treatment† | AC level, pmole/mg protein/min ± S.D. | | |
| --- | --- | --- | --- | --- |
| | | 100 $\mu$molar | 10 $\mu$molar | 1 $\mu$molar |
| Control | No treatment | 15 ± 1.4 | | |
| Control | Apomorphine | 32 ± 2 | | 27 ± 1 |
| Differentiated | No treatment | 21 ± 1 | | |
| Differentiated | Apomorphine | 36 ± 2.1 | | 33 ± 1 |
| Control | Acetylcholine | 18 ± 1.4 | 17 ± 1 | |
| Differentiated | Acetylcholine | 22 ± 1 | 23 ± 1 | |

*From K. N. Prasad and K. N. Gilmer, Demonstration of Dopamine-Sensitive Adenylate Cyclase in Malignant Neuroblastoma Cells and Change in Sensitivity of Adenylate Cyclase to Catecholamines in "Differentiated" Cells, *Proc. Nat. Acad. Sci. U.S.A.*, in press.

†R020-1724, an inhibitor of PDE, was used to induce differentiation in neuroblastoma cells in culture. Cells (0.5 x $10^6$) were plated in large Falcon plastic flasks (75 $cm^2$), and R020-1724 (200 $\mu$g/ml) was added 24 hr later. Controls were treated with an equivalent volume of solvent. The drug and medium were changed 2 days after treatment, and the AC activity in homogenate was measured 3 days after treatment according to a modified procedure[52] of Krishna, Weiss, and Brodie.[53] Various agents were added separately in the incubating mixture. Each value represents an average of six samples.

TABLE 8

EFFECT OF SODIUM FLUORIDE, PROSTAGLANDIN $E_1$ AND
EPINEPHRINE ON THE ADENYLATE CYCLASE IN HOMOGENATE OF
NEUROBLASTOMA CELLS*

| Treatment† | AC activity, pmole/mg protein/min ± S.D. | | | |
|---|---|---|---|---|
| | Basal | NaF | $PGE_1$ | EP |
| Control | 15 ± 1.4 | 26 ± 1.9 | 36 ± 3.8 | 19 ± 1.9 |
| RO20-1724 (200 μg/ml, 3 days) | 21 ± 1 | 38 ± 4.2 | 46 ± 6.3 | 46 ± 7.5 |
| $PGE_1$ (10 μg/ml, 3 days) | 22 ± 1.5 | 38 ± 2.5 | 60 ± 8 | 41 ± 2.1 |

*From K. N. Prasad and K. N. Gilmer, Demonstration of Dopamine-Sensitive Adenylate
Cyclase in Malignant Neuroblastoma Cells and Change in Sensitivity of Adenylate Cyclase to
Catecholamines in "Differentiated" Cells, *Proc. Nat. Acad. Sci. U.S.A.*, in press.

†Cells $(0.5 \times 10^6)$ were plated in large Falcon plastic flasks $(75 \text{ cm}^2)$ and $PGE_1$,
(stimulator of AC) and RO20-1724 (inhibitor of PDE) were used to induce differentiation.
These drugs were added separately 24 hr after plating. The drug and medium were changed
2 days after treatment, and the AC activity in homogenate was measured 3 days after
treatment. Control cells were treated with an equivalent volume of solvent and were
analyzed in a similar fashion. EP (100 μmolar), $PGE_1$ (0.1 μg/ml) and NaF (10.0 mmolar)
were added separately in the incubating mixture. Each value represents an average of six
samples.

(Table 9). A concentration of 11 μmolar haloperidol reduced DA-stimulated
enzyme activity by 50%; however, even a high concentration (100 μmolar) of
haloperidol decreased NE-stimulated enzyme activity only by about 30%.
Haloperidol by itself produced no significant effect on the AC activity.

A concentration of about 0.43 μmolar phentolamine (α-blocking agent)
reduced DA-stimulated AC activity by 50%, whereas a similar amount of
inhibition of NE-stimulated enzyme activity was achieved with about 2.3 μmolar
phentolamine (Table 9). A concentration of about 180 μmolar propranolol
(B-blocking agent) produced a 50% inhibition of DA-stimulated AC activity,
whereas NE-stimulated enzyme activity required only 1.7 μmolar propranolol
for a similar amount of inhibition (Table 9). Neither α-adrenergic nor B-
adrenergic blocking agent affected the basal level of AC activity.

The combination of DA (100 μmolar) and NE (100 μmolar) had an additive
stimulatory effect on AC activity (Table 10); however, when NE (100 μmolar)
was combined with a lower concentration of DA (10 μmolar), no such effect was
observed. The $PGE_1$ increased AC activity to about the same level as that
produced by DA and NE. The combination of NE and $PGE_1$ produced an
additive stimulatory effect on AC activity (Table 10); however, the combination
of DA and $PGE_1$ caused no such effect. The $PGE_1$-stimulated AC activity was

TABLE 9

CONCENTRATIONS OF BLOCKING AGENTS THAT
PRODUCE 50% INHIBITION OF CATECHOLAMINES-
STIMULATED ADENYLATE CYCLASE ACTIVITY IN
HOMOGENATE OF DIFFERENTIATED MOUSE
NEUROBLASTOMA CELLS*

| | Concentrations, $\mu$molar | | |
| --- | --- | --- | --- |
| | Haloperidol | Phentolamine | Propranolol |
| DA-stimulated AC activity | 11 | 0.43 | 180 |
| NE-stimulated AC activity | >100 | 2.3 | 1.7 |

*From K. N. Prasad and K. N. Gilmer, Demonstration of Dopamine-Sensitive Adenylate Cyclase in Malignant Neuroblastoma Cells and Change in Sensitivity of Adenylate Cyclase to Catecholamines in "Differentiated" Cells, *Proc. Nat. Acad. Sci. U.S.A.*, in press.

TABLE 10

EFFECT OF PROSTAGLANDIN AND CATECHOLAMINES
ON ADENYLATE CYCLASE ACTIVITY IN HOMOGENATE
OF DIFFERENTIATED MOUSE NEUROBLASTOMA CELLS*

| Treatment† | AC activity, pmole/mg protein/min ± S.D. |
| --- | --- |
| Basal level | 21 ± 1 |
| Dopamine (100 $\mu$molar) | 36 ± 4 |
| Norepinephrine (100 $\mu$molar) | 42 ± 5.2 |
| PGE$_1$ (10 $\mu$molar) | 41 ± 1 |
| DA + NE | 69 ± 3 |
| NE + PGE$_1$ | 74 ± 2 |
| DA + PGE$_1$ | 38 ± 1 |
| PGE$_1$ + propranolol (10 $\mu$molar) | 40 ± 2 |
| PGE$_1$ + phentolamine (10 $\mu$molar) | 20 ± 1 |

*From K. N. Prasad and K. N. Gilmer, Demonstration of Dopamine-Sensitive Adenylate Cyclase in Malignant Neuroblastoma Cells and Change in Sensitivity of Adenylate Cyclase to Catecholamines in "Differentiated" Cells, *Proc. Nat. Acad. Sci. U.S.A.*, in press.

†Cells ($0.5 \times 10^6$) were plated in large Falcon plastic flasks (75 cm$^2$) and R020-1724 (200 $\mu$g/ml) was added 24 hr later. Controls were treated with an equivalent volume of solvent. The drug and medium were changed 2 days after treatment and the AC activity in homogenate was measured 3 days after treatment. Each value represents an average of six samples.

blocked by a low concentration of phentolamine but was not affected significantly by propranolol (Table 10).

Table 11 shows that the AC activity in cells in SFM 3 days after treatment was similar to that in control cells. In addition, the AC activity was not significantly stimulated either by DA or NE. In cells treated with sodium butyrate (3 days after treatment), the basal activity of AC was increased by about 230% of control, and DA and NE further increased the enzyme activity about twofold.

Our data demonstrate the presence of an adenylate cyclase, sensitive to a very low concentration of dopamine, in homogenate of mouse neuroblastoma cells. The occurrence of DA-sensitive adenylate cyclase was demonstrated by Kebabian et al.[36,37] in homogenates of mammalian superior cervical ganglia and basal ganglia and by Brown and Makman[38] in mammalian retina. The AC has been suggested[38] to be the receptor for DA in mammalian brain. Our data indicate that the AC also may be linked to the dopamine receptor in neuroblastoma cells. For example, apomorphine, which mimics the actions of DA on the dopamine receptor of the caudate nucleus,[39,40] increases AC activity of neuroblastoma cells. Haloperidol, which antagonizes the DA receptors within the caudate nucleus,[41] also blocks DA-stimulated AC activity in NB cells. It has been shown that DA receptors of the caudate nucleus are not blocked by B-adrenergic blocking agents but are weakly antagonized by α-blocking agents.[42] The AC activity of the caudate nucleus shows a similar response with respect to

TABLE 11

EFFECT OF DOPAMINE AND NOREPINEPHRINE ON ADENYLATE
CYCLASE ACTIVITY IN HOMOGENATES OF NEUROBLASTOMA
CELLS TREATED WITH SERUM-FREE MEDIUM AND
SODIUM BUTYRATE*

| Treatment† | AC activity pmole/mg protein/min ± S.D. | | |
|---|---|---|---|
| | Basal | DA (100 μmolar) | NE (100 μmolar) |
| Control | 15 ± 1.4 | 32 ± 1 | 18 ± 2.2 |
| Sodium butyrate | 35 ± 1.4 | 60 ± 1.8 | 68 ± 1.5 |
| SFM | 16 ± 1.5 | 19 ± 1.2 | 17 ± 1 |

*From K. N. Prasad and K. N. Gilmer, Demonstration of Dopamine-Sensitive Adenylate Cyclase in Malignant Neuroblastoma Cells and Change in Sensitivity of Adenylate Cyclase to Catecholamines in "Differentiated" Cells, *Proc. Nat. Acad. Sci. U.S.A.,* in press.

†Cells (0.5 x 10$^6$) were plated in large Falcon plastic flasks (75 cm$^2$) and SFM and sodium butyrate (0.5 mmolar) were given separately 24 hr later. The drug and medium were changed 2 days after treatment, and the AC activity in homogenate was measured 3 days after treatment. Each value represents an average of six samples.

B- and α-blocking agents.[37] Our results show that the DA-stimulated activity of NB cells is not affected by a low concentration of B-blocking agent but is markedly inhibited by a low concentration of α-blocking agent. Thus the AC activity of NB cells and the caudate nucleus shows a quantitatively different response with respect to α-blocking agent.

The mouse NB cells also appear to contain NE-sensitive AC, which has pharmacological properties different from those of DA-sensitive AC. In cAMP-induced differentiated cells, the effective concentration of NE needed for a half-maximal and maximal stimulation of AC activity is about 10 times less than that needed for a similar increase in control cells, whereas only a maximal response of DA-sensitive AC reveals such a shift in concentration requirement. Unlike DA-sensitive AC, NE-sensitive AC is markedly inhibited by a low concentration of B-blocking agent but affected little by a low concentration of α-blocking agent and haloperidol. The fact that DA and NE produce an additive stimulatory effect on the AC activity of differentiated NB cells suggests that DA and NE interact at different receptor sites. This suggestion is further supported by the observation that the combination of $PGE_1$ and NE produces an additive stimulatory effect on AC activity, whereas the combination of DA and $PGE_1$ does not. The observation that the effects of DA and $PGE_1$ are not additive, coupled with the observation that a low concentration of phentolamine blocks the effect of $PGE_1$, suggests the interesting possibility that these two agents may interact at a common site.

Our study shows that the regulation of AC activity in malignant NB cells in culture is different from that in malignant glial cells in culture. This is demonstrated by the fact that the AC activity of malignant NB cells is stimulated by a low concentration of DA but not by a low concentration of NE, whereas the AC activity of malignant glial cells[43,44] is stimulated by a low concentration of NE but not by a low concentration of DA. Since DA stimulates AC activity and cAMP causes differentiation and inhibition of cell division in NB cells, an addition of exogenous DA to NB culture should mimic the effects of cAMP. Indeed, we have shown[45] that DA reversibly inhibits cell division when NB cells in culture are exposed to DA for 1 hr, whereas NE and EP under a similar experimental condition have no such effect. Thus DA-induced inhibition of cell division may be related to an increase in the cAMP level. Since the induction of an irreversible differentiation and inhibition of cell growth by cAMP requires a drug exposure time of at least 3 days, the DA exposure time of 1 hr was inadequate to mimic the effect of cAMP. Dopamine is auto-oxidized in solution; therefore, the removal of drug was necessary to avoid the effect of oxidative products.

In differentiated cells the basal activity of AC increases by about 40% of control, and the sensitivity of AC to DA and NE also increases. We showed previously[19,46] that the levels of cAMP and PDE increase in cAMP-induced differentiated cells. These data indicate that the levels of AC, cAMP, and PDE and the sensitivity of AC to DA and NE increase during differentiation of mouse neuroblastoma cells in culture; therefore, we suggest here that the reverse may be true during malignant transformation of nerve cells. It is interesting to note that the AC and PDE activities in adult hamster cerebrum increase twofold in comparison to the activities in newborn animals[47] and that the brain AC undergoes an age-dependent increase in its sensitivity to NE.[48]

## DIFFERENTIATION OF HUMAN NEUROBLASTOMA CELL CULTURE AND CYCLIC AMP

As with mouse neuroblastoma tumors,[22,26] human tumors contain more than one neuronal cell type.[49] Human neuroblastoma cells in culture also show morphological differentiation after treatment with dbcAMP (2.0 mmolar), papaverine (1 to 10 $\mu g/ml$) [Fig. 5(B)], and $PGE_1$ (10 $\mu g/ml$). The time of expression and the extent of differentiation are concentration dependent. The combination of $PGE_1$ (10 $\mu g/ml$) and papaverine (2.5 $\mu g/ml$) allows the expression of differentiated phenotype much earlier and to a much greater extent than that produced by each agent individually. Among all cAMP agents, papaverine was most potent in causing morphological differentiation. Sodium butyrate, a degradative product of dbcAMP in solution, induced neurite formation in a dose-dependent fashion [Fig. 5(C)]. This is in contrast to mouse cells[1] in which sodium butyrate reversibly inhibits the cell division without causing morphological differentiation. Serum-free medium [Fig. 5(D)], 5-BrdU [Fig. 5(E)], and X ray also induced neurite formation similar to that observed in mouse cells. Table 12 shows that sodium butyrate increased the cAMP level about twofold but that SFM, X ray, and 5-BrdU did not. Thus, as in mouse cells, the neurites in human NB cells can be induced by agents that do not change the intracellular level of cAMP. The control culture had an extremely low level of TH (5 ± 2.0 pmole/mg protein), but cells treated with dbcAMP (0.5 mmolar) and sodium butyrate (0.5 mmolar) had about 550 ± 102 and 72 ± 19 pmole/mg protein, respectively.

## CONCLUSION

The fact that dbcAMP also induces neurite formation in human neuro-blasts,[29] chick-embryo dorsal-root ganglion,[50] and mouse-embryo sensory ganglion[51] indicates that mouse NB cell culture is a pertinent model for a study of the neuronal differentiation. Among various agents that are known to induce some differentiated functions in mouse neuroblastoma cells in culture, cAMP is the only one which induces at least eight differentiated functions, some of which can be induced by agents that do not change the intracellular level of cAMP. Neurite formation and biochemical differentiation are independently regulated since one can be expressed in the absence of the other. The mechanism of cAMP-induced differentiation of NB cells remains to be elucidated.

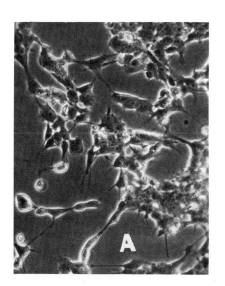
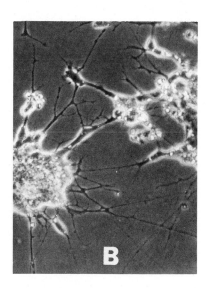
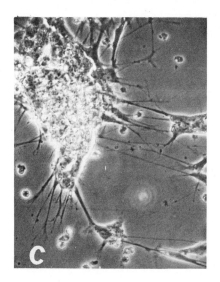
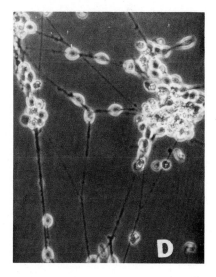

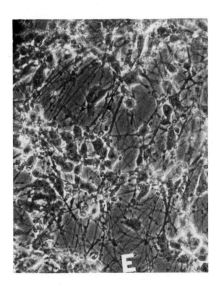

Fig. 5   Phase contrast photomicrographs of human neuroblastoma cells in culture (IMR-32 clone). Cells were plated in Falcon plastic dishes (60 mm); and papaverine (2.5 μg/ml), sodium butyrate (0.5 mmolar), SFM, and 5-BrdU (2.5 μmolar) were added individually 4 days after plating. The drug and medium were changed every 2 to 3 days, and the cultures were maintained for 10 to 13 days. The control culture (A) shows that cells grow in clumps and exhibit no spontaneous morphological differentiation (cytoplasmic processes greater than 50 μm in length). Papaverine-treated culture 10 days after treatment (B) shows the formation of extensive neurites. Many cell deaths occurred during this period. Sodium butyrate-treated culture 10 days after treatment (C) also shows the formation of extensive neurites. Some cell death occurred during this period. SFM-treated culture 3 days after treatment (D) and 5-BrdU-treated cultures 10 days after treatment (E) show extensive neurite formation.[46]

TABLE 12

EFFECT OF VARIOUS AGENTS ON THE LEVEL OF
CYCLIC AMP IN HUMAN NEUROBLASTOMA CELL
CULTURE

| Treatment* | cAMP level, pmole/mg protein ± S.D. |
|---|---|
| Control | 10 ± 1.8 |
| Sodium butyrate (1 mmolar), 3 days | 20 ± 3.0 |
| SFM, 3 days | 10 ± 1.4 |
| X ray (400 rads), 4 days | 9 ± 2.0 |

*Cells were plated in large Falcon plastic flasks (75 cm²). Sodium butyrate (1.0 mmolar) and SFM were added separately to the flasks 6 days after plating. At this time there were enough exponentially growing cells in each flask. Cells after specified periods of treatment were washed twice with PDS solution and then removed from the flask in PDS solution by shaking the flask surface. Cells were loosely attached to the flask surface and therefore came off with the above procedure. Cells were centrifuged, and 2 ml of 5% cold TCA was added. The cAMP level was determined according to the method of Gilman,[55] and the protein was determined according to the method of Lowry et al.[54] Each value represents an average of six samples.

## ACKNOWLEDGMENTS

This work was supported by U. S. Public Health Service grants NS-09230 and CA-12247. We thank H. Sheppard of Hoffman-La Roche, Inc., and J. E. Pike of The Upjohn Company for supplying R020-1724 and prostaglandin, respectively. We thank April Montgomery, Katrina Gilmer, and Marianne Gaschler for their technical help.

## REFERENCES

1. K. N. Prasad and A. W. Hsie, Morphological Differentiation of Mouse Neuroblastoma Cells Induced in vitro by Dibutyryl Adenosine 3',5'-Cyclic Monophosphate, *Nature (London) New Biol.,* **233**: 141-142 (1971).
2. K. N. Prasad, Morphological Differentiation Induced by Prostaglandin in Mouse Neuroblastoma Cells in Culture, *Nature (London) New Biol.,* **236**: 49-52 (1972).
3. K. N. Prasad and J. R. Sheppard, Inhibitors of Cyclic Nucleotide Phosphodiesterase Induced Morphological Differentiation of Mouse Neuroblastoma Cell Culture, *Exp. Cell Res.,* **73**: 436-440 (1972).
4. K. N. Prasad, S. Kumar, K. Gilmer, and A. Vernadakis, Cyclic AMP-Induced Differentiated Neuroblastoma Cells: Changes in Total Nucleic Acid and Protein Contents, *Biochem. Biophys. Res. Commun.,* **50**: 973-977 (1973).
5. J. C. Waymire, N. Weiner, and K. N. Prasad, Regulation of Tyrosine Hydroxylase Activity in Cultured Mouse Neuroblastoma Cells. Elevations Induced by Analogs of Adenosine 3',5'-Cyclic Monophosphate, *Proc. Nat. Acad. Sci. U.S.A.,* **69**: 2241-2242 (1972).
6. E. Richelson, Stimulation of Tyrosine Hydroxylase Activity in an Adrenergic Clone of Mouse Neuroblastoma by Dibutyryl Cyclic AMP, *Nature (London) New Biol.,* **242**: 175-177 (1973).
7. K. N. Prasad and B. Mandal, Choline Acetyltransferase Level in Cyclic AMP and X-Ray Induced Morphologically Differentiated Neuroblastoma Cells in Culture, *Cytobios,* **8**: 75-80 (1973).
8. K. N. Prasad and A. Vernadakis, Morphologic and Biochemical Study in X-Ray and Dibutyryl Cyclic AMP-Induced Differentiated Neuroblastoma Cells, *Exp. Cell Res.,* **70**: 27-32 (1972).
9. P. Furmanski, D. J. Silverman, and M. Lubin, Expression of Differentiated Functions in Mouse Neuroblastoma Mediated by Dibutyryl Cyclic Adenosine Monophosphate, *Nature,* **233**: 413-415 (1971).
10. K. N. Prasad, Cyclic AMP-Induced Differentiated Mouse Neuroblastoma Cells Lose Tumourgenic Characteristics, *Cytobios,* **6**: 163-166 (1972).
11. K. N. Prasad and K. N. Gilmer, Demonstration of Dopamine-Sensitive Adenylate Cyclase in Malignant Neuroblastoma Cells and Change in Sensitivity of Adenylate Cyclase to Catecholamines in "Differentiated" Cells, *Proc. Nat. Acad. Sci. U.S.A.,* in press.
12. N. W. Seeds, A. G. Gilman, T. Amano, and M. W. Nirenberg, Regulation of Axon Formation by Clonal Lines of a Neural Tumor, *Proc. Nat. Acad. Sci. U.S.A.,* **66**: 160-167 (1970).
13. J. R. Kates, R. Winterton, and K. Schlessinger, Induction of Acetylcholinesterase Activity in Mouse Neuroblastoma Tissue Culture Cells, *Nature,* **224**: 345-346 (1971).
14. D. Schubert and F. Jacob, 5-Bromodeoxyuridine-Induced Differentiation of a Neuroblastoma, *Proc. Nat. Acad. Sci. U.S.A.,* **67**: 247-254 (1970).
15. K. N. Prasad, Differentiation of Neuroblastoma Cells Induced in Culture by 6-Thioguanine, *Int. J. Cancer,* **12**: 631-635 (1973).

16. K. N. Prasad, K. Gilmer, and S. Kumar, Morphologically "Differentiated" Mouse Neuroblastoma Cells Induced by Non-Cyclic AMP Agents: Levels of Cyclic AMP, Nucleic Acid and Protein, *Proc. Soc. Exp. Biol. Med.,* **143:** 168-171 (1973).

17. K. N. Prasad, X-Ray-Induced Morphologic Differentiation of Mouse Neuroblastoma Cells in vitro, *Nature,* **234:** 471-474 (1971).

18. K. N. Prasad, Role of Cyclic AMP in the Differentiation of Neuroblastoma Cell culture, in *The Role of Cyclic Nucleotides in Carcinogenesis,* H. Gratzner and J. Schultz (Eds.) Proceedings of the Miami Winter Symposium, Vol. 6, pp. 207-237, Academic Press, Inc., New York, 1973.

19. K. N. Prasad and S. Kumar, Cyclic $3',5'$-AMP Phosphodiesterase Activity During Cyclic AMP-Induced Differentiation of Neuroblastoma Cells in Culture, *Proc. Soc. Exp. Biol. Med.,* **142:** 406-409 (1973).

20. J. R. Sheppard and K. N. Prasad, Cyclic AMP Levels and Morphological Differentiation in Mouse Neuroblastoma Cells, *Life Sci.,* **12:** 431-439 (1973).

21. A. Sakamoto and K. N. Prasad, Effect of DL-Glyceraldehyde on Mouse Neuroblastoma Cell Culture, *Cancer Res.,* **32:** 532-534 (1972).

22. K. N. Prasad, B. Mandal, J. C. Waymire, G. J. Lees, A. Vernadakis, and N. Weiner, Basal Level of Neurotransmitter Synthesizing Enzymes and Effect of Cyclic AMP Agents on the Morphological Differentiation of Isolated Neuroblastoma Clones, *Nature (London) New Biol.,* **241:** 117-119 (1973).

23. G. Augusti-Tocco and G. Sato, Establishment of Functional Clonal Lines of Neurons from Mouse Neuroblastoma, *Proc. Nat. Acad. Sci. U.S.A.,* **64:** 311-315 (1969).

24. K. N. Prasad and B. Mandal, Catechol-*o*-Methyltransferase Activity in Dibutyryl Cyclic AMP, Prostaglandin and X-Ray Induced Differentiated Neuroblastoma Cell Culture, *Exp. Cell Res.,* **74:** 532-535 (1972).

25. A. Blume, F. Gilbert, S. Wilson, J. Farber, R. Rosenberg, and M. W. Nirenberg, Regulation of Acetylcholinesterase in Neuroblastoma Cells, *Proc. Nat. Acad. Sci. U.S.A.,* **67:** 786-792 (1970).

26. A. Amano, E. Richelson, and M. Nirenberg, Neurotransmitter Synthesis by Neuro-blastoma Clones, *Proc. Nat. Acad. Sci. U.S.A.,* **69:** 258-263 (1972).

27. R. Prasad, N. Prasad, and K. N. Prasad, Esterase, Malate and Lactate Dehydrogenesis Activity in Murine Neuroblastoma, *Science,* **181:** 450-451 (1973).

28. J. G. Hardman, G. A. Robison, and E. W. Sutherland, Cyclic Nucleotides, *Ann. Rev. Physiol.,* **33:** 311-386 (1971).

29. E. H. Macintyre, J. P. Perkins, C. J. Wintersgill, and A. W. Vatter, The Responses in Culture of Human Tumor Astrocytes and Neuroblasts to $N^6O'_2$-Dibutyryl Adenosine $3',5'$-Cyclic Monophosphoric Acid., *J. Cell Sci.,* **11:** 639-667 (1971).

30. A. W. Hsie and T. T. Puck, Morphological Transformation of Chinese Hamster Cells by Dibutyryl Adenosine Cyclic $3',5'$-Monophosphate and Testosterone, *Proc. Nat. Acad. Sci. U.S.A.,* **68:** 358-361 (1971).

31. G. S. Johnson, R. M. Friedman, and J. Pastan, Restoration of Several Morphological Characteristics of Normal Fibroblasts in Sarcoma Cells Treated with Adenosine $3',5'$-Cyclic Monophosphate and Its Derivatives, *Proc. Nat. Acad. Sci. U.S.A.,* **68:** 425-429 (1971).

32. R. van Wijk, W. D. Wicks, and K. Clay, Effect of Derivatives of Cyclic $3',5'$-Adenosine Monophosphate on the Growth, Morphology and Gene Expression of Hepatoma Cells in Culture, *Cancer Res.,* **32:** 1905-1911 (1972).

33. J. R. Sheppard, Restoration of Contact-Inhibited Growth to Transformed Cells by Dibutyryl $3',5'$-Monophosphate, *Proc. Nat. Acad. Sci. U.S.A.,* **68:** 1316-1320 (1971).

34. A. Guidotti and E. Costa, Involvement of Adenosine $3',5'$-Monophosphate in the Activation of Tyrosine Hydroxylase Elicited by Drugs, *Science,* **179:** 902-904 (1973).

35. L. W. Lapham, Tetraploid DNA Content of Purkinje Neurons of Human Cerebellar Cortex, *Science,* **159**: 310-312 (1968).

36. J. W. Kebabian and P. Greengard, Dopamine-Sensitive Adenyl-Cyclase: Possible Role in Synaptic Transmission, *Science,* **174**: 1346-1349 (1971).

37. J. W. Kebabian, G. L. Petzold, and P. Greengard, Dopamine-Sensitive Adenylate Cyclase in Caudate Nucleus of Rat Brain and Its Similarity to the "Dopamine-Receptor," *Proc. Nat. Acad. Sci. U.S.A.,* **69**: 2145-2149 (1972).

38. J. H. Brown and M. H. Makman, Stimulation by Dopamine of Adenylate Cyclase in Retinal Homogenates and of Adenosine $3',5'$-Cyclic Monophosphate Formation in Intact Retina, *Proc. Nat. Acad. Sci. U.S.A.,* **69**: 539-543 (1972).

39. U. Ungerstedt, L. L. Butcher, S. G. Butcher, N. E. Andén, and K. Fuxe, Direct Chemical Stimulation of Dopaminergic Mechanisms in the Neostriatum of the Rat, *Brain Res.,* **14**: 461-471 (1969).

40. N. E. Andén, A. Rubenson, K. Fuxe, and T. Hökfelt, Evidence for Dopamine Receptor Stimulation by Apomorphine, *J. Pharm. Pharmacol.,* **19**: 627-629 (1967).

41. A. Carlsson and M. Lindquist, Effect of Chlorpromazine or Haloperidol on Formation of 3-Methoxytyramine and Normetanephrine in Mouse Brain, *Acta. Pharm. Toxicol.,* **20**: 140-144 (1963).

42. N. E. Andén, A. Dahlström, K. Fuxe, and K. Larsson, Functional Role of the Nigro-Neostriatal Dopamine Neurons, *Acta. Pharm. Toxicol.,* **24**: 263-274 (1966).

43. R. B. Clark and J. P. Perkins, Regulation of Adenosine $3',5'$ Cyclic Monophosphate Concentration in Cultured Human Astrocytoma Cells by Catecholamines and Histamine, *Proc. Nat. Acad. Sci. U.S.A.,* **68**: 2757-2760 (1971).

44. A. G. Gilman and M. Nirenberg, Effect of Catecholamines on the Adenosine $3',5'$-Cyclic Monophosphate Concentrations of Clonal Satellite Cells of Neurons, *Proc. Nat. Acad. Sci. U.S.A.,* **68**: 2165-2168 (1971).

45. K. N. Prasad, Effect of Dopamine and 6-Hydroxy-Dopamine on the Mouse Neuroblastoma Cells in vitro, *Cancer Res.,* **31**: 1457-1460 (1971).

46. K. N. Prasad and S. Kumar, Cyclic AMP and the Differentiation of Neuroblastoma Cells, in *Control of Proliferation in Animal Cells,* B. Clarkson and R. Baserga (Eds.), pp. 581-594, Cold Spring Harbor Laboratory, Cold Spring Harbor, N. Y., 1974.

47. B. Weiss, H. M. Shein, and R. Snyder, Adenylate Cyclase and Phosphodiesterase Activity of Normal and $SV_{40}$ Virus Transformed Hamster Astrocytes in Cell Culture, *Life Sci.,* **10**: 1253-1260 (1971).

48. M. J. Schmidt and G. A. Robison, Cyclic AMP, Adenyl Cyclase, and the Effect of Norepinephrine in the Developing Rat Brain, *Fed. Proc.,* **29**: 479 (1970).

49. K. N. Prasad, B. Mandal, and S. Kumar, Demonstration of Cholinergic Cells in Human Neuroblastoma and Ganglio Neuroma, *J. Pediat.,* **82**: 677-679 (1973).

50. F. J. Roisen, R. A. Murphy, M. E. Pichichero, and W. G. Braden, Cyclic Adenosine Monophosphate Stimulation of Axonal Elongation, *Science,* **175**: 73-74 (1972).

51. D. C. Hass, D. B. Hier, B. G. W. Aranson, and M. Young, On a Possible Relationship of Cyclic AMP to the Mechanism of Action of Nerve Growth Factor, *Proc. Soc. Exp. Biol. Med.,* **140**: 45-47 (1972).

52. J. P. Perkins and M. M. Moore, Adenylate Cyclase of Rat Cerebral Cortex, *J. Biol. Chem.,* **246**: 62-68 (1971).

53. G. Krishna, B. Weiss, and B. B. Brodie, A Simple Sensitive Method for the Assay of Adenyl Cyclase, *J. Pharmacol. Exp. Ther.,* **163**: 379-385 (1968).

54. O. H. Lowry, N. J. Rosebrough, A. L. Farr, and R. J. Randall, Protein Measurement with the Folin Phenol Reagent, *J. Biol. Chem.,* **193**: 265-275 (1951).

55. A. Gilman, A Protein Binding Assay for Adenosine $3',5'$-Cyclic Monophosphate, *Proc. Nat. Acad. Sci. U.S.A.,* **67**: 305-312 (1971).

# PERTURBATIONS OF CELLULAR KINETICS BY PHYSICAL AND CHEMICAL AGENTS

E. FRINDEL
Institut de Radiobiologie Clinique, INSERM, Institut Gustave-Roussy, Villejuif, France

Modifications caused by drugs and radiation, particularly effects on the duration of the cell cycle, the growth fraction, and the temporary blocks in the cycle, are studied. The consequences of these modifications and of selective killing lead to two types of phenomena: (1) A reassortment of the age distribution in the population studied. This reassortment is reflected by a semisynchronization of the cells. (2) Recruitment of quiescent cells. These phenomena must be taken into consideration when dealing with phase-dependent drugs because recruitment and synchronization occur not only in tissues to be eradicated but also in normal tissues. It is important to keep this in mind during fractionated treatments with physical or chemical agents.

Rational tumor therapy should depend on a thorough understanding of the kinetics of tumor growth, of the homeostatic mechanisms in critical normal tissues, and of the cell kinetics of critical normal tissues as well as on the specific effects of radiation and drugs on normal tissues. In the last decade techniques using labelled DNA precursors combined with autoradiography, cyto-photometry, mathematical models, cell synchronization, etc., made it possible to obtain information concerning the necessary parameters. Many of the drugs used in cancer therapy are phase dependent. Response to radiation is also cycle dependent but not as clearly as it is in the case of drugs.

Radiation and drugs synchronize cells of a heterogeneous population by selective killing of cells in particular phases of the cell cycle, mitotic delay, recruitment of quiescent cells, and triggering of homeostatic mechanisms. The exploitation of these effects and knowledge of the age distribution in a given population should make it theoretically possible to select combinations of drugs and radiotherapy at precise schedules to maximize the therapeutic effects and minimize the effects on normal tissues.

An ideal therapeutic agent should have a differential effect on tumor tissues and normal tissues. It should have cycle-dependent effects and/or effects on progress through the cell cycle in such a manner as to result in an accumulation of cells in the stage of the cell cycle most sensitive to the agent in the tumor. We shall consider two types of therapeutic agents: radiation and chemical drugs.

Kinetically the main effect of radiation is either cell death, or, if the dose is sublethal, a mitotic delay. Both of these phenomena result in cell synchronization, which should be taken into account when fractionated doses are delivered. Drugs are even more efficient in selective killing, and some chemotherapeutic agents block cells in the $G_1$ —S and S—$G_2$ transitions.

## SELECTIVE KILLING

Since the pioneering work of Terasima and Tolmach,[1] the radiosensitivity of a cell is known to vary throughout the cell cycle (Fig. 1). In vitro there are two

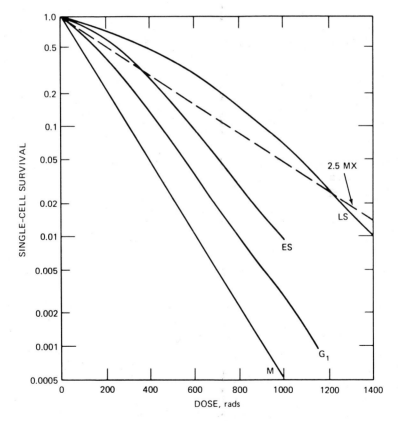

Fig. 1   Single-cell survival curves for chinese hamster cells obtained by mitotic selection plus HSA—$^3$HTdR. LS, late S. ES, early S. M, mitosis. 2.5 M, anoxic cells. [From W. K. Sinclair, Cyclic X-Ray Responses in Mammalian Cells in Vitro, *Radiat. Res.*, 33: 632 (1968).]

peaks of radioresistance in most cell lines, the early part of $G_1$ and the late part of S, and two peaks of sensitivity, at mitosis and at the $G_1-S$ transition. However, cells with a short $G_1$ phase do not show peak resistance characteristic of the $G_1$ phase. In vivo the cyclic effects of radiation were studied in mammals, but the results initially were not as clear as those found in vitro. However, the main features observed in mammalian cells in vitro, namely, radiosensitivity in mitosis and resistance in S, are also observed in vivo.

Thus, the overall radiosensitivity of a tissue will depend not only on the characteristics of the particular types of cells that constitute the tissue but also on the age distribution of these cells. Very few data are available on the effects on quiescent cells. These cells constitute an important proportion of the tumor population, and information on $G_0$ cells would be very valuable.

Most of the drugs used in cancer chemotherapy have even more selective effects than radiation has. Drugs such as hydroxyurea, cytosine arabinoside, and methotrexate are specific for the S phase as are most antimitotics. Alkylating agents are most effective on cells when exposed during mitosis.[2-6] Figure 2 summarizes the effects of some drugs on the various phases of the cell cycle.

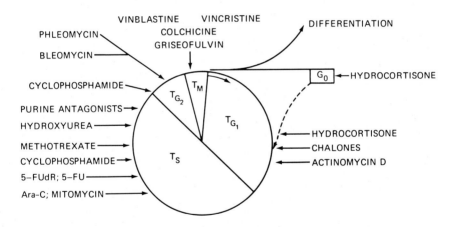

Fig. 2   Relation between action of drugs and phase of cell cycle [From H. O. Klein, Synchronization of Tumor Cell Proliferation and the Timing of Cytostatic Drugs, Rev. Eur. Etud. Clin. Biol., 17: 836 (1972).]

## DIVISION DELAY AND EFFECT ON THE DIFFERENT PHASES OF THE CELL CYCLE FOLLOWING IRRADIATION

In 1927 Canti and Spear[7] used chick tissue growing in culture to demonstrate that mitosis is delayed by ionizing radiation. The duration of the delay increases with increasing dose, and, contrary to the killing effects of radiation, it is not an all or none phenomenon. To study division delay, investigators try to identify the four phases of the cell cycle by autoradiography after administering a radioactive precursor of DNA for the S phase and to determine $G_1$ and $G_2$ phases by various methods of microdensitophotometry. The duration of mitotic delay is dose dependent (Fig. 3), as is the interval between irradiation and the minimum mitotic activity. At high doses the duration of the delay depends on the logarithm of the dose,[8] but at lower doses a linear relationship applies. With Chinese hamster cells Elkind, Han, and Volz[9] found a delay equivalent to 0.1 of the mean generation time per 100 rads. However, Yamada and Puck[10] have found a much longer delay with HeLa cells as did Caldwell[11] with mouse leukemic cells.

The duration of the mitotic delay of a given cell is also dependent on the phase of the cycle of that cell at the time of irradiation (Fig. 4). With 100 R

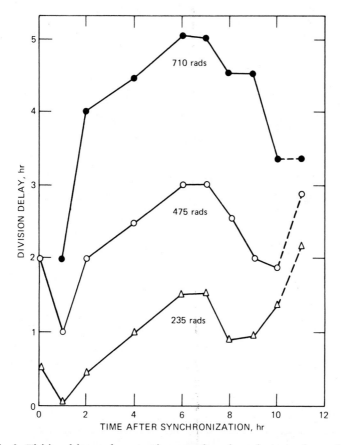

Fig. 3   Division delay vs. dose at various ages throughout the generation cycle. [From W. K. Sinclair, Sensitivity to Mitotic Delay and Stage in the Cycle, *Curr. Top. Radiat. Res.*, 7: 325 (1972).]

Puck and Yamada[12] were able to illustrate that the delay in mitosis in the HeLa S3 cells was approximately 0.1 min/rad for cells irradiated in $G_2$. Cells irradiated in S and $G_1$ were not immediately affected but showed a mitotic lag on reaching the $G_2$ stage.

Froese[13] and Yu and Sinclair[14] have shown that hamster cells have a small delay, ranging between about 0.1 min/rad in $G_1$ and an average of about 0.5 min/rad in S. HeLa cells studied by Terasima and Tolmach[15] and human kidney cells studied by Bootsma[16] have delays from about 0.1 min/rad in $G_1$ to about

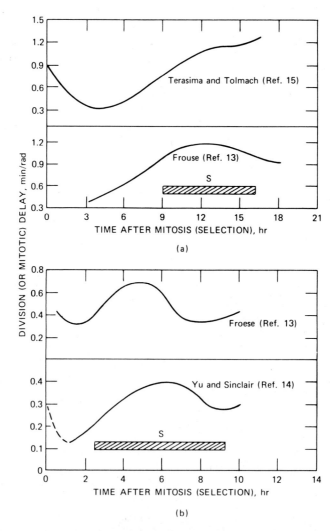

Fig. 4 Division (or mitotic) delay vs. age of the cell. (a) HeLa cells. (b) Hamster (V79) cells. (By Courtesy of W. K. Sinclair).

1 min/rad when irradiated in S. The longest delays were found by Dewey and Humphrey[17] and Whitmore, Till, and Gulyas[18] on L cells. When irradiated in $G_1$, these cells exhibited a delay of the order of 0.5 min/rad and, when irradiated in late S and $G_2$, 2 min/rad or more. Mak and Till[19] found that the block occurs immediately before mitosis and prevents cells from leaving $G_2$ to enter mitosis but allows cells initially in $G_1$ to enter S. Thus, when the last cell in $G_1$ has entered S, the increase in the percentage of labelled cells ceases. The cells initially in $G_2$ at the time of irradiation cannot enter S until the mitotic block is overcome.

Kim and Evans[20] studied mitotic delay on Ehrlich ascites tumor cells in vitro. The doses varied from 300 to 1000 rads. Their evidence for the prolongation of $G_2$ was the immediate reduction in mitotic activity. In cultured mouse leukemic (L5178Y) cells, Doida[21] observed that 200 rads of X rays induced a block in the middle of the $G_2$ phase. Little[22] studied the progression through the life cycle in very slowly proliferating cells. He observed a delay in the passage of cells from $G_1$ to S following exposures to doses as low as 10 rads, whereas doses of up to 1000 rads were without effect on rapidly growing cells. In synchronized Chinese hamster ovary cells,[23] the radiation-induced division delay increased exponentially with age between early—mid $G_1$ and late S—early $G_2$ from 0.29 min/rad to 0.8 min/rad, respectively. This delay increased linearly with dose at any phase of the cycle.

Walters and Petersen[24] examined division delay in terms of both time of onset and duration in several established mammalian cell lines. Their results indicated that onset of the delay is dose independent and that the duration of delay is proportional to dose in the range of 25—800 rads. Moreover, in contrast to work cited previously, they found that Chinese hamster cells are equally sensitive to division delay throughout their life cycle. Miller, Dewey, and Miller[25] irradiated synchronized Chinese hamster ovary (CHO) cells and found that after 300 rads of X rays, mitotic cells were delayed longer than early—mid $G_1$ cells and that delay then increased with cell age. A maximum division delay was found in late S in contrast to a minimum for cell killing and chromosome aberrations in that phase. In vivo studies have been done more rarely than in vitro. Odartchenko et al.[26] reported a mitotic delay in erythroblasts of the dog.

Ladinsky and Gruchow[27] showed that cells in $G_1$ are relatively insensitive and continue to progress through the generative cycle in estrogen-stimulated vaginal epithelium. Radiation reduces the rate of DNA synthesis, thus prolonging the S phase. There is no evidence of a radiation-induced $G_1$ to S block in this system. Frindel, Tubiana, and Vassort[28] found a block in $G_2$ after irradiation in mouse bone marrow with a dose of 250 rads of X rays. Ten hours after irradiation, the shape of the labelled mitosis curve shows a lengthening of the mean value of $G_2$ and a large fluctuation of its duration. Most of the cells that divide between 10 and 20 hr after irradiation were probably in $G_2$ during irradiation. About 15 hr after treatment, the mitotic index, after reaching very low values, overshoots probably owing to a reversal of the $G_2$ postirradiation block.

Sinclair[29] considers that mitotic delay seen after irradiation is the result of two processes, one indirect and one direct:

1. S-cell retention. After 710 rads Chinese hamster cells remain in S 2.5 hr longer than in controls. The rate of DNA synthesis is reduced and recovers slowly.

2. $G_2$ block. After 710 rads the total mitotic delay is about 5 hr, 2.5 hr of which are spent in $G_2$.

Sinclair suggests that cells are blocked in $G_2$ regardless of their position in the cell cycle when irradiated but that the duration of the block appears to be greater for cells nearest to $G_2$.

Cysteamine shortens division delay.[30] This protective effect is age dependent, and cysteamine is more efficient for cells irradiated during $G_2$ than for cells irradiated during S. The mechanism of division delay has been investigated by a number of workers. Bachetti and Sinclair[31] suggested that the block in division induced by X rays is due to interference with the synthesis of proteins necessary for division. In effect, protein synthesis is required during the delay period for cells to resume division. Moreover, ionizing radiation and inhibitors of protein synthesis induce comparable delays, and the two agents are additive in their effects.

Doida and Okada[21] observed that puromycin blocked cells in $G_2$ as did 200 rads of X rays; puromycin interfered with recovery from the mitotic block. They speculated that radiation-induced mitotic delay involves inhibition of protein synthesis. Walters and Petersen[24] suggest that the biochemical defect resulting in division delay is completely reversible and probably unrelated to the genetic effect responsible for cell death. Miller, Dewey, and Miller[25] observed that division delay was not increased by incorporating BUdR into the DNA, whereas BUdR increased mortality and chromosome aberrations. Grote and Revell[32] found that after 150 rads the radiation-induced mitotic delay in Syrian hamster cells was not related to the content of chromosome aberrations. On the other hand, the content of chromosome aberrations was directly related to the proliferating capacity of the cells.

Another difference between age response for survival and division delay is the fact that the latter is not influenced by the concentration of oxygen. These results tend to suggest that X-ray-induced division delay differs from that involved in chromosomal aberrations and cell killing.

In conclusion, the age response for division delay is different from that for survival. This suggests that the sites of action in the cell concerned with these two responses are different. It is possible that survival and division delay depend on each other but inversely. For instance, an S cell may survive well because it has a long delay before division during which damage can be repaired prior to expression.

## SYNCHRONIZATION OF CELLS

The combination of mitotic delay and selective killing of cells changes the age distribution of a given population and increases the cells in one of the phases of the cell cycle. We will call this phenomenon synchronization. This results in cyclic variations in radiosensitivity when fractionated doses are administered. In effect, this was found by acute lethality experiments in which mice were irradiated whole body with sublethal first doses, then with second doses at frequent intervals thereafter.[33,34] A cellular basis for these cyclic variations was provided by their similarity to the cyclic variations in the survival of mouse bone-marrow stem cells, assayed by spleen colonies, during two-dose irradiation treatments.[35] This was also shown by Rockwell and Kallman[35a] in mouse mammary tumors irradiated in vivo where cell survival was assayed in vitro. The cyclic pattern of cellular radiosensitivity persisted for about 40 hr. This periodicity was in agreement with that predicted for a synchronous cohort of surviving cells moving through the different states of radiosensitivity of the cell cycle. When solid mouse tumors were irradiated in situ, their clonogenic cells were found to describe a cyclic fluctuation in sensitivity to a second test dose[36] as determined by quantitative transplantation assay. Data suggestive of radiation-induced cyclicity in normal mouse epidermal cells have been provided by experiments on acute skin damage[37] and clonal growth of surviving cells.[38] Fluctuations in survival of intestinal crypt cells irradiated with split doses[39] are consistent with conditions based on cell-cycle and age—response data determined for these cells[40] (Fig. 5).

All systems, both normal and neoplastic, showed cyclic radiosensitivity variations that persisted for two or more cycles. This implies that such fluctuations are not short-term effects of theoretical interest only but that they may persist for days and therefore be of importance in clinical treatment, if the chronology is different for normal and neoplastic tissues.

Synchronization by chemotherapeutic agents has also been obtained.[41] The temporary inhibition of DNA replication by hydroxyurea and selective killing of cells in DNA synthesis have resulted in the modification of the age distribution of surviving cells. Bleomycine has also been used as a synchronizing agent for human tumor cells in vivo[6] because it delays the $S-G_2$ flow of cells. Klein[42] synchronized human tumor cells with vincristine. Others[43,44] synchronized human tumor cells with cytosine arabinoside, fluorouracil, or hydroxyurea.

## EFFECTS OF RADIATION AND DRUGS ON THE CELL CYCLE AND THE KINETICS OF CELL PROLIFERATION

Kinetics following irradiation or chemotherapy vary with the various characteristics of the tissue: cell turnover, which determines the rate at which

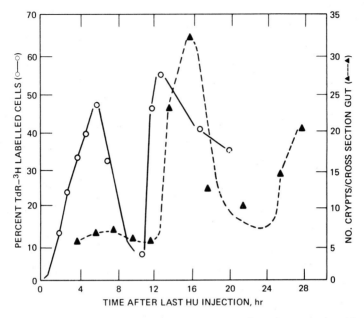

Fig. 5   Time relationship of intestinal crypt stem-cell synchrony produced by
HU and survival pattern following 1150 rads given at various intervals
following HU injections. [From E. L. Gillette, H. R. Withers, and I. F.
Tannock, *Radiology*, 96: 642 (1970).]

lesions appear, the eventual existence of several compartments in the tissue, and
mechanisms of homeostasis that are triggered by increased demands provoked by
cell death. The study of these effects is of paramount importance in
radiotherapy where fractionated doses are used for treatment.

In normal tissues cell depletion triggers homeostatic mechanisms that
hopefully compensate for damage when doses are sublethal and when the
intervals between iterative irradiations permit these mechanisms to operate. This
would be an ideal situation. In tumors the modification of cell-population
kinetics induced by each dose fraction will influence the response to the next
fraction. A high proportion of cells are in a condition of malnutrition and may
recover more slowly than the normal tissue. Moreover, homeostatic
mechanisms seem to exist in the tumor but may be less   efficient
than they are in normal tissues. Theoretically, the difference in the timing  of
compensating mechanisms in normal and neoplastic tissues should be useful in
scheduling therapy. Thus, in radiotherapy as well as in chemotherapy, two main
phenomena must be considered: cell synchronization of surviving cells and the
rate of repopulation of normal and neoplastic tissues.

Having discussed the synchronizing effects of physical and chemical agents,
we turn to the problem of repopulation. One may ask by what mechanism cell

repopulation is made possible and what is the signal received by the surviving stem cells as a consequence of a depletion of the maturation compartment. Perhaps there is a decrease in the concentration of chalones,[45] which play a role in the control of cell division. Another possibility would be the secretion of some stimulating factor by cells that are doomed to die. Whatever the signal may be, one of the consequences is an increase in the pool of dividing cells. This increase is due to a number of factors, some of which are an increase of the growth fraction, which is in turn a consequence of cell recruitment into cycle. A decrease in the rate of differentiation may also increase the pool of proliferating cells. Another response to the signal is the acceleration of proliferation of the surviving cells by shortening the cell cycle. The time sequence of these phenomena and the return to a normal status should be studied and compared with the events in tumors.

## Normal Tissues

The normal tissues that interest the therapist most are the renewal tissues in the body. These are made up of three main compartments:[46] the stem cells, the maturing cells, and the differentiated or functional cells. Proliferation of the tissue is due to the first two compartments, which are the only ones that divide.

The stem-cell compartment is self maintaining and responds to homeostatic mechanisms by varying its proliferation rate and its differentiation rate (Fig. 6). The size of the maturation compartment depends on the inflow from the stem-cell compartment, its own proliferation rate, and the outflow toward the differentiated compartment. It also responds to homeostatic mechanisms by modifying these variables. The functional compartment consists of cells with a finite life-span which are unable to divide. The modification of any one of these compartments triggers homeostasis to operate. We will consider three of these tissues: the intestinal epithelium, the skin, and the bone marrow.

### Intestine

Cell proliferation in the intestine occurs in the lower half of Lieberkühn's crypt, where the average cell-cycle time is about 10 hr in mice and rats.[46] After doses of acute irradiation, the steady state between cell production in the crypt and cell loss from the tips of the villi is disturbed by a block in the production of the proliferating cells as a result of mitotic delay and cell death. Morpho-

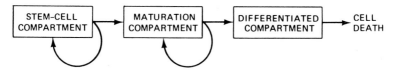

Fig 6   Three main compartments in normal renewal tissues.

logically, after doses of less than 800 rads,[47] cell production is gradually restored, and the crypts are repopulated within 72 to 84 hr after irradiation. After another 24 hr the villi also show a normal microscopic structure. Kinetically the number of mitoses in the crypt cells decrease. The duration of division delay is dose dependent. A gradual increase in the number of mitoses and labelled cells occurs from about 12 hr after irradiation. The pool of proliferating cells is extended at the expense of the maturing crypt-cell population. Thus, during repopulation the crypt cell obtains information to proliferate after 400 to 700 rads. The expansion of the proliferating pool is over by about 7 to 10 days, and normal cell kinetics are restored. The increase in the proliferating pool occurs between 36 to 48 hr after irradiation independent of the dose in conventional rats and between 60 to 72 hr in germ-free animals. The decrease in the maturation pool occurs 24 hr later in the germ-free animals than in the conventional animals. Since there is no difference in cell kinetics in the crypt or in the enzyme activities of the maturation pool in these two types of rats and since the migration rate is the same, we can conclude that the regulation of cell proliferation in the crypt is related to information from the functional villus cells.

To summarize, there is a speeding up of the proliferation rate of the lowest cells in the crypt. After acute irradiation[48] and after continuous irradiation,[49] a shortening of the cell-cycle time and a temporary extension of the zone of proliferation occur. Thus, more cells divide and at a faster rate during the regeneration period.

After local irradiation at 1000 rads of the rat ileum, Poulakos and Osborne[50] found the maximum recovery rate between 5 and 7 days after irradiation. Crypt cellularity decreased until a new steady state occurred in crypt cell population between days 17 and 21. It was an interesting observation that the adjacent shielded crypt (5 cm distal to RX segment) also underwent compensatory changes. There was an increase above normal values in the number of total and labelled cells though they were not as pronounced as in the recovering irradiated intestine. This was also found by Swift and Taketa[51] and Brandt.[52] Crypt regeneration following local intestinal irradiation in which the relative size of the proliferative compartment does not change contrasts with crypt regeneration following whole-body irradiation in which the entire crypt becomes a proliferative compartment.[47] In the latter case, since there is no undamaged intestine to take over function, each individual crypt must become entirely proliferative in order to accomplish recovery in the shortest possible time.

As for effects of drugs, the response of the small intestine to selective killing of proliferating cells by phase-specific drugs[53] did not cause gut failure. There seems to be therefore a sparing effect of noncyclic cells. The effects of hydroxyurea (HU) on duodenal crypt-cell kinetics of the $C_3H$ mouse were studied by Dethlefsen and Riley[54] and Gillette, Withers, and Tannock[40]

(Fig. 5). They observed an inhibition of DNA synthesis from 4 to 5 hr after a dose of 3 mg per gram of body weight. On recovery there was a definite synchronization of the duodenal crypt cells, which was still evident through the second post-HU mitotic phase. Duodenal recovery was accomplished by a shortening of the crypt-cell cycle and an increase in the size of the proliferating pool as after irradiation.

In conclusion, the results obtained suggest that the functional status of the intestine may be an important part of the mechanism regulating the kinetics of crypt regeneration that occurs after cell depletion either by radiation or drugs. A negative feedback control of crypt-cell proliferation by functional villus cells plays an important role. Whatever the mechanism, it seems that the depletion of the functional compartment is the signal for the proliferating compartment to divide at an increased rate.

### Stratified Squamous Epithelium

Two cellular compartments can be distinguished in the skin: the basal cells that proliferate and differentiate and give rise to the second compartment of differentiated, keratinized cells. In the normal epidermis there is a balance between cell production in the layer of the basal cells and the loss of keratinized cells from the surface. Devik reviewed the kinetics of normal skin after irradiation.[55] Irradiation has an immediate effect on the number of mitoses. The mitotic index in the skin of hairless mice following 50 to 1500 rads is illustrated in Fig. 7. After 1500 rads normal values were obtained at 4 to 6 days followed by an overshoot. When the labelling index was followed after this dose, an initial decrease of the proportion of labelled cells was observed followed by a dramatic overshoot at 5 to 8 days. Normal values in both the labelling index and mitotic index were reached by about 14 days. We can conclude from these results that initially cell production is considerably reduced and this is followed by increased production. The generation time is reduced when regeneration starts in a way comparable to that of intestinal epithelium. By split-dose methods[56] and cloning techniques,[57,58] it was established that at the 4th hour after irradiation with a few hundred rads,[57] the progression of cells in the mitotic cycle is resumed and that before the 24*th* hour the cells had time to terminate a cell cycle. Regeneration is then continued with a doubling of the number of basal cells every 24 hr. This is obtained in spite of the rate of differentiation, which is increased from 0.5 in the steady state to 0.75 during the phase of regeneration. More recently Denekamp[59] has shown that the dose increment necessary to counteract repopulation is different after 1, 2, or 3 weeks of daily irradiation. After 4 daily 300-rad fractions, there was no repopulation. After 9 fractions, 60 rads per day was required, and after 14 fractions about 100 to 150 rads per day was required. Repair of sublethal injury in the skin within 24 hr was the most important factor in tolerance to short-term fractionation. In extended fractionation the increased rate of proliferation was a factor equally important.

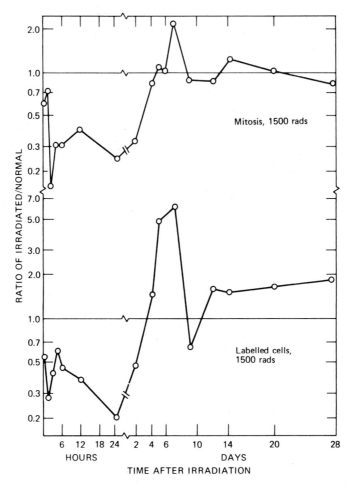

Fig. 7 Mitotic index and labelling index in irradiated epidermis of the hairless mouse. (From F. Devik, The Skin. Kinetics in Normal Skin After Irradiation and After Wounding, in Seminaire: La Cinétique de Prolifération Cellulaire, p. 225, INSERM, 1971.)

## Bone Marrow

The kinetics of proliferation of bone marrow during the regenerative phase after irradiation is more difficult to study than that of tissues of the intestine and the stratified squamous epithelium because the stem cells are not morphologically identified and are studied by cloning methods in recipient mice.[60] The kinetics of this compartment is limited to the study of cells in DNA synthesis.[61]

In the bone marrow the stem-cell compartment is quiescent, and hemopoiesis is maintained mostly by the maturation compartment in normal animals. The average cell-cycle time of this compartment was found to be 8 hr in mice.[28] Ten hours after 250 R a lengthening of the mean value of $G_2$ and a large fluctuation of its duration were found. About 15 hr after irradiation, the mitotic index, after reaching very low values, overshoots probably because of the reversal of the $G_2$ postirradiation block. Thirty-six hours after irradiation, which corresponds to about 4.5 cycles, the parameters of the generation cycle were almost back to normal, with a smaller fluctuation in the duration of $G_1$ and a shorter $G_2$ than in control marrow. The narrowing in the fluctuations of the duration of the cell cycle from one cell to another seems to be confirmed by the fact that the second wave of labelled mitoses is similar to the first wave, whereas in the normal mouse the second wave is quite different. This is also observed in the intestinal epithelium.

In the stem-cell compartment (CFU) of the mouse, 80 to 90% of the cells are quiescent[61] in $G_0$. After irradiation the proportion of stem cells in DNA synthesis increases, which indicates that a certain proportion of quiescent stem cells enters the mitotic cycle. The subsequent evolution of the number of stem cells depends on the rate of proliferation and of differentiation. If the latter increases, the number of CFU may decrease. This evolution depends on the scheme of irradiation. The proliferative activity of bone-marrow stem cells of mice was studied after single and multiple total or subtotal irradiation.[62] After single partial-body irradiation with 150 rads, the number of CFU in the shielded marrow, after a transitory decrease (which seems to be dose dependent), increases to a maximum at about 7 hr. The number of CFU in S increases at about 14 hr. This seems to indicate that the increase in the stem-cell pool is due to a delay in differentiation. The number of CFU in the circulating blood is reduced after partial-body irradiation with 150 rads and drops from 80 to 38 in 15 min. By comparing partial-body and whole-body irradiations, H. Croizat, E. Frindel, and M. Tubiana (unpublished) showed that CFU in circulation are produced by both the shielded zone and the irradiated one. During a course of subtotal daily irradiations, the number of stem cells in the shielded area decreases. This decrease is due to migration and accelerated differentiation. Accelerated differentiation was also found by Vos,[63] who studied the effects of one, two, and three doses of 440 rads on bone-marrow stem cells.

Using the method of numerating the stem cells by the exocolonizing assay, Byron[64] observed, after a dose of 150 rads, a recovery pattern characterized by a long postirradiation lag and dip lasting 4 to 6 days followed by a return to normal values by about the 14*th* to 16*th* day. A similar pattern of recovery was found by Blackett, Roylance, and Adams[65] in the repopulating capacity of rat femoral bone marrow after 200 rads.

To summarize, bone marrow responds to irradiation by mechanisms similar to those of other renewal systems, but, in addition, quiescent stem cells are triggered to divide and migrate in a more effective manner. Moreover, the rate of differentiation can be modulated in response to irradiation. The most striking fact is the rapidity with which bone marrow responds to both radiation and chemical drugs.

During antitumor chemotherapy the hematopoietic tissue is one of the most critical and most sensitive to the cytotoxic effects of drugs. This tissue limits the therapeutic possibilities of some active drugs. It is therefore of prime importance to study the effects of drugs on the kinetics of bone-marrow stem cells. In mice and rats these studies are possible in vivo with the Till and McCulloch techniques.[60] Human bone-marrow stem cells have thus far only been studied in vitro and differ from the murine cells in that they are already committed to the granulocytic series whereas the murine stem cells assessed are pluripotential in vivo or unipotential in vitro.

The administration in vivo of an antitumor drug can have certain effects at the stem-cell level:

1. Death of a certain proportion of cells. The chemosensitivity varies throughout the cell cycle, which results in selective killing of the cells in the sensitive phase of the cycle.

2. Block of cells in certain phases of the cell cycle. Certain drugs block the progression of cells through the cell cycle and especially at the frontier of $G_1 - S$. The cells are thus arrested for a few hours depending on the nature and the dose of the drug.

3. The recruitment of quiescent cells into the cycle.

4. The stimulation of the proliferative activity of surviving cells.

5. Lastly, as a consequence of these effects, there is a reassortment of the age-distribution of cells which results in a partial synchronization.

We studied[66] the effects of HU on stem cells in the mouse by the methods of Till and McCulloch[60] and determined their percentage in the DNA synthesis phase by the method of Becker et al.[61] These studies were carried out on two types of mice, the $C_3H$, which in our animal quarters have 20% of their CFU in the S phase, and the $C_{57}B1$, with virtually quiescent CFU. The comparison of these two types of stem-cell populations made it possible to study the relative importance of direct and indirect effects of HU on this cell compartment. The number of CFU decreases 3 hr after treatment, probably owing to an increased differentiation of the stem cells as a result of a homeostatic response to the depletion of the mature compartment or to some signal arriving from doomed cells. In the $C_{57}B1$ mice the proportion of cells in S, negligible in the controls, remains unmodified for several hours after the injection of HU. The percentage of cells in S then increases at about 7 hr after the injection and reaches its maximum at 12 hr. About half the quiescent cells enter the cycle simultaneously. After traversing the $G_1$ phase, they start synthesizing DNA synchronously. The stimulus that triggers the quiescent cells into cycle may be the same which accelerated the differentiation of the stem cells or may be a consequence of the depletion of the stem-cell compartment itself (Fig. 8).

When HU is administered to $C_3H$ mice, 20% of the CFU are killed since 20% of the cells are in DNA synthesis. Therefore, there is a decrease in the number of CFU from the first hour after the injection of the drug, and this decrease continues for a few hours owing to differentiation. The percentage of CFU in S decreases to zero immediately after HU administration and remains nil up to about 4 hr (Fig. 9). The fact that the number of CFU decreases before the increase in the proliferation of these cells indicates that differentiation precedes multiplication in cases of emergency. Thus it seems that depletion of the maturation compartment triggers CFU to differentiate because it is urgent to repopulate this compartment. The consequence of the accelerated differentiation is a depletion of the pool of CFU. When the number of CFU reaches a certain threshold, these cells are triggered to divide. This is in agreement with Boggs, Chervenick, and Boggs,[67] who state that when the CFU compartment is

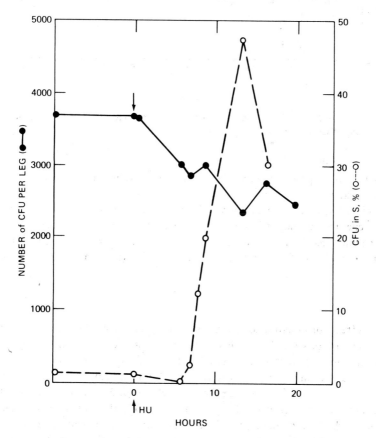

Fig. 8 Evolution of the number of CFU and the percent CFU in S after 10 mg of HU in $C_{57}Bl$ mice.

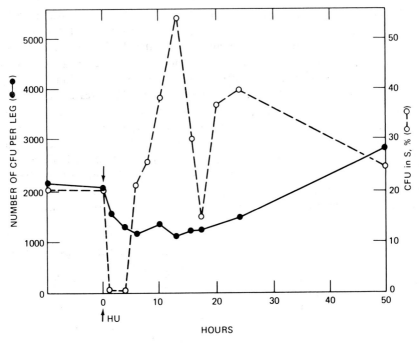

**Fig. 9  Evolution of the number of CFU and the percent CFU in S after 10 mg of HU in C₃H mice.**

reduced below approximately 10% of its size proliferation occurs without differentiation.

Radiotherapy and chemotherapy should try to exploit these various phenomena to minimize the effects of drugs and radiation on normal tissues while augmenting the effects on tumor cells. It is therefore important to try to use the eventual differences between the kinetics of normal and neoplastic tissues.

## Tumor

The effects of radiation and drugs on tumor cells must take into account the rate of division of cells after their temporary arrest and the modification of the growth fraction. These two factors will influence the rate of tumor growth after irradiation and chemotherapy. Using the NCTC fibrosarcoma in the ascites form, we[68] found a marked difference between the effects of 250 R on the cells of the young exponentially growing 4-day tumors and on the slow-growing 12-day tumors. In the 4-day tumors, the S phase is about twice normal at 20 hr after irradiation, and it decreases slightly by 48 hr. At this time the shape of the labelled mitosis curves seems to be going back to normal. There is no evidence of a block in $G_2$ after time intervals greater than 20 hr. Cytophotometric data do not show any pile-up of cells in $G_2$, but they do show a pile-up in $G_1$, which suggests a block in this phase. Forty-eight hours after irradiation, the importance of this block has decreased. The distribution of the duration of the cell cycle, $T_c$, shows that the model and the mean duration of $T_c$ are lengthened 20 hr and 48 hr after irradiation. In both cases, but especially at 20 hr, there is a noticeable proportion of cells with a $T_c$ longer than 50 hr.

In the 12-day tumors, the duration of the $G_2$ phase is noticeably increased 20 and 48 hr after irradiation. Cytophotometric data confirm the pile-up in $G_2$, whereas the proportion of cells in $G_1$ remains constant. When the effects of 250 R on young and old tumors are compared at equal cycle times after irradiation, i.e., 20 hr for the 4-day tumors and 48 hr for the 12-day tumors, there is still a marked difference between the effects on the respective cycles.

The same dose of radiation does not have the same effect on slowly growing tumors and rapidly growing tumors as far as the blocks in $G_2$ and $G_1$ are concerned. The recovery of the duration of the cell cycle is faster in young than in old tumors. This may be due to the different abilities of cells to repair some of the damage or to the fact that radiation does not have the same effect on cells in the different phases of the cycle. Using the NCTC fibrosarcoma in the solid form, Frindel, Vassort, and Tubiana[68] found that at 48 hr after 600 R the cell cycle was slightly reduced, whereas the S phase increased by about 30%. The $G_1$ phase was about 25% of the unirradiated value. The duration of the $G_2 + M$ phases was not changed (Fig. 10).

The difference in the response of the same cell type growing as a solid tumor and as an ascitic tumor underlines the importance of environmental factors. These results suggest that in the solid tumors, where there are zones of cells with longer cycle times, those cells may also exhibit a longer recovery time. Brown and Berry[69] found that in the tumors of the hamster cheek pouch 24 hr after an irradiation of 500 R there is a slight lengthening of the cell cycle owing to the elongation of $G_2 + M$ and to an increase in the variation in the length of the S phase among individual cells. Denekamp and Thomlinson,[70] working on four different experimental solid tumors, found that after a dose of 1000 to 1500 rads, the mean cell-cycle time remained unchanged. The growth fraction diminished only slightly. However, volume growth rates diminished, and this was attributed to a greater cell loss. In some other studies, a change in the cell cycle has been observed. Hermens[71] studied changes in tumor volume and cell kinetics of R-I rhabdomyosarcoma tumors after a single X-ray dose of 2000 rads. Changes in volume are shown in Fig. 11. The recurrent tumor regained a relative volume equal to 1 at about 12 to 14 days. The growth rate of the tumor increased gradually between days 8 and 14. In his study of the cell kinetic parameters of these tumors, Hermens[71] observed a reduction in cell-cycle time due to the absence of the $G_1$ phase. Subsequent lengthening of the cell-cycle time at day 14 in the tumor center results from reappearance of the $G_1$ phase. Sixteen days after a dose of 2000 rads to the NCTC fibrosarcoma of

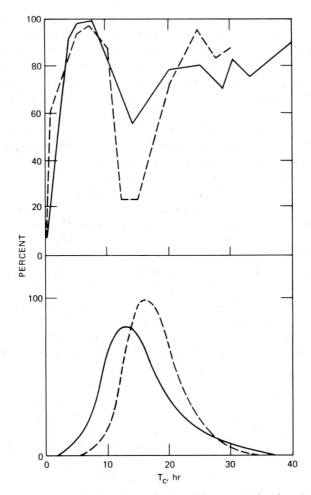

**Fig. 10   Cell cycle of NCTC fibrosarcoma solid tumor 48 hr after 600 rads.
—, 48 hr after 600 rads. - - -, no irradiated tumors.**

the mouse, during recurrence of tumor growth, the average volume doubling time was shorter than in controls. This was due to an increase in the growth fraction since there was no change in the cell-cycle time after irradiation.[72] Hermens' results suggest that the growth fraction increases in the central part of the tumor. However, the autoradiographic methods he used at that time could not distinguish between viable and doomed cells. Barendsen,[72a] using the cloning methods in vitro, showed that the rate of proliferation of clonogenic cells increases after a lag period of 2 days subsequent to 1000 to 2000 rads. When the tumor reaches its original size, the growth rate of the tumor decreases.

We can conclude that in many experimental tumors the rate of proliferation is increased after irradiation. This increase is dose dependent and persists after

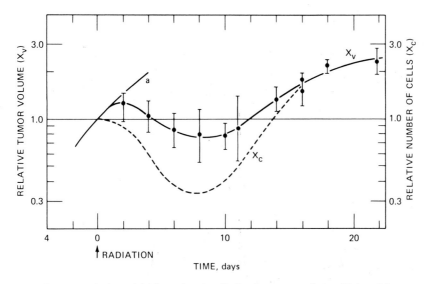

Fig. 11   Variation with time after irradiation in tumor volume ($X_V$) and in total number of cells ($X_c$). Curve a represents the growth of unirradiated controls. (From A. F. Hermens, Variations in the Cell Kinetics and the Growth Rate in an Experimental Tumour During Natural Growth and After Irradiation, Thesis, Radiobiologisck Instituut, Rijswijk, Netherlands, 1973.)

multiple doses of radiation. The delay between radiation and increased proliferation varies from one tumor to another and in different zones of the same tumor. The degree of acceleration varies with time. It decreases progressively and stops when the number of viable cells returns to the original number. The acceleration of cell proliferation and recruitment of cells have also been observed after chemotherapy. Skipper[73] found that after administration of cytoxan in a plasmocytoma of the hamster, the doubling time of clonogenic cells was 0.53 day during the repopulation period as compared to 3 days in the controls. Rajewsky[74] induced synchronization of a carcinoma of the rat, and Madoc-Jones and Mauro[75] were able to synchronize a lymphoma of the mouse. In the carcinoma the maximum of cells in S appeared 7 to 8 hr after HU injection, and in the lymphoma it appeared 15 hr after drug administration. Thus, after HU injection, a cohort of CFU of the marrow enter DNA synthesis every 12 hr; cells of the carcinoma of the rat have about the same rhythm, and the lymphoma of the mouse enters DNA synthesis every 16 hr (Fig. 12).

All these studies have been done on experimental tumors, and little information on spontaneous animal tumors is available. Little work on human tumors has thus far been reported. Rambert et al.,[76] Van Peperzeel,[77] and Malaise et al.[78] have found an acceleration of the rate of growth after irradiation in pulmonary and in skin metastases.

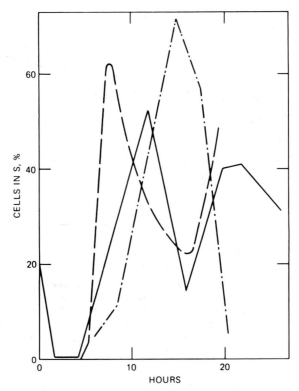

Fig. 12  Comparison  of  effects  of  HU  on  bone  marrow.  ——  CFU.  - - -,
carcinoma.  — · —, lymphoma.

After  chemotherapy  Ernst,  Faille,  and  Killman[79]  found  that  cytosine
arabinoside  injected  into  patients  with  acute  myeloid  leukemia  recruited
quiescent  cells  into  cycle.  This  phenomenon  has  also  been  observed  by  Griswold
et  al.,[80]  Gabbutti  et  al.,[81]  Van  Putten,[82]  Lampkin,  Nagao,  and  Mauer,[83]  and
Pouillard  et  al.[84]  It  is  evident  that  surviving  tumor  cells  respond  to  treatment  by
modifying  their  kinetic  parameters.  The  mechanism  of  homeostasis  may  be
similar  to  that  found  in  normal  tissues,  but  it  seems  to  be  slower  and  less
efficient.

It  seems  that  theoretically  a  differential  effect  on  tumor  tissues  and  normal
tissues  can  be  obtained  when

(1) The  bone-marrow  stem  cells  are  quiescent  and  tumor  cells  are  in  cycle.
This  situation  occurs  when  the  first  dose  of  drug  is  administered.

(2) Bone-marrow  stem cells,  as  well  as  cells  in  the  other  renewal  systems,  turn
back  to  their  quiescent  state  following  intensive  proliferation  due  to  restoration.
In  effect,  it  seems  that  after  chemotherapy,  as  well  as  after  radiotherapy,  the
period  of  active  proliferation  in  tumors  is  of  a  longer  duration  than  it  is  in
normal  tissues.

Since repopulation kinetics of tumors vary with each tumor type, it seems that fractionation of treatment can be based more easily on data obtained with normal tissues that one wishes to protect.

Thus, theoretically, by studying the kinetic parameters of normal and neoplastic tissues and by exploiting the differences in the timing of synchronization and repopulation of these two types of tissues, we should be able to improve schedules for chemotherapy and radiotherapy.

In conclusion, in spite of the pessimistic remarks of Hall,[85] who states that "cell kinetics has been a relatively unproductive area and shows little sign of changing this position," we must admit that cell kinetics have clarified our understanding of homeostatic processes and may contribute to better cancer therapy.

## REFERENCES

1. T. Terasima and L. J. Tolmach, Changes in X-Ray Sensitivity of HeLa Cells During the Division Cycle, *Nature,* **190**: 1210-1211 (1961).
2. F. Mauro and H. Madoc-Jones, Age Responses of Cultured Mammalian Cells to Cytotoxic Drugs, *Cancer Res.,* **30**: 1397-1408 (1970).
3. S. Bacchetti and G. F. Whitmore, Actinomycin D and X-Ray Sensitivity in Synchronized Mouse L-Cells, *Radiat. Res.,* **31**: 577-578 (1967).
4. F. L. Graham and G. F. Whitmore, Studies in Mouse L-Cells on the Incorporation of 1-β-D-Arabino-Furanosycytosine into DNA and on Inhibition of DNA Polymerase by 1-β-D-Arabinofuranosyl-Cytosine-S'-Triphosphate, *Cancer Res.,* **30**: 2636-2644 (1970).
5. B. Djordjevic and J. H. Kim, Different Lethal Effects of Mitomycin D and Actinomycin D During the Division Cycle of HeLa Cells, *J. Cell Biol.,* **38**: 477-483 (1968).
6. S. C. Barranco, J. K. Luce, M. M. Romsdahl, and R. M. Humphrey, Bleomycin as a Possible Synchronizing Agent for Human Tumor Cells In Vivo, *Cancer Res.,* **33**: 882-887 (1973).
7. R. G. Canti and F. G. Spear, The Effect of Gamma Irradiation on Cell Division in Tissue Culture In Vitro, *Proc. Roy. Soc. (London), Ser. B,* **102**: 92 (1927).
8. D. O. Schneider and G. F. Whitmore, Comparative Effects of Neutrons and X-Rays on Mammalian Cells, *Radiat. Res.,* **18**: 286-306 (1963).
9. L. Elkind, A. Han, and K. W. Volz, Radiation Response of Mammalian Cells Grown in Culture. IV. Dose Dependence of Division Delay and Post-Irradiation Growth of Surviving and Non-Surviving Chinese Hamster Cells, *J. Nat. Cancer Inst.,* **30**: 705-721 (1963).
10. M. M. Yamada and T. T. Puck, Action of Radiation on Mammalian Cells. IV. Reversible Mitotic Lag in the $S_3$ HeLa Cells Produced by Low Doses of X-Rays, *Proc. Nat. Acad. Sci. U. S. A.,* **47**: 1181-1191 (1961).
11. W. L. Caldwell, L. F. Lamerton, and D. K. Bewley, Increased Sensitivity of In Vitro Murine Leukemia Cells to Fractionated X-Rays and Fast Neutrons, *Nature,* **208**: 168-170 (1965).
12. T. T. Puck and M. A. Yamada, Chromosomal Dynamics in Irradiated Mammalian Cells, *Radiat. Res.,* **16**: 589 (1962).
13. G. Froese, Division Delay in HeLa Cells and Chinese Hamster Cells. A Time-Lapse Study, *Int. J. Radiat. Biol.,* **10**: 353-367 (1966).
14. C. K. Yu and W. K. Sinclair, Division Delay and Chromosomal Aberrations Induced by X-Rays in Synchronized Chinese Hamster Cells In Vitro, *J. Nat. Cancer Inst.,* **39**: 619-632 (1967).

15. T. Terasima and L. J. Tolmach, Variations in Several Responses of HeLa Cells to X-Irradiation During the Division Cycle, *Biophys. J.,* **3**: 11(1963).

16. D. Bootsma, Mitotic Delay of Human Cells in Tissue Culture Irradiated at Different Phases of the Generation Cycle, in Progress in Radiobiology, 11*th* International Congress of Radiology, Rome, Sept. 24, 1965, p. 1404, Excerpta Medica Foundation, New York, 1967.

17. W. C. Dewey and R. M. Humphrey, Relative Radiosensitivity of Different Phases in the Life Cycle of L-P59 Mouse Fibroblasts and Ascites Tumor Cells, *Radiat. Res.,* **16**: 503-530 (1962).

18. G. F. Whitmore, J. E. Till, and S. Gulyas, Radiation Induced Mitotic Delay in L Cells, *Radiat. Res.,* **30**: 155-171 (1967).

19. S. Mak and J. E. Till, The Effects of X-Rays on the Progress of L Cells Through the Cell Cycle, *Radiat. Res.,* **20**: 600-618 (1963).

20. J. H. Kim and T. C. Evans, Effects of X-Irradiation on the Mitotic Cycle of Ehrlich Ascites Tumor Cells, *Radiat. Res.,* **21**: 129-143 (1964).

21. Y. Doida and S. Okada, Radiation-Induced Mitotic Delay in Cultured Mammalian Cells, *Radiat. Res.,* **38**: 513-529 (1969).

22. J. B. Little, Irradiation of Primary Human Amnion Cell Cultures: Effects on DNA Synthesis and Progression Through the Cell Cycle, *Radiat. Res.,* **44**: 674-699 (1970).

23. D. B. Leeper, M. H. Schneiderman, and W. C. Dewey, Radiation-Induced Division Delay in Synchronized Chinese Hamster Ovary Cells in Monolayer Culture, *Radiat. Res.,* **53**: 326-337 (1973).

24. R. A. Walters and D. F. Petersen, Radiosensitivity of Mammalian Cells. I. Timing and Dose-Dependence of Radiation-Induced Division Delay, *Biophys. J.,* **8**: 1475-1486 (1968).

25. D. R. Miller, W. C. Dewey, and H. H. Miller, X-Ray-Induced Delay in the Chinese Hamster Cell-Cycle: Dependence on Phase Irradiated Under Different Culturing Conditions, BuDR Incorporation and Hypertonic Treatment, *Int. J. Radiat. Biol.,* **23**: 591-602 (1973).

26. N. Odartchenko, H. Cottier, L. E. Feinendegen, and P. V. Bond, Mitotic Delay in More Mature Erythroblasts of the Dog, Induced In Vivo by Sublethal Doses of X-Rays, *Radiat. Res.,* **21**: 413-422 (1964).

27. J. L. Ladinsky and H. W. Gruchow, The Effects of Irradiation on the Generative Cycle of the Estrogen Stimulated Vaginal Epithelium, *Cell Tissue Kinet.,* **3**: 175-184 (1970).

28. E. Frindel, M. Tubiana, and F. Vassort, Generation Cycle of Mouse Bone Marrow, *Nature,* **214**: 1017-1018 (1967).

29. W. K. Sinclair, Cell Cycle Dependence of the Lethal Radiation Response in Mammalian Cells, *Curr. Top. Radiat. Res.,* **7**: 264-285 (1972).

30. C. K. Yu and W. K. Sinclair, Protection by Cysteamine Against Mitotic Delay and Chromosomal Aberrations Induced by X-Rays in Synchronized Chinese Hamster Cells, *Radiat. Res.,* **43**: 357-371 (1970).

31. S. Bachetti and W. K. Sinclair, The Effects of X-Rays on the Synthesis of DNA, RNA, and Proteins in Synchronized Chinese Hamster Cells, *Radiat. Res.,* **45**: 598-612 (1971).

32. S. J. Grote and S. H. Revell, Mitotic Delay in Syrian Hamster Cells in Relation to Chromosome Aberrations, *Curr. Top. Radiat. Res.,* **7**: 334-335 (1972).

33. R. F. Kallman and G. Silini, Recuperation from Lethal Injury by Whole-Body Irradiation. I. Kinetic Aspects and the Relationship with Conditioning Dose in $C_{5\,7}B1$ Mice, *Radiat. Res.,* **22**: 622-642 (1964).

34. R. F. Kallman, G. Silini, and H. M. Taylor, Recuperation from Lethal Injury by Whole-Body Irradiation. II. Kinetic Aspects in Radiosensitive Balb/c Mice, and Cyclic Fine Structure During the Four Days After Conditioning Irradiation, *Radiat. Res.,* **29**: 362-394 (1966).

35. E. Frindel, F. Charruyer, M. Tubiana, H. S. Kaplan, and E. L. Alpen, Radiation Effects on DNA Synthesis and Cell Division in the Bone Marrow of the Mouse, *Int. J. Radiat. Biol.*, **11**: 435-443 (1966).

35a. S. Rockwell and R. Kallman, Cellular Radiosensitivity and Tumor Radiation Response in the EMT$_6$ Tumor Cell System, *Radiat. Res.*, **53**: 281 (1973).

36. R. F. Kallman and N. M. Bleehen, Post-Irradiation Cyclic Radiosensitivity Changes in Tumors and Normal Tissues, in Proceedings of a Symposium on Dose Rate in Mammalian Radiation Biology, April 29—May 1, 1968, D. G. Brown, R. G. Cragle, T. R. Noonan (Eds.), USAEC Report CONF-680410, UT-AEC Agricultural Laboratory, Oak Ridge, Tenn., July 12, 1968.

37. J. Denekamp, M. M. Ball, and J. F. Fowler, Recovery and Repopulation in Mouse Skin as a Function of Time After X-Irradiation, *Radiat. Res.*, **37**: 361-370 (1969).

38. H. R. Withers, Recovery and Repopulation In Vivo by Mouse Skin Epithelial Cells During Fractionated Irradiation, *Radiat. Res.*, **32**: 227-239 (1967).

39. H. R. Withers and M. M. Elkind, Radiosensitivity and Fractionation Response of Crypt Cells of Mouse Jejunum, *Radiat. Res.*, **38**: 598-623 (1969).

40. E. L. Gillette, H. R. Withers, and I. F. Tannock, The Age Sensitivity of Epithelial Cells of Mouse Small Intestine, *Radiology*, **96**: 639-643 (1970).

41. M. F. Rajewsky, Synchronization In Vivo: Kinetics of Mammalian Cell Populations Following Blockage of DNA Synthesis with Hydroxyurea, p. 68, Abstract, 2nd Meeting European Study Group for Cell Proliferation (ESGCP), Schloss Reisensburg, Germany, 1968.

42. H. O. Klein, K. J. Lennartz, and R. Gross, Investigation on Cell Kinetics and the Possibility of Synchronization of Lymphoreticular Tumor Cells, Its Importance for Cytostatic Treatment, Abstract Volume, p. 10, 3rd International Congress of Lymphology, Aug. 27—Sept. 1, 1970, Brussels, 1970.

43. P. Kissel, A. Duprez, and M. Bessot, Essais de Synchronization in Vivo de la Synthèse de l'ADN de Cellules Malignes Humaines par le 5-Fluoro-Uracile. Etude Autohisto-radiographique, *C.R. Acad. Sci. Ser. D*, **262**: 2558 (1966).

44. A. M. Mauer, B. C. Lampkin, and T. Nagao, Prospects for New Directions in Therapy of Acute Lymphoblastic Leukemia, in *Hemopoietic Cellular Proliferation*, p. 260, Grune & Stratton, Inc., New York, 1970.

45. W. S. Bullough and E. B. Laurence, Mitotic Control by Internal Secretion: The Role of the Chalone-Adrenaline Complex, *Exp. Cell Res.*, **33**: 176-194 (1964).

46. L. F. Lamerton, Cell Proliferation and the Differential Response of Normal and Malignant Tissues, *Brit. J. Radiol.*, **45**: 161-170 (1972).

47. H. Galjaard, Cellular Kinetics in Normal Intestine and After Acute X-Irradiation, in Seminaire sur la Cinétique de Proliferation Cellulaire, pp. 217-223, INSERM, 1971.

48. S. Lesher, A. Sallese, and M. Jones, Effects of 1000 R Whole-Body X-Irradiation on DNA and Mitosis in Duodenal Crypts of the BCF-1 Mouse, *Z. Zellforsch. Mikroskop. Anat.*, **77**: 144-146 (1967).

49. A. B. Cairnie, Cell Proliferation Studies in the Intestinal Epithelium of the Rat; Response to Continuous Irradiation, *Radiat. Res.*, **32**: 240-264 (1967).

50. L. Poulakos and J. W. Osborne, The Kinetics of Cellular Recovery in Locally X-Irradiated Rat Ileum, *Radiat. Res.*, **53**: 402-413 (1973).

51. M. N. Swift and S. T. Taketa, Modification of Acute Intestinal Radiation Syndrome Through Shielding, *Amer. J. Physiol.*, **185**: 85-91 (1956).

52. K. B. Brandt, Migration Rates of Duodenal Epithelial Cells After X-Irradiation of Exteriorized Jejunum and Ileum, M. S. Thesis, State University of Iowa, Iowa City, Iowa, 1971.

53. H. E. Skipper and F. M. Schabel, Quantitative and Cytokinetic Studies in Experimental Tumor Models, in *Cancer Medicine,* J. F. Holland and E. Frei, III (Eds.), Lea and Febiger, Philadelphia, in press.

54. L. A. Dethlefsen and R. M. Riley, Hydroxyurea Effects in the $C_3H$ Mouse. I. Duodenal Crypt Cell Kinetics, *Cell Tissue Kinet.,* **6**: 3-16 (1973).

55. F. Devik, The Skin. Kinetics in Normal Skin, After Irradiation, and After Wounding, in Seminaire: La cinétique de Prolifération Cellulaire, pp. 225-251, INSERM, 1971.

56. J. Denekamp, M. M. Ball, and J. F. Fowler, Recovery and Repopulation in Mouse Skin as a Function of Time After X-Irradiation, *Radiat. Res.,* **37**: 361-370 (1969).

57. H. R. Withers, Recovery and Repopulation In Vivo by Mouse Skin Epithelial Cells During Fractionated Irradiation, *Radiat. Res.,* **32**: 227-239 (1967).

58. E. W. Emery, J. Denekamp, M. M. Ball, and S. Field, Survival of Mouse Skin Epithelial Cells Following Single and Divided Doses of X-Rays, *Radiat. Res.,* **41**: 450-466 (1970).

59. J. Denekamp, Changes in the Rate of Repopulation During Multifraction Irradiation of Mouse Skin, *Brit. J. Radiol.,* **46**: 381-387 (1973).

60. J. E. Till and E. A. McCulloch, A Direct Measurement of the Radiation Sensibility of Normal Mouse Bone Marrow Cells, *Radiat. Res.,* **14**: 213-222 (1961).

61. A. J. Becker, E. A. McCulloch, L. Siminovitch, and J. E. Till, The Effect of Differing Demands for Blood Cell Production on DNA Synthesis by Hemopoietic Colony Forming Cells of Mice, *Blood,* **26**: 296-308 (1965).

62. H. Croizat, E. Frindel, and M. Tubiana, Proliferative Activity of the Stem Cells in the Bone-Marrow of Mice After Single and Multiple Irradiations (Total or Partial-Body Exposure), *Int. J. Radiat. Biol.,* **18**: 347-358 (1970).

63. O. Vos, Stem Cell Renewal in Spleen and Bone-Marrow of Mice After Repeated Total-Body Irradiations, *Int. J. Radiat. Biol.,* **22**: 41-50 (1972).

64. J. W. Byron, Recovery of the Erythropoietin Sensitive Stem-Cell Population Following Total Body X-Irradiation, in *Effects of Radiation on Cellular Proliferation and Differentiation,* Symposium Proceedings, Monaco, Apr. 1–5, 1968, pp. 173-185, International Atomic Energy Agency, Vienna, 1968 (STI/PUB/186).

65. N. M. Blackett, P. J. Roylance, and K. Adams, Studies of the Capacity of Bone-Marrow Cells to Restore Erythropoiesis in Heavily Irradiated Rats, *Brit. J. Haematol.,* **10**: 453-467 (1964).

66. F. Vassort, M. Winterholer, E. Frindel, and M. Tubiana, Kinetic Parameters of Bone-Marrow Stem Cells Using In Vivo Suicide by Tritiated Thymidine or by Hydroxyurea, *Blood,* **41**: 789-795 (1973).

67. S. S. Boggs, P. A. Chervenick, and D. R. Boggs, The Effect of Post-Irradiation Bleeding or Endotoxin on Proliferation and Differentiation of Hematopoietic Stem Cells, *Blood,* **40**: 375-388 (1972).

68. E. Frindel, F. Vassort, and M. Tubiana, Effects of Irradiation on the Cell Cycle of an Experimental Ascites Tumor of the Mouse, *Inter. J. Radiat. Biol.,* **17**: 329-337 (1970).

69. J. M. Brown and R. J. Berry, Effects of X-Irradiation on Cell Proliferation in Normal Epithelium and in Tumors of the Hamster Cheek Pouch, in *Effects of Radiation on Cellular Proliferation and Differentiation,* Symposium Proceedings, Monaco, Apr. 1–5, 1968, pp. 475-488, International Atomic Energy Agency, Vienna, 1968 (STI/PUB/186).

70. J. Denekamp and R. H. Thomlinson, The Cell Proliferation Kinetics of Four Experimental Tumors After Acute X-Irradiation, *Cancer Res.,* **31**: 1279-1284 (1971).

71. A. F. Hermens, Variations in the Cell Kinetics and the Growth Rate in an Experimental Tumour During Natural Growth and After Irradiation, Thesis, Radiobiologisch Instituut, Rijswijk, Netherlands, 1973.

72. E. Malaise and M. Tubiana, Croissance des Cellules d'un Fibrosarcome Expérimental Irradié Chez la Souris $C_3H$, *C.R. Acad. Sci., Ser. D,* **263**: 292-295 (1966).

72a. G. W. Barendsen and J. J. Brevevr, Experimental Radiotherapy of Rat Rhabdomyo-sarcoma, *Eur. J. Cancer,* **5**: 313 (1969).

73. H. E. Skipper, Kinetic Behavior Versus Response to Chemotherapy, *Nat. Cancer Inst. Monogr.,* **34**: 2-14 (1971).

74. M. F. Rajewsky, Synchronization In Vivo: Kinetics of a Malignant Cell System Following Temporary Inhibition of DNA Synthesis with Hydroxyurea, *Expt. Cell Res.,* **60**: 269-276 (1970).

75. H. Madoc-Jones and F. Mauro, Age-Response to X-Rays, Vinca Alkaloids and Hydroxyurea of Murine Lymphoma Cells Synchronized In Vivo, *J. Nat. Cancer Inst.,* **45**: 1131 (1970).

76. P. Rambert, E. Malaise, A. Laugier, M. Schlienger, and M. Tubiana, Données sur la Vitesse de Croissance des Tumeurs humaines, *Bull. Cancer,* **55**: 323-342 (1968).

77. H. A. Van Peperzeel, Effects of Single Doses of Radiation on Lung Metastase in Man and Experimental Animals, *Eur. J. Cancer,* **8**: 665-675 (1972).

78. E. Malaise, A. Charbit, N. Chavaudra, F. F. Combes, J. Douchez, and M. Tubiana, Changes in Volume of Irradiated Human Metastases, *Brit. J. Cancer,* **26**: 43-52 (1972).

79. P. Ernst, A. Faille, and S. A. Killman, Perturbation of Cell Cycle of Human Leukemia Myeloblasts In Vivo by Cytosine Arabinoside, *Scand. J. Haematol.,* **10**: 209-218 (1973).

80. D. P. Griswold, F. M. Schabel, W. S. Wilcox, L. Simpson-Herren, and H. E. Skipper, Success and Failure in the Treatment of Solid Tumors, *Cancer Chemother. Rep.,* **52**: 345-387 (1968).

81. J. V. Gabbutti, A. Pilert, R. P. Tarocco, F. Gavosto, and E. H. Cooper, Proliferative Potential of Out-of-Cycle Leukemia Cells, *Nature,* **224**: 375-376 (1969).

82. L. M. Van Putten, Recruitment, a Two-Sided Sword in Cancer Chemotherapy, *Bull. Cancer,* **60**: 131 (1973).

83. B. C. Lampkin, T. Nagao, and A. M. Mauer, Synchronisation and Recruitment in Acute Leukemia, *J. Clin. Invest.,* **50**: 2204-2214 (1971).

84. P. Pouillard et al., Essai clinique de Combinaisons chimiothérapiques basées sur la Notion de Synchronisation cellulaire. Administration première d'un Antimitotique suivie de l'Application de Produit(s) cycle ou Phase Dépendant(s), *Nouv. Presse Med.,* **1**: 1757-1762 (1972).

85. T. C. Hall, Limited Role of Cell Kinetics in Clinical Cancer Chemotherapy, *Nat. Cancer Inst. Monogr.,* **34**: 15-17 (1971).

# CHROMATID AND HALF-CHROMATID ABERRATIONS IN CHINESE HAMSTER CELLS X-IRRADIATED IN METAPHASE, PROPHASE, OR G$_2$

W. C. DEWEY

Department of Radiology and Radiation Biology, Colorado State University, Fort Collins, Colorado

## ABSTRACT

The types and frequencies of chromosomal aberrations were studied both in cells not delayed in their cycle by X-irradiation, i.e., located beyond an X-marker existing 10 min prior to prophase, and in cells delayed by irradiation, i.e., located in G$_2$ prior to the X-marker. Cells located beyond the X-marker at the time of irradiation, i.e., cells in metaphase, prophase, and in late G$_2$ within 10 min of prophase, were physically separated from cells located prior to the X-marker by mitotic selection to collect the cells as they entered metaphase and anaphase. These mitotic cells were fixed immediately or were allowed to traverse one cell cycle before they were fixed. When cells reached their first metaphase following irradiation, those irradiated prior to the X-marker manifested chromatid deletions and exchanges, but those irradiated beyond the X-marker sustained no visible aberrations. However, when prophase and metaphase cells were treated with Colcemid for 60 min following irradiation, gaps and chromatid deletions appeared. Thus, in cells located beyond the X-marker, there was neither division delay nor evidence of aberrations. Only when a delay was artificially produced with Colcemid did aberrations begin to appear. When cells reached their second metaphase following irradiation, both those prior to and beyond the X-marker at the time of irradiation sustained only chromosome deletions and exchanges. This finding contrasts with a previous observation of a high frequency of chromatid type deletions and exchanges in cells X-irradiated in metaphase following a 2-hr treatment with Colcemid and then scored for aberrations in the next metaphase. Thus, true half-chromatid exchanges, which are evidenced by chromatid exchanges in the second metaphase, normally do not occur to any appreciable extent in cells irradiated in metaphase, prophase, or in G$_2$ prior to the X-marker. However, the bineme nature of the mitotic chromatid can be readily observed in radiation studies if metaphase cells are treated with Colcemid prior to X-irradiation.

As reviewed recently by Kihlman,[1] the presence of half-chromatid exchanges reported[2-5] for cells irradiated in prophase is controversial. Supposedly, studies of the type of exchanges in the second division after irradiation should resolve this controversy because true half-chromatid exchanges should appear as chromatid exchanges in the second division, and masked chromatid exchanges[6] should appear as chromosome exchanges in the second division. However, both types of exchanges have been reported in the second division, and these differences have been attributed to uncertainties in timing or to the effects of drugs, such as Colchicine, used in the experiments to obtain tetraploid or binucleated cells. In fact, previous studies[7] have shown that X-irradiation of metaphase cells produces only chromosome exchanges in the second metaphase unless the cells are treated with Colcemid for 2 hr before irradiation; then, there is an approximately equal number of chromatid and chromosome exchanges.

Therefore, instead of drugs, we have used mitotic selection, normally used for obtaining synchronous populations of mitotic cells,[7] to investigate the types of aberrations in both the first and second metaphases following irradiation. Cells located at the time of irradiation in metaphase, prophase, and in $G_2$ past a point 10 min prior to prophase (the X-marker)[8] were collected as they entered metaphase and anaphase without any delay following irradiation. Also, cells irradiated in $G_2$ prior to the X-marker were collected after they recovered from their delay. Then, these mitotic cells were either fixed immediately or were allowed to traverse one cell cycle before they were arrested in metaphase with Colcemid. Thus, the frequencies and types of aberrations in cells located either before or beyond the X-marker at the time of irradiation could be compared. Of particular interest was whether or not there would be an appreciable frequency of aberrations produced during prophase which would result in chromatid exchanges in the second metaphase, as was observed when metaphase cells were X-irradiated following Colcemid treatment.[7]

## MATERIALS AND METHODS

Chinese hamster ovary (CHO) cells,[9] 95% near diploid, were cultured in McCoy's 5a medium as monolayers in Falcon T-60 plastic flasks at $37°C$. As described in Ref. 8, the flasks were shaken in a reciprocating shaker for 10 sec, and the medium containing the mitotic cells was poured off and rapidly cooled to $4°C$ to prevent cell division. The number of cells entering mitosis was monitored by the concentration of cells in 8 ml of medium poured from a flask immediately after it was shaken. Conditioned medium was returned to the flasks, and 10 min later the procedure was repeated. After about 60 min the cells in the flasks were irradiated[7] (immediately after the shake) at $37°C$ with an X-ray machine, and the shaking procedure was continued. The mitotic cells collected over intervals A, B, and C (Fig. 1) were either fixed immediately by the hypotonic method[10] (group 1 in Table 1) or were incubated at $37°C$ and fixed 20 hr later after they traversed one cell cycle (group 2). In the second case, Colcemid (0.06 μg/ml) was added at 11 hr to arrest the cells in metaphase (mitotic indices of 23 to 70%). As observed previously,[8] the durations of anaphase—telophase, metaphase, and prophase were 6.2, 25.6, and 9.5 min,

## TABLE 1

CHROMOSOMAL ABERRATIONS IN METAPHASE CELLS IRRADIATED IN METAPHASE, PROPHASE, OR LATE S TO $G_2$*

| Sample, dose in rads or min fixed after irrad. | No. of cells | Normal cells | Gaps | Chromatid deletions | Isolocus deletions | Chromatid exchanges | Chromosome exchanges | Total No. of aberrations† | Aberrations per cell | Gaps per cell‡ | Isolocus deletions, % | Chromosome exchanges, % |
|---|---|---|---|---|---|---|---|---|---|---|---|---|
| Group 1. Scored in first division, no Colcemid § | | | | | | | | | | | | |
| Control | 17 | 16 | 1 | 1 | 0 | 0 | 0 | 1 | 0.06 | | | |
| 150 A | 16 | 13 | | 1 | 0 | 2? | 0 | 3? | 0.19 | | | |
| 150 B | 22 | 8 | | 9 | 7 | 8 | 0 | 24 | 1.09 | | 44 | 0 |
| 150 C | 19 | 11 | | 6 | 4 | 6 | 0 | 16 | 0.84 | | 40 | 0 |
| Group 2. Scored in second division, Colcemid before fixation | | | | | | | | | | | | |
| Control | 50 | 50 | 4 | 0 | 0 | 0 | 0 | 0 | 0.00 | 0.08 | | |
| 100 A | 50 | 21 | | 0 | 32 | 1? | 10 | 43 | 0.86 | | 100 | 91 |
| 200 A | 50 | 2 | 6 | 0 | 66 | 1? | 28 | 95 | 1.90 | 0.12 | 100 | 97 |
| 100 B | 50 | 33 | | 0 | 18 | 0 | 4 | 22 | 0.44 | | 100 | 100 |
| 200 B | 50 | 33 | | 0 | 16 | 0 | 1 | 17 | 0.34 | | 100 | 100 |
| 100 C | 50 | 41 | | 0 | 8 | 0 | 2 | 10 | 0.20 | | 100 | 100 |
| 200 C | 50 | 33 | 3 | 0 | 18 | 0 | 4 | 22 | 0.44 | 0.06 | 100 | 100 |

## Group 3. Scored in first division, Colcemid 1 hr before 300 rads

| | | | | | | | | |
|---|---|---|---|---|---|---|---|---|
| Control | 50 | 47 | 6 | 1 | 1 | 0 | 3 | 0.06 | 0.12 |
| 0.5 min | 50 | 49 | 5 | 1 | 0 | 0 | 1 | 0.02 | 0.10 |
| 20 min | 50 | 48 | 10 | 2 | 0 | 0 | 2 | 0.04 | 0.20 |
| 30 min | 50 | 46 | 17 | 2 | 1 | 1 | 4 | 0.08 | 0.34 |
| 45 min | 50 | 45 | 27 | 4 | 2 | 0 | 7 | 0.14 | 0.54 |
| 60 min | 50 | 42 | 52 | 10 | 5 | 0 | 15 | 0.30 | 1.04 |

(brace grouping the last column: 30)

*No obvious half-chromatid exchanges were detected. In the A samples the metaphase cells analyzed for aberrations were irradiated in early metaphase, prophase, and 10 min before prophase and in the B and C samples, cells were irradiated in $G_2$ and late S. In group 1 the cells were analyzed in the first metaphase following irradiation, and in group 2 the synchronous cells divided once following irradiation and then traversed a complete cell cycle before they were fixed. For group 3 asynchronous cells were treated with Colcemid for 1 hr before receiving 300 rads and for 0.5 to 60 min thereafter. The metaphase index increased from 7.5% at the time of irradiation to 11% at 20 min after irradiation and then remained at 11% until 60 min after irradiation. Since prophase is 10 min in duration and the X-marker is located 10 min before prophase, the metaphase cells fixed at 0.5 min after irradiation were irradiated in metaphase. In samples fixed from 20 to 60 min after irradiation, about 30% of the metaphase cells (i.e., 3.5/11.0 x 100) had been irradiated in prophase or in the 10-min period before prophase, and the remaining 70% had been irradiated in metaphase.

†Number of aberrations equals the sum of deletions plus exchanges.

‡Gaps were scored only where values are indicated.

§These metaphase cells in group 1 were difficult to analyze because they had not been treated with Colcemid. Therefore, the data for the few cells scored provide only an estimate of the actual number of aberrations. The question marks indicate that the exchanges were questionable.

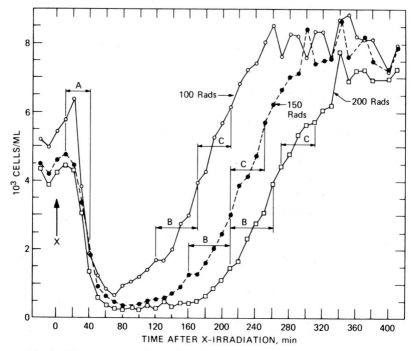

**Fig. 1** Time sequence of sampling showing the number of mitotic cells per milliliter at various times after irradiation.

respectively. The cells removed in mitosis were located between 4 and 22 min before the completion of division; therefore, the mitotic cells in sample A had not been delayed by irradiation and were located at the time of irradiation in the first 10 min of metaphase, in prophase, and in the 10-min interval between the X-marker and the beginning of prophase. The mitotic cells in samples B and C had been delayed by irradiation and were located in $G_2$ and late S at the time of irradiation.

Chromosomal aberrations were scored in metaphase cells as described in Refs. 7 and 11. Cells in anaphase of the first division were observed but not scored in detail because of uncertainty in distinguishing between true half-chromatid exchanges[12] and the phenomenon of two chromosomes appearing to be stuck together (observed in less than 5% of the anaphase cells).

In one experiment, asynchronous cells were treated with Colcemid (0.06 μg/ml) 1 hr before they were irradiated [Table 1 (group 3)]. Then, after the cells continued to incubate in the presence of Colcemid for 0.5 to 60 min, they were fixed and scored for chromosomal aberrations. The increase in the percent of cells in metaphase and the decrease in the percent in prophase following irradiation are plotted in Fig. 4, Ref. 8, for this experiment.

## RESULTS

The different types of aberrations scored in the first or second metaphase after irradiation are shown schematically in Figs. 2 and 3, and results are tabulated in Tables 1 and 2. For comparative purposes, the results from previous studies, Refs. 7 and 14, are included in Table 2 for cells irradiated in $G_1$ or metaphase after they had been synchronized following a 2-hr Colcemid treatment. Cells irradiated in the first half of metaphase, prophase, and in $G_2$ within 10 min of prophase did not manifest any definite half-chromatid exchanges in the first metaphase after irradiation (groups 1 and 3 in Table 1). Furthermore, the aberration frequency was no higher than that observed in the controls (0.06 aberrations per cell), unless the cells had been treated with Colcemid for 60 min after irradiation (0.30 aberrations per cell) (see group 1, 150 A, and group 3 in Table 1). In conjunction with the increase in aberrations in the cells treated with Colcemid, the frequency of gaps also increased considerably, i.e., from 0.10 for 0.5 min of treatment to 1.04 for 60 min of treatment after irradiation. The most interesting observation, however, was that in the second metaphase none of the aberrations were of the chromatid type; they consisted instead entirely of the chromosome type (group 2, 100 A and 200 A).* Thus, although the lack of half-chromatid exchanges between sister chromatids cannot be established by the scoring of metaphase cells in the first division, the lack of chromatid type aberrations in metaphase cells in the second division indicates that true half-chromatid exchanges between different chromatids must be nonexistent or at least very low in frequency.

Cells irradiated in S or $G_2$ and scored in the first metaphase after irradiation manifested chromatid and isochromatid deletions and only chromatid type exchanges (group 1, 150 B and 150 C). Then, in the second division only chromosome type aberrations were observed (group 2, 100 B, 200 B, 100 C, and 200 C).

## DISCUSSION

The argument can be presented that half-chromatid exchanges were not observed in this experiment because the cells containing the aberration did not survive to be scored with a chromatid aberration in the second metaphase. This is highly unlikely because, when half-chromatid exchanges were induced by treating with Colcemid before irradiation of metaphase cells,[7,14] the aberrations did persist to the second metaphase where there was approximately an equal number of chromatid and chromosome exchanges. Furthermore, when cells were

---

*The frequency of aberrations, 0.86 and 1.90 for 100 and 200 rads, respectively, agrees well with the values of 1.0 and 1.8 reported for cells irradiated in metaphase and anaphase and then analyzed in the next metaphase.[13]

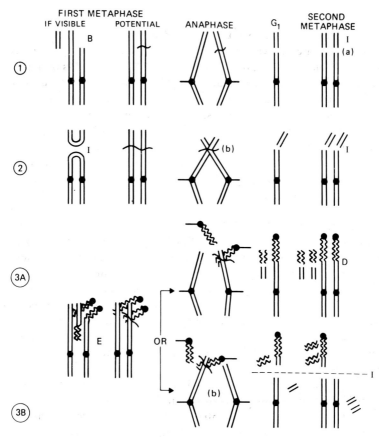

Fig. 2  Aberrations involving whole chromatids at the time of the first division. Each line represents a half-chromatid, two parallel lines represent a chromatid, and two sister chromatids constitute a chromosome. Aberrations that might be observed are illustrated schematically in the first and last columns; after the cell divides, only chromosomes with aberrations are illustrated. In the second and third columns, potential aberrations, which may or may not be observed, are illustrated by the wavy line. Aberrations are designated as follows: chromatid deletions, B; isolocus deletions, I; and chromosome exchanges, D. Notes: (a) Although the isolocus deletions (I) are shown without sister union, this is not meant to imply that sister union could not occur; sister union would imply that an exchange had occurred between two half-chromatids in the same chromatid. The fragments shown with I and D in the second metaphase would not necessarily be located in the cell containing the particular chromosome from which the fragment was derived. (b) If a bridge actually formed, it would break as the cell completed division; then, an isolocus deletion would be seen in each daughter cell, one above the dashed line and the other below.

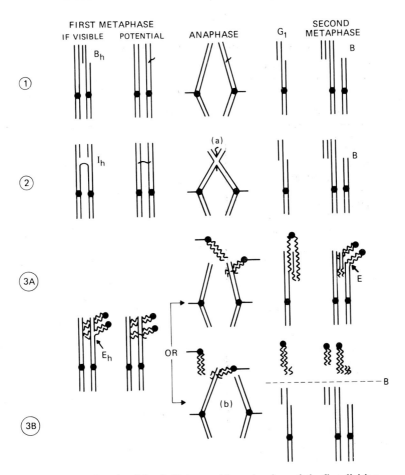

Fig. 3   Aberrations involving half-chromatids at the time of the first division. See the caption for Fig. 2 for notation. Aberrations are designated as follows: chromatid deletions, B; chromatid exchanges, E; half-chromatid deletions, $B_h$, which may be gaps; and half-chromatid exchanges, $I_h$ and $E_h$, which would be difficult to observe. Notes: (a) These half-chromatid exchanges at anaphase have been observed[2-5] as side-arm bridges, but they were not scored in this experiment. Any side-arm bridges, as well as a half-chromatid bridge between two different chromosomes (b) would break as the cell divided; then, a chromatid deletion would be seen in each daughter cell, one above the dashed line and the other below.

irradiated prior to the X-marker (B and C in Table 1), many cells survived to manifest chromosome aberrations (0.4 per cell) in the second metaphase although they had manifested chromatid aberrations (1 per cell) in the first metaphase. In other words, if many whole-chromatid exchanges like 3A and other aberrations in Fig. 2 can reach the second metaphase to give chromosome

**TABLE 2**

SYNCHRONIZED CELLS IRRADIATED BEFORE OR
BEYOND THE X MARKER

| | Observed aberrations* | |
|---|---|---|
| Phase irradiated | First metaphase | Second metaphase |
| Before X-marker, S and $G_2$ | B, I, E | I, D |
| Beyond X-marker, prophase, metaphase | None | I, D |
| Beyond X-marker, prophase, metaphase (60-min Colcemid treatment after irradiation) | Gaps $\overset{2}{=}$ $B_h$ B, I | Not scored |
| Metaphase (2-hr Colcemid treatment before irradiation)† | None | B, E I, D |
| $G_1$ † | I, D | Not scored |
| $G_1$ (2-hr Colcemid treatment of metaphase during synchrony)† | B, E I, D | Not scored |

*See Figs. 2 and 3 for definition of symbols and Table 1 for compilation of the data.

†These data were reported previously.[7,14] Note that for $G_1$ irradiation, the first metaphase would correspond to the second metaphase in Figs. 2 and 3.

exchanges and isolocus deletions, many half-chromatid aberrations like 1 and 3A in Fig. 3, if they existed, certainly should reach the second metaphase to give chromatid deletions and exchanges because any loss of genetic information should be less for half-chromatid aberrations than for whole-chromatid aberrations. One would also expect many aberrations resulting from side-arm bridges [Fig. 3, note(a)] if they existed, to reach the second metaphase, but at this point we cannot exclude the possibility that a few side-arm bridges did occur. Also, it is quite possible that exchanges between half-chromatids of the same chromatid occurred (1 in Fig. 2), which would produce in the second metaphase isolocus deletions with sister union. The frequency of real sister union is being studied by comparing the frequency of sister union with that of any anaphase bridges resulting from them. However, the main conclusion from this experiment is that the frequency of half-chromatid exchanges resulting from irradiation during metaphase, prophase, or $G_2$ is virtually nonexistent compared with the high frequency observed[7,14] when metaphase cells were treated with Colcemid before X-irradiation.

An interesting observation was that when prophase and metaphase cells were treated with Colcemid for about 1 hr after irradiation, which prevented the cells from dividing by arresting them in metaphase, some of the lesions appeared as gaps and deletions (group 3 in Table 1). This effect of Colcemid may result either from the delay allowing time for expression of the lesions or from the same phenomenon that resulted in the X-ray induction of half-chromatid exchanges in cells treated with Colcemid for 2 hr before irradiation in metaphase.[7,14] Concerning the Colcemid effect, two basic questions still remain to be answered: (1) Are any of the aberrations appearing when Colcemid is added after irradiation of the half-chromatid type? (2) Do half-chromatid exchanges induced during metaphase when Colcemid is added before irradiation actually occur prior to anaphase and thus appear during anaphase as half-chromatid exchanges, or do they occur only after the cell enters $G_1$ or S? Their occurrence during $G_1$ is very likely because, when cells were irradiated in prophase or metaphase without any Colcemid treatment, the lack of visible aberrations in the first metaphase (group 1 150 A in Table 1) and anaphase (data not shown) indicates that the aberrations must have been expressed after the cells had divided.

In summary, this study shows that at a point about 10 min before prophase (X-marker), there is a dramatic change in the cell, such that beyond this point, X-irradiation results neither in division delay nor in visible aberrations in the ensuing metaphase. The fundamental mechanism associated with this transition should be worthy of investigation. Furthermore, the $G_2$, prophase, and metaphase chromatid, as well as the $G_1$ chromosome, normally responds to X-irradiation as a unineme structure, although following Colcemid treatment the metaphase chromatid and $G_1$ chromosome can be made to respond to X-irradiation as a bineme structure.[7,14] Wolff[15] also has been able to get the $G_1$ chromosome to respond as a bineme structure. This bineme structure either could represent the loosening of two separate structures, each of which consists of a DNA double helix, or it could represent alterations in the DNA double helix and associated chromosomal protein which allow exchanges to occur between single strands of DNA. The latter possibility is preferred because of the observed[16-18] semiconservative distribution of DNA between the daughter chromatids at the time of division and the lack of genetic redundancy inferred from mutation and crossover data.[19]

## ACKNOWLEDGMENTS

The work reported here was supported in part by U. S. Public Health Service grant CA 08618. The technical assistance of Hannah Miller and Don Highfield is greatly appreciated.

## REFERENCES

1. B. A. Kihlman, Molecular Mechanisms of Chromosome Breakage and Rejoining, in *Advances in Cell and Molecular Biology*, Vol. 1, pp. 59-107, E. J. Dupraw (Ed.), Academic Press, Inc., New York, 1971.

2. B. R. Brinkley and R. M. Humphrey, Evidence for Subchromatid Organization in Marsupial Chromosomes, *J. Cell Biol.*, **42**: 827-839 (1969).

3. J. A. Heddle and D. J. Bodycote, The Strandedness of Chromosomes, *J. Cell Biol.*, **39**: 60a (1968).

4. L. F. LaCour and A. Rutishauser, X-Ray Breakage Experiments with Endosperm. I. Sub-Chromatid Breakage, *Chromosoma*, **6**: 696-709 (1954).

5. W. J. Peacock, Sub-Chromatid Structure and Chromosome Duplication in *Vicia faba*, *Nature*, **191**: 832-833 (1961).

6. G. Östergren and T. Wakonig, True or Apparent Sub-Chromatid Breakage and Induction of Labile States in Cytological Chromosome Loci, *Bot. Notis.*, **4**: 357-375 (1954).

7. W. C. Dewey and H. H. Miller, X-Ray Induction of Chromatid Exchanges in Mitotic and $G_1$ Chinese Hamster Cells Pretreated with Colcemid, *Exp. Cell Res.*, **57**: 63-70(1969).

8. M. H. Schneiderman, W. C. Dewey, D. B. Leeper, and H. Nagasawa, Use of the Mitotic Selection Procedure for Cell Cycle Analysis, *Exp. Cell Res.*, **74**: 430-438 (1972).

9. J. H. Tjio and T. T. Puck, Genetics of Somatic Mammalian Cells. II. Chromosomal Constitution of Cells in Tissue Culture, *J. Exp. Med.*, **108**: 259-268 (1958).

10. T. C. Hsu and D. S. Kellogg, Mammalian Chromosomes In Vitro. Evolution of Cell Populations, *J. Nat. Cancer Inst.*, **24**: 1067-1083 (1960).

11. S. H. Revell, The Accurate Estimation of Chromatid Breakage, and Its Relevance to a New Interpretation of Chromatid Aberrations Induced by Ionizing Radiations, *Proc. Roy. Soc. (London), Ser. B*, **150**: 563-589 (1959).

12. H. J. Evans, Chromosome Aberrations Induced by Ionizing Radiations, *Int. Rev. Cytol.*, **13**: 221-321 (1962).

13. W. C. Dewey, L. E. Stone, H. H. Miller, and R. E. Giblak, Radiosensitization with 5-Bromodeoxyuridine of Chinese Hamster Cells X-Irradiated During Different Phases of the Cell Cycle, *Radiat. Res.*, **47**: 672-688 (1971).

14. W. C. Dewey and H. H. Miller, Effects of Cycloheximide on X-Ray Induction of Chromatid Exchanges in Synchronous Chinese Hamster Cells, *Exp. Cell Res.*, **66**: 283-288 (1971).

15. S. Wolff, The Splitting of Human Chromosome into Chromatids in the Absence of Either DNA or Protein Synthesis, *Mutat. Res.*, **8**: 207-214 (1969).

16. D. M. Prescott and M. A. Bender, Autoradiographic Study of Chromatid Distribution of Labeled DNA in Two Types of Mammalian Cells In Vitro, *Exp. Cell Res.*, **29**: 430-442 (1963).

17. Larrie E. Stone, William C. Dewey, and Hannah H. Miller, Segregation of DNA and Sister Chromatid Exchanges in Chinese Hamster Chromosomes, *Cytobiologie*, **5**: 324-334 (1972).

18. J. H. Taylor, P. S. Woods, and W. L. Hughes, The Organization and Duplication of Chromosomes as Revealed by Autoradiographic Studies Using Tritium-Labeled Thymidine, *Proc. Nat. Acad. Sci. U. S. A.*, **43**: 122-127 (1957).

19. E. J. DuPraw, *Cell and Molecular Biology*, pp. 476, 567-569, Academic Press, Inc., New York, 1968.

# RADIATION-INDUCED DIVISION DELAY
# IN CHO CELLS: REPAIR KINETICS

DENNIS B. LEEPER
Department of Radiation Therapy and Nuclear Medicine, Thomas Jefferson University
Hospital, Philadelphia, Pennsylvania

## ABSTRACT

The kinetics of the recovery from radiation damage manifest as division delay has been analyzed in Chinese hamster ovary fibroblasts in monolayer culture using two-dose fractionation schemes and suboptimal postirradiation temperatures in a manner similar to the analysis of the repair of sublethal and potentially lethal radiation damage. Mitotic-cell selection was used to assess the rate of cell division.

Fractionation of a single dose of 300 rads into two 150-rad fractions separated by intervals of time and analysis of the division delay remaining at the time of the second dose have shown that the damage resulting in division delay is repaired at a constant rate of 1 min of delay per minute between dose fractions. However, when a 600-rad single dose was fractionated into two 300-rad fractions, a bimodal-recovery pattern resulted. After a dose of 300 rads, damage manifest as division delay was repaired initially (up to 0.4 hr postirradiation) by a rapid recovery process at the rate of 3.6 min of delay per minute between dose fractions, after which a second and slower recovery process became operant, with damage being repaired at the rate of 0.55 min of delay per minute between dose fractions. Lowering the postirradiation incubation temperature to 4, 20, or 30°C or lowering the temperature between two-dose fractions reduced the rate of recovery. The construction of an Arrhenius plot showed that the repair process was enzymatic with an activation energy of 11,000 cal/mole and a $Q_{10}$ of 1.82.

Neither fractionation nor postirradiation treatment with suboptimal incubation temperatures modified the recovery from division delay in a way that resembled the recovery from sublethal or potentially lethal radiation damage. This provides further evidence that the respective radiosensitive targets are distinct.

The use of ionizing radiation for the treatment of human cancer is predicated on the fact that radiation inhibits tissue proliferation and causes the death of cells when proliferation resumes. The curative goal of radiation therapy is to reduce the probability that a clonogenic cell remains within a tumor to some value less than one. Radiotherapists, following the leadership of Coutard,[1] have successfully employed fractionated radiation schemes to eliminate malignant disease since the early 1920s. During the past two decades, a number of significant processes that occur within malignant and normal proliferative tissues between fractionated doses of radiation have been described, the more important of which are intracellular repair of radiation damage, redistribution of cells within their life cycle, repopulation, and reoxygenation.[2,3] However, data from the American Cancer Society[4] indicate that approximately one-third of the annual cancer deaths in the United States occur in patients in which treatment failed to control the local disease. Therefore, in spite of recent advances in techniques and understanding, an optimal treatment regime for the radiation therapy of cancer has yet to be established.

The biological response of proliferating mammalian cells to modest doses of X rays can be summarized as follows. Cell division ceases for a period of time proportional to the X-ray dose,[5] and normal cell-cycle progression is altered.[6] During this period of cell-cycle perturbation and division delay, cells repair the radiation damage to the extent that cell-cycle progression and division can resume. Owing to the differential effectiveness of radiation on cell-cycle progression, irradiated cells accumulate in $G_2$; and, at the end of the division-delay period, the rate of cell division may temporarily exceed the control level.[6-8] Radiation also produces lethal, sublethal, and potentially lethal lesions within the nucleoprotein complex which may manifest themselves at the next cell division in the form of chromosome aberrations.[9-11] The sublethal and potentially lethal lesions may interact to become lethal, or they may be repaired.[2,3,12-15] The capacity of the cell to accumulate and to repair sublethal and potentially lethal lesions and its sensitivity to radiation-induced division delay, although distinct from survival functions, are strongly dependent on the position of the cell in its life cycle at the time of irradiation (Refs. 5, 9, and 14–23).

Further development of effective radiotherapy would be facilitated by a greater understanding of the biochemistry of cellular radiosensitivity and of the mechanism by which radiation damage, both cell killing and perturbation of cell-cycle progression, is repaired. The split-dose technique for determining the accumulation and repair of sublethal radiation damage (Refs. 2, 3, 14, and 17) and the use of suboptimal postirradiation growth conditions for evaluating repair of potentially lethal radiation damage,[12-14,18] which have been so successfully applied to survival, have not as yet been employed for the rigorous analysis of recovery from radiation-induced cycle delay. Previous studies with the Sarcoma-180 mouse ascites tumor indicated that dose fractionation can be used successfully in the study of the recovery from radiation-induced cycle delay. The results showed that, when the fractionation interval was long with respect to the initial division-delay period, the resultant division delay was longer than that caused by an equivalent single exposure[24] but that, when the fractionation interval was shortened, the resultant delay became less than that caused by the equivalent single exposure. Analysis of the recovery kinetics indicated a two-component repair process.[25] The kinetics of the recovery from radiation-induced division delay in Chinese hamster ovary cells have been obtained by using mitotic-cell selection for cell-cycle analysis[8] and the split-dose technique combined with postirradiation cooling to suboptimal temperatures to analyze repair of accumulated radiation damage.

## METHODS AND MATERIALS

Chinese hamster ovary fibroblasts (CHO cells, 98% near diploid, modal chromosome number = 21) were propagated as monolayers on Falcon plastic in McCoy's 5a medium supplemented with 10% calf and 5% fetal calf serum in a humidified atmosphere of 6% $CO_2$. Stock cells were carried in the absence of antibiotics and were routinely tested to be free of mycoplasma contamination.[26] Growth medium used in experiments contained the antibiotics potassium penicillin G (0.07 g/liter) and streptomycin sulfate (0.1 g/liter).

Schneiderman et al.[8] have reported that the mitotic-cell selection procedure previously used to obtain highly synchronous populations of mitotic cells[27] could be used to greatly enhance precision in the analysis of mammalian-cell-cycle kinetics and control of cell division. Mitotic cells were removed from an asynchronous monolayer of CHO cells grown on Falcon 75-$cm^2$ T-flasks by vigorous shaking in a mechanical shaker (260 strokes/min, 1.5 in./stroke) for 20 sec every 10 min.[8] The flasks were shaken in a constant-temperature walk-in incubator, and the pH of the 10 ml of overlying medium was maintained at approximately 7.2 with a constant flow of $CO_2$. The mitotic cells collected per shake were decanted into test tubes immersed in ice and subsequently counted with a Coulter counter. The frequency—volume distribution of the cell population was analyzed by a 200-channel pulse-height analyzer interfaced with the counter and was either recorded graphically or presented on a video monitor and, if desired, photographed. The frequency—cell volume distribution spectrum of mitotic cells was positively correlated to the percent of cells in mitosis (mitotic index determined by mild centrifugation and the squash technique[28] to score the frequency of mitotic figures in 1000 cells).

A typical experiment was performed with eight 75-$cm^2$ culture flasks, each containing approximately $10^7$ cells in exponential growth. Shaking began at zero time, and, after good synchrony was established in 4 to 6 shakes, the flasks were individually irradiated and treated appropriately. Unirradiated and single-dose-only controls were maintained during every experiment. Except for the duration of the postirradiation suboptimal temperature treatment, shaking was continued at 10-min intervals throughout an experiment until cell division in all flasks returned to control levels. The culture flasks were transported to and from the X-ray machine and irradiated in a temperature-controlled water bath at the desired temperature, depending on the particular experiment, of 0 to 4, 20, 30, or 37°C. The conditions of X-irradiation were 250 kVcp, 15 mA; 2 mm of aluminum added filtration; 60 cm source to sample distance; a half-value layer of 0.5 mm of copper; and a dose rate of 125 rads/min. Dosimetry was accomplished with a thimble ionization chamber calibrated against a LiF thermoluminescent dosimeter.

## RESULTS

The results obtained using mitotic-cell collection to compute radiation-induced division delay are shown in Fig. 1. Populations of collected mitotic cells normally exhibited a mitotic index of approximately 95%. Approximately 85% of the mitotic cells were in metaphase, 15% in anaphase–telophase, and less than

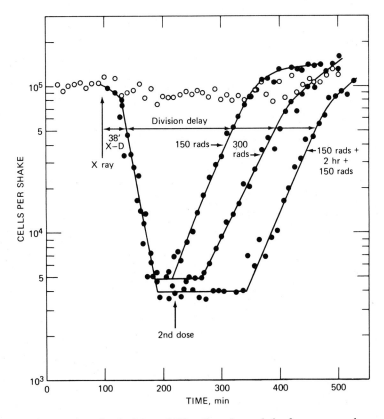

Fig. 1  Number of cells (M.I. = 96%) collected per shake from an asynchronous monolayer of $1.64 \times 10^7$ cells every 10 min after initiation of the mitotic-cell collection procedure. ○, control. ●, cells from populations that were irradiated at 100 min. Irradiated populations received 150 rads, 300 rads, or a 150-rad fraction and 2 hr later another 150-rad fraction. The X–D interval was 38 min for all three populations.

1% in prophase. After irradiation the rate of cell division continued at the normal level for approximately 27 min but then began to decline so that by 86 min postirradiation cell division had virtually ceased. The time from irradiation until the rate of cell division was reduced to one-half was 38 min. It is referred to as the X–D interval, i.e., the time from metaphase to the X-ray sensitive marker in $G_2$. The resumption of cell division after the period of division delay can be observed in Fig. 1; the mean division delay is the interval between the points when the number of mitotic cells per shake fell to one-half and recovered to one-half of the unirradiated control rate. The division delay was 3.0 hr after 150 rads, 4.3 hr after 300 rads, and 5.4 hr after 150 rads + 2 hr at $37°C$ + 150 rads. During division delay there was parasynchronization of the asynchronous population,[6,8] which resulted in an overshoot in the rate of cell division, e.g., 30% over that of the nonirradiated control for a dose of 150 rads (Fig. 1). The curves showing the recovery of cell division each exhibited similar slope constants of approximately 0.009 $min^{-1}$ for all three dose conditions but were not as steep as the immediate postirradiation decline in cell division, which exhibited a slope constant of 0.023 $min^{-1}$.

The degree of synchrony of the populations obtained during the selection procedure was monitored by analyzing the frequency–cell volume distributions with the pulse-height analyzer as the cells were being counted. The frequency–cell volume distribution exhibited by trypsinized asynchronous populations of cells is shown in Fig. 2. Since more $G_1$ cells ($1285 \mu m^3$) exist in a population exponentially distributed throughout the cell cycle, more cells exhibited smaller volumes. In contrast to the asynchronous frequency–cell volume distribution, synchronous mitotic cells (Fig. 2) displayed a modal volume of 2570 $\mu m^3$ with a complete absence of small cells ($1285 \mu m^3$), a finding that was verified microscopically by a mitotic index of 97%. Figure 2 also shows the size (peak $1470 \mu m^3$) of the nonmitotic cells collected during the division-delay period after a dose of 300 rads. The resumption of cell division resulted in mitotic cells that exhibited a modal volume of $2990 \mu m^3$, and, after full recovery of cell division, the collected mitotic cells exhibited a modal volume of $3100 \mu m^3$, 20% greater than nonirradiated mitotic cells.

The effect of reduced temperature on the rate of cell division as determined by mitotic-cell collection is shown in Fig. 3. The number of mitotic cells per shake from $9 \times 10^6$ asynchronous cells in monolayer culture was reduced to 50% of the $37°C$ control by lowering the temperature to $30°C$ and to 13% of control by reducing the temperature to $20°C$. The harvested cells exhibited a mitotic index greater than 90% and a normal size range. The nature of the dip in the rate of cell division 90 min after the temperature was reduced to $30°C$ was observed in duplicate experiments. Since there was no overshoot in the rate of cell division after the reestablishment of the normal metabolic temperature (data not shown), the temperature-dependent reduction in the rate of cell division shown in Fig. 3 probably reflects the overall rate of cell-cycle progression for the later part of the cell cycle.

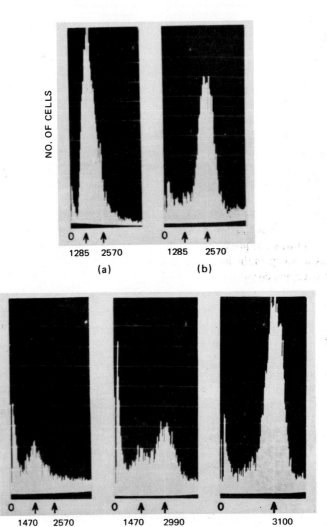

Fig. 2  Video monitor display of frequency vs. cell volume distributions for asynchronous and mitotic populations before and after a dose of 300 rads. Each panel displays 100 channels at 52.5 $\mu m^3$ per channel. (a) Asynchronous population. (b) Synchronized population of mitotic cells (M.I. = 97%); 82% metaphase cells. Note the absence of $G_1$ and S sized cells. (c) Cells removed by mitotic-cell collection during the division-delay period after a dose of 300 rads. Note the absence of mitotic cells. (d) Appearance of mitotic cells as cell division resumed after a dose of 300 rads. (e) Mitotic cells collected after complete recovery from division delay after 300 rads. The average volume of the mitotic cells was increased by 20% during the period of division delay.

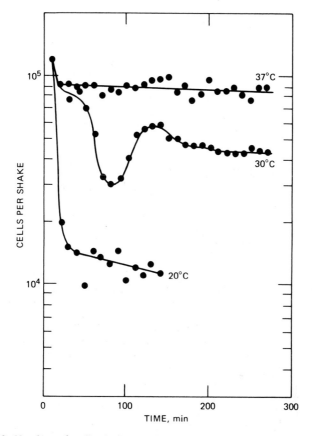

Fig. 3 Number of cells (M.I. = 95%) collected per shake from $9 \times 10^6$ asynchronous cells every 10 min after initiation of the mitotic-cell collection procedure at temperatures of 37, 30, and 20° C.

The kinetics of the recovery from radiation damage manifest as division delay were analyzed in the CHO cells in a manner similar to the analysis of accumulation and repair of sublethal radiation damage by separating two doses of radiation with varying intervals of time and comparing the biological response to that of the single dose.[2,3,14] Mitotic-cell selection was used to analyze the rate of cell division after fractionated irradiation as shown in Fig. 1 for two doses of 150 rads separated by an interval of 2.0 hr at 37°C. The effect of varying the fractionation interval between two doses of 150 rads is shown in Fig. 4. The overall division delay was measured from the decline in the rate of cell division to 50% of control after the first radiation dose to the recovery of cell division to 50% of the control rate after the second radiation dose. The division delay remaining from the first dose of irradiation was determined by subtracting the duration of the fractionation interval from the total division

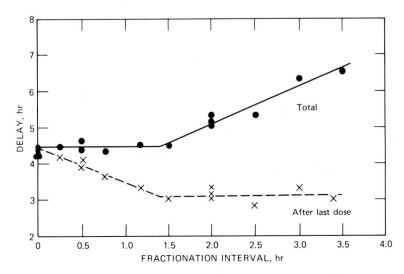

Fig. 4 Division delay plotted as a function of the interval at 37°C between two doses of 150 rads. The curve labelled "total" is the entire period from the midpoint of the decline of cell division after the first dose of 150 rads to the midpoint of the recovery wave of cell division after the second dose of 150 rads. The curve "after last dose" represents the division delay remaining after the second dose of radiation (i.e., total delay less the fractionation interval). The division delay of 3 hr observed after fractionation intervals longer than 1.5 hr is that produced by a single dose of 150 rads.

delay. If a fractionation interval greater than 2.0 hr was used, cell division after the first dose of 150 rads would resume, to then fall again after the second dose (data not shown). Therefore, the total division delay is a summation of the damage in hours of delay remaining from the first dose in addition to the damage in hours of delay imparted by the second dose. If the fractionation interval is greater than the time to recover from the damage imparted by the first dose, then the computed total division delay will incorporate that additional time. The total division delay as shown in Fig. 4 increased after a fractionation interval greater than 1.5 hr, and the division delay remaining after the first dose of X rays decreased to a plateau at a fractionation interval of 1.5 hr. The slope of that curve indicated that the damage resulting in division delay after a dose of 150 rads was repaired at a constant rate of 1 min of delay per minute between dose fractions. Owing to the two relative sensitivities of division delay at high and low total doses (data to be published elsewhere), the division delay for a dose of 150 rads was 3 hr, and that for a dose of 300 rads (fractionation interval = zero) was 4.5 hr (Fig. 4). The damage equivalent to 1.5 hr of division delay was repaired during the first 1.5 hr of fractionation, and additional time between the two 150-rad doses was merely additive to the radiation-induced division delay imparted by the second dose.

The effect of separating two 300-rad fractions with intervals of time at 37°C compared to the division delay resulting from a single dose of 600 rads is shown in Fig. 5. A striking feature was that a bimodal recovery process was operant. The total division delay decreased as the fractionation interval was increased up to an interval of 0.4 hr. However, the total division delay increased again with fractionation intervals greater than 0.4 hr between the 300-rad dose fractions. The repair kinetics can be visualized by considering only the division delay remaining after the second dose of 300 rads (i.e., total delay between the midpoints of the decline and recovery of cell division after the first and second doses, respectively, less the fractionation interval). The initial, more rapid repair process proceeded at a rate of 3.6 hr of delay repaired per hour of fractionation, but this repair process became inoperative by 0.4 hr postirradiation. After 0.4 hr a slower repair process became dominant and proceeded at a rate of 0.55 hr of delay repaired per hour between dose fractions.

The effect of postirradiation cooling on the repair of radiation damage manifest as division delay was studied in much the same way as the repair of

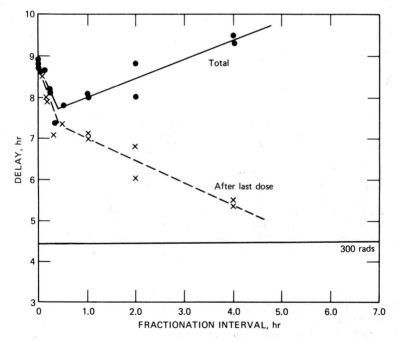

Fig. 5 Division delay plotted as a function of the interval at 37°C between two doses of 300 rads. The curve labelled "total" is the entire period of division delay from both doses of 300 rads. The curve "after last dose" depicts the division delay remaining after the second dose of 300 rads (i.e., total delay less the fractionation interval). Note the inflection point at 0.4 hr of fractionation. The 300-rad curve indicates the delay from a single dose of 300 rads.

potentially lethal radiation damage in CHO cells has been studied.[14,19] Reducing the temperature of mammalian cells to 20°C immediately after irradiation enhances survival by permitting the repair of potentially lethal radiation damage before it becomes permanently fixed as a lethal lesion.[15] Figure 3 shows that maintaining CHO cells at a temperature of 20°C reduced the rate of cell division to 13% of that at 37°C. The effect of reducing the temperature of cells to 20°C during the fractionation interval between two 150-rad fractions is shown in Fig. 6. The division delay remaining from the first

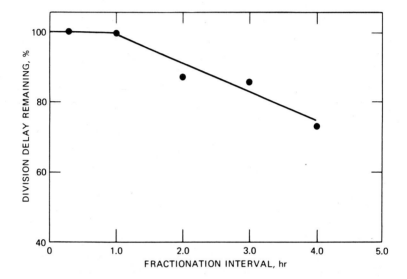

Fig. 6  Division delay after two fractionated doses of 150 rads when the cells were maintained at 20°C during the fractionation interval. The cells were returned to 37°C immediately after the second dose of 150 rads. Division delay is presented as the delay remaining after the second dose of 150 rads in percent of the division delay produced by a single dose of 300 rads (i.e., the interval from the second dose, when the temperature was raised to 37°C, to the midpoint of the recovery of cell division divided by the mean delay after 300 rads).

dose in percent of a single dose of 300 rads is plotted as a function of time at 20°C between the two 150-rad fractions. Little or no damage was repaired during the first hour of fractionation at 20°C, but then repair commenced at the rate of 8.2% of the delay from the single dose per hour of fractionation. This is compared to the repair rate of 23% per hour when the cells remained at 37°C (Fig. 4). Also, at 37°C there was no threshold for the onset of the repair process (Fig. 4).

The effect of postirradiation temperature on the repair rate of division delay is shown in Fig. 7. Asynchronous monolayers were cooled to 0 to 4, 20, or

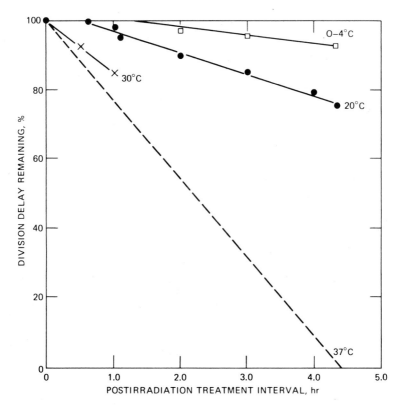

Fig. 7  Division delay remaining after cooled, irradiated cells were returned to 37°C in percent of the division delay from a single dose of 300 rads plotted as a function of the postirradiation interval for which irradiated cells were maintained at the indicated temperature.

30°C, immediately irradiated with 300 rads, left at the respective temperature for up to 4 hr, and then returned to 37°C until cell division returned to control levels. The division delay remaining after the postirradiation cooling interval is plotted in percent of the 37°C control as a function of time at a particular temperature. The curve for 37°C is simply a line drawn from 100% to the division delay period observed when cells are left at 37°C, namely, 4.4 hr. The rates of repair at 0 to 4 (in an ice bath), 20, 30, and 37°C were, respectively, 2.4, 6.1, 15.0, and 22.7% per hour. Repair did not begin until 0.65 and 1.3 hr postirradiation when the cells were held at 20 and 0 to 4°C, respectively. At 30°C fractionation intervals of only up to 1 hr could be analyzed since longer intervals at that postirradiation temperature resulted in the detachment of asynchronous cells during shaking.

The effect of temperature on the recovery from radiation-induced division delay was analyzed by constructing an Arrhenius plot for the temperature dependence of the repair process,[29] i.e., the logarithm of the recovery coefficient (slope of curves in Figs. 6 and 7, in percent per hour) vs. the reciprocal of the absolute temperature. A linear fit implies that a single enzymatic process is effective over the temperature range explored. The Arrhenius equation is:

$$k = Ae^{-E_a/RT}$$

where k = the specific reaction rate
    A = constant
    $E_a$ = energy of activation
    T = absolute temperature
    R = 1.98 cal/deg/mole

When log k is plotted against $1/T$, the slope of the line equals $E_a/2.303R$, and for the division delay repair system $E_a = 11,020$ cal/mole. Most enzymes exhibit activation energies in the range[30] of 10,000 to 25,000 cal/mole. When the reduction of the normal division rate by suboptimal incubation temperatures (Fig. 3) was analyzed in a similar fashion, a linear Arrhenius plot was also obtained, and the activation energy was computed to be 22,900 cal/mole.

The $Q_{10}$ of an enzyme is its temperature coefficient and is a factor whereby the velocity is reduced when the temperature is lowered by $10°C$. The $Q_{10}$ is predicted by the equation

$$\log Q_{10} = \frac{10E_a}{2.303 \, RT \, (T + 10)}$$

and was 1.82 between 27 and $37°C$ for this repair system. The temperature coefficients of most enzymatic reactions[29] fall between 1 and 2. One can then hypothesize that the repair process for the recovery from radiation-induced division delay is enzymatic and is characterized by an $E_a$ of 11,000 cal/mole and a $Q_{10}$ of 1.82. In the Arrhenius plot in Fig. 8, the recovery data derived both from cooling between 150-rad fractions and from postirradiation cooling after 300 rads fall on the same calculated regression line.

## DISCUSSION

Interest in radiation-induced cycle delay derives not only from the biology of cell-cycle progression and cell division but also from the possibility of establishing multiple-fractionation schemes in the radiation therapy of cancer which will optimize parasynchronization of cells into radiosensitive states during the periods of division delay. Toward this end the mitotic-cell collection procedure has been adapted to carefully analyze the repair kinetics of

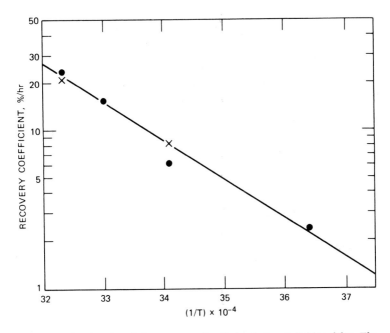

Fig. 8 Arrhenius plot of the recovery of radiation-induced division delay. The recovery coefficient of division delay, defined as the slope of the delay remaining after postirradiation lowered-temperature treatment, is plotted as a function of the reciprocal of the absolute temperature. As calculated in the text, the activation energy was 11,020 cal/mole, and the $Q_{10}$ was 1.82. •, data from single-dose experiments. X, data from two-dose fractionation experiments.

radiation-induced division delay in CHO cells. These results have shown that the radiation damage manifest as division delay from a dose of 150 rads is repaired linearly with time at the rate of 1 min of delay per minute postirradiation. The damage produced by 300 rads is repaired in a bimodal fashion with approximately one-third of the damage repaired initially at the rate of 3.6 min of delay per minute up to 0.4 hr postirradiation, whereas the remaining two-thirds of the initial damage is repaired at the rate of 0.55 min of delay per minute.

The temperature dependence of the division-delay repair process was determined by lowering the postirradiation temperature for various intervals and constructing an Arrhenius plot of the repair rate against the reciprocal of the absolute temperature. Since the biochemical damage responsible for division delay remains obscure, as does the nature of the repair mechanisms, this type of analysis provides one means of characterization. The recovery rate from division delay is assumed proportional to the reaction rate of enzymatic repair at the biochemical level, and a linear Arrhenius plot (Fig. 8) implies the existence of a single enzyme as the dominant repair mechanism.[29,30] This enzyme is characterized by an activation energy of 11,000 cal/mole and a $Q_{10}$ of 1.82. Both these values are in the range of those commonly observed for enzymatic systems.[29,30]

The decreased rate of repair of division delay at a given temperature was similar regardless of whether the incubation temperature was lowered between two 150-rad fractions or whether it was lowered immediately after a single dose of 300 rads (Figs. 6 to 8). However, at 37°C the repair of damage from 150 rads was a simple linear function of time (Fig. 4), whereas the repair of damage from 300 rads occurred in two steps (Fig. 5). There was no suggestion of two-step repair at the suboptimal temperatures shown in Fig. 7. Until confirmatory experiments, which will employ two doses of 300 rads separated by intervals of suboptimal incubation temperatures, can be performed, it must be concluded that at reduced temperatures, as opposed to 37°C, the repair rate of division-delay damage is independent of the degree of damage incurred.

The observed variations of radiation-induced division delay at 37°C after two-dose fractionation result from repair processes. That they are not a simple function of redistribution in the cell cycle by the time the second dose is given is suggested by the following points:

1. The most sensitive stage in the cell cycle to radiation-induced division delay, as determined in synchronous populations, is late S through $G_2$ [0.80 min/rad in late S and 0.78 min/rad in $G_2$ (Ref. 5)].

2. The delay coefficient for asynchronous CHO cells was 0.88 min/rad compared to 0.77 min/rad reported in Ref. 5; so in all probability it is the $G_2$ cells that are the first to recover from division delay after doses of less than 450 rads.

3. The radiation-induced delay in the termination of DNA replication (radiation-induced S delay) after doses of 150 or 300 rads in late S is significantly less than the division delay exhibited by those cells (Ref. 6); so movement out of S is not influencing the division delay.

4. A period of 0.4 hr is not sufficient for cell-cycle progression to account for the 30% reduction in the division delay remaining after the first dose observed when two doses of 300 rads were separated and the effect was compared to a single dose of 600 rads.

5. The activation energy of the division-delay repair system was 11,000 cal/mole compared to an activation energy of cell-cycle progression of 23,000 cal/mole.

A comparison of repair of division-delay damage in irradiated CHO cells and in irradiated mouse Sarcoma-180 (S-180) ascites tumor cells[24,25] reveals striking similarities in the two systems and suggests a common mechanism. Both cell lines are equally sensitive to radiation-induced division delay, exhibiting delay coefficients[5,24] of approximately 0.8 min/rad. The CHO cells recover from division-delay damage from 150 rads at the rate of 1 min of delay per minute postirradiation, but, after larger doses and greater damage, recovery occurs in a bimodal fashion. In the S-180 ascites tumor, as well, when a 400-rad dose of X-rays is fractionated into two 200-rad doses, approximately 22% of the damage from the first dose is repaired at the rate of 3.3 min of delay per minute; and, from 0.5 hr postirradiation until recovery is complete, repair occurs at the rate of 0.28 min of delay per minute. In CHO cells, when 600 rads is fractionated into two 300-rad doses, 33% of the damage from the first dose is repaired initially at the rate of 3.6 min of delay per minute up to 0.4 hr postirradiation; thereafter repair occurs at the rate of 0.55 min of delay per minute until recovery is complete. In fact, when the S-180 ascites tumor cells are irradiated with doses greater than 200 rads in any of several fractionation schedules, 30 to 40% of the damage is repaired initially at the rate of approximately 3 min of delay per minute, and the remaining 60 to 70% is repaired at the rate of approximately 0.3 min of delay per minute. Therefore it appears that in both cell systems the division-delay damage from a dose of 150 rads may be repaired linearly at the rate of 1 min of delay per minute. When greater damage is incurred, however, approximately 40% is repaired at the rate of approximately 3 min of delay per minute postirradiation, and 60% is repaired much more slowly at a rate of 0.3 min per minute in the S-180 ascites tumor cell and 0.6 min per minute in the CHO cell.

Temperature reduction does exhibit a stage-dependent effect on subsequent cycle progression in human amnion cells which is particularly apparent[31] at 30°C. The rate of DNA synthesis was three to four times slower at 30 than at 37°C, the $G_2$ phase was approximately doubled in length, and metaphase was extended at 30°C to four to five times its normal length.[31] This might explain the dip in the mitotic-cell collection curve observed 90 min after the temperature was lowered to 30°C (Fig. 3). The rate of cell division would decline at 90 min if DNA synthesis in CHO cells, as in human amnion cells, was considerably more affected than $G_2$ progression so that the rate of entry of cells into $G_2$ after the temperature shift was less than the rate at which cells were completing $G_2$. Eventually, fewer cells would enter metaphase at a time equal to the length of $G_2$ plus prophase. However, if this model is valid, $G_2$ plus prophase in CHO cells must not be appreciably affected by incubation at 30°C since $G_2$ is 60 to 90 min in duration in synchronous monolayer cultures[6,32] at 37°C. After the cells that were in $G_2$ and prophase at the time of the temperature shift divided, a new situation would be established in which cells would be leaving S, progressing through $G_2$ and prophase, to be collected in metaphase at the rates characteristic of S cells at that particular temperature.[31]

It is interesting that irradiated CHO cells incubated at 30°C for postirradiation intervals greater than 1 hr rounded up and detached from the Falcon plastic culture flasks (Fig. 7). This may be a characteristic of the liquid-water phase transition[33,34] at 30°C. Such an effect on growth rate was described in unirradiated L929 cells by Lau.[34] Unirradiated rat epithelial cells in culture also detached and died after a 12-hr exposure at 30°C but remained relatively unaffected by prolonged incubation at temperatures[35] of 31 and 27°C. However, unirradiated CHO cells remained fibroblastic and firmly attached to the surface for up to 6 hr of incubation at 30°C (Fig. 3), and CHO cells did not exhibit a change in the energy of activation at 30°C as Lau[34] described for L929 cells (16,800 cal above 30°C to 99,600 cal below 30°C).

Neither fractionation nor postirradiation treatment with suboptimal culture conditions modified the recovery from radiation-induced division delay in CHO cells in a way that resembled the recovery from sublethal or potentially lethal radiation damage. In CHO cells both sublethal and potentially lethal radiation damage are repaired with the same kinetics ($T_{1/2} \approx 15$ min), and both forms of damage probably represent lesions in the nucleoprotein complex which are manifest as chromosome aberrations at mitosis.[14,15,19] The repair of sublethal radiation damage occurs at 20 and 37°C, but not at 0 to 4°C, whereas the repair of potentially lethal damage is observed[14,15,19] only at 20°C and not at 37 or 0 to 4°C. In contrast, the repair of the radiation damage that results in division delay is rate dependent on temperature but continuous between 0 to 4 and 37°C (Figs. 7 and 8). The bimodal kinetics of the repair of division delay after larger doses (Fig. 6 and Ref. 25) are also dissimilar to the single exponential kinetics of the repair of sublethal and potentially lethal radiation damage.[14,15,19] These observations on repair rates provide further evidence that the respective radiosensitive targets for lethality and division delay are distinct.

## ACKNOWLEDGMENTS

The author acknowledges the expert technical assistance of Robin Putzrath. The research reported here was supported by National Institutes of Health grant CA-11602.

## REFERENCES

1. H. Coutard, Roentgen Therapy of Epitheliomas of the Tonsillar Region, Hypopharynx and Larynx from 1920 to 1926, *Am. J. Roentgenol., Radium Ther. Nucl. Med.*, **28**: 313-331(1932).
2. H. R. Withers, Capacity for Repair in Cells of Normal and Malignant Tissues, in Time and Dose Relationships in Radiation Biology as Applied to Radiotherapy, USAEC Report BNL-50203, pp. 54-69, Brookhaven National Laboratory, 1970.
3. T. L. Phillips, Split-Dose Recovery in Euoxic and Hypoxic Normal and Tumor Cells, *Radiology*, **105**: 127-134(1972).
4. H. D. Suit, Statement of the Problem Pertaining to the Effect of Dose-Fractionation and Total Treatment Time on Response of Tissue to X-Irradiation, in Time and Dose Relationships in Radiation Biology as Applied to Radiotherapy, USAEC Report BNL-50203, pp. vii-x, Brookhaven National Laboratory, 1970.
5. D. B. Leeper, M. H. Schneiderman, and W. C. Dewey, Radiation-Induced Cycle Division Delay in Synchronized Chinese Hamster Ovary Cells in Monolayer Culture, *Radiat. Res.*, **50**: 401-417 (1972).
6. D. B. Leeper, M. H. Schneiderman, and W. C. Dewey, Radiation-Induced Cycle Delay in Synchronized Chinese Hamster Cells: Comparison Between DNA Synthesis and Division, *Radiat. Res.*, **53**: 326-337 (1973).

7. G. R. Shepherd, R. A. Walters, J. M. Hardin, and B. J. Nolan, The Effects of X-Irradiation on Histone Acetylation and Methylation in Cultured Mammalian Cells, *Arch. Biochem. Biophys.*, 149: 175-182 (1972).

8. M. H. Schneiderman, W. C. Dewey, D. B. Leeper, and H. Nagasawa, Use of the Mitotic Selection Procedure for Cell Cycle Analysis: Comparison Between the X-Ray and Cycloheximide $G_2$ Markers, *Exp. Cell Res.*, 74: 430-438 (1972).

9. W. C. Dewey, S. C. Freeman, and H. H. Miller, Comparison of Lethality and Chromosomal Damage Induced by X-Rays in Synchronized Chinese Hamster Cells In Vitro, *Radiat. Res.*, 43: 561-581 (1970).

10. A. V. Carrano, Chromosome Aberrations and Radiation-Induced Cell Death. I. Transmission and Survival Parameters of Aberrations, *Mutat. Res.*, 17: 341-353 (1973).

11. A. V. Carrano, Chromosome Aberrations and Radiation-Induced Cell Death. II. Predicted and Observed Cell Survival, *Mutat. Res.*, 17: 355-366 (1973).

12. J. S. Belli, G. J. Dicus, and W. Nagle, Repair of Radiation Damage as a Factor and Preoperative Radiation Therapy, in The Interrelationship of Surgery and Radiation Therapy in the Treatment of Cancer, J. M. Vaeth (ed.), Proceedings of the 5th Annual San Francisco Cancer Symposium, *Frontiers of Radiation Therapy and Oncology*, Vol. 5, pp. 40-47, University Park Press, Baltimore, 1971.

13. J. B. Little, G. M. Hahn, E. Frindel, and M. Tubiana, Repair of Potentially Lethal Radiation Damage In Vitro and In Vivo, *Radiology*, 106: 689-694 (1973).

14. W. C. Dewey, H. H. Miller, and D. B. Leeper, Chromosomal Aberrations and Mortality of X-Irradiated Mammalian Cells: Emphasis on Repair, *Proc. Nat. Acad. Sci. U. S. A.*, 68: 667-671 (1971).

15. W. C. Dewey, J. S. Noel, and C. M. Dettor, Changes in Radiosensitivity and Dispersion of Chromatin During the Cell Cycle of Synchronous Chinese Hamster Cells, *Radiat. Res.*, 52: 373-394 (1972).

16. W. C. Dewey, L. E. Stone, H. H. Miller, and R. E. Giblak, Radiosensitization with 5-Bromodeoxyuridine of Chinese Hamster Cells X-Irradiated During Different Phases of the Cell Cycle, *Radiat. Res.*, 47: 672-688 (1971).

17. W. K. Sinclair, Dependence of Radiosensitivity upon Cell Age, in Time and Dose Relationships in Radiation Biology as Applied to Radiotherapy, USAEC Report BNL-50203, pp. 97-107, Brookhaven National Laboratory, 1970.

18. G. F. Whitmore, S. Gulyas, and J. Kotalik, Recovery from Radiation Damage in Mammalian Cells, in Time and Dose Relationships in Radiation Biology as Applied to Radiotherapy, USAEC Report BNL-50203, pp. 41-46, Brookhaven National Laboratory, 1970.

19. L. F. Winans, W. C. Dewey, and C. M. Dettor, Repair of Sub-Lethal and Potentially Lethal X-Ray Damage in Synchronous Chinese Hamster Cells, *Radiat. Res.*, 52: 333-351 (1972).

20. C. K. Yu and W. K. Sinclair, Mitotic Delay and Chromosomal Aberrations Induced by X-Rays in Synchronized Chinese Hamster Cells In Vitro, *J. Nat. Cancer Inst.*, 39: 619-632 (1967).

21. L. J. Tolmach, T. Terasima, and R. A. Phillips, X-Ray Sensitivity Changes During the Division Cycle of HeLa S3 Cells and Anomalous Survival Kinetics of Developing Microcolonies, in *Cellular Radiation Biology*, pp. 376-393, The Williams and Wilkins Company, Baltimore, 1965.

22. G. F. Whitmore, J. E. Till, and S. Gulyas, Radiation-Induced Mitotic Delay in L Cells, *Radiat. Res.*, 30: 155-171 (1967).

23. L. H. Thompson and H. D. Suit, Proliferation Kinetics of X-Irradiated Mouse L Cells Studied with Time-Lapse Photography. II, *Int. J. Radiat. Biol.*, 15: 347-362 (1969).

24. T. C. Evans, R. F. Hagemann and D. B. Leeper, Mitotic Inhibition and Its Relation to Survival in S-180 Ascites Tumor Cells In Vivo Following Fractionated Exposures of X-Irradiation, *Radiat. Res.*, **45**: 85-93 (1971).

25. D. B. Leeper and R. F. Hagemann, Repair Kinetics of Radiation-Induced Mitotic Delay, *Biophys. J.*, **13**: 179-185 (1973).

26. E. M. Levine, Mycoplasma Contamination of Animal Cell Cultures: A Simple, Rapid Detection Method, *Exp. Cell Res.*, **74**: 99-109 (1972).

27. T. Terasima and L. J. Tolmach, Growth and Nucleic Acid Synthesis in Synchronously Dividing Populations of HeLa Cells, *Exp. Cell Res.*, **30**: 344-362 (1963).

28. T. C. Hsu and O. Klatt, Mammalian Chromosomes In Vitro. ix. On Genetic Polymorphism in Cell Populations, *J. Nat. Cancer Inst.*, **21**: 437-473 (1958).

29. M. Dixon, *Enzymes*, pp. 150-170, Academic Press, Inc., New York, 1958.

30. A. White, T. Handler, and E. L. Smith, *Principles of Biochemistry*, 3rd ed., pp. 219-240, McGraw-Hill Book Company, New York, 1964.

31. J. E. Sisken, L. Morasca, and S. Kibby, Effect of Temperature on the Kinetics of the Mitotic Cycle of Mammalian Cells in Culture, *Exp. Cell Res.*, **39**: 103-116 (1965).

32. D. R. Miller, W. C. Dewey, and H. H. Miller, X-Ray Induced Delay in the Chinese Hamster Cell Cycle: Dependence on Phase Irradiated Under Different Culturing Conditions, BUdR Incorporation and Hypertonic Treatment, *Int. J. Radiat. Biol.*, **23**: 591-602 (1973).

33. J. A. Glasel, A Study of Water in Biological Systems by $O^{17}$ Magnetic Resonance Spectroscopy, I. Preliminary Studies and Xenon Hydrates, *Proc. Nat. Acad. Sci. U. S. A.*, **55**: 479-485 (1966).

34. L. C. Lau, Effects of Liquid Water Phase Transition on the Growth of L929 Cells, *Exp. Cell Res.*, **71**: 475-477 (1972).

35. H. Katsuta and T. Takaoka, Effects of Suboptimal Temperatures on the Growth of Rat Epithelial Cells in Tissue Culture, *Jap. J. Exp. Med.*, **43**: 191-200 (1973).

# CELL KINETICS IN THE SKIN OF MICE ONE YEAR AFTER IRRADIATION WITH CYCLOTRON-ACCELERATED HELIUM IONS

JOHN T. LEITH, W. A. SCHILLING, G. P. WELCH, and C. A. TOBIAS
Lawrence Berkeley Laboratory and Donner Laboratory of Medical Physics, University of California, Berkeley, California

## ABSTRACT

The cell kinetics of the dorsal skin of the mouse were studied 1 year after irradiation with low-energy helium ions. The labelled mitoses curves of mouse epidermis for dose levels of 75 to 2000 rads indicate that the lowest dose at which definite disturbance in epidermal cell kinetics may be found is 1200 rads. At this dose level and higher levels, the epidermis is characterized morphologically by the presence of a persistent hyperplastic epithelium. This acanthotic epidermis is associated with an increased duration of the $G_1$ phase of the cell cycle, a slower turnover time, and a greater number of cells with the ability to synthesize DNA per unit length of epidermis.

The effects of ionizing radiation on the cell kinetics of skin represent an important area of investigation, particularly since radiation appears to induce a dose-dependent persistent acanthosis or hyperplasia of epidermis, a fact that differentiates radiation from the transient cell kinetic changes occurring after wound healing, for example.[1-4] Acute changes occurring in epidermal cell kinetics after irradiation have been well studied. For example, Song and Tabachnick[5] studied the kinetics of cell-population turnover in the guinea pig after 3000 rep of $^{90}Sr-^{90}Y$ beta rays. However, although acute changes have been well studied, there is a relative paucity of cell kinetic data on nontumorous irradiated skin at long postirradiation times.

With the exception of the work done by Yamaguchi and Tabachnick[6] dealing with local beta-particle irradiation of guinea pig skin at 150 days postirradiation and the morphology presented by Lippincott, Baker, and Stickley[7] on changes in mouse skin 1 year after irradiation with protons of helium ions, there are few data available. The question of the actual time persistence of hyperplastic epidermis and its relationship to dose level, to long-term production of skin tumors, and to the disturbance in regulatory control mechanisms permitting establishment of such a new steady state have yet to be investigated.

We previously reported[8] that irradiation of the entire surface of the mouse with helium ions of an energy sufficient to penetrate maximally only 0.5 mm into the animal would produce a dose-dependent life shortening, a dose-dependent moist desquamation and epilation, and a dose-dependent production of skin tumors. At the time of the report, the means by which the life-shortening effect was brought about was not known. In this report we present data on survivors of the helium-ion irradiations at 1-year postirradiation. Specifically cell kinetic data on the irradiated skin are presented as a function of dose level; other findings at necropsy are also included.

## MATERIALS AND METHODS

Male CD-1 mice, obtained from the Charles River Breeding Laboratories, were used. They were irradiated at 70 days of age and housed singly for the duration of their life-spans in pint mason jars. At this age the mice should be in the telogen of hair growth.[9,10] They were given food and water ad libitum. The water was slightly chlorinated to prevent growth of *Pseudomonas* organisms.

The detailed irradiation procedures for the helium-ion exposures were previously reported.[8] Briefly, the mice are held in tubular Mylar holders (7.5 by 2.5 cm) and rotated, while in an upright position, in front of a helium-ion beam of 40-MeV initial energy. The exposures covered the entire surface of the mouse. Considering the absorption of the helium-ion beam by the Mylar holder and the hair of the mouse, the residual maximum penetration range in tissue is approximately 0.5 mm with an energy at the surface of 26 MeV. The rotation of the beam also creates a family of Bragg ionization curves that superimpose to produce a relatively flat depth—dose distribution over this 0.5-mm range (Fig. 1).

One year after irradiation, the mice were sacrificed for histological and autoradiographic studies. To obtain labelled mitoses curves for the skin of the irradiated mice, we injected the mice intraperitoneally with 1 $\mu$Ci of $^3$H—thymidine ($^3$H—TdR) (6.7 Ci/mmole) in 0.85% sodium chloride per gram of body weight between 0800 and 1000. Keeping a more or less constant time of label injection reduces the effect of diurnal rhythms in skin mitotic activity, a prominent feature of mouse skin. Mice were maintained on a 12-hr light—dark cycle (0700 to 1900). At varying times postinjection, animals were sacrificed, and the following tissue samples were obtained: right kidney, a section of the median lobe of the kidney, the spleen, a sample of peripheral blood from the orbital venous sinus, and two dorsal and two ventral samples of skin. The tissues were immediately fixed in Bouin's solution, embedded in Tissueprep, and sectioned at 5-$\mu$m thickness. For skin, care was taken to cut sections perpendicular to the skin surface.

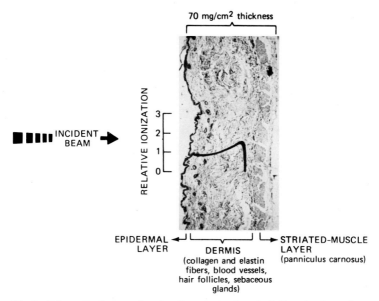

**Fig. 1** Schematic diagram showing the penetration of a helium-ion beam into the skin of the mouse.

Autoradiographs of skin were made by dipping slides in Kodak NTB-2 emulsion. They were developed in Kodak D-19 developer after 2 weeks of exposure with desiccant at 4°C. The developed autoradiographs were stained with hematoxylin and eosin. The liver, kidney, and spleen tissues were not processed for autoradiography. For them and for the skin samples, hematoxylin and eosin, Mallory's trichrome, and Feulgen stainings were used. In counting labelled mitoses, we used a minimum of three grains to identify a labelled cell, and, in counting labelled cells and labelled mitoses, we scored only interfollicular epidermis. Slides were counted using a 100X oil-immersion objective with 10X eyepieces.

## CLINICAL OBSERVATIONS OF MICE 1 YEAR AFTER IRRADIATION

Animal weights as a function of dose level are shown in Table 1. Although there is a slight tendency for average weight to decrease with increasing dose, there is no significant difference between dose groups. Helium-ion irradiations produce an acute syndrome consisting of dose-dependent epilation and moist desquamation. The epilation is persistent, indicating permanant damage to the hair follicle cells. The degree of damage is presented in Table 2 as a function of dose level. The amount of the surface of the mouse (about 55 cm$^2$) involved in

TABLE 1

WEIGHTS OF MICE 1 YEAR AFTER IRRADIATION
WITH LOW-ENERGY HELIUM IONS

| Dose, rads | No. of mice | Mean wt.,*<br>g | S.D., g | Range, g |
|:---:|:---:|:---:|:---:|:---:|
| 0 | 80 | 48.0 | 5.5 | 39.0−64.0 |
| 75 | 17 | 51.5 | 5.5 | 44.0−64.0 |
| 150 | 19 | 47.0 | 6.5 | 34.5−60.0 |
| 300 | 17 | 49.5 | 5.0 | 42.0−62.0 |
| 600 | 16 | 44.0 | 4.0 | 39.0−52.0 |
| 1200 | 16 | 47.0 | 6.0 | 37.0−55.0 |
| 1400 | 14 | 42.5 | 6.0 | 34.0−51.0 |
| 2000 | 16 | 42.0 | 8.5 | 23.0−56.0 |

*To the nearest 0.5 g.

TABLE 2

PERCENT OF MOUSE SURFACE PERMANENTLY
EPILATED 1-YEAR AFTER IRRADIATION WITH
HELIUM IONS

| Dose, rads | No. of mice | Surface<br>epilated,* % | Range, % |
|:---:|:---:|:---:|:---:|
| 0 | 80 | 0 | |
| 75 | 17 | 0 | |
| 150 | 19 | 0 | |
| 300 | 17 | 3 | 0−20 |
| 600 | 16 | 6 | 0−30 |
| 1200 | 16 | 16 | 0−55 |
| 1400 | 14 | 30 | 5−70 |
| 2000 | 16 | 41 | 8−80 |

*The body surface was estimated at 55 $cm^2$. Results are
expressed to the nearest percent.

permanent epilation was estimated and expressed as a percent of the total
surface; the percentage increased with increasing dose level. Mice were also
examined for the presence of cataracts and tumors, and neither cataracts nor the
number or type of tumors found showed any dose dependence. (Table 3).

Hematological values of peripheral blood are presented in Table 4. None of
the peripheral-blood parameters examined showed any obvious dose dependence.

**TABLE 3**

OTHER CLINICAL FINDINGS AT SACRIFICE
OF MICE

| Dose, rads | No. of cataracts | No. of tumors | Type of tumor |
|---|---|---|---|
| 0 | 0/80 | 3 | Hepatomas |
| 75 | 0/17 | 2 | Hepatomas |
| 150 | 0/19 | 0 | |
| 300 | 1/17 | 2 | Hepatoma/skin tumor (squamous-cell carcinoma) |
| 600 | 1/16 | 0 | |
| 1200 | 1/16 | 2 | Hepatoma/leukemia (myelogenous) |
| 1400 | 1/14 | 0 | |
| 2000 | 1/16 | 0 | |

## CELL KINETICS OF DORSAL SKIN

The typical histologic appearance of irradiated dorsal skin at the different dose levels used is shown in Figs. 2 and 3. No areas of active ulceration were taken for histologic and autoradiographic processing. The labelling and mitotic indexes of interfollicular basal cells were estimated by counting at least 2000 basal cells. At least 100 mitotic cells were counted, and all stages of mitosis were scored.

### Results for Control Dorsal Epidermis

The variation of mitotic index with time of day was studied. Two peaks of mitotic activity were seen, at 0600 and 1400. The average mitotic index over the 24-hr period was 1.0% with a range of 0.8 to 1.6%.

The curve for percent labelled mitoses showed two clear waves of labelled mitoses, the second wave rising to about 50% of the first wave at 105 to 108 hr postinjection. Two animals were used per time interval. The duration of the cell cycle and the duration of its phases are shown in Table 5 and are best fit by eye values.

### Results for Irradiated Dorsal Epidermis

One year after irradiation not enough mice per dose level were alive to allow us to perform as complete a labelled-mitoses curve as was done with unirradiated mice. Only the first wave of labelled mitoses could be seen; therefore one mouse

TABLE 4

HEMATOLOGICAL VALUES FOR MICE 1 YEAR AFTER WHOLE-EPIDERMIS IRRADIATION WITH HELIUM IONS

| Dose, rads | No. | Packed cell volume, % | Spleen wt., mg | WBC count, x $10^3$/mm$^3$ | Peripheral WBC differential,* % | | | | |
|---|---|---|---|---|---|---|---|---|---|
| | | | | | Neut. | Im. neut. | Lympho. | Mono. | Eos. |
| C | 68 | 38.1 ± 5.3 | 80.6 ± 23.4 | 4.4 ± 0.5 | 31.7 | 0.4 | 66.1 | 0.4 | 1.4 |
| 75 | 18 | 35.5 ± 8.2 | 106.6 ± 46.6 | 4.8 ± 0.6 | 37.2 | 1.2 | 60.0 | 0.1 | 1.5 |
| 150 | 16 | 38.9 ± 4.6 | 99.6 ± 68.5 | 5.2 ± 0.4 | 41.4 | 0.3 | 56.8 | 0.4 | 1.1 |
| 300 | 17 | 39.2 ± 3.7 | 92.5 ± 32.2 | 4.5 ± 0.8 | 39.3 | 0.3 | 58.8 | 0.0 | 1.6 |
| 600 | 16 | 38.0 ± 5.5 | 133.4 ± 67.3 | 4.6 ± 0.3 | 40.5 | 0.2 | 58.1 | 0.1 | 1.1 |
| 1200 | 16 | 39.1 ± 2.1 | 96.2 ± 42.8 | 5.2 ± 0.9 | 38.3 | 0.2 | 58.9 | 0.1 | 2.5 |
| 1400 | 15 | 36.5 ± 4.1 | 134.0 ± 79.4 | 5.4 ± 0.4 | 49.7 | 0.4 | 49.4 | 0.0 | 0.5 |
| 2000 | 14 | 35.6 ± 6.4 | 105.5 ± 55.5 | 5.5 ± 0.5 | 45.1 | 0.1 | 53.5 | 0.2 | 1.1 |

*Neut., neutrophils; Im. neut., immature neutrophils; lympho., lymphocytes; mono., monocytes; and eos., eosinophils.

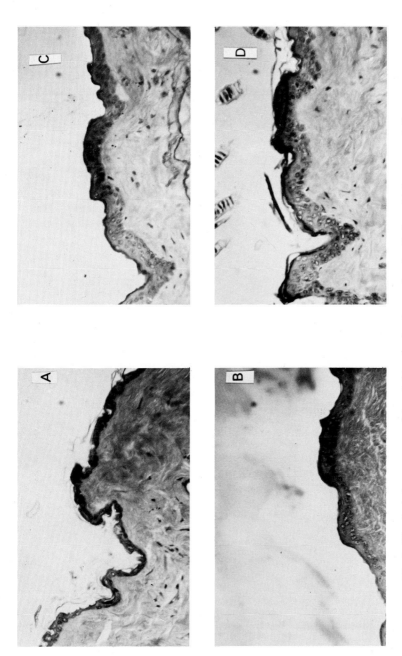

Fig. 2 Histological appearance of dorsal skin of mice 1 year after irradiation with low-energy helium ions. The absorbed doses were A, control; B, 75 rads; C, 150 rads; and D, 300 rads. (Hematoxylin–eosin stain; magnification, 288 x.)

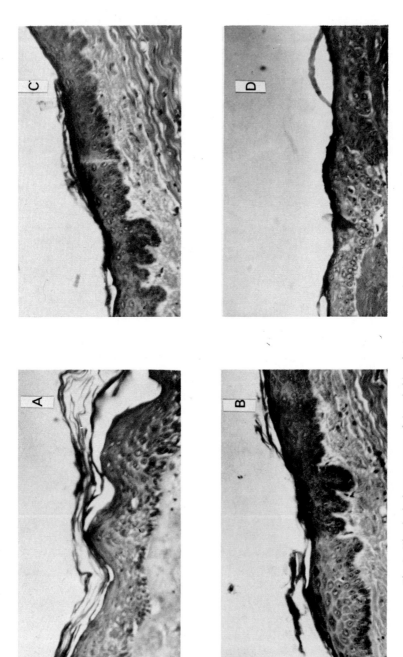

Fig. 3 Histological appearance of dorsal skin of mice 1 year after irradiation with low-energy helium ions. The absorbed doses were A, 600 rads; B, 1200 rads; C, 1400 rads; and D, 2000 rads. (Hematoxylin—eosin stain; magnification, 288 x.)

## TABLE 5
## DURATIONS (HOURS) OF CELL-CYCLE PHASES OF DORSAL EPIDERMIS 1 YEAR AFTER IRRADIATION*

| | Dose level, rads | | | | | | | |
|---|---|---|---|---|---|---|---|---|
| | 0† | 75 | 150 | 300 | 600 | 1200 | 1400 | 2000 |
| $T_c$, hr | 95.0 | 95.0 | 96.0 | 92.0 | 96.0 | 102.0 | 106.0 | 110.0 |
| $T_s$, hr | 10.3 | 10.3 | 10.3 | 10.2 | 10.4 | 10.4 | 10.3 | 10.5 |
| $T_{g_2}$ + $(T_{m2})$,‡ hr | 2.6 | 2.5 | 2.4 | 2.1 | 2.4 | 2.5 | 2.5 | 2.2 |
| $T_{g_1}$, hr | 81.4 | 81.5 | 82.6 | 79.0 | 82.5 | 88.4 | 92.5 | 96.6 |
| $(LI)_{bs}$,§ hr | 5.52 | | | | | | | 3.85 |
| $(LI)_b$, hr | 8.00 | 7.90 | 7.84 | 8.13 | 7.94 | 7.48 | 7.10 | 6.91 |
| N(b)/mm | 117 | 124 | 119 | 124 | 130 | 169 | 177 | 180 |
| $T_{bs}$,¶ days | 7.8 | | | | | | | 11.4 |

*Estimated by eye from percent labelled mitoses curves.

†The cell-cycle time ($T_c$) was determined from the time between the first and second waves of percent labelled mitoses; all other $T_c$ values for other doses were determined from the first wave of mitoses only, using a second-order approximation method.

‡The duration of mitoses ($T_m$) for controls (only) was calculated to be about 1.4 hr, using the relationship $T_m = T_c \times (MI)_b/\ln 2$, where the average 24-hr mitotic index of the basal cells was 1%. This yields a $T_{g_2}$ for controls of about 1.9 hr.

§ $(LI)_{bs}$, labelling index for a single population of basal cells and spinous cells.

¶Approximate rates of differentiation (turnover time) of the epidermal basal and spinous cells were calculated using $T_{bs}$ (days) = $T_s/(LI)_{bs}$.

was used per time period postinjection, and the cell-cycle time and length of subphases were calculated[6,11] from the equation

$$T_c = \frac{Ts + [Ts^2 + 2(2T_2 Ts + Ts^2)(LI)_b]^{\frac{1}{2}}}{2(LI)_b/\ln 2}$$

where $T_s$ = the DNA synthetic time and is taken from the 50% points on the first wave of labelled mitoses

$T_2$ = the time from the beginning of the G$_2$ phase to halfway through mitosis, $T_{g_2} + (T_m/2)$ and was estimated from the 50% point on the ascending limb of the percent labelled mitosis curve

$(LI)_b$ = the basal-cell labelling index and was determined by counting 5 different sections and 500 cells in each section on mice at the 1-hr point after the $^3$H—TdR injection. Values for all dose levels studied are shown in Table 5.

## DISCUSSION

One of the primary objectives of this research was to provide an answer to the dose-dependent life-shortening effect found after irradiation of the entire surface of the mouse.[8] Disappointingly, our data obtained by sacrificing the mice 1-year after irradiation do not provide such insight. The data presented in Tables 1 through 4 show no obvious dose dependence of tumorigenesis or other physiological change. The fact that peripheral-blood hematological values are not widely disparate between dose levels was not expected. An early hypothesis had been that irradiation of the entire skin would produce an environment such that red blood cells in skin capillary beds might be damaged in their passage, predisposing the animal to an anemic situation. Such a response was not found. Our value of 38% for the hematocrit at 1-year postirradiation is in poor agreement with a value of about 52% reported by the Charles River Breeding Laboratories for these mice[12] at 20 weeks of age. The Charles River Laboratories also report that the differential peripheral-blood count for 20-week old mice is about 75% lymphocytes and 25% neutrophils; our control mice showed about 66% lymphocytes and 32% neutrophils. There is evidence of slight neutrophilia in the irradiated mice. Also, histological sections of liver and kidney do not show any dose-dependent degenerative changes that could be correlated with decreased life-span.

With regard to the histological and kinetic changes in irradiated mouse skin, acute inflammation of the mucous membranes of the eyes and of the mouth region is seen at about 14 days postirradiation. The time of maximal involvement of skin in an early reaction is about 28 days postirradiation. The lowest dose of helium ions at which rare areas of early moist desquamation could be seen is about 800 rads. However, from a dose—response curve obtained for production of moist desquamation, a tentative threshold dose of about 1150 rads is found, with about 50% of the entire surface of the mouse involved in moist desquamation at a dose of 2900 rads (area involved at time of maximal development of early reactions). This early threshold of about 1150 rads for production of moist desquamation correlates surprisingly well with the fact that at a dose level of about 1200 rads clear signs of a late persistent hyperplasia are first seen.

With regard to changes in the cell kinetics of irradiated skin, use of the second-order approximation for estimation of intermitotic times assumes that the growth fraction of the labelled epidermal cells is 1 and that cells are distributed exponentially along the cell cycle. We have not shown that the growth fraction is indeed 1 in these irradiated mice, because there were not enough mice to allow us to perform continuous labelling experiments to show that all cells were cycling. However, it has been shown[13-15] that the growth fraction of normal epidermal cells, either unstimulated or stimulated by hair plucking, is 1.

As Yamaguchi and Tabachnick[6] pointed out, even though there is a decrease in the labelling index at the higher dose levels in the established hyperplastic epithelium, this is misleading because there are more basal cells per unit length of epidermis. Table 5 shows that mice irradiated with 2000 rads have about 50% more basal cells than control mice of comparable age. In control mice there are about 9.4 DNA synthesizing cells per millimeter, whereas, in the epidermis receiving 2000 rads of helium ions, there are about 12.4 per millimeter.

Our intermitotic time in control mice of 95 hr compares well with values of 91 to 92 hr for the guinea pig,[6] 101 hr for mice,[16] and 83 to 110 hr for hairless mice.[13] Yamaguchi and Tabachnick[6] also reported no significant change in epidermal cell-cycle parameters in irradiated guinea pigs at ages of 3 to 8 months.

Table 5 shows that the turnover time of the epidermal cells increased by about 45% in the mice irradiated with 2000 rads (7.8 to 11.4 days).

In summary, a dose of about 1200 rads or more of low-energy helium ions with a relatively high linear energy transfer (LET) (average LET may be given as about 50 keV/$\mu$m) will produce in CD-1 albino mice a persistent hyperplasia. This acanthotic epidermis is characterized by an increased $G_1$ duration, a slower turnover time, and a greater number of cells with DNA synthetic ability per unit length of epidermis. Similar results have been shown after a dose of 3000 rep of beta particles in the guinea pig.[7]

Why this persistent alteration in tissue organization occurs is not known. However, several possibilities include

1. Damage to dermal structures, such as blood vessels and connective-tissue elements, to the extent that some epidermal process dependent on dermal integrity is impaired. One could hypothesize a decrease in the availability of some nutrient that would produce increased cell activity. (One might ask, What has happened to the fraction of hypoxic cells thought to be present in epidermis[17] in the established hyperplastic epithelium?) In this regard, it should be possible to study the cell kinetics of capillary endothelial cells in the skin, for example by using the technique developed by Tannock and Hayashi.[18] Concerning the dependency of epidermal activity on dermal integrity, Leith et al.[8] have shown that, for the same dose to the epidermis, if one does or does not also irradiate the dermis, the ability of the epidermis to form visible clones will be significantly higher following epidermis-only irradiation. The critical depth at which such epidermal sparing would not occur was between 220 to 310 $\mu$m deep in skin.

2. Possible interference with normal growth-regulation processes. Much research has been directed toward the epidermal chalone, which is broadly described as a tissue-specific species-nonspecific protein that regulates the rate of epidermal-cell production by a process of negative feedback inhibition,[19] possibly[20] at $G_1$, with the inhibitory action being potentiated by epinephrine.[21,22] To date, there have been no studies of the level and action of such a chalone after radiation damage to skin. It would be of interest to see if

there were a correlation between chalone level, degree of histological hyper-plasia, and changes in cell kinetics.

## ACKNOWLEDGMENTS

The research reported here was supported jointly by the U. S. Atomic Energy Commission and by the National Aeronautics and Space Administration. The authors wish to thank the skillful operators of the Lawrence Berkeley Laboratory 88-in. cyclotron for their help.

## REFERENCES

1. G. D. Winter, Movement of Epidermal Cells Over the Wound Surface, in *Wound Healing*, W. Montagna and R. E. Billingham (Eds.), pp. 113-117, The Macmillan Company, New York, 1964.
2. P. Block, I. Seiter, and W. Oehlert, Autoradiographic Studies of the Initial Cellular Response to Injury, *Exp. Cell Res.*, **30**: 311-321 (1963).
3. F. Devik, Studies on Cell Population Kinetics of X-Irradiated and Shielded Mouse Epidermis by Autoradiographs After Administration of Trititated Thymidine, *Acta Pathol. Microbiol. Scand., Suppl.*, **148**: 35-41 (1961).
4. F. Devik, Studies on the Duration of DNA-Synthesis and Mitosis in Irradiated and Regenerating Epidermis Cells in Mice, by Means of Tritium-Labelled Thymidine, *Int. J. Radiat. Biol.*, **5**: 59-66 (1962).
5. C. W. Song and J. Tabachnick, Cell Population Kinetics in Radiation-Induced Hyperplastic Epidermis of Guinea Pig Skin, *Int. J. Radiat. Biol.*, **15**: 171-174 (1969).
6. T. Yamaguchi and J. Tabachnick, Cell Kinetics of Epidermal Repopulation and Persistent Hyperplasia in Locally $\beta$-Irradiated Guinea Pig Skin, *Radiat. Res.*, **50**: 158-180 (1972).
7. S. W. Lippincott, C. P. Baker, and E. E. Stickley, A Study of the Influence of Spatial Distribution of Ionization on Skin Carcinogenesis Using Proton and Alpha-Particle Bombardment, *Radiology*, **91**: 537-539 (1968).
8. J. T. Leith, G. P. Welch, W. A. Schilling, and C. A. Tobias, Life-Span Measurements and Skin Tumorigenesis in Mice Following Total-Body Helium-Ion Irradiation of the Skin to Different Maximum Penetration Depths, in *Radionuclide Carcinogenesis*, Richland, Wash., May 10—12, 1972, C. L. Sanders et al. (Eds.), AEC Symposium Series, No. 29(CONF-720505), pp. 90—105, 1973.
9. H. B. Chase, H. Rauch, and V. W. Smith, Critical Stages of Hair Development and Pigmentation in the Mouse, *Physiol. Zool.*, **24**: 1-53 (1951).
10. C. S. Potten, B. A. Jessup, and M. B. Croxson, Incorporation of Tritiated Thymidine into the Skin and Hair Follicles. I. Oscillatory Changes Through the Hair Growth Cycle, *Cell Tissue Kinet.*, **4**: 241-254 (1971).
11. A. B. Reiskin and M. L. Mendelsohn, A Comparison of the Cell Cycle in Induced Carcinomas and Their Normal Counterparts, *Cancer Res.*, **24**: 1131-1136 (1946).
12. *Charles River Digest*, Vol. 10, No. 4, Charles River Breeding Laboratories, Wilmington, Mass., 1971.
13. O. H. Iversen, R. Bjerknes, and F. Devik, Kinetics of Cell Renewal, Cell Migration and Cell Loss in the Hairless Mouse Dorsal Epidermis, *Cell Tissue Kinet.*, **1**: 351-367 (1968).

14. J. M. Brown and R. Oliver, A New Method of Estimating the Cell Cycle Time in Epithelial Tissues of Long Generation Time, *Cell Tissue Kinet.*, **1**: 11-21 (1968).
15. M. A. H. Hegazy and J. F. Fowler, Cell Population Kinetics of Plucked and Unplucked Mouse Skin. I. Unirradiated Skin, *Cell Tissue Kinet.*, **6**: 17-33 (1973).
16. M. A. Hegazy and J. F. Fowler, Effect of Hair Plucking on the Kinetics of Methylcholanthrene-Induced Skin Tumors in Mice, *Cell Tissue Kinet.*, **3**: 317-319 (1970).
17. S. B. Field and S. Hornsey, RBE Values for Cyclotron Neutrons for Effects on Normal Tissues and Tumours as a Function of Dose and Dose Fractionation, *Europ. J. Cancer*, **7**: 161-170 (1971).
18. I. F. Tannock and S. Hayashi, The Proliferation of Capillary Endothelial Cells, *Cancer Res.*, **32**: 77-82 (1972).
19. W. S. Bullough and E. B. Laurence, The Control of Epidermal Mitotic Activity in the Mouse, *Proc. Roy. Soc. (London), Ser. B*, **151**: 417-536 (1960).
20. C. L. Wiley, W. W. Williams, and C. J. McDonald, The Effects of the Epidermal Chalone on DNA Synthesis in Mammalian Epidermal Cells, *J. Invest. Dermatol.*, **60**: 160-165 (1973).
21. W. S. Bullough and E. B. Laurence, Mitotic Control by Internal Secretion: the Role of the Chalone-Adrenalin Complex, *Exp. Cell Res.*, **33**: 176-194 (1964).
22. W. A. Schilling, G. Magilen, and J. T. Leith, Response of Human Primary Foreskin Cells to a Cell-Extract Obtained From Skin, *Experientia*, **28**: 161-162 (1972).

# EFFECT OF PULMONARY IRRADIATION FROM INTERNAL EMITTERS ON THE TRANSFORMATION AND KINETICS OF CANINE LYMPHOCYTES IN VITRO

STEPHEN A. BENJAMIN, ANTONE L. BROOKS, and ROBERT K. JONES
Inhalation Toxicology Research Institute, Lovelace Foundation
for Medical Education and Research, Albuquerque, New Mexico

## ABSTRACT

Beagle dogs exposed via inhalation to $^{144}$Ce in fused clay exhibited a profound and persistent lymphopenia and developed primary pulmonary neoplasms 2 to 3 years after exposure. Experiments were designed to evaluate the functional characteristics of the residual lymphocyte populations in these dogs. Lymphocyte transformation and the kinetics of the lymphocyte response to plant mitogens in vitro were studied in $^{144}$Ce-exposed and control dogs. Normal beagle dog lymphocytes responded to both phytohemagglutinin (PHA) and pokeweed mitogen (PWM) although the responses varied quantitatively. Compared to controls, lymphocytes from dogs with radiation-induced lymphopenia had a reduced ability to respond to both mitogens. Lymphocyte kinetic studies indicated that the time before initial DNA synthesis varied between individual cells. The kinetics of lymphocyte response to PHA and PWM also differed although it varied between dogs. This was true of lymphocytes from both irradiated and control animals. These data suggest that two different populations of canine lymphocytes may be stimulated by PHA and PWM and that both are affected by chronic irradiation. The combined effect of the lymphopenia and the functional lymphocyte depression on the general immune response coupled with the direct carcinogenetic effect of chronic pulmonary irradiation could lead to early development of pulmonary neoplasms.

The lymphocyte is extremely sensitive to cell killing from radiation.[1] In addition, external high-dose-rate radiation has a definite suppressive effect on both humoral and cellular immunity.[2] Two major functional classes of lymphocytes have been described: those responsible for cell-mediated immunity (T lymphocytes) and those responsible for humoral immunity (B lymphocytes).[3-5] Functional differences between T and B lymphocytes are reflected in their responses to stimulatory agents, including plant mitogens, in vitro.[6-8] Response to phytohemagglutinin (PHA) is a property of T lymphocytes,[8-11] and the major cell type responding to pokeweed mitogen (PWM) appears to be the B lymphocytes (Refs. 8, 10, 12, and 13). Some effects of high-dose-rate irradiation on lymphocytes have been elucidated by using mitogenic stimulants. Canine lymphocytes X-irradiated in vitro have an impaired ability to respond to PHA.[14] Human lymphocytes irradiated in vitro and lymphocytes from patients receiving radiation therapy also have an impaired response to PHA.[15] In addition, thoracic irradiation of human cancer patients can lead to prolonged lymphopenia[16-19] with evidence that T lymphocytes are selectively depressed.[18]

Lymphocyte depression has been observed in beagle dogs receiving protracted low-dose-rate pulmonary irradiation after inhalation of alpha- and beta-emitting radionuclides.[20-22] This is a somewhat surprising effect considering the localization of radiation dose to the respiratory system. The chronic pulmonary irradiation in these animals also resulted in the development of primary pulmonary neoplasms at a time when the lymphopenia was still manifest.[23,24] The potential regulatory role of cell-mediated and humoral immunity in oncogenesis is the subject of much current research.[25,26] Clinical and experimental studies have shown that both naturally occurring and induced immune deficiencies are associated with an increased incidence of malignancy.[27] The relationship between the lymphopenia and the pulmonary neoplasms in beagle dogs is not clear. The potential selective effect of radiation on T and B lymphocytes is important since this could influence the type of immune capability impaired. This is especially true since cell-mediated immunity has been implicated as the major line of immunological defense against neoplasia.[25]

Our experiments were designed to evaluate the relative effect of protracted low-dose-rate pulmonary beta radiation on lymphocyte subpopulations. The data were obtained from studies on beagle dogs which were exposed by inhalation to $^{144}$Ce in fused clay and subsequently developed persistent lymphopenia.

## METHODS

### Exposure, Dosimetry, and Clinical Methods

The 24 beagle dogs used for this study were selected from a group of 50 that were being used to study the pathogenesis of the toxic effects of inhalation of $^{144}$Ce in fused clay. At 12 to 14 months of age, 14 of these dogs received a single nose-only exposure to $^{144}$Ce, and 10 were exposed to stable cerium in fused clay. The breeding and management procedures have been described,[28,29] and detailed descriptions of the exposure methods and radioactive-aerosol preparation have been reported.[30,31] The dogs were exposed to the experimental aerosols for various periods of time so as to achieve initial lung burdens (ILB) of approximately 45, 25, or 12.5 $\mu$Ci/kg of body weight. The particle-size distributions of the $^{144}$Ce—fused-clay aerosols were log normal with an activity median aerodynamic diameter (AMAD) of approximately 1.4 to 2.7 $\mu$m and a geometric standard deviation of approximately 1.5 to 2.3. The dogs were whole-body counted periodically, and the data for the first 14 days postinhalation exposure were used to graphically determine the ILB. The ILB of the dogs reported here ranged from 24 to 41 $\mu$Ci/kg. Absorbed beta doses to lung were calculated on the basis of the whole-body counting data for each dog, as previously described.[32]

All dogs were housed individually in metabolism cages after exposure and then transferred to the kennel where two of the same sex and comparable activity level were housed in each run. Each dog was observed daily, and detailed physical examinations, EKG recordings, and thoracic radiography were performed every 6 months through 1.5 years postexposure. Samples for hematology were obtained weekly for the first 28 days, monthly to 180 days, every 90 days to 1 year, and semiannually thereafter. In addition, samples for clinical chemistry were obtained every 6 months.

## Lymphocyte Culture Methods

Dogs were sampled at least twice between 52 and 66 weeks postexposure. At each sampling a minimum of 25 ml of peripheral blood was drawn in sterile sodium heparin. Aseptic techniques were used in all procedures. A smaller blood sample was always drawn concurrently in sodium ethylenediaminetetraacetic acid (EDTA) for hematological examination. Lymphocytes were separated by the addition of 6% dextran in isotonic saline to the whole blood in the amount of one-half the total blood volume. This solution was gently and thoroughly mixed and incubated at 37°C for 60 min. The suspension was then centrifuged at 430 rpm for 20 min. The leukocyte-rich plasma was separated, and total, differential, and viability counts were made on the separated cells. The lymphocytes in the plasma were centrifuged at 1500 rpm and resuspended in about 5 to 10 ml of the autologous plasma. The final culture medium was adjusted with this lymphocyte suspension to contain $0.5 \times 10^6$ viable lymphocytes per milliliter. Cultures were grown in glass screw-cap culture tubes containing 2 ml of Eagle's minimal essential medium, Spinner modification, supplemented with 10% inactivated fetal calf serum, 4 $\mu$moles of L-glutamine/ml, 100 units of penicillin G/ml, and 100 $\mu$g of streptomycin sulfate/ml. The pH was adjusted to $7.2 \pm 0.1$ with sodium bicarbonate. Lymphocyte transformation was measured by uptake of tritiated thymidine ($^3$H−TdR) into DNA. Three groups of five replicate cultures were set up for each animal. These culture groups were supplemented with 10 $\mu$l/ml of either PHA-m (DIFCO), PWM (Grand Island Biological Co.), or Hank's balanced salt solution (HBSS). The stock mitogen was reconstituted as directed by the manufacturer. These mitogen concentrations had been previously found to give optimal $^3$H−TdR uptake. Cultures were mixed gently and incubated horizontally at 37°C in a humidified atmosphere of 5% $CO_2$ and air. After 72 hr of incubation, 2 $\mu$Ci of $^3$H−TdR (24 to 29 Ci/mmole) was added to each tube. Two different batches of $^3$H—TdR were used for the first and second sampling of the dogs. After 24-hr labelling time, a 100-fold excess of cold thymidine was added to each tube. The tubes were incubated for 10 min and then centrifuged at 2000 rpm; the supernatant was discarded. The cells were washed three times with HBSS and then precipitated twice with 2 ml of cold 2% perchloric acid in isotonic saline. Next, 2 ml of 10% aqueous perchloric acid was added to the precipitate, and the mixture was incubated at $70°C$ for 30 min to hydrolyze the DNA. After centrifugation a 1.0-ml aliquot of the supernatant was added to 10 ml of a toluene-based scintillation cocktail and counted by liquid scintillation. Results were evaluated for quench, and, since this was a negligible factor, they are expressed as the gross counts per minute (cpm) per culture.

Lymphocyte kinetics were studied to elucidate the underlying cellular bases for differences in total DNA synthesis between $^{144}$Ce-exposed and control dogs by following the number of cells labelled with $^3$H—TdR and, hence, in DNA synthesis, between initiation of the cultures and 96 hr. Counts of labelled mitoses were also performed to evaluate cell-cycle times in the lymphocytes from irradiated and control dogs. For these studies 75-ml blood samples were drawn from three control and two $^{144}$Ce-exposed dogs. One of the latter dogs was sampled twice. Lymphocytes were separated and cultured as described. The number of lymphocytes available limited the total number of cultures for individual dogs. The cultures from each animal were split into two groups and stimulated with either PHA or PWM. Equal numbers of cultures containing PHA or PWM were then further split into groups for harvest at 12-hr intervals from 48 to 96 hr. Table 1 shows the harvest groups set up for each dog, and Table 2 shows the experimental design for a representative group harvested at 96 hr. At each labelling time, duplicate or triplicate cultures were pulse labelled with $^3$H—TdR for 30 min. All the labelled cultures in a group were treated with 0.4 μg of colchicine per milliliter 4 hr before harvesting. Cells were harvested by

TABLE 1

GROUPS OF CULTURES HARVESTED
FOR INDIVIDUAL DOGS

| Treatment | Harvest times, hr | | | | |
|---|---|---|---|---|---|
| | 48 | 60 | 72 | 84 | 96 |
| Control | | | | | |
| Dog 1 | X | X | | | |
| Dog 2 | | X | X | X | X |
| Dog 3 | X | X | X | | |
| $^{144}$Ce-exposed | | | | | |
| Dog 4 (first sampling) | X | X | | | |
| Dog 4 (second sampling) | X | X | X | | |
| Dog 5 | | X | X | X | X |

TABLE 2

REPRESENTATIVE EXAMPLE FOR CULTURES HARVESTED AT 96 HR

| Mitogen Treatment | Hours of Culture* | | | | | | | | | | | | | |
|---|---|---|---|---|---|---|---|---|---|---|---|---|---|---|
| | 24 | 30 | 36 | 42 | 48 | 54 | 60 | 66 | 72 | 78 | 84 | 90 | 92 | 96 |
| PHA | PL | PL | PL | PL | PL | PL | PL | PL | PL | PL | PL | PL | C | H |
| PWM | PL | PL | PL | PL | PL | PL | PL | PL | PL | PL | PL | PL | C | H |

*PL, pulse label with $^3$H—TdR (30 min). C, colchicine treatment. H, harvest. The entire group of labelled cultures was treated with colchicine at 92 hr and harvested at 96 hr.

treating with 1.1% sodium citrate, fixing with Carnoy's fixative, and preparing chromosome spreads by flaming. Autoradiographs were prepared using NTB emulsion and exposed for either 2 or 14 days depending on the apparent specific acitivity of the $^3$H—TdR used. Labelled interphase cells and labelled mitoses were counted.

# RESULTS

The radiation dose and the dose rate to the lungs of a typical dog exposed to $^{144}$Ce in fused clay are illustrated in Fig. 1. The curves are representative of the approach used for each dog in determining these parameters. The range of ILB in these animals was from 24 to 41 $\mu$Ci/kg. The beta dose rate to the lung in the 14 $^{144}$Ce-exposed dogs in this experiment ranged from 110 to 190 rads/day shortly after exposure to 11 to 19 rads/day at about 500 days postexposure. The dose rate decreased relatively rapidly over the first 6 months and then at a slower rate. Calculated cumulative doses to lung ranged from 21,000 to 36,000 rads. If 6% of the total blood volume is assumed to be in the lung at any one time, then the blood in these animals would have received a cumulative dose of from 1260 to 2160 rads.

The results of the hematological findings through 66 weeks postexposure are shown in Fig. 2. The points on the graph are based on the absolute lymphocyte counts, which were compared with preexposure counts for each dog to derive a percent of the preexposure values. Although control dogs demonstrated some variability, this group did not show a significant deviation from the preexposure values and remained between 75 and 105%. The $^{144}$Ce-exposed dogs, however, showed a significant reduction in absolute lymphocyte counts. There was a relatively rapid drop during the first 3 weeks after exposure, followed by a more protracted decline out to 66 weeks. During the period of sampling for lymphocyte-function testing (52 to 66 weeks postexposure), the peripheral lymphocyte counts in the irradiated dogs were 40% of their preexposure values, and the difference between the control and irradiated groups was highly significant.

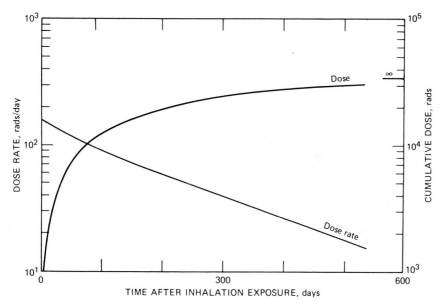

Fig. 1 Absorbed beta dose to lung for dog 541U following inhalation of $^{144}$Ce in fused clay. (ILB, 35 µCi/kg.)

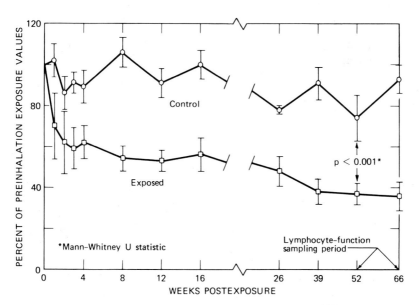

Fig. 2 Absolute lymphocyte values in beagle dogs exposed to $^{144}$Ce in fused clay. The control values represent the mean of 10 dogs. The exposed values represent the mean of 14 dogs with an ILB of 24 to 41 µCi/kg. Vertical bars represent standard error.

The responses of lymphocytes from individual dogs to plant mitogens are shown in Fig. 3. These scattergrams represent two sequential samplings on each dog. Variations between replicate cultures were considerable in most dogs despite the great care taken to keep conditions and numbers of cells constant. The use of five replicate cultures, however, minimized the effect of outlying results. There was also considerable variation between dogs in the level of response to mitogen as well as in overlap between the control and $^{144}$Ce-exposed groups. The principal finding, however, was that the dogs exposed to $^{144}$Ce tended, as a group, to respond poorly to both PHA and PWM. At the first sampling time, 11 of 14 irradiated dogs had less than 2000 cpm per culture while only 2 of 10 controls were this low. The upper range of response in the controls was also considerably higher than that in the irradiated animals. At the second sampling time, a new batch of $^3$H—TdR with an apparently higher specific activity was used. The absolute response was higher, but the same relationships held true. The $^{144}$Ce-exposed dogs again tended to respond poorly to both mitogens. Twelve of 14 irradiated dogs had fewer than 10,000 cpm per culture, whereas only 4 of 10 controls were this low in their response to PHA. Response to PWM showed 10 of 14 irradiated animals below 10,000 cpm and 4 of 10 controls at this level. The unstimulated cultures that had HBSS added instead of mitogen showed little uptake of $^3$H—TdR at 96 hr. There was no significant difference between the uptake in these cultures in control and $^{144}$Ce-exposed groups. Uptake in individual cultures ranged from 100 to 600 cpm. The means in the control and irradiated groups were 300 and 320 cpm, respectively, at the first sampling and 375 and 300 at the second sampling. Figure 4 graphically presents these data as means for each treatment in each group. The differences in lymphocyte response between the irradiated and control dogs were significant and repeatable. The $^{144}$Ce-exposed groups showed a 50 to 75% reduction in ability to respond to PHA and PWM as compared to controls.

Studies of the kinetics of the lymphocyte response to plant mitogens were carried out to further define the decreased DNA synthesis in cultures from irradiated animals. Figure 5 shows the labelling index for lymphocytes following stimulation with PHA and PWM in the three control dogs tested. The manner in which lymphocytes from an individual animal responded to the two mitogens varied in that in dog 1 the response to PHA was earlier and greater than the response to PWM, and in dog 2 PWM produced the greater response. Dog 3 had an almost equivalent response to these two mitogens. Similar results were seen in the cultures from the two irradiated dogs. Figure 6 demonstrates the kinetics of the response to PHA and PWM, respectively, in control and $^{144}$Ce-exposed dogs. In both cases the control dogs as a group appeared to have a higher labelling index than the irradiated animals, since two of the three control-dog curves tended to be above the others. There was, however, considerable variation in absolute response (DNA synthesis) at 96 hr between dogs, as well as considerable overlap between the control and $^{144}$Ce-exposed groups. The relatively small number of animals sampled for kinetic studies, therefore, makes drawing any

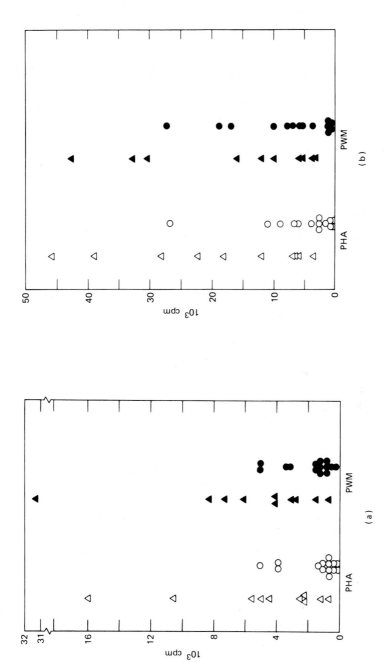

Fig. 3 Beagle dog lymphocyte response to plant mitogens (PHA and PWM) in vitro following inhalation exposure to $^{144}$Ce in fused clay. (a) 52 to 59 weeks postexposure. (b) 60 to 66 weeks postexposure. Each point represents the mean of five replicate cultures for a single dog. △ and ▲, controls (10). ○ and ●, exposed (14).

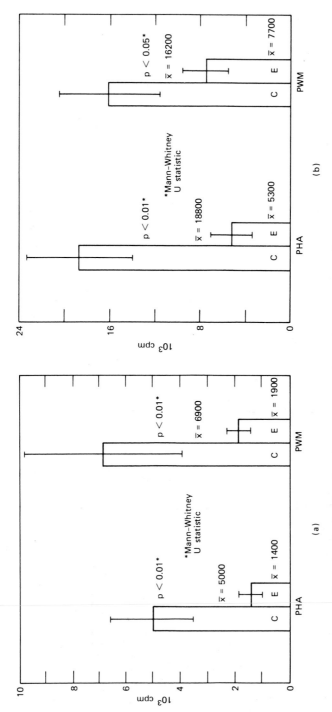

Fig. 4 Beagle dog lymphocyte response to plant mitogens (PHA and PWM) in vitro following inhalation exposure to $^{144}$Ce in fused clay. (a) 52 to 59 weeks postexposure. (b) 60 to 66 weeks postexposure. C, controls (10). E, exposed (14). The mean and the standard error are shown for both groups.

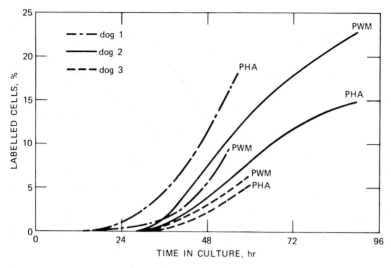

**Fig. 5    Kinetics of the lymphocyte response to PHA and PWM in control dogs.**

firm conclusions hazardous. Although actual cell counts were not performed on these cultures at the various harvest times, the number of cells per culture could be estimated. Each tube was centrifuged, and the entire fixed cell pellet was resuspended in a few drops of fixative and placed on a single slide. From this, cultures from the irradiated dogs appeared to have fewer lymphocytes remaining, expecially at later times (72 to 96 hr).

A few cells (less than 0.1%) were in DNA synthesis (S phase) as early as 16 hr after culture initiation. Significant numbers of cells synthesizing DNA were not found until after 24 hr of culture. Figure 7 illustrates the early portion of the cell cycle of canine lymphocytes. The cell-cycle curve shown is based on the first major wave of mitoses occurring 48 hr after mitogen stimulation. This is a generalized curve drawn from data on control and irradiated animals as well as from PHA- and PWM-stimulated cultures. There was no apparent difference in the cell cycle due to either the radiation exposure or the use of different mitogens. A similar curve generated for the population of lymphocytes in mitosis at 60 hr revealed no significant differences between the cell-cycle times for 48- and 60-hr harvests. The 48-hr cultures, however, had less than half the mitotic index seen in cells cultured for 60 hr, 0.22% and 0.52%, respectively.

## DISCUSSION

Beagle dogs exposed by inhalation to relatively high levels of [144]Ce in fused clay developed a severe and persistent lymphopenia. All the exposed dogs showed some degree of lymphocyte depression, and as a group the absolute lymphocyte counts were reduced to 40% of the preexposure values. This

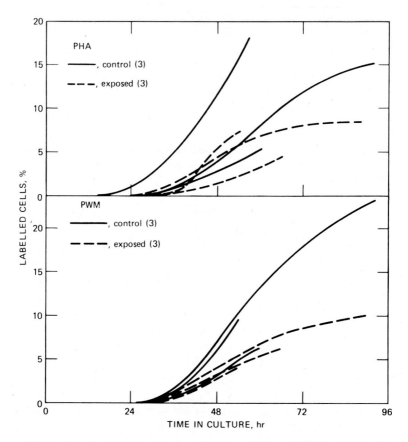

**Fig. 6   Kinetics of the lymphocyte response to PHA and PWM in control and**
**[144] Ce-exposed dogs.**

lymphopenia is probably due to the protracted low-dose-rate irradiation of
lymphocytes as they circulate through the lung. Similar results can be produced
in humans by extracorporeal irradiation of blood, and, although there have been
conflicting data reported concerning the ability of remaining lymphocytes to
respond to PHA in these patients, their immune responses do appear to be
depressed.[33,34] Furthermore, prolonged beta irradiation of canine blood by
intravascular implants[35] of [90]Y or [90]Sr also produced persistent lymphopenia,
and the animals had decreased immune responses. The decreased ability of the
remaining lymphocytes in the dogs exposed to [144]Ce in fused clay to transform
in response to plant mitogens in vitro indicates that the residual lymphocyte
population is functionally impaired; however, mitogen response is not a measure
of total immunological capability and only subpopulations of lymphocytes are
involved in the mitogen response.[8] The hypothesis that PHA is a T-cell stimulant
and that the majority of the cells stimulated by PWM are B cells is based on

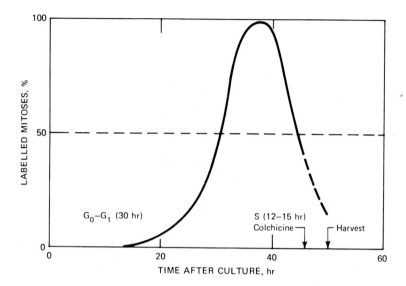

Fig. 7  Cell cycle of canine lymphocytes after in vitro stimulation with plant mitogens (PHA and PWM).

studies in other species. If this is true in the dog, it would appear that both cell types are equally affected by chronic irradiation. The differential kinetic response of canine lymphocytes to PHA and PWM also suggests that two distinct lymphocyte subpopulations were stimulated, although a less likely possibility is that a single population responded differently to the two mitogens.

Lymphocyte kinetic studies were performed to evaluate the cellular basis for the decreased transformation in our dogs. Human lymphocyte kinetic studies have shown results similar to those reported here. The pre-DNA synthetic phase of stimulated and cultured lymphocytes appears to be quite variable,[36-38] and the findings in canine lymphocytes appear consistent with these studies. Further, the length of S phase as determined in our studies (12 to 15 hr) is consistent with that reported for human lymphocytes in culture.[39-41] Studies on the effect of radiation on the cell cycle of lymphocytes have shown conflicting results. Sasaki and Norman[40] reported no change in cell-cycle parameters with X-ray doses of up to 500 rads delivered before culture. Rickinson and Ilbery,[41] using $^{60}$Co-irradiated lymphocyte cultures that received 250 to 2000 rads, found a dose-dependent delay of entry of some cells into the first DNA synthesis and complete blockage of others. The S phase was unchanged, and there was a further delay in $G_2$. There were no differences in the cell-cycle curves between cultures from control and irradiated dogs in our studies, and mitotic indexes were also similar. Thus, little change is suggested in the early cell-cycle parameters ($G_0$, $G_1$, and S) for the lymphocytes that were capable of responding to the mitogens. A lower labelling index in the irradiated dog cultures, as compared to controls, however, could indicate that some of the lymphocytes were not capable of entering S. The reasons for the decrease in lymphocyte transformation remain unclear. The data presented here suggest that two factors, decreased labelling index and decreased lymphocyte viability, may contribute to the depression of in vitro DNA synthesis in [144]Ce-exposed dogs. Two major possibilities exist as to the mechanisms responsible for the differences in lymphocyte function. First, differences could result from the accumulation of extensive damage in circulating lymphocytes over a long period of time. Since most of these lymphocytes are irradiated in $G_0$, they might not express the damage until they were stimulated to undergo division either in vivo or in vitro. Second, there could be an overall change in the residual lymphocyte population in these dogs from irradiation-induced cell killing over a long period of time. Thus, such animals might be depleted of the lymphocyte subpopulations that can respond to mitogenic stimulus.

In summary, the dogs in this study that were exposed by inhalation to [144]Ce fused clay developed a severe and persistent lymphopenia. The lymphocytes remaining in these animals at 1-year postexposure showed an impaired ability to respond to plant mitogens in vitro. Comparable dogs exposed to [144]Ce fused clay at similar activity levels for other studies have developed primary pulmonary neoplasms, mainly hemangiosarcomas, at 2 to 3 years postexposure.[24] The combined effect of the lymphopenia and the functional depression of the remaining lymphocytes is likely to produce some level of immune suppression. The combination of the direct carcinogenetic effect of radiation on the lung and immune suppression could well be related to early development of pulmonary neoplasms.

## ACKNOWLEDGMENTS

The generous assistance of the entire staff of the Lovelace Foundation Inhalation Toxicology Research Institute is gratefully acknowledged. Specifically we thank F. C. Rupprecht for his editorial assistance and Ann C. Ferris and Leslie A. Wofford for their technical assistance. The research reported here was performed under U. S. Atomic Energy Commission contract AT-(29-2)-1013 in animal facilities fully accredited by the American Association for Accreditation of Laboratory Animal Care.

## REFERENCES

1. O. A. Trowell, The Sensitivity of Lymphocytes to Ionizing Radiation, *J. Pathol. Bacteriol.*, **64**: 687-704 (1952).
2. G. Mathe and H. DaCosta, Effect of Irradiation on Immunity, in *Nuclear Hematology*, E. Szirmai (Ed.), pp 339-356, Academic Press, Inc., New York, 1965.
3. D. G. Osmond, The Origins, Lifespans and Circulation of Lymphocytes, in *Proceedings of the Sixth Leukocyte Culture Conference*, University of Washington, June 19-24, 1971, Academic Press, Inc., New York, 1972.

4. O. Stutman and R. A. Good, Heterogeneity of Lymphocyte Populations, *Rev. Eur. Etud. Clin. Biol.,* **17:** 11-14 (1972).

5. N. L. Warner, Differentiation of Immunocytes and the Evolution of Immunological Potential in Immunogenicity, *Frontiers of Biology,* Vol. 25, pp. 467-537, American Elsevier Publishing Company, Inc., New York, 1972.

6. H. Huber and S. D. Douglas, Functional Impairment of Lymphocytes and Monocytes: Assessment In Vitro, *Seminars Hematol.,* **8:** 192-215 (1971).

7. S. D. Douglas, Human Lymphocytic Growth In Vitro: Morphologic, Biochemical and Immunologic Significance, *Int. Rev. Exp. Pathol.,* **10:** 41-114 (1971).

8. F. Daguillard, Immunologic Significance of In Vitro Lymphocyte Responses, *Med. Clin. N. Amer.,* **56:** 293-304 (1972).

9. H. Blomgren and E. Svedmyr, Evidence of Thymic Dependence of PHA-Reactive Cells in Spleen and Lymph Nodes and Independence in Bone Marrow, *J. Immunol.,* **106:** 835-841 (1971).

10. G. Janossy and M. F. Greaves, Lymphocyte Activation. II. Discriminating Stimulation of Lymphocyte Subpopulations by Phytomitogens and Heterologous Antilymphocyte Sera, *Clin. Exp. Immunol.,* **10:** 525-536 (1972).

11. S. J. Shacks, J. Chiller and G. A. Granger, The In Vitro Role of Thymus-Dependent Cells in DNA Synthesis and LT Secretion by PHA-Stimulated Mouse Lymphoid Cells, *Transplant. Proc.,* **4:** 303-305 (1972).

12. S. D. Douglas and H. H. Fudenberg, In Vitro Development of Plasma Cells from Lymphocytes Following Pokeweed Mitogen Stimulation: A Fine Structural Study, *Exp. Cell Res.,* **54:** 277-279 (1969).

13. G. Janossy and M. F. Greaves, Lymphocyte Activation. I. Response of T and B Lymphocytes to Phytomitogens, *Clinc. Exp. Immunol.,* **9:** 483-498 (1971).

14. M. Goldman, K. K. Wolf, A. K. Klein, and B. F. Nehman, Radiosensitivity of Cultured Beagle Lymphocytes, *Radiat. Res.,* **31:** 597-598 (1967).

15. P. L. T. Ilbery, A. B. Rickinson, and C. E. Thrum, Blood Lymphocyte Replicating Ability as a Measurement of Radiation Dosage, *Brit. J. Radiol.,* **44:** 834-840 (1971).

16. K. K. Meyer, D. R. Weaver, W. C. Luft, and B. D. Boselli, Lymphocyte Immune Deficiency Following Irradiation for Carcinoma of the Breast, in The Interrelationship of the Immune Response to Cancer, *Front. Radiat. Ther. Oncol.,* **7:** 179-198 (1971).

17. J. A. McCredie, W. R. Inch, and R. M. Sutherland, Effect of Post-Operative Radiotherapy on Peripheral Blood Lymphocytes in Patients with Carcinoma of the Breast, *Cancer,* **29:** 349-356 (1971).

18. J. Stjernsward, M. Jondal, F. Vanky, H. Wigzell, and R. Sealy, Lymphopenia and Change in Distribution of Human B and T Lymphocytes in Peripheral Blood Induced by Irradiation for Mammary Carcinoma, *Lancet,* **1:** 1352-1356(1972).

19. V. K. Jenkins, M. H. Olson, and H. N. Ellis, In Vitro Methods of Assessing Lymphocyte Transformation in Patients Undergoing Radiotherapy for Bronchogenic Cancer, *Tex. Rep. Biol. Med.,* **31:** 19-28 (1973).

20. J. F. Park, E. B. Howard, B. O. Stuart, A. P. Wehner, and J. V. Dilley, Cocarcinogenic Studies in Pulmonary Carcinogenesis, in *Morphology of Experimental Respiratory Carcinogenesis,* Gatlinburg, Tenn., May 13—16, 1970, P. Nettesheim, M. G. Hannah, Jr., and J. W. Deatherage, Jr. (Eds.), AEC Symposium Series, No. 21 (CONF-700501), pp. 417-436, 1970.

21. C. L. Yuile, F. R. Gibb, and P. E. Morrow, Dose-Related Local and Systemic Effects of Inhaled Plutonium-238 and Plutonium-239 Dioxide in Dogs, *Radiat. Res.,* **44:** 821-834 (1970).

22. R. K. Jones, B. B. Boecker, C. H. Hobbs, A. J. Hulbert, and R. O. McClellan, Hematologic Effects of Inhaled $^{90}$Y, $^{91}$Y, $^{144}$Ce or $^{90}$Sr Fused Clay in Beagle Dogs, *Radiat. Res.,* **51:** 470-471 (1972).

23. E. B. Howard, The Morphology of Experimental Lung Tumors in Beagle Dogs, in *Morphology of Experimental Respiratory Carcinogenesis*, Gatlinburg, Tenn., May 13– 16, 1970, P. Nettesheim, M. G. Hannah, Jr., and J. W. Deatherage, Jr. (Eds.), AEC Symposium Series, No. 21 (CONF-700501), pp. 147-160, 1970.

24. F. F. Hahn, S. A. Benjamin, B. B. Boecker, T. L. Chiffelle, C. H. Hobbs, R. K. Jones, R. O. McClellan, J. A. Pickrell, and H. C. Redman, Primary Pulmonary Neoplasms in Beagle Dogs Exposed to Aerosols of $^{144}$Ce in Fused Clay Particles, *J. Nat. Cancer Inst.*, **50**: 675-698 (1973).

25. F. M. Burnet, Immunological Surveillance in Neoplasia, *Transplantation Reviews*, Vol. 7, pp. 3-25, Munksgaard, Copenhagen, Denmark, 1971.

26. M. G. Lewis, Circulating Humoral Antibodies in Cancer, *Med. Clin. N. Amer.*, **56**: 481-499 (1972).

27. R. A. Good, Relations Between Immunity and Malignancy, *Proc. Nat. Acad. Sci., U. S. A.*, **69**: 1026-1032 (1972).

28. H. C. Redman, A. J. Wilson, S. W. Bielfelt, and R. O. McClellan, Beagle Dog Production Experience at the Fission Product Inhalation Program (1961-1968), *Lab. Anim. Care*, **20**: 61-68 (1970).

29. S. W. Bielfelt, A. J. Wilson, H. C. Redman, R. O. McClellan, and L. S. Rosenblatt, A Breeding Program for the Establishment and Maintenance of a Stable Gene Pool in a Beagle Dog Colony to be Used for Long-Term Experiments, *Amer. J. Vet. Res.*, **20**: 2221-2229 (1969).

30. O. G. Raabe, G. M. Kanapilly, and G. J. Newton, New Methods for the Generation of Aerosols of Insoluble Particles for Use in Inhalation Studies, in *Third International Symposium on Inhaled Particles*, Symposium Proceedings, London, England, Sept. 16- 23, 1970, pp. 3-18, Unwin Brothers, Ltd., Surrey, England, 1971.

31. B. B. Boecker, F. L. Aguilar, and T. T. Mercer, A Canine Inhalation Exposure Apparatus Utilizing a Whole-Body Plethysmograph, *Health Phys.*, **10**: 1077-1089 (1964).

32. B. B. Boecker, Toxicity of $^{144}$Ce in Fused Clay Particles Inhaled by the Beagle Dog: Metabolism and Dosimetry, to be submitted to *Health Physics*.

33. B. Rosengren, S. E. Bergentz, K. Lindahl-Kiessling, L. Lindholm, and B. Persson, Incorporation of $^{14}$C- and $^{3}$H-Thymidine in Lymphocytes after Extracorporeal Irradiation of the Blood, *Rev. Eur. Etud. Clin. Biol.*, **15**: 778-782 (1970).

34. E. Weeke, Lymphocyte Transformation Tests Before, During and After Extracorporeal Irradiation of the Blood, *Acta Med. Scand.*, **192**: 271-279 (1972).

35. J. S. Wolf and D. M. Hume, Alteration of the Immune Response to Transplantation by Beta Irradiation of Circulating Blood, *Bull. Soc. Int. Chir.*, **5**: 433-476 (1967).

36. J. Jasinska, J. A. Steffen, and A. Michalowski, Studies on In Vitro Lymphocyte Proliferation in Cultures Synchronized by the Inhibition of DNA Synthesis, *Exp. Cell Res.*, **61**: 333-341 (1970).

37. L. H. Younkin, In Vitro Response of Lymphocytes to Phytohemagglutinin (PHA) as Studied with Antiserum to PHA. I. Initiation Period, Daughter-Cell Proliferation and Restimulation, *Exp. Cell Res.*, **75**: 1-10 (1972).

38. L. Soren, Variability of the Time at Which PHA-Stimulated Lymphocytes Initiate DNA Synthesis, *Exp. Cell Res.*, **78**: 201-208 (1973).

39. M. A. Bender and D. M. Prescott, DNA Synthesis and Mitosis in Cultures of Human Peripheral Leukocytes, *Exp. Cell Res.*, **27**: 221-229 (1962).

40. M. S. Sasaki and A. Norman, Proliferation of Human Lymphocytes in Culture, *Nature*, **210**: 913-914 (1966).

41. A. B. Rickinson and P. L. T. Ilbery, The Effect of Radiation Upon Lymphocyte Response to PHA, *Cell Tissue Kinet.*, **4**: 549-562 (1971).

# TUMOR AGE COHORT VARIATION
# AND SENSITIVITY TO DNA SYNTHESIS
# DIRECTED CHEMOTHERAPY

Y. MARUYAMA, T. C. LEE, and R. D. McMILLIN
Department of Radiation Medicine, University of Kentucky, Lexington, Kentucky

## ABSTRACT

Tumor growth is accompanied by changing states and physiological activities of the tumor cells. The tumor at different ages is comprised of varying cell age distributions that can be determined in part by mitotic and $^3$H−TdR labelling, DNA per cell, and ploidy. These parameters change considerably but in a characteristic manner after transplantation for an ascites lymphoma. Anti-DNA−S chemotherapy or high-specific-activity $^3$H−TdR reveals a sensitivity pattern with maximum sensitivity in the early exponential phase where DNA−S activity is great; 5-FU exposure is more potent against the proliferating tumor presumably because of RNA and DNA antimetabolite activity. Reactivation of proliferation appeared to follow exposure to an alkylating agent as determined by the reappearance of a characteristic chemosensitivity pattern.

It is now abundantly clear that the intermitotic activity of proliferating cells undergoes a characteristic sequence of physiological changes. Before mitosis a mammalian cell doubles its deoxyribonucleic acid (DNA) content during a discrete period of DNA synthetic activity, the S phase. This phase is characterized by the uptake of radioactively labelled precursors into the polymeric macromolecule, DNA. Likewise during this phase the DNA macromolecular content per cell rises and doubles as a prerequisite to mitosis. The S phase is separated from mitosis, M, by two time intervals $G_1$ and $G_2$, which either precede or follow S. During mitosis a cell undergoes cytokinesis and divides into two identical daughter cells.[1] This activity moreover is common to both normal and malignant cells.

The evidence that actively cycling cells have large proportions of the population in active DNA−S has been advantageously applied to the study and therapeutics of malignant disease. At the same time it has been recognized that certain fractions of the cell population are not in active cell cycle. This noncycling or nonproliferating fraction would interfere with the effective therapy of tumors with any noncycling fraction, especially where the therapeutic agent exhibits strictly cycle-specific activity.

The relevance of noncycling or nonproliferating cells in therapy requires study in animal model systems where the nonproliferating stage and its significance can be studied experimentally. As a model for tumor growth, we have used an ascites lymphoma system that provides an accurate and precise in vivo model of tumor growth. The system behaves as an exponential-growth model during much of its course in the animal.[2] Growth curves obtained in vivo trace accurately the stage of tumor growth and proliferative activity. Late in growth a plateau or stationary phase is reached, and markers of proliferative activity become very low. During these later stages of tumor growth, the animals become listless, toxic, cease to eat and drink, and shortly thereafter die. We have regarded the tumor residing in these latter animals as nonproliferating on the basis of host physiology and cell markers, which include a long doubling time, a low mitotic activity, and a low labelling index.

Using this model system we have studied the changes from an exponentially proliferating tumor to a tumor of reduced proliferative activity, to one in the near terminal animal. We were able to identify different activities and different corresponding sensitivities of the tumor at different times during the process of tumor growth and thus to gain further insight into the nonproliferating state of tumor cells in the advanced tumor of the preterminal animal (Fig. 1).

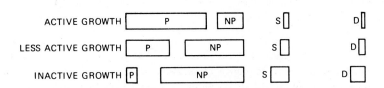

**Fig. 1 Schematic diagram of proliferative activities of tumors at different stages of growth. P, proliferating. NP, nonproliferating. S, sterile. D, dead.**

Study of this tumor system has shown that the model system used in these experiments is one of induced proliferative activity. The inducing procedure is the transfer of the tumor from a nonproliferative state in the terminal animal into a fresh recipient. On transfer to a fresh animal, cells reenter active cycle, and the tumor proliferates anew to eventually reach again in the recipient a nonproliferating state.

Our recent studies with this system are reviewed in this paper. We also present evidence that the nonproliferating cells in the animal may be induced to reenter active cycle in the host following therapy.

## MATERIALS AND METHODS

### Animals

Inbred C57BL mice produced in our laboratory by a single-line breeding system were used throughout these experiments. Mature animals weighing about 20 to 25 g were used. They were housed in clear Lucite cages with laboratory animal chow and water ad libitum.

### Tumor

The LSA tumor, a transplant tumor, has been described elsewhere.[3] It was transferred at weekly intervals and was always obtained on the 7th day of growth. Tumor inoculum was $1 \times 10^6$ cells unless otherwise specified.

### Biochemical Procedures

Cells were collected and extracted with cold (0 to $4°C$) 5% perchloric acid (PCA). The residues were extracted first with a mixture of chloroform and methanol (2:1), then ethyl ether, and then with hot 5% PCA. The DNA was determined using the method of Dische modified by Siebert[4] by mixing one volume of the hot PCA extracts with two volumes of the diphenylamine reagent. The reaction mixture was heated at $100°C$ for 10 min, cooled to room temperature, and read at 595 nm in a spectrophotometer. The RNA was determined using the orcinol reaction.

Uptake data with tritiated thymidine $^3H–TdR$ was obtained using a dose of 0.16 $\mu Ci/g$ $^3H–TdR$ obtained commercially at a specific activity of 6.7 Ci/mmole. The uptake period was 30 min and was terminated by the injection of 10 $\mu$moles of unlabelled thymidine per mouse. An aliquot of the extracted DNA sample was measured for DNA content, and a separate aliquot was counted in a vial with PPO, POPOP, toluene, and ethanol in a liquid scintillation counter to determine radioactive uptake.

### Treatment with Drugs

The following supplies were used: 5-FU (5-fluorouracil), HU (hydroxyurea), 5-FUdR (5-fluorodeoxyuridine), HSATT (high-specific-activity tritiated thymidine), BCNU [1,3-bis(2-chloroethyl)-1-nitrosourea] (courtesy, Steve Carter, National Cancer Institute), $HN_2$ [Mustargen (mechlorethamine HCl)], and Cytoxan (cyclophosphamide). Drugs were administered intraperitoneally in a volume of 0.2 to 0.5 ml of normal saline. All drugs were freshly prepared daily before administration. All drug exposures were made at about the same time daily. Following treatment with drugs, animals were observed and scored daily until they died. Mean survival time was calculated using the geometric mean.[2]

## EXPERIMENTAL PROTOCOL

Ascites tumor cells were injected intraperitoneally into normal recipients in an inoculum of $1 \times 10^6$ cells in a 0.2-ml volume. For all determinations of macromolecular content or $^3H-TdR$ uptake, animals were irradiated with 400 rads of total-body-radiation dose to reduce the normal cellular content of the peritoneal cavity. Cells were collected for analysis by multiple washes using normal saline and were washed with normal saline to remove interfering substances.

Chemotherapeutic agents when used were injected a single time at the time specified. Drugs were freshly prepared and injected intraperitoneally in a volume of 0.2 to 0.5 ml. Injections were performed at the same time daily. In the case of 5-FUdR and HSATT, 5-FUdR always preceded HSATT by 30 min., but this combination was given only once on the specified day.

## METHOD OF IDENTIFYING ACTIVITIES OF CELLS

Several parameters are useful in assessing the positions of the cells in the cell cycle. First, the mitotic index identifies cells undergoing mitosis. This fraction, however, was always small and accounted for less than 5% of the cells. Another parameter is the uptake of $^3H-TdR$ per cell as measured by counts per minute per microgram of cell DNA or labelling index. A third parameter is DNA per cell (picograms). The measurement of DNA per cell gives an assessment of the portion of the cell population in S, $G_2$, and early M. Finally, it is necessary to determine whether the chromosome number of the tumor is euploid or aneuploid. Significant tetraploidy or higher ploidies would give higher DNA per cell data and interfere with accurate positioning of the cell in the cell cycle. The LSA tumor does not exhibit gross polyploidy or variation in chromosome number.

The DNA was determined according to the method of Dische as modified by Seibert[4] using the diphenylamine reagent. This method gives a specific color reaction for deoxypentose when mixed in hot acid solution with the hydrolyzed nucleotides. The $^3H-TdR$ uptake was used as a measure of DNA-S activity assessed as counts per minute per microgram of DNA. For RNA determination the orcinol reaction was used.[4]

### Macromolecular Synthesis During Ascites Growth

Three separate experiments were carried out with a starting inoculum of $1 \times 10^6$ cells. Cell-growth curves show a short lag period followed by an exponential increase in cell numbers. The doubling time during this phase was 12 hr. The data from the three experiments are shown in Fig. 2. Following the logarithmic growth phase, a stationary phase is reached at approximately

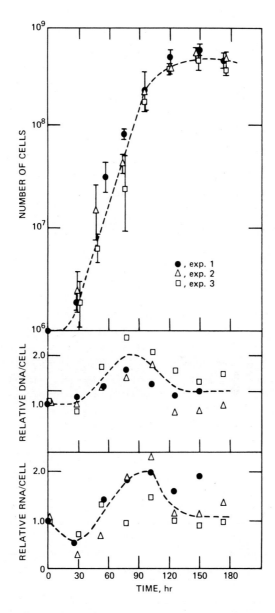

Fig. 2  Growth curve for LSA ascites tumor and DNA and RNA per cell with growth from three experiments on macromolecular synthesis during ascites growth (inoculum of 1 x 10⁶ cells).

$5 \times 10^8$ cells beyond which no further increase occurs. Still later, the number of cells declines.

Concomitant determination of DNA and RNA per cell was carried out, and the data of the three experiments are also presented in Fig. 2. The DNA per cell rises with the growth phase, peaking in the mid-exponential growth phase and falling thereafter. During mid-exponential growth, the population shifts to one containing, on the average, a larger quantity of DNA, which then falls during the later stages of growth.

The RNA per cell declined as cells entered the logarithmic growth phase and then rose as DNA per cell increased. As with DNA, a fall occurred as cells entered the stationary phase.

The DNA per cell for normal spleen cells was used as a reference standard. The cells, obtained from mature, normal, and nonstimulated animals, presumably were largely noncycling cells containing a diploid content of DNA. The DNA content of normal spleen cells was a reproducible and reliable reference, whereas tumor-cell DNA was found to vary with stage of ascites growth.

### $^3$H—TdR Uptake and Ascites Tumor Growth

A 30-min pulse of $^3$H—TdR was given to tumor cells on different days of growth. Uptake was terminated by the injection of 10 $\mu$mole of unlabelled thymidine. The results of such an experiment starting with an inoculum of $1 \times 10^6$ cells is shown in Fig. 3. The DNA-S activity preceded and rose concurrently with the cell-number increase. Peak activity was attained on day 2, or during early tumor growth. During the mid-exponential phase, a slowing began, and during the stationary phase DNA—S activity declined. During the mid-growth cycle, DNA—S was still active but was minimal in the aged tumor. These data show that ascites tumors in vivo behave much as cultured cells in vitro where similar results have been reported.

The DNA per cell as a measure of DNA synthesis lags behind the $^3$H—TdR data but shows that, as the population enters S and with continued S activity, ultimately a larger DNA per cell content results.

For the data shown in Fig. 4, a starting inoculum of $1 \times 10^5$ cells was used. The growth phase was prolonged over an approximate 6-day period. The DNA—S activity rose and peaked while cell number was still increasing. The peak activity was reached on day 3, however, 1 day after the same peak was observed for the larger $10^6$ cell inoculum. Again during the mid-exponential phase, a fall in $^3$H—TdR uptake was found.

Of particular interest are our results with the 8-day-old tumor. A fall in cell numbers was noted, indicating cell loss in the peritoneal cavity of the terminal mouse. At the same time, a 10-fold drop in DNA synthesis was also observed on the last day of ascites growth. The terminal animal supports cell growth poorly, and tumor cells residing in the terminal animal reduce their cell proliferative and

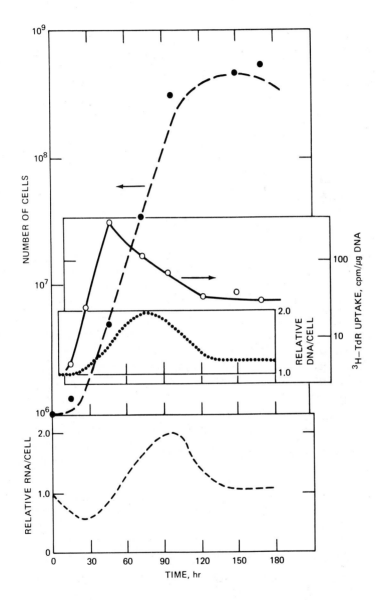

Fig. 3   ³H–TdR uptake with growth. ●, cell-growth curve. ○, ³H–TdR uptake. Starting inoculum, 1 x 10⁶ cells.

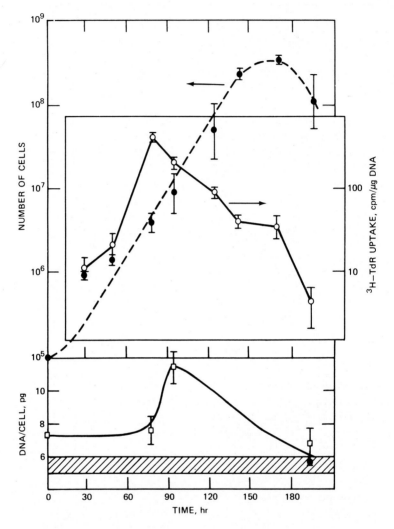

Fig. 4  Tumor growth (●), $^3$H—TdR uptake (○), and DNA per cell (□) for starting inoculum of $1 \times 10^5$ cells. Hatched bar represents normal spleen cell DNA per cell.

DNA synthesis activity. The studies indicate that activity varies considerably during early, mid-, and late tumor growth.

## CHEMOTHERAPEUTIC TEST OF AGE COHORT VARIATION

During tumor growth chemotherapeutic agents may be grouped into categories of specificities depending on the proliferative state of cells.[5] Applying this approach to the LSA tumor suggested that therapeutic strategy may be based in part on the composition and age cohorts present at a particular moment. For an advanced tumor or a solid tumor, it is likely that radiotherapy, because of its cycle nonspecificity, is an effective modality to use. If the cell age composition varies greatly, differing potencies of phase- and cycle-specific drugs should be seen at every stage of growth.

We ran an experiment to test this model approach. The results are given in Fig. 5. Hydroxyurea (HU) in a dose of 50 mg per mouse was most potent in the early stages when $^3$H—TdR uptake was high. Hydroxyurea is an agent with specificity and toxicity for DNA synthesis. That a greater potency was not observed indicates that cell toxicity is not a simple process. Interestingly, 5-fluorouracil (5-FU), which is an antimetabolite against DNA and RNA synthesis, showed great potency during the entire stage of tumor growth where DNA and RNA metabolism was active. However, in the end-stage tumor, all antitumor activity also vanished.

## HIGH-SPECIFIC-ACTIVITY RADIOACTIVE THYMIDINE EFFECT

The specific DNA precursor, thymidine in a highly radioactive form, is another specific agent cytotoxic for DNA synthesis.[6] We have used thymidine tritiated to a specific activity of 55 Ci/mmole and have found that it can greatly alter the biological behavior of this experimental ascites lymphoma. This activity was greatest (Fig. 6) during periods that correspond to those where greatest DNA synthesis is going on during a period of tumor growth, i.e., in the early and mid-exponential growth phase. It declined in the advanced tumor and nearly disappeared in the preterminal animal. This too, corresponded to the pattern of DNA synthesis. The data indicate that for age cohorts of pre-dominantly S phase, cells sensitive to radioactive thymidine are distributed identically to DNA—S activity and thus support the hypothesis of age-cohort variation during tumor growth.

The 5-fluorodeoxyuridine (5-FUdR), a specific agent interfering with the enzyme thymidylate synthetase, would be expected to act in a similar manner.[7] The data for combined 5-FUdR and radiothymidine indicate that the salvage pathway is a strongly competing one for this tumor. Blockade of the endogenous thymidine synthesis pathway by 5-FUdR permits larger quantities of exogenous precursors to be used (reused) and thereby permits expression of the HSATT-specific-tumor growth alteration. Thus a much greater increase in potency was observed for the combined agents compared to the single agent.

In conclusion, our experiments using 5-FUdR and $^3$H—TdR have shown a correspondence of tumor sensitivity to a DNA—S specific agent and DNA—S phase activity. The considerable variation in potency of these agents at different stages of tumor growth indicates that there is varying S activity at the different tumor stages.

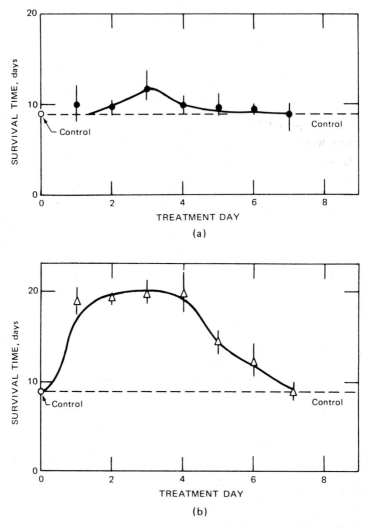

Fig. 5  Effect of (a) hydroxyurea (50 mg per mouse) or (b) 5-fluorouracil
(1.0 mg per mouse) on survival time of tumor-injected animals. Inoculum,
$1 \times 10^6$ cells given intraperitoneally.

## EFFECT OF ALKYLATING AGENTS FOLLOWED BY ANTIMETABOLITES

Figure 7 shows the sensitivity of the tumor to nitrogen mustard (0.04 mg per
mouse) and hydroxyurea (100 mg per mouse) after exposure to $HN_2$ on day 3
of tumor growth. Table 1 details the results of the experiment where animals
had received this combination of drugs. Hydroxyurea was given intraperitoneally
in five 20-mg doses at hourly intervals for a total daily dose of 100 mg. When

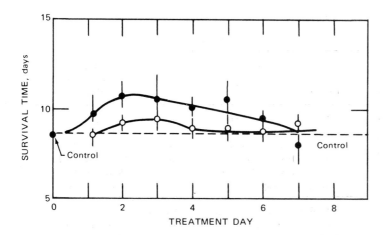

Fig. 6 Effect of (○) 5-FUdR (1 mg per mouse) or (●) 5-FUdR and HSATT (250 μCi) on the survival time of tumor-injected animals. Inoculum, 1 × 10⁶ cells.

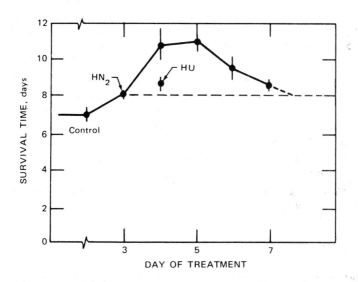

Fig. 7 Response of LSA tumor to HN₂ (0.04 mg) exposure on day 3.5 followed by 100 mg (20 mg × 5 at hourly intervals) of HU on subsequent treatment day noted. Inoculum, 1 × 10⁷ cell given intraperitoneally. - - -; tumor-bearing mice treated with both agents (HN₂ and antimetabolite).

TABLE 1

SURVIVAL TIMES*

| Group | | No. of mice | Mean survival time† |
|---|---|---|---|
| 1 | Untreated control | 8 | 6.9(6.6—7.3) |
| 2 | HN$_2$ day 3.5 | 8 | 8.0(7.8—8.2) |
| 3 | HN$_2$ + HU day 4 | 8 | 10.7(9.9—11.6) |
| 4 | HN$_2$ + HU day 5 | 8 | 10.9(10.5—11.3) |
| 5 | HN$_2$ + HU day 6 | 8 | 9.5(9.1—10.0) |
| 6 | HU day 4 | 8 | 8.6(8.3—8.8) |

*Animals were inoculated with $1 \times 10^7$ cells of LSA ascites tumor. They were treated on day 3.5 of growth with 0.04 mg of HN$_2$ given intraperitoneally and daily thereafter with 100 mg of HU given intraperitoneally in divided doses of 20 mg every hour for five consecutive doses.

†Geometric mean (±1 S.E.).[2]

HU followed HN$_2$, a great increase in sensitivity to HU was found. These data show that optimizing the sequencing of this combination of agents potentiated its activity with the reappearance of proliferative-phase sensitivity in this tumor. Figure 8 shows the sensitivity of the tumor to 5-FU after BCNU given on day 5. The animals received $1 \times 10^7$ cells intraperitoneally as a starting inoculum. They were treated with 0.18 mg of BCNU on day 5 and then had one exposure to 1 mg of 5-FU on varying days afterwards for an additional week. These data also indicate the reappearance of 5-FU chemosensitivity after BCNU exposure.

Figure 9 shows the sensitivity of the tumor to HU and 5-FU following exposure to Cytoxan. Cytoxan alone in this system exhibits greater potency than HN$_2$. These data also show the reappearance of a 5-FU and HU chemosensitivity following Cytoxan exposure.

These results showing reappearance of proliferative-phase chemotherapeutic sensitivity are not unexpected when considered in the view of the cell-cycle model.[1] At different intervals after injection of the alkylating agent, the tumor cell population again reverted to and was in active cycle and proliferation; therefore, activity against the tumor was again found.

## DISCUSSION

Most cell populations are not synchronized to any extent but instead contain cells distributed throughout the whole cell cycle. In a steady-state population, there is a balance between cell production and cell loss and a constant total number of cells at all times. An expanding population, the exponentially growing one, where the total cell number increases exponentially with time, is

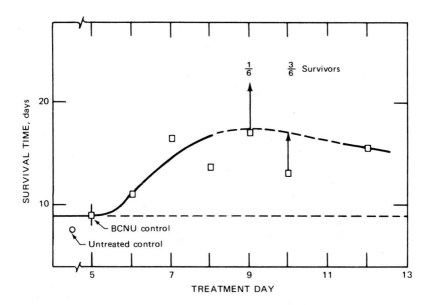

**Fig. 8** Response of LSA tumor to BCNU (0.18 mg) exposure on day 5 followed by 1 mg of 5-FU on subsequent days noted. Inoculum, $1 \times 10^7$ cells given intraperitoneally. - - -, data from tumor-bearing mice treated with both BCNU and 5-FU. □, mean survival time of animals dying with tumor.

the most readily analyzed. In tumors cell populations are increasing but do not usually expand exponentially. In those situations cell-cycle times can vary widely for subpopulations which appear randomly,[8] or there are fractions of the population which are growing or nongrowing.[9] Operationally, a population that has an extremely long cell-cycle time cannot be distinguished from a nongrowing one and effectively becomes one.

For ascites tumors one may encounter situations where the growth fractions change with tumor growth[10] or where the cycle time becomes progressively longer in duration but the growth fraction remains essentially about 1.0.[11] The situation studied here is one in which the growth slowing associated with stationary phase is followed shortly by host toxicity and then by the death of the host animal. We have used this advanced tumor to simulate a non-proliferating situation for this experimental tumor.

For the LSA ascites lymphoma, there was a great change in $^3$H—TdR uptake and DNA per cell content with stage of growth. These data indicated that the age cohort composition of the tumor cell population varied greatly at different times during tumor growth. Both $^3$H—TdR uptake and DNA content per cell were greatest during the early and mid-exponential growth phase. On the basis of this evidence, the age composition of the population would heavily favor S-, $G_2$-, and early M-phase cells. In the advanced and aged tumor, $^3$H—TdR uptake was

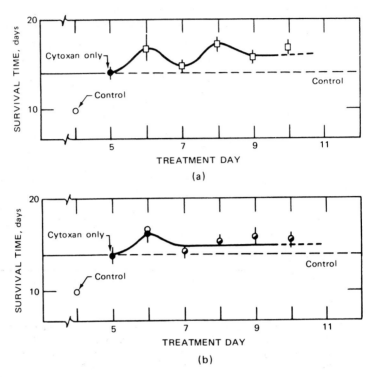

Fig. 9   Response of LSA tumor to Cytoxan (4 mg) exposure on day 5 followed by (a) 0.5 mg of 5-FU or (b) 100 mg of HU on subsequent day noted. Starting inoculum, 1 x 10⁶ cells.

low, DNA per cell content was near diploid, and the mitotic index was low, indicating a population that would be predominantly $G_1$-phase cells.

From these considerations S-phase-specific agents would be expected to exert their greatest cytotoxic activity during the early exponential phase. This was observed for HSATT, HU, and 5-FUdR, although this activity was weak for all these agents. The combinations of 5-FUdR and HSATT increased incorporation of exogenous thymidine and thus the potency of the drug.

The 5-FU, an agent active against both DNA and RNA biosynthesis, showed a great potency against the tumor at different times and behaved entirely consistently with the concept of considerable age cohort variation of the tumor cell population at different times during growth. Thus, it exhibited maximum potency on day 2 and day 3 of growth and minimal activity in the advanced and aged tumor. The change from marked potency to little effect is stepwise with a day-by-day gradual decline in potency until virtually no effect was obtained on the advanced tumor preterminally. Therefore, 5-FU was effective as a marker for the cycling or proliferative cell.

The advanced ascites tumor used in this study is one whose proliferative activity was slowed considerably. Mice bearing the advanced day-5 tumors were exposed to an alkylating agent followed by antimetabolite chemotherapy. The 5-day-old tumor would be expected to be in the early stationary phase. Our data show a return of sensitivity to the antimetabolites studied here following the exposure of this tumor to the alkylating agents. This would correspond to the pattern of sensitivity we have observed following transplantation-induced cell proliferation.

The experiments reported here for the LSA ascites lymphoma show that

1. Transplantation induces proliferative activity.

2. A characteristic sequence of macromolecular events accompanies the proliferation.

3. The exposure of the growing tumor to HU, 5-FUdR, HSATT, 5-FUdR and HSATT, or 5-FU shows a characteristic sequence of chemosensitivity.

4. An alkylating agent applied to the advanced tumor may or may not alter survival, but exposure of the ascitic tumor to Cytoxan, $HN_2$, or BCNU and subsequently to 5-FU or HU was followed by a characteristic pattern of chemosensitivity which resembled that induced by transplantation. The reappearance of this pattern of sensitivities is consistent with reentry of the tumor into proliferative phase.

It should be noted that the present data deal with the length of survival rather than with "cell kill" or fractional survivorship. We have reported on this problem elsewhere.[12,13]

Figure 10 is a representation of the cell cycle as currently viewed. Slow proliferation or nonproliferation in the LSA ascites tumor is a feature that begins to appear in the tumor residing in the advanced preterminal animal. In this system collection of the cells in that clinical state appears to be in $G_1$ phase as growth slowing occurs. All those cells are very much capable of promptly returning to proliferation and actively cycling states. This was evidenced by marked increases in sensitivity to 5-FU and slight increases in sensitivity to HU

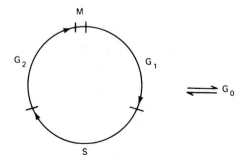

**Fig. 10 Representation of cell cycle and nonproliferating state ($G_0$) for LSA tumor in peritoneal cavity.**

shortly after treatment with the alkylating agents. Solid tumors are likely to be much more complex, with cells actually removed from active cycle.[9] However, there may be sites where many of the tumor cells enter an irreversible "noncycling" and nonproliferating state[14] even for leukemia. For example, such a site may occur in extremely advanced tumors or in the skin.[15] Both Cytoxan and BCNU were more effective against the $G_1$-arrested tumor cell in this system than $HN_2$.

Clinical therapeutical strategy planning should define the kinetics and the proliferative state of the tumor cells present. In addition, the age cohort composition of slowly or nonproliferating states of tumor is also desirable. The tumor cells in the advanced and terminal animal tumor in this system appear to collect in $G_1$. To return this tumor to a proliferative state requires an agent active in $G_1$ for the advanced tumor, which can be followed by standard cycle specific antimetabolite drugs to be effective. The recovery of a cell from radiation[16-18] or chemotherapeutic effects probably causes it to reenter the active proliferative phase with a greater likelihood of being affected by S-phase active chemotherapeutic agents. Transplantation may act similarly.[19] Radiation by virtue of its relative cycle nonspecificity and its ability to be concentrated on a localized tumor may represent a potent means of stimulating proliferation as well as destroying tumor. At any rate, when multiple agents or modalities are combined, the proper sequence of therapies is likely to greatly affect their effectiveness and would be as relevant to human therapy as we have found for the mouse in this system.

In conclusion, modifications are produced by therapeutic agents whether they be cancer chemotherapeutic drugs or radiation. These include cell killing and production of perturbations in the cell cycle of surviving (as well as the reproductively dead) cells. As the surviving population recovers from that effect, there is a reassortment of the cells to one of a younger age distribution. There may also be a "reactivation" of the nonproliferating cells into a proliferating compartment. There may also be a temporary distortion of the recovering cell population to one of more closely grouped age cohorts. The most important consideration for tumor therapy would be to transfer the nonproliferating compartment to the proliferating compartment whereupon the greatest variety of potential cancer antimetabolite drugs can be applied. At the same time, if therapeutic ratio and normal tissue tolerance are to be optimized, one must consider the cell kinetics of normal tissues by sequencing and scheduling therapy to minimize the toxic effects of the drugs. With these guiding principles, cancer chemotherapy should be more effective.

## ACKNOWLEDGMENTS

We acknowledge the permission of the publishers of *Cancer and Radiology* to use figures published previously.

Susan Sullivan and Eva Graybeal provided able assistance on these experiments. The research for this paper was supported by National Institutes of Health grants CA 13849, RR 05374, CA 08832, and CA 05528 and by the University of Kentucky Research Foundation.

# REFERENCES

1. A. Howard and S. C. Pelc, Synthesis of Deoxyribosenucleic Acid in Normal and Irradiated Cells and Its Relation to Chromosome Breakage, *Heredity Suppl.*, **6**: 261-273 (1953).

2. Y. Maruyama and B. W. Brown, The Growth of Murine Lymphomatous Tumour Cells as Determined by Host Survival Time, *Int. J. Radiat. Biol.*, **8**: 59-73 (1964).

3. G. Silini and Y. Maruyama, Studies of the LSA Ascites Lymphoma of C57 BL Mice. I. Transplantation Characteristics and Radiosensitivity of Cells During Serial Passages, *J. Nat. Cancer Inst.*, **35**: 841-849 (1965).

4. Y. Maruyama and T. C. Lee, Evidence for and Therapeutic Implications of Cell Age Cohort Variation During Tumor Growth, *Cancer*, **30**: 84-90 (1972).

5. W. R. Bruce, B. E. Meeker, and F. A. Valeriote, Comparison of the Sensitivity of Normal Hematopoietic and Transplanted Lymphoma Colony-Forming Cells to Chemotherapeutic Agents Administered In Vivo, *J. Nat. Cancer Inst.*, **37**: 233-245 (1966).

6. R. B. Painter, R. M. Drew, and W. L. Hughes, Inhibition of HeLa Growth by Intranuclear Tritium, *Science*, **127**: 1244-1245 (1958).

7. C. Heidelberger, Fluoridated Pyrimidines, in *Progress in Nucleic Acid Research and Molecular Biology*, Vol. 4, pp. 1-50, Academic Press, Inc., New York, 1965.

8. R. Barrett, A Mathematical Model of the Mitotic Cycle and Its Application to the Interpretation of Percentage Labelled Mitosis Data, *J. Nat. Cancer Inst.*, **37**: 443-450 (1966).

9. M. L. Mendelsohn, Autoradiographic Analysis of Cell Proliferation in Spontaneous Breast Cancer of C3H Mouse III. The Growth Fraction, *J. Nat. Cancer Inst.*, **28**: 1015-1029 (1962).

10. E. Frindel, A. J. Valleron, F. Vassort, and M. Tubia, Proliferation Kinetics of an Experimental Ascites Tumor of the Mouse, *Cell Tissue Kinet.*, **2**: 51-65 (1969).

11. P. K. Lala and H. M. Patt, Cytokinetic Analysis of Tumor Growth, *Proc. Nat. Acad. Sci. U. S. A.*, **56**: 1735-1742 (1966).

12. Y. Maruyama, F. W. Briese, and B. W. Brown, Jr., X-Radiation Response by $TD_{50}$ and Survival Time Assays for Murine Lymphoma, *Radiat. Res.*, **30**: 96-115 (1967).

13. Y. Maruyama, Indirect Effects of Radiation Upon Tumor Response In Vivo, *Radiology*, **91**: 657-668 (1968).

14. A. M. Mauer, E. F. Saunders, and B. C. Lampkin, Possible Significance of Nonproliferating Cells, *Nat. Cancer Inst. Monogr.*, **30**: 63-79 (1972).

15. Y. Maruyama, T. Mariani, E. P. Engels, and R. A. Good, Analogies Between Experimental and Human *Lymphoma Cutis*, *Cancer*, **31**: 1106-1113 (1973).

16. S. Lesher, Compensatory Reactions in Intestinal Crypt Cells After 300 Roentgens of Cobalt-60 Gamma Irradiation, *Radiat. Res.*, **32**: 510-519 (1967).

17. R. F. Hagemann and S. Lesher, Irradiation of the G. I. Tract: Compensatory Response of Stomach, Jejunum and Colon, *Brit. J. Radiol.*, **44**: 559-602 (1971).

18. A. F. Hermens and G. W. Barendsen, Changes of Cell Proliferation Characteristics in a Rat Rhabdomyosarcoma Before and After X-Irradiation, *Eur. J. Cancer*, **5**: 173-189 (1969).

19. Y. Maruyama, Changes in Spleen Cell CFU Radiosensitivity Following Transplantation, *Radiology*, **90**: 353-355 (1968).

# THE EFFECT OF CYCLOPHOSPHAMIDE ON THE KINETICS OF THORACIC-DUCT LYMPHOID CELLS AND BLOOD LEUKOCYTES OF CALVES

H. P. WAGNER,* M. TROXLER,* H. COTTIER,† A. D. CHANANA,‡ E. P. CRONKITE,‡ and D. D. JOEL‡

*Institute for Clinical and Experimental Cancer Research, University of Bern, Switzerland; †Institute of Pathology, University of Bern, Switzerland; and ‡Medical Research Center, Brookhaven National Laboratory, Upton, New York.

## ABSTRACT

The effect of a single intravenous dose of cyclophosphamide (20 mg per kilogram of body weight) on the cellular output, mitotic index, labelling intensity, and pyknotic index of thoracic-duct lymphocytes was investigated. The output of proliferating large thoracic-duct lymph cells was reduced to approximately one-third of pretreatment values within 2 days. The findings were consistent with the interpretation that (1) cells were killed in various phases of the mitotic cycle, (2) DNA synthesis rate was reduced, and (3) cells were blocked in $G_2$ by cyclophosphamide. Regenerative processes characterized by rising labelling and mitotic indices started 20 to 40 hr following cyclophosphamide and became most evident at 100 to 150 hr. The pyknotic index of thoracic-duct lymph cells showed an initial peak at 12 hr followed by a second peak at 157 hr after drug injection. The changes with time of the pyknotic index and DNA content of nonfragmented pyknotic nuclei support the hypothesis that cyclophosphamide destroyed more small lymphocytes than large proliferating lymphoid cells.

The numbers of large mononuclear cells, small lymphocytes, and neutrophils in blood decreased, reaching minimum values within 2, 3 to 5, and 7 days, respectively. The most important numerical reduction was observed in neutrophils.

Immunosuppressive agents are used extensively for the management of patients receiving bone marrow or organ transplants and for the treatment of neoplastic, autoimmune, and other diseases.[1] Although the effect of such agents on humoral and cellular immune responses has been studied in detail, little is actually known about the cytokinetic effects of these agents on normal lymphoid cells. In part this is probably due to the rather laborious methodology that is required for such investigations. Such information would be particularly valuable, from both a theoretical and a practical point of view. Therefore, a

256

detailed study of the cytokinetic effects of a single intravenous (i.v.) dose of cyclophosphamide (Cytoxan) on proliferating and resting bovine thoracic-duct lymph (TDL) and blood leukocytes was performed. Results of this investigation are presented in this paper.

## MATERIALS AND METHODS

A total of three healthy calves were used in this study (Table 1). In two of these calves, the effect of Cytoxan on blood leukocytes alone was investigated. In the third calf a thoracic-duct-jugular shunt was established,[2] and TDL flow was continuously monitored. At different time intervals before and after a single i.v. dose of 20 mg of Cytoxan per kilogram of body weight, samples of lymph and peripheral blood were obtained. Absolute numbers of neutrophils and mononuclear cells in the blood were determined from total and differential leukocyte counts and estimated blood volumes. The output of large and small TDL cells was assessed as described previously.[3] Aliquots of each lymph sample were incubated for 30 min at 38°C with $^3$H—TdR (New England Nuclear, specific activity 6.7 Ci/mmole, concentration 1 mCi/ml) at a concentration of 1 $\mu$Ci/ml. After incubation the lymph was centrifuged at 1000 rpm for 5 min at 4°C. Following decantation of the supernatant, cells were spread on slides by a spinner or a brush and fixed in absolute methyl alcohol for 3 X 5 min. Spinner smears were processed for radioautography (dipping emulsion NTB-2; exposure time, 4 days) and stained with Giemsa solution 1:50 at pH 6.0. Brush smears were Feulgen stained as described previously.[4] The Giemsa-stained radioauto-graphs were used for determinations of the mitotic index (mitotic figures/10,000 cells), the labelling index (2000 cells counted/sample), and the labelling intensity (median grain count/labelled cell). Only cells with 4 or more grains were considered to be labelled. The Feulgen-stained smears were used for the determination of the pyknotic index (nonfragmented pyknoses/10,000 cells) and for the cytophotometric determination of the DNA content of pyknotic nuclei. The DNA content of labelled and unlabelled nonpyknotic nuclei was determined after the film was removed from autoradiographically processed,

TABLE 1

DETAILS OF CYCLOPHOSPHAMIDE STUDIES

| | Calf | | | | Samples | |
|---|---|---|---|---|---|---|
| Strain | Weight, kg | Age, months | Cytoxan, mg/kg | | Lymph | Blood |
| Holstein | 186 | 7 | 10 | | No | Yes |
| Holstein | 165 | 7 | 20 | | No | Yes |
| Holstein | 134 | 5.5 | 20 | | Yes | Yes |

Feulgen-stained smears. Cytophotometry was performed with a Zeiss scanning spectrophotometer (objective: Ultrafluar X 100, nA 1.25, immersed in glycerine; condensor, LD Planachromat X 40 nA 0.6; illumination field diameter representing 5 $\mu$m at the cellular level; measurement field diameter, 0.5 $\mu$m; wave length, 525 nm; distance of scanning lines, 0.5 $\mu$m) and a digital PDP 12 computer (data processing, Apamos I or II).

## RESULTS

The total output of TDL cells, as well as the output of large and small TDL cells, before and at various time intervals following a single dose of 20 mg of Cytoxan per kilogram of body weight, is shown in Fig. 1. The output of large cells decreased during the first 20 to 30 hr following Cytoxan and then gradually rose to a level above pretreatment values before returning to preinjection levels. The

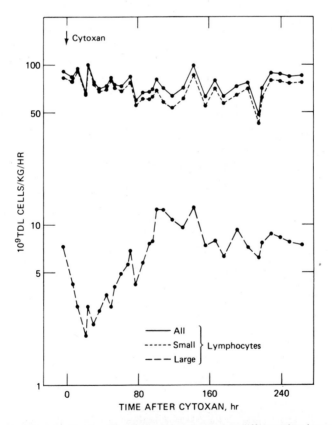

Fig. 1   Thoracic-duct lymph-cell output before and at different time intervals following the injection of 20 mg of Cytoxan per kilogram of body weight.

output of small TDL cells decreased more slowly and returned to pretreatment values later than that of large TDL cells.

The Cytoxan-induced changes in the labelling index and labelling intensity of TDL cells are shown in Fig. 2. Both the labelling index and the labelling intensity decreased within 10 hr post Cytoxan and remained low for approximately 20 to 30 hr. Subsequently these values rose to a peak at 110 hr post Cytoxan and returned to approximately the pretreatment value at about 170 hr following drug injection.

The variation in the mitotic index as a function of time following Cytoxan injection is shown in Fig. 3. The complete disappearance of mitotic figures during the first 25 hr was followed by the reappearance of some mitotic figures at 30 hr. During the next 90 hr, there was a more or less stepwise increase in

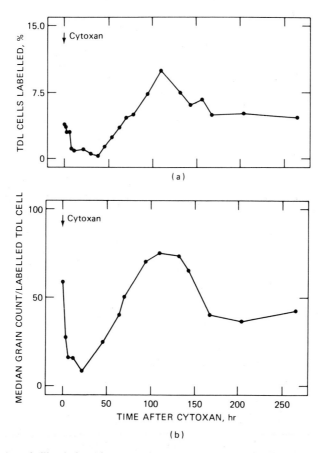

Fig. 2 Labelling index (a) and labelling intensity (b) of TDL cells before and at different time intervals following the injection of 20 mg of Cytoxan per kilogram of body weight.

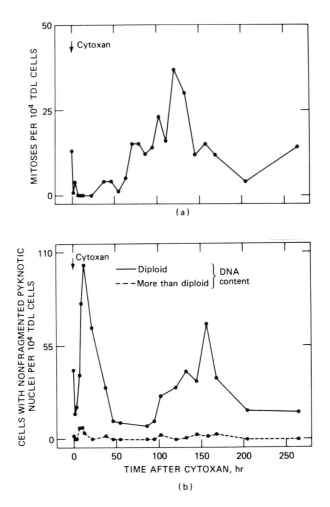

Fig. 3 Mitotic index (a) and pyknotic index (b) of TDL cells before and at different time intervals following the injection of 20 mg of Cytoxan per kilogram of body weight.

mitotic index with a peak value at 120 hr. At approximately 145 hr the values had returned to the pretreatment levels.

The changes in relative numbers of cells with nonfragmented pyknotic nuclei having diploid or more than diploid DNA content, respectively, are also represented in Fig. 3. Following drug injection, the pyknotic index of cells with diploid DNA content decreased and then rose sharply, reaching an initial peak at 12 hr. Minimum values were observed between 50 and 90 hr with a subsequent rise to a second peak at 157 hr. Pyknotic nuclei with more than diploid DNA content represented a very small fraction of total pyknotic cells. The pyknotic index of these cells reached a maximum value as early as 6 to 9 hr postinjection. At this time DNA contents were distributed over the whole range from 2 to 4 c.

The frequency distribution of surviving labelled and unlabelled large lymphoid cells at 9-hr post Cytoxan indicated a minor relative numerical reduction of cells with approximately 2-c DNA content and a slightly increased relative number of cells with approximately 4-c DNA content.

Following both 10 and 20 mg/kg doses of Cytoxan, the numbers of large mononuclear cells, small lymphocytes, and neutrophils in the blood decreased, reaching minimal values within 2, 3 to 4, and 7 days, respectively. The numbers of small lymphocytes in the blood showed a more pronounced diminution following Cytoxan than the output of TDL cells (Figs. 1 and 4). In the calf that received a dose of 20 mg of Cytoxan per kilogram of body weight (Fig. 4), the recovery time for small lymphocytes and neutrophils in blood approached 18 days.

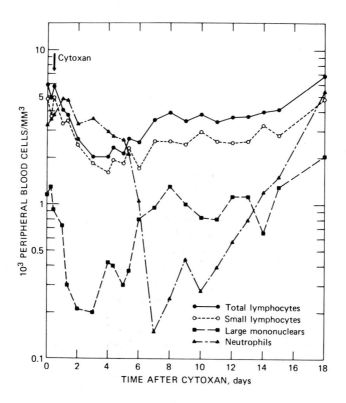

Fig. 4 Blood leukocyte counts before and at different time intervals following the injection of 20 mg of Cytoxan per kilogram of body weight.

## DISCUSSION

These findings indicate that the majority of cells with pyknotic nuclei found in TDL during the first 50 hr following 20 mg of Cytoxan per kilogram had a DNA content of approximately 2 c (Fig. 3). Most TDL cells have a diploid DNA content and are nonproliferating $G_0$ small lymphocytes. However, a small fraction of the small lymphocyte population is a part of the proliferative pool, and, in addition, approximately 25% of large lymphocytes have a diploid DNA content. The data in Fig. 3 show that a maximum of 1% of the diploid lymphocytes are pyknotic. Accordingly one cannot conclude with certainty whether cells are damaged in $G_0$, $G_1$, or early S. Pyknotic cells with DNA contents intermediate between 2 c and 4 c as registered 6 and 9 hr following Cytoxan showed a frequency distribution consistent with the view that proliferating lymphoid cells were killed by Cytoxan in various phases of the cell cycle. The early drop in median grain counts of DNA synthesizing cells and the distribution of these cells with respect to DNA content 9 hr following Cytoxan may be explained in part by a reduction of DNA synthesis rate and/or arrest of cells in various phases of S as reported for other cell systems.[5,6] The increase in relative numbers of unlabelled large lymphoid cells with a DNA content near 4 c, as observed 9 hr after administration of Cytoxan, may reflect an arrest of cells in $G_2$. Similar observations were made on transplantable fibrosarcoma cells in rats.[7]

The interpretation with regard to the effects of Cytoxan on lymphoid cell numbers in TDL and blood is based on the assumption that changes in these populations largely reflected alterations in lymphoreticular tissues and were not heavily influenced by factors such as disparate release into the lymph stream of different cell types. Although the large majority of lymphoid cells killed within 3 to 9 hr after Cytoxan had a DNA content of 2 c and may have been small lymphocytes, the relative sensitivity of these elements appears to be markedly less than that of large proliferating lymphoid cells. This interpretation is supported by the fact that the output of large lymphoid TDL cells and large mononuclear blood cells within 30 hr after Cytoxan decreased to lower relative values than that of small lymphocytes. The output of DNA-synthesizing TDL cells corresponded satisfactorily with the output of large cells. Sizing of cells may, therefore, serve as a method for rapid evaluation of the kinetic effects of the Cytoxan. Damage to the proliferating pool of lymphoid cells must have contributed to the reduction in numbers of small lymphocytes. It is of particular interest in this context that the output of long-lived small lymphocytes in the TDL was less reduced by Cytoxan than was the number of small lymphocytes in the peripheral blood, which contains more short-lived elements than TDL.[8]

Regenerative processes characterized by rising relative numbers of DNA synthesizing cells and mitotic figures were first observed 20 to 40 hr post Cytoxan. Further experimentation is necessary to examine if and to what extent the oscillations in the mitotic-index curve as found during this period were due to partial synchronization of the lymphoid cell system. The peak labelling and mitotic indexes at 110 and 120-hr post Cytoxan, respectively, were two to three times the pretreatment values. It is of interest that pyknotic indices showed a second peak shortly after the regenerative peak of mitotic activity. Since most of these disintegrating cells had a DNA content of approximately 2 c, this may largely represent a fragile population of newly formed small lymphocytes.

The present results also demonstrate that the dose of Cytoxan used had a marked effect on other cell renewal systems, such as bone marrow. Although recovery of the neutrophils was slower than that of large TDL cells, additional studies are needed to evaluate differences in the regenerative pattern of lymphoid and myeloid cell systems.

## ACKNOWLEDGMENTS

The research reported in this paper was supported by the Swiss National Foundation for Scientific Research and the U. S. Atomic Energy Commission.

## REFERENCES

1. M. D. Skinner and R. S. Schwartz, Immunosuppressive Therapy, *New Eng. J. Med.*, **287**: 221-227 and 281-286 (1972).
2. A. D. Chanana and E. P. Cronkite, Semipermanent Extracorporeal Arteriovenous and Thoracic Duct-Venous Shunts in Cattle, *Amer. J. Vet. Res.*, **27**: 683-688 (1966).
3. C. R. Sipe, A. D. Chanana, E. P. Cronkite, D. D. Joel, and L. M. Schiffer, Studies on Lymphopoiesis. VII. Size Distribution of Bovine Thoracic Duct Lymphocytes, *Proc. Soc. Exp. Biol. Med.*, **123**: 158-161 (1966).
4. M. Sordat et al., Studies on Lymphocytes. XV. Analysis of the In Vivo Division Cycle of Large Lymphoid Cells in Calf Thoracic Duct Using Combined Microspectrophotometry and Autoradiography, *Exp. Cell Res.*, **70**: 145-153 (1972).
5. P. Brookes and P. D. Lawley, Evidence for the Action of Alkylating Agents on Deoxyribonucleic Acid, *Exp. Cell Res. Suppl.*, **9**: 521-524 (1963).
6. K. J. Lennartz, K. D. Siemoneit, K. U. Bahntje, and M. Eder, Autoradiographische Untersuchung über die Aenderung des Zellcyclus und der $^3$H—Thymidin-Einbaurate durch Cyclophosphamid bei zwei verschiedenen Ehrlich-Ascitestumoren, *Z. Krebsforsch.*, **73**: 110-121 (1969).
7. S. Peel and D. M. Cowen, The Effect of Cyclophosphamide on the Growth and Cellular Kinetics of a Transplantable Rat Fibrosarcoma, *Brit. J. Cancer*, **26**: 304-314 (1972).
8. H. Cottier, R. Schindler, H. Bürki, B. Sordat, D. D. Joel, and M. W. Hess, Kinetic Aspects of Lymphocyte Recirculation, *Int. Arch. Allergy Appl. Immunol.*, **41**: 4-12 (1971).

# HYDROXYUREA AND IN VIVO SYNCHRONIZATION OF PROLIFERATING CELLS: PROBLEMS AND PROMISES

LYLE A. DETHLEFSEN

Department of Radiology, University of Utah Medical Center, Salt Lake City, Utah

## ABSTRACT

Many reports have shown that hydroxyurea, in vivo, can cause partial synchronization of proliferating cells in both normal and malignant tissue. Theoretically, clinical use for such agents could be rewarding. This paper reviews the murine data within the framework of two models as an aid in evaluating the practicality of cell synchronization in cancer therapy.

The first model uses a disseminated malignancy that is sensitive to hydroxyurea. Each dose kills S-phase cells and causes partial cell synchrony in tumor, bone marrow, and intestinal epithelium; thus, data from all three tissues are crucial. The second model uses a localized tumor, relatively unresponsive to the drug and adjacent to a critical normal tissue, such as intestine. Hydroxyurea is used primarily to synchronize the intestinal cells; then X-irradiation is given to the tumor. In both situations the hydroxyurea must synchronize the cells in such a manner that a subsequent administration of a drug or X-irradiation will kill relatively more tumor than normal cells.

In general, the murine data suggest that one must not be too optimistic about the routine use of synchronizing agents in the clinic. The detailed information needed to make such a procedure feasible is substantial, and the finding of a so-called "optimum interval" that spares normal tissue while increasing the kill of tumor cells may only be fortuitous and, therefore, not applicable in a general sense. In a few selected situations, however, the procedure does have the potential for being appreciably more effective than conventional therapy if the necessary kinetic data can be obtained. In these cases the extra investment in time and expense should be well worth the effort.

Since the initial work on the current concept of the cell cycle by Howard and Pelc[1] and the mammalian cell cloning and single-cell survival techniques by Puck and Marcus,[2] it has been the hope of tumor biologists and oncologists that formal cellular kinetic analysis of normal and malignant tissue would lead to logical improvement in the protocols for radiation and chemotherapy. Unfortunately direct impact on the clinic has been minimal. The reasons are multiple and complex, but they center around the fact that rigorous kinetic data are rarely available in clinical situations because most of the laboratory procedures are too cumbersome and time-consuming to be used. Although basic research on cellular kinetics has presented some valuable insights to the clinical oncologists, a healthy skepticism has prevailed as to the direct use of cellular kinetic data for human patients. Recently, however, several reports concerning cell synchronization in vivo have rekindled interest in potential clinical applications.

Hydroxyurea (HU) has been reported to kill the cells synthesizing DNA and cause a reversible $G_1/S$ block, thereby producing a partial cell synchronization in mouse skin,[3-5] rat and mouse bone-marrow cells,[6-9] mouse spleen erythropoietic cells,[10] mouse duodenal-crypt cells,[11,12] rat cartilage cells,[13] murine lymphoma,[14] rat carcinoma, liver and spleen,[15] C3H mouse mammary tumors,[16] and mouse hair matrix cells.[17] Thus, the thought prevails that HU may be used to synchronize cells in vivo so that one can administer a second therapeutic agent at a time that will minimize damage to the normal tissues and enhance the killing effect on malignant cells. Other cycle-specific agents, such as cytosine arabinoside[18,19] and bleomycin,[20] have also been reported to cause cell synchrony in vivo; however, this paper will not compare drugs per se but review only the HU data from mice as an aid in evaluating those clinical situations which may be amenable to such an approach and then discuss the problems inherent in these clinical situations.

## MODEL 1: DISSEMINATED DISEASE

In this model the malignancy is a systemic disease such as leukemia or a widely disseminated lymphoma such that the multiple foci exclude the possibility for only localized treatment. The assumptions are that the majority of the tumor cells are proliferating (i.e., growth fraction $\simeq 1.0$), there is recruitment from the nonproliferating to proliferating fraction, and the cycle time is quite short (about equal to that for the duodenal-crypt cells). This tumor is sensitive to HU. For simplicity, only two normal tissues, i.e., bone marrow and small intestine, will be considered. The HU obviously affects the proliferating cells in other normal tissues; however, when used in clinical trials the untoward effects were manifested primarily as gastrointestinal and hematologic toxicity.[21] Thus, a limited concern for only two of the various normal tissues should be quite adequate.

Figure 1 shows one example of how the HU perturbations in these three tissues may take place. In such a situation the HU dose is large enough to kill all the S-phase cells and produce a $G_1/S$ block that is significantly long in relation to the total duration of $G_2$, M, and $G_1$. For example, the $G_1/S$ block in the duodenal-crypt cells is 4 to 5 hr, whereas the transient time for $G_2$, M, and $G_1$ equals about 8.4 hr and the S phase is about 7 hr. Thus, an appreciable proportion of the surviving cells will be found in mid and late $G_1$ when the $G_1/S$

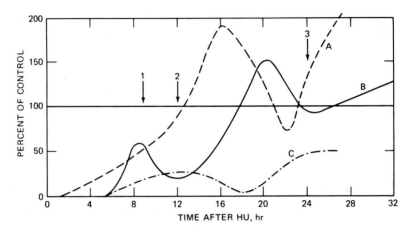

Fig. 1  Model 1. A disseminated malignancy that is sensitive to HU. The arrows indicate selected times when a second dose of HU or some other S-phase specific cytotoxic agent may be given. A, bone marrow, colony-forming units (CFU)/leg × % CFU in S (modified from data in Table 2 of Ref. 8). B, duodenum, DNA radioactivity (modified from data in Fig. 1 of Ref. 12). C, lymphoma, CFU in S (modified from data in Ref. 14, particularly Fig. 4); first 18 hr are taken from reported data and the next 10 hr are hypothesized on the bases of cell cycle and no recruitment.

block is removed. The three numbered arrows indicate times when one may choose to give a second dose of HU or some other S-phase-specific agent.

If the dose is given at arrow 1, then the duodenum should be severely damaged since the first post-HU peak in DNA synthesis is at this time; however, the effect on the bone marrow and lymphoma and especially the lymphoma should be relatively minor since a smaller proportion of these cells are in the S phase. Thus, one would predict that this 9-hr interval between doses of HU would be a poor choice. In contrast, an interval of 12 hr (arrow 2) should spare the duodenum since most of the cells have moved into $G_2$ and beyond, but the bone marrow will be affected quite severely since the number of cells in S are almost back to control levels. The lymphoma should also be severely affected because this is the peak for the first post-HU wave of DNA synthesis. Even though many tumor cells may be killed at this time, the 12-hr interval may not be optimum because of the potential damage to the bone marrow. Arrow 3 suggests an interval that actually may be the optimum one for such an animal-tumor system. By 24 hr the bone-marrow and duodenal-crypt cells have undergone one and two rounds of DNA synthesis, respectively, and have recruited cells from the nonproliferating fractions. Thus, even though a second dose of HU at this time would kill quite a few S-phase cells in both tissues, there may be enough new cells in resistant phases to allow adequate recovery. In contrast, the lymphoma cells are in the second post-HU wave of DNA synthesis, and another dose of HU now may have maximum toxic effects on the tumor. This model assumes no significant lethal effects from the temporary $G_1/S$ block.

It is important to appreciate that Fig. 1 does not indicate the degree of synchrony but only the relative number of cells in S phase at a given time after HU perturbation as compared to the number of cells in S in unperturbed tissues. The criteria for determining synchrony, as discussed by Sinclair and Morton,[22] require more detailed and different data than presented here; however, a crude indication of the extent of synchrony can be obtained by comparing the pulse labelling index or the proportion of colony-forming units (CFU) in S of the control tissue to the respective initial peaks in the perturbed tissue. At 9 hr post-HU, the [3]H—IUdR pulse labelling index for duodenal-crypt cells was 43% as compared to 22% for controls.[12] In the normal bone marrow, the proportion of CFU in S was 20%, and a peak of 57% was reported at 16 hr after HU perturbation.[8] In the lymphoma the percent of CFU in S was 65 to 80% for control tumors and about 95% at 12 hr post-HU for the treated tumors.[14,23] The CFU data are not based on [3]H—TdR pulse labelling but instead are based on cell killing from a second dose of HU. Perfect synchrony, of course, would find 100% of the cells in S; thus, the synchrony in the lymphoma appears quite good, but the normal tissue synchrony is modest. These results appear to be typical for in vivo synchronization attempts in normal tissues.

Skipper et al.[24] have reported on the toxic effects of HU in the $BDF_1$-L1210 mouse tumor system. (The median $T_c$ for the L1210 cells is 12.8 hr, approximating the $T_c$ for the lymphoma tumor in Fig. 1). They first established the $LD_{10}$ dose for five different protocols and then, using these respective doses and protocols, measured the increase in life-span and so-called "cures" when mice were injected intraperitoneally with L1210 cells. A cure is defined as an animal living at least 45 days after treatment without evidence of disease. They reported that a daily dose given for 15 days was more effective than either a single dose, 8 doses every 2 days, or 4 doses every 4 days. The increased life-span (as percent of untreated controls) was 61, 11, 55, and 11%, respectively, with no cures in any group. They also reported that the most effective protocol was 8 doses every 3 hr on days 2, 6, 10, and 14 after the injection of the L1210 cells. In this group the life-span was increased by more than 100%, and there were 10 cures out of 40 mice. The curves in Fig. 1 do not allow a prediction of the effects of a split-dose procedure, but the agreement between the model in Fig. 1 and the data from the 24 hr-interval trial of Skipper et al.[24] is very encouraging. However, a crucial question is: Will the perturbed cellular kinetics be the same after two or more doses as they are after the initial dose of HU? We are currently testing this by setting up groups of tumor-bearing (S102F line) mice for the three two-dose protocols as suggested by the arrows in Fig. 1. In each of the three groups, one set of animals was observed for weight loss and perturbations in the tumor growth curves (clinical effects), and in a second set the rates of [3]H—TdR incorporation were measured in the duodenum and tumors after the second dose of HU. The mice were injected with two doses of HU (3 mg per gram of body weight) at either 9-, 12-, or 24-hr intervals; then at various times five or six mice were injected with 20 $\mu$Ci of $^3$H—TdR (New England Nuclear, 6.7 Ci/mmole) and killed 1 hr later. The duodenal and tumor DNA were extracted and radioactivity was determined and reported as a percent of control tissue. The clinical data for some recently completed experiments are summarized in Table 1 and the $^3$H-incorporation data are given in Table 2.

**TABLE 1**

CLINICAL EFFECTS: TWO DOSES OF HU

| Time between HU doses, hr | No. of mice | Body weight* | | No. of mice | Tumor growth† | |
|---|---|---|---|---|---|---|
| | | 1 day post-HU | 3 days post-HU | | 1 day post-HU | 3 days post-HU |
| 9 | 10 | 97.7 ± 0.9 | 87.4 ± 0.8 | 6 | 84.6 ± 6.5 | 65.2 ± 4.4 |
| 12 | 11 | 93.4 ± 2.2 | 94.0 ± 2.2 | 11 | 58.4 ± 3.5 | 60.3 ± 6.8 |
| 24 | 9 | 99.2 ± 1.7 | 97.3 ± 3.1 | 13 | 85.7 ± 3.5 | 75.8 ± 7.6 |

*Data are mean percent of control (weight on day of first HU injection) weight ± standard error of the mean.

†Data are mean percent inhibition ± standard error of the mean (percent inhibition = [(measured tumor volume)/(predicted tumor volume)] x 100). Predicted volume comes from a computer-fitted growth curve.[31]

**TABLE 2**

$^3$H—TdR INCORPORATION: TWO-DOSE EFFECTS OF HU

| Time between HU doses, hr | Time of first post-HU peak in DNA synthesis* | | DNA radioactivity, percent of control† | | Time of subsequent minimum* | |
|---|---|---|---|---|---|---|
| | Duodenum | Tumor | Duodenum | Tumor | Duodenum | Tumor |
| 9 | 8 | 14 | 7.4 ± 2.6  (6) | 40.4 ± 15.3 (7) | 12 | 16 |
| 12 | 8 | 14 | 19.3 ± 9.6  (5) | 55.0 ± 4.0  (7) | 10 | 16 |
| 24 | 10 | 14 | 99.1 ± 31.1 (6) | 77.6 ± 12.7 (8) | 12 | 16 |

*The sampling intervals were 2 hr so these times are at least ±1 hr.

†Data are group means ± standard error of the means and (n) = number of observations.

If body weight is a reasonable indirect reflection of gastrointestinal toxicity (the cellular toxicity causes reduced food intake, fluid loss, etc.), then model 1 predicts that two doses of HU at a 9-hr interval should cause more weight loss than the 12- or 24-hr intervals. The data in Table 1 are for measurements on day 1 and day 3 post-HU. The 1-day data are inconclusive. This may be related to the time it takes to reflect cellular toxicity, but, by 3 days post-HU, the trend is as predicted. The body weights for the mice in the 9-hr interval averaged 87%

of control, and those for the 12- and 24-hr intervals are 94 and 97%, respectively. The tumor data at 3 days post-HU also follow predictions. The measured volume in the 9-hr group averaged 65% of the predicted volume, and the 12- and 24-hr-interval measurements are 60 and 75% of predicted volumes, respectively. The data are preliminary and the sources of error are quite substantial, but the agreement with prediction is encouraging.

Qualitative predictions can also be made about the relative rates of $^3$H–TdR incorporation during the first post-HU round of DNA synthesis. The actual value cannot be established, because we do not know the efficiency of synchronization or the extent of recruitment from the nonproliferating fraction; but in the duodenum the peak for the 9-hr group should be considerably lower than that in the 12-hr group. Also, the peak for the 24-hr group should be markedly higher than either. For the tumor a gradual increase in the peak as the intervals between HU doses increase would be expected owing to recovery from the $G_1/S$ block and recruitment. The data in Table 2 confirm these predictions. The first peaks for $^3$H–TdR incorporation in the duodenal DNA are 7 and 19% of control, respectively, for the 9- and 12-hr data, whereas the 24-hr group shows incorporation that is 99% of control. These peaks for the tumor DNA radioactivity are 40, 55, and 78%, respectively, for the 9-, 12- and 24-hr group. This index (relative incorporation of $^3$H–TdR) admittedly is rather crude as compared to formal autoradiographic analysis; however, Dethlefsen and Riley[12] have shown that the index correlates very well with the labelling index following a perturbation with HU. Moreover, this procedure is much more practical to use in the clinic, as has been demonstrated by Lampkin, Nagao, and Mauer[18] for leukemia and by Barranco et al.[20] for malignant melanoma. Both reports demonstrated that the $^3$H–TdR incorporation data adequately reflect the pulse labelling index.

The specific timing of these peaks cannot be predicted a priori; however, if the method is to be used in the clinic, one must hope that the times for maximum incorporation would be the same after two or more doses as they are after one; and, indeed, this appears to hold true in the mouse duodenum and mammary tumor. The first peaks in the duodenum occur between 8 and 10 hr with the subsequent lows occurring at 10 to 12 hr. The initial peaks in the tumor cells are all around 14 hr, the subsequent minimums being around 16 hr. These data suggest that the kinetics of the surviving cells are the same after two doses (regardless of the interval) as they are after a single dose of HU.

Barranco et al.[20] reported similar results from human malignant melanomas. They used bleomycin (25 mg total dose per 24 hr) for synchronization and found in the four patients studied that the peak incorporation occurred 2 days later. Unfortunately, the report by Lampkin, Nagao, and Mauer[18] did not show this uniformity for human leukemia. They used single doses of cytosine arabinoside and found that the peak labelling index varied between 25 and 96 hr in seven patients with acute lymphoblastic leukemia and two patients showed no apparent response.

If it is assumed that something analogous to model 1 may actually be achieved in the clinic and that the kinetics posttreatment are relatively stable, then we must ask what information is needed. One set of data that is not needed is formal kinetic (autoradiographic) analysis of the unperturbed tissue. Such data can be helpful for making predictions about perturbed kinetics, but the crucial data are the $^3$H—TdR incorporation data as a function of time after one, two, and more doses of the perturbing agent. Of course, these data must be obtained on all relevant tissues. This information is adequate for predicting the time for second and subsequent doses. Besides the correct intervals, the optimum dose for each drug used singly and in combination with other drugs must be established. When two or more drugs are given in sequence, then, of course, the kinetics after each drug in the sequence and between sequences must be established. In brief, any perturbation in dose, type of drug used, combination of drugs, and particular sequence will require the collecting of $^3$H—TdR incorporation data so as to establish the subsequent optimal intervals. One is quickly impressed with the voluminous amount of data that is required for even this rather crude analysis. However, the techniques have already been demonstrated as feasible in the clinic; thus, clinicians must decide if the potential payoff will be worth the extra investment in time, material, and labor.

## MODEL 2: LOCALIZED TUMOR ADJACENT TO A CRITICAL NORMAL TISSUE

In this model the assumptions are as follows:

1. The solid, localized tumor is slow growing and relatively unresponsive to HU.

2. The fraction of proliferating cells is small.

3. The mean cell-cycle time is considerably longer than the cell cycle in the intestinal epithelial cells.

4. The intestine is the only normal tissue of concern.

In this situation HU is used primarily for synchronization of the normal tissue cells. Either single or multiple doses can be used to achieve a reasonable degree of cell synchrony; however, there will be some gastrointestinal toxicity from the HU, per se. This may not have to be the case, but for now it seems to be a valid conservative assumption since doses large enough to arrest cells for more than 1 hr are cytotoxic.[25] Figure 2 shows some stylized data for the mouse duodenum and mammary tumor as well as a hypothetical tumor that is completely resistant to HU.

If the tumor in question responds like curve A, Fig. 2, then the only hope is that partial synchronization of the intestinal-crypt cells will allow the X-irradiation to be given at a time when more of the intestinal cells are in a relatively radioresistant phase (see Sinclair[26] for a review on relative radiosensitivity about the cell cycle). If so, a larger dose may be delivered to the tumor. The theoretical

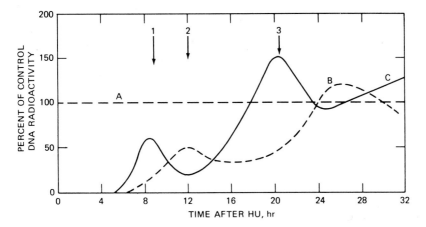

Fig. 2 Model 2. A localized tumor that is either completely insensitive, A (hypothetical tumor), or partially sensitive, B (C3H mammary tumor), to HU and is growing close to a critical normal tissue, C (intestine). This tumor is slow growing and has a low growth fraction. Curve A shows that the HU kills few or no S-phase cells and does not produce a detectable $G_1$/S block. Curve B shows that a single dose of HU does kill some of the S-phase cells and causes an appreciable delay at the $G_1$/S interphase. The three arrows indicate times when X-irradiation may be delivered to the localized tumor and adjacent small bowel. The curve for the C3H mouse mammary-tumor data (curve B) is suggested by first-generation transplants in Ref. 16, Fig. 1, p. 176, and the duodenal (curve C) data are the same as in Fig. 1.

gain in such a situation could be substantial since the change in cellular radiosensitivity can vary by a factor of 10 to 40. For example, single cell survival for Chinese hamster V79 cells that received a dose of 710 rads ranged between 0.005 for mitotic cells to 0.2 for late S-phase cells, whereas, for HeLa cells that received 500 rads, this range was from 0.01 to 0.1 (see Fig. 1, Sinclair[26]). However, this potential gain is minimized substantially because the current in vivo synchronizing methods are quite inadequate; i.e., the relative increase in the proportion of cells that can be accumulated in any particular phase is small.

If the tumor responds like curve B, Fig. 2, then one may find a time when a higher proportion of the intestinal-crypt cells are in a relatively radioresistant part of the cell cycle while a higher proportion of the tumor cells are in a more radiosensitive phase of the cycle. Again, a larger dose may be tolerated by the intestine, but, in addition, each rad of this larger dose may be more effective in reducing tumor-cell survival. The potential gain is still expected to be modest, but a small increase in dose, along with improved efficiency, may yield an enhanced inhibitory effect on the tumor without increasing the untoward effects on the normal tissue (see Shukovsky[27] for an example of a steep control probability curve). Arrows 1 and 3 (Fig. 2) indicate two times when more of the duodenal-crypt cells (curve C) are in the relatively radioresistant S phase; thus, these should be optimal times for X-irradiation. In contrast, arrow 2 suggests a time that would be more detrimental to the duodenum, curve C (relatively more cells in $G_2$, M, and early $G_1$), and the mammary tumor, curve B, may actually be spared since more cells are in the S phase.

These specific procedures remain to be tested in C3H mammary tumors; but Malkinson, Griem, and Marianovic[17] have actually conducted such an experiment on anagen hair follicles of $CF_1$ mice, and Gillette, Withers, and Tannock[11] have reported a similar experiment on the jejunum of $BDF_1$ mice. Malkinson, Griem, and Marianovic[17] injected HU (1.2 mg per gram of body weight) followed by 650 rads of X-irradiation at various times and reported an initial sensitive period (i.e., about 10% hair survival), then a resistant period that corresponds to the initial peak in DNA synthesis, and then another sensitive phase. The maximum survival at 6 hr post-HU was 35% as compared to 44% when only X-irradiation was given.

Gillette, Withers, and Tannock[11] used multiple doses of HU and demonstrated a periodicity in the number of surviving crypts when single doses (1150 rads) of $^{137}Cs$ gamma rays were administered at various times after the injections of HU. The peak survival (about 30 crypts per cross section) corresponded with the mid to late S phase; at other times the survival was 5 to 10 crypts per cross section. However, one must again bear in mind that the combined treatment, regardless of time, is much more toxic than gamma irradiation alone. The crypt survival following 1150 rads of $^{137}Cs$ gamma irradiation without previous HU administration is about 100 crypts per cross section; thus, in terms of toxicity, one has gone from an approximate $LD_{10/5}$ dose to something significantly greater than $LD_{50/5}$ (Dr. H. R. Withers, M. D. Anderson Hospital and Tumor Institute, personal communication). If such a situation holds when irradiation is given at the time of arrow 3 and even if the tumor response is similar to the mammary tumor (curve B, Fig. 2) (i.e., a modest increase in the proportion of relatively more radiosensitive cells), then one may actually reduce instead of increase the therapeutic index. Gillette, Withers, and Tannock[11] also reported that the first peak of DNA synthesis (arrow 1) was not radioresistant but actually quite radiosensitive and suggested that this may be due to direct radiosensitization by the HU still present in the tissue.[11] However, in a subsequent series of experiments also using HU and $^{137}Cs$ irradiation, Mason and Withers (unpublished, personal communication) found that a resistant phase does occur with the initial peak of DNA synthesis; thus they do not feel that direct sensitization by HU is involved. Obviously, for the technique to be clinically effective, normal tissue toxicity from the synchronizing agents must be minimal and not synergistic with the irradiation toxicity.

In contrast to this model, Sinclair[26] has proposed a model based on his in vitro results with HU. In his model, HU is used to kill the S-phase cells, which are relatively more radioresistant, produce a $G_1/S$ block, and directly sensitize the arrested $G_1$ cells. In this situation, the irradiation must be given within a few hours of the HU administration. Piver et al.[28] used this model for evaluating the combined effects of HU and X-irradiation in a C3H mouse mammary tumor and reported a small effect with HU if the irradiation was fractionated and administered under hypoxic conditions but no effect with single-dose irradiations. These data suggest that the tumor response to HU was somewhere between the response curves for the hypothetical tumor and mammary tumor of Fig. 2 and more probably closer to the hypothetical curve (curve A). Thus, few S-phase cells were killed, the $G_1/S$ block was short, and, presumably, the tumor concentration of HU was low; thus sensitization was minimal or nonexistent. Therefore, one would not expect an appreciable reduction in the dose needed for a 50:50 chance of local control.

If one assumes that the problems suggested by the reports of Gillette, Withers, and Tannock[11] and Piver et al.[28] can be overcome and that something analogous to the C3H mammary tumor curve (curve B, Fig. 2) can be achieved, then what information does a therapist need to make this clinically feasible? Obviously, the same type of information is needed here as was discussed for model 1. Fortunately, one needs the data on only two instead of three tissues. This is an appreciable reduction in time and expense. Once again, the important question about uniformity of the cellular kinetics in the normal tissues of the patients as well as in tumors of the same histological type confronts the therapist. Furthermore, the present data do not allow one to predict the kinetics of the surviving cells after one or more treatments with synchronizing agent and ionizing radiation. Another relevant problem is the relative importance of early vs. late effects of ionizing radiation on normal tissue in the assessment of the clinical outcome. Stewart and Fajardo[29] have reported that myocardial fibrosis, a late effect, is related to capillary endothelial-cell damage, which is followed by loss of capillaries and a failure of the microcirculation. If the late effects in the intestine are also due to a similar phenomenon, will a reduction in the killing of lining epithelial cells be of significance? In studying early and late reactions in the skin on the feet of rats, Field[30] reported that the dose—response curve for late effects is much steeper than the curve for early effects, and he concluded that the early reactions are an insensitive measure for determining late reaction. Thus, one could be confronted with the problem of an unacceptably high incidence of severe late effects with only modest increases in patient survival times.

## EPILOGUE

The murine data for HU-produced synchronization of proliferating cells have been reviewed, and some of the problems and promises have been cataloged. The question now is, Where do we go from here? In spite of the general pessimistic tone of this paper, I see two areas with potential payoff.

1. An ideal situation analogous to model 1. Skipper et al.[24] have already set the stage for animal experimentation, and Lampkin, Nagao, and Mauer[18] and Barranco et al.[20] have given us glimpses of potential benefits that may be

obtained in the clinic. Multiple doses, combination of drugs, and optimum intervals (when they exist and if they can be determined) of administration can most certainly improve the effectiveness of cancer therapy.

2. If normal cells can be partially synchronized with minimal toxicity, then there are probably a limited number of situations where model 2 (i.e., drug plus localized X-irradiation) may function. At the moment, this potential does not seem as likely as model 1, but the possibility should not be forgotten.

Optimistically, these two areas together will constitute only a small fraction of all cancer patients, but the improvement in therapy for these patients should be substantial.

Much more work needs to be done on experimental solid tumor systems, and the clinical investigator must be persuaded to make an extra effort to collect data that will allow logical choices instead of empiricism in cancer therapy. It is of utmost importance that the initial cases be selected carefully and then worked up logically and in depth. The time course will be long, the work arduous and tedious, and the potential rewards relatively small as compared to finding cancer causes, but, until the causes are found and eliminated, we are duty bound to improve cancer therapy by whatever small percentages we can.

## ACKNOWLEDGMENTS

I wish to thank Reba Riley, Michael Maack, and Steve Sorenson for their competent technical assistance, H. R. Withers, for unpublished data and a critical reading of the manuscript, and J. Robert Stewart, for a critical review and discussion of this report.

The research reported in this paper was supported in part by the U. S. Atomic Energy Commission (COO-2269-3) and the National Cancer Institute (1 R01-CA-14165-01).

## REFERENCES

1. A. Howard and S. R. Pelc, Nuclear Incorporation of P-32 as Demonstrated by Autoradiographs, *Expt. Cell Res.*, **2**: 178-187 (1951).
2. T. T. Puck and P. I. Marcus, Action of X-Rays on Mammalian Cells, *J. Expt. Med.*, **103**: 653-666 (1956).
3. R. Süss and H. R. Maurer, Reduced Binding of Carcinogenic Hydrocarbons to DNA of Mouse Skin During Inhibition of DNA Synthesis, *Nature*, **217**: 752-753 (1968).
4. H. C. Smith, R. K. Boutwell, and V. R. Potter, Effects of Hydroxyurea on DNA and RNA Synthesis in Mouse Skin, Liver, and Thymus and on Skin Tumorigenesis Initiated by $\beta$-Propiolactone, *Cancer Res.*, **28**: 2217-2227 (1968).
5. R. M. Singer and S. Gelfant, Continuous Inhibition of DNA Synthesis in Mouse Ear Epidermis Using Hydroxyurea, *Exp. Cell Res.*, **73**: 270-271(1972).
6. F. Bohne, R. J. Haas, T. M. Fliedner, and I. Fache, The Role of Slowly Proliferating Cells in Rat Bone Marrow During Regeneration Following Hydroxyurea, *Brit. J. Hematol.*, **19**: 533-542(1970).

7. Von R. J. Haas, I. Fache, F. Bohne, and T. M. Fliedner, Die Wirkung von Hydroxyharnstoff auf die Hämopoese der Ratte nach einmaliger oder fraktionierter Gabe, *Arzneim.-Forsch.,* **7**: 974-978(1971).

8. F. Vassort, E. Frindel, and M. Tubiana, Effects of Hydroxyurea on the Kinetics of Colony Forming Units of Bone Marrow in the Mouse, *Cell Tissue Kinet.,* **4**: 423-431(1971).

9. J. T. Chaffey and S. Hellman, Differing Responses to Radiation of Murine Bone Marrow Stem Cells in Relation to the Cell Cycle, *Cancer Res.,* **31**: 1613-1615(1971).

10. Y. Najean, Action de la Chimiothérapie sur la Cinétique Cellulaire. I. Evolution, en Fonction du temps, de la Prolifération Érythroblastique. Influence de Cette Donnée pour le Choix de L'espacement des drogues dans un Traitement Séguential, *Nouv. Rev. Fr. Hematol.,* **11**: 185-202 (1971).

11. E. L. Gillette, H. R. Withers, and I. F. Tannock, The Age Sensitivity of Epithelial Cells of Mouse Small Intestine, *Radiology,* **96**: 639-643(1970).

12. L. A. Dethlefsen and R. M. Riley, Hydroxyurea Effects in the C3H Mouse. I. Duodenal Crypt Cell Kinetics, *Cell Tissue Kinet.,* **6**: 3-16(1973).

13. N. F. Kember, Hydroxyurea and the Differentiation of Growth Cartilage Cells in the Rat, *Cell Tissue Kinet.,* **5**: 199-201(1972).

14. H. Madoc-Jones and F. Mauro, Age Responses to X-Rays, Vinca Alkaloids, and Hydroxyurea of Murine Lymphoma Cells Synchronized in Vivo, *J. Nat. Cancer Inst.,* **45**: 1131-1143(1970).

15. M. F. Rajewsky, D. F. Hülser, and E. Fabricus, Untersuchungen zur Synchronisation in vivo: Temporäre Inhibition der DNA-Synthese durch Hydroxyharnstoff in normalen und malignen Säugerzellsystemen, *Z. Krebsforsch,* **76**: 266-292(1971).

16. L. A. Dethlefsen and R. M. Riley, Hydroxyurea Effects in the C3H Mouse II. Mammary Tumor Cell Kinetics, *Cell Tissue Kinet.,* **6**: 173-184(1973).

17. F. D. Malkinson, M. L. Griem, and R. Marianovic, Effects of Hydroxyurea and Radiation on Hair Matrix Cells, *Cell Tissue Kinet.,* **6**: 395-405(1973).

18. B. C. Lampkin, T. Nagao, and A. M. Mauer, Synchronization and Recruitment in Acute Leukemia, *J. Clin. Invest.,* **50**: 2204-2214(1971).

19. M. H. L. Gibson and F. D. Bertalanffy, In Vivo Synchrony of Solid B16 Melanoma by Cytosine Arabinoside, an Inhibitor of DNA Synthesis, *J. Nat. Cancer Inst.,* **49**: 1007-1018(1972).

20. S. C. Barranco, L. K. Luce, M. M. Romsdahl, and R. M. Humphrey, Bleomycin as a Possible Synchronizing Agent for Human Tumor Cells In Vivo, *Cancer Res.,* **33**: 882-887(1973).

21. D. L. Ahmann, R. G. Hahn, and H. F. Bisel, Clinical Evaluation of 5-(3,3-Dimethyl-1-triazeno) imidazole-4-carboxamide (NSC-45388), Melphalan (NSC-8806) and Hydroxyurea (NSC-32065) in the Treatment of Disseminated Malignant Melanoma, *Cancer Chemother. Rep.,* **56**: 369-372(1972).

22. W. K. Sinclair and R. A. Morton, X-Ray and Ultraviolet Sensitivity of Synchronized Chinese Hamster Cells at Various Stages of the Cell Cycle, *Biophys. J.,* **5**: 1-25(1965).

23. F. Mauro and H. Madoc-Jones, Age Response to X-Radiation of Murine Lymphoma Cells Synchronized In Vivo, *Proc. Nat. Acad. Sci. U.S.A.,* **63**: 686-691 (1969).

24. H. E. Skipper et al., Implications of Biochemical, Cytokinetic Pharmacologic, and Toxicologic Relationships in the Design of Optimal Therapeutic Schedules, *Cancer Chemother. Rep.,* **54**: 431-450(1970).

25. H. Hennings and F. Devik, Comparison of Cytotoxicity of Hydroxyurea in Normal and Rapidly Proliferating Epidermis and Small Intestine in Mice, *Cancer Res.,* **31**: 277-282(1971).

26. W. K. Sinclair, Dependence of Radiosensitivity upon Cell Age, in Conference on Time and Dose Relationships in Radiation Biology as Applied to Radiotherapy Held at

Carmel, California, September 15—18, 1969, pp. 97-107, USAEC Report BNL-50203, Brookhaven National Laboratory, August 1970.

27. L. J. Shukovsky, Dose, Time, Volume Relationships in Squamous Cell Carcinoma of the Supraglottic Larynx, *Amer. J. Roentgenol., Rad. Ther. Nucl. Med.,* **108**: 27-29(1970).

28. M. S. Piver, A. E. Howes, H. D. Suit, and N. Marshall, Effect of Hydroxyurea on the Radiation Response of C3H Mouse Mammary Tumors, *Cancer,* **29**: 407-412(1972).

29. J. R. Stewart and L. F. Fajardo, Radiation-Induced Heart Disease. Clinical and Experimental Aspects, *Radiol. Clin. N. Amer.,* **9**: 511-531(1971).

30. S. B. Field, Early and Late Reactions in Skin of Rats Following Irradiation with X-Rays or Fast Neutrons, *Radiology,* **92**: 381-384(1969).

31. L. A. Dethlefsen, J. M. S. Prewitt, and M. L. Mendelsohn, Analysis of Tumor Growth Curves, *J. Nat. Cancer Inst.,* **40**: 389-405(1969).

# PERTURBATIONS OF ERYTHROBLASTIC KINETICS IN THE SPLEEN OF MICE INFECTED BY THE FRIEND VIRUS

F. SMADJA-JOFFE,* C. JASMIN,* P. E. TAMBOURIN,† and E. P. MALAISE‡
*Institut de Cancérologie et d'Immunogénétique (I.N.S.E.R.M.
et Association Claude-Bernard), Hôpital Paul-Brousse, Villejuif, France.
†Institut du Radium, Faculté de Sciences, University of Paris, Orsay, France.
‡Institut Gustave-Roussy, Villejuif, France.

## ABSTRACT

The kinetic parameters of the polycythemic variety of Friend leukemia have been studied in DBA/2 mice inoculated with the virus. Almost all leukemic cells (hyperbasophilic proerythroblasts) are in active stages of the cell cycle (mean duration, 7.6 hr). This intense and massive proliferation is unaffected even during the hours preceding death. The multiplication of leukemic cells results in three different phenomena: a very small fraction ($\frac{1}{20}$) of the proliferation accounts for the growth of the spleen and the progressive invasion of the liver and the blood; $\frac{1}{3}$ of leukemic cells differentiate into short-lived erythrocytes; and $\frac{2}{3}$ disappear apparently owing to massive cellular death. From these results it can be concluded that Friend leukemia is a proliferative disease and that the cumulative model proposed to explain the poor transplantability of Friend cells cannot be accepted. The patterns of proliferation in Friend leukemia differ with the kinetic parameters of transplantable leukemias such as L 1210, for example. The role of the viral infection is discussed.

The kinetic and physiological characteristics of cellular proliferation at the very beginning of the disease are now under study.

The injection of Friend virus (FV) into a sensitive strain of mice induces the appearance of leukemic cells belonging to the erythropoietic line, as has been shown by cytological[1] and physiological[2] studies. These pathological cells called Friend cells (FC) are poorly differentiated proerythroblasts with a hyperbasophilic cytoplasm.[3] These cells appear in the spleen, which they invade diffusely, provoking a splenomegaly; during the disease, pathological cells are disseminated throughout all the organs but mainly in the liver and in the peripheral blood.

Though they are leukemic, these cells are able to differentiate along the erythropoietic line up to the erythrocyte stage; this has been shown by measuring the production of differentiated cells (reticulocytes and erythrocytes) in the peripheral blood of leukemic mice.[4] Two strains of FV have been isolated: an anemia-inducing strain, characterized by a low hematocrit that results from hypervolemia[4] and the polycythemia-inducing strain, isolated by Mirand.[5] In these two varieties of the disease, the hyperbasophilic cell proliferation can be lowered by injecting washed isogenic red blood cells,[6] but the physiological steady-state equilibrium can never be completely reached again. This lack of control confirms the neoplasic nature of FC. Stimulation of erythroblastosis and an increased red-cell production in the peripheral blood are observed in the two kinds of Friend leukemias. The anemia-inducing variety is the most susceptible to this artificial polyglobulia.

Two hypotheses can be proposed to explain the splenomegaly characterizing the Friend disease: (1) a cumulative model in which hyperbasophilic cells would multiply very slowly or even not at all and accumulate in the spleen and other organs and (2) a proliferative model in which transformed cells are rapidly dividing (Fig. 1).

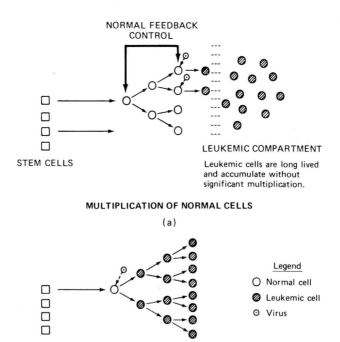

NORMAL FEEDBACK
CONTROL

STEM CELLS

LEUKEMIC COMPARTMENT
Leukemic cells are long lived
and accumulate without
significant multiplication.

MULTIPLICATION OF NORMAL CELLS

(a)

Legend
○ Normal cell
⊘ Leukemic cell
⊙ Virus

STEM CELLS          LEUKEMIC COMPARTMENT

MULTIPLICATION OF LEUKEMIC CELLS

(b)

Fig. 1 Two hypotheses to explain the splenomegaly in Friend disease.
(a) A cumulative model. (b) A proliferative model.

Therefore, a comprehensive study of Friend disease requires a knowledge of the characteristics of proliferation of FC. Using autoradiographic techniques, we have studied: (1) the proliferation rate of leukemic cells in the spleen, which appears to be the first organ involved in their production, and in the liver and peripheral blood and (2) the growth rate of the leukemic spleen.

## MATERIAL AND METHODS

The polycythemia-inducing strain of Friend virus used was obtained from supernatants of homogenates of leukemic spleens following centrifugation. The titre of the viral preparations expressed in spleen dose 50% ($SD_{50}$) was determined using the technique of Rowe and Brodsky.[7] In our experiments each mouse was inoculated intravenously (i.v.) with 0.2 ml of viral suspension containing 50 $SD_{50}$.

Female DBA/2 mice, approximately 2 months old, were used. The mean spleen weight of a normal mouse is 106 ± 13.8 mg. Tritiated thymidine, $^3H-TdR$ (0.2 ml; specific activity, 9.3 Ci/mmole), was injected into the retro-orbital sinus of each mouse.

To study the mitotic cycle, we gave each leukemic mouse 2.5 $\mu$Ci/g of $^3H-TdR$. Half an hour after injection and then every hour for 25 hr, four leukemic animals were killed. In another experimental group, 1 $\mu$Ci/g of $^3H-TdR$ was injected every 3 hr for 15 hr. Four leukemic mice were killed 1 hr after each injection. With the doses of $^3H-TdR$ we used, labelled spleen cells had a modal number of 30 to 35 grains per cell 15 days after exposure; this value was determined on 2000 cells per point.

After the mice were anesthetized with ether, the organs under study were removed and imprints were made. The imprints were fixed for 1 hr in Carnoy's fixative. This technique allowed adhesion of a continuous monolayer of morphologically well preserved cells on the glass slide (Fig. 2).

Labelling indexes on imprints, on histological sections, and on smears of spleen and liver were determined by counting 2000 cells per mouse. Mitotic indexes and the percentage of labelled mitoses were calculated on the basis of 400 mitoses (100 per mouse) from imprints of spleen.

Peripheral blood was drawn into heparin from a section of the axillary artery, and blood smears were fixed in absolute methanol. Labelling indexes of peripheral blood cells were determined on 1000 nucleated cells per mouse using four mice per point (see Fig. 9).

Slides were dipped into autoradiographic emulsion and exposed for about 2 weeks at +4°C. They were stained with Romanovsky stain. The background of the emulsion was determined on autoradiographs of control imprint slides. Usually, under our experimental conditions a cell was considered labelled when there were three grains over its nucleus.

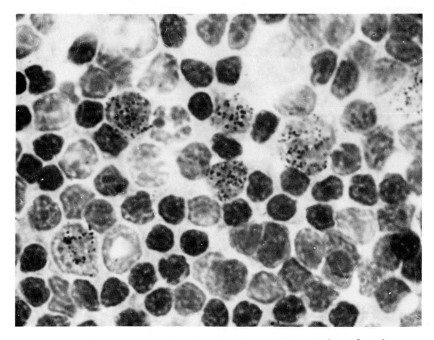

Fig. 2 Autoradiograph of a Friend leukemic spleen 15 days after the injection of 50 $SD_{50}$ of viral suspension. (Romanovsky stain; 576 x.)

Differential counts of cell populations were also made from imprints, smears, and histological sections of nonautoradiographed organs.

Growth curves for the spleen, liver, and peripheral blood have been established. Of the mice inoculated with 50 $SD_{50}$ of viral suspension given i.v., seven DBA/2 mice were killed on days 4, 7, 21, and 28 after injection of the virus. Spleens and livers were weighed, and counts of nucleated cells per cubic millimeter of peripheral blood were performed in a counting chamber.

The daily production rate of reticulocytes in peripheral blood was calculated with the formula:[4]

Daily production rate = (total number of reticulocytes in peripheral blood)/
(mean life-span of reticulocytes in peripheral blood)

The number of reticulocytes for 1000 erythrocytes was determined with water-soluble brilliant Cresyl Blue. The blood volume was determined by the $^{59}$Fe-labelled red-cell dilution method.[8] The mean life-span was calculated according to Ganzoni.[9]

The duration of the mitotic cycle and its phases has been determined following the method of Quastler and Sherman[10] with the aid of a mathematical model described by Valleron, Mary, and Frindel.[11]

# RESULTS

## Evolution of Spleen and Liver Weights and the Number of Nucleated Cells in the Peripheral Blood of Leukemic Mice

### Growth Curve and Cytological Formula of the Spleen

From the 7th day after injection of 50 $SD_{50}$ of virus, growth of the leukemic spleen is composed of two distinct phases (Fig. 3): an exponential phase to the 21st day, characterized by a doubling time of 6 days (144 hr) and, beginning with the 21st day, the terminal phase, characterized by a doubling time of 18 days. Mice begin to die 30 days after virus infection, the mean weight of their spleens being then 2.5 ± 0.6 g.

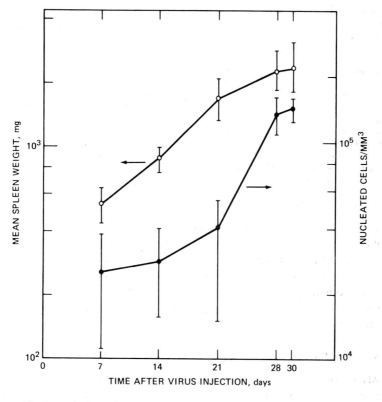

Fig. 3 Evolution of the mean spleen weights and of the number of nucleated cells in the peripheral blood after Friend virus injection (50 $SD_{50}$ at day 0). Each point is the mean calculated from 10 mice. Exponential growth phase spans day 7 to day 21 and has a doubling time of 144 hr. Terminal phase spans day 21 to day 30 and has a doubling time of 432 hr.

Cytological formulas determined from imprints of leukemic spleens taken during the exponential growth and during the terminal phase of the disease and cytological formulas of normal spleens are given in Table 1. We can see that 80 to 85% of leukemic spleen cells are erythroblastic (hyperbasophilic proerythroblasts, proerythroblasts, basophilic, polychromatophilic, and acidophilic erythroblasts). Less than 5% of reticular, granular, and monocytic cells are found in either normal or leukemic spleen.

**TABLE 1**

**CYTOLOGIC FORMULAS AND MITOTIC INDEXES OF NORMAL AND LEUKEMIC SPLEENS FROM IMPRINTS AND SMEARS\***

|  | Normal mice | | Leukemic mice | |
| --- | --- | --- | --- | --- |
| Time after virus injection, days | 0 | 14 | 28 | 28 |
| Mean spleen weights, mg | 106 ± 13.8 | 860 ± 49 | 2090 ± 181 | 2090 ± 181 |
| Technique used | Imprint | Imprint | Imprint | Smear |
| Erythroid cells: | | | | |
| Proerythroblastic, % | 2.52 | 48.46 | 51.94 | 45.73 |
| Erythroblastic, % | 15.00 | 35.14 | 32.92 | 34.99 |
| Total, % | 17.50 ± 5.30 | 83.60 ± 5.74 | 84.86 ± 3.20 | 80.79 ± 6.62 |
| Reticular cells, % | 1.50 ± 0.71 | 2.64 ± 1.96 | 1.79 ± 0.62 | 10.29 ± 5.72 |
| Lymphoid cells, % | 77.00 ± 5.76 | 14.50 ± 3.04 | 12.79 ± 3.26 | 8.93 ± 0.76 |
| Granulocytic and | | | | |
| monocytic cells, % | 2.88 ± 0.63 | 1 | 1 | 1 |
| Mitotic indexes | | 2.64 ± 0.42 | 2.40 ± 0.20 | 2.10 ± 0.50 |

\*Each value is the mean calculated on seven DBA/2 mice.

### Growth of the Liver

The liver increases in weight later and more slowly than the spleen. Its weight is multiplied by 2 during the disease (from $1 \pm 0.1$ g in normal mice, it reaches $2 \pm 0.2$ g before death in leukemic mice). On microscopic examination the appearance of small islands of leukemic cells in perivascular zones can be observed beginning 1 week after viral infection (Fig. 4). These blast cells, which are very easily distinguished from hepatocytes, can almost entirely infiltrate the liver at a later stage of disease.

### Nucleated Cells in Peripheral Blood

After a slow increase up to day 21, the number of nucleated cells per cubic millimeter in peripheral blood increases regularly until the 28th day, reaching more than $2 \times 10^5$ cells per cubic millimeter. As indicated in Table 2, the peripheral blood is already invaded by erythroblastic cells when the spleen weighs about 1 g. But it is only at the advanced stage of the disease that the erythroblastic infiltration becomes very large, representing 24 to 77% of nucleated cells.

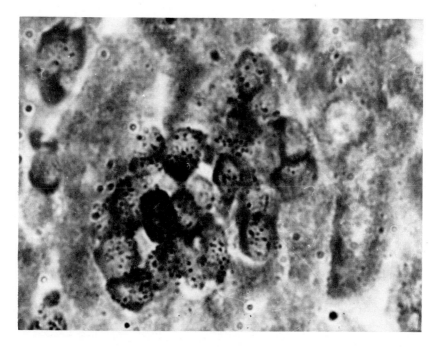

Fig. 4 Autoradiograph of a histological section of Friend leukemic liver 1 week after the injection of 50 $SD_{50}$ of viral suspension. Note the island of labelled leukemic cells among unlabelled hepatocytes. (Hemotoxylin—eosin stain; 576 x.)

## Daily Output of Reticulocytes in Peripheral Blood

The daily production rate of reticulocytes in peripheral blood is $0.8 \times 10^9$ at the 14*th* day after viral infection, and it reaches $3 \times 10^9$ at the terminal phase of the disease (Table 3).

## Study of the Phase of Exponential Growth

### Duration of the Mean Mitotic Cycle of Spleen Cells

From the curves of labelled mitoses for the exponential-growth phase (Fig. 5), the durations of the mitotic cycle and of its different phases have been calculated with the aid of the mathematical model described by Valleron et al.[11] The results are as follows:

1. Duration of mitotic cycle (which corresponds to the mean mitotic cycle of cell populations of leukemic spleen): $T_C = 7.6$ hr.

2. Durations of:

DNA synthesis phase, $T_S = 5.40 \pm 1.14$ hr.

Postsynthetic phase, $T_{G_2} = 1.10 \pm 1.29$ hr.

TABLE 2

NUMBER AND TYPE OF NUCLEATED CELLS IN
PERIPHERAL BLOOD OF NORMAL AND LEUKEMIC MICE

|  | Normal mice* | Leukemic mice† | |
|---|---|---|---|
| Time after virus injection, days | 0 | 14 | 28 |
| Mean spleen weights, mg | 160 ± 14 | 860 ± 49 | 2,060 ± 181 |
| Mean number of nucleated cells in peripheral blood | 3,140 ± 870 | 28,187 ± 12,520 | 140,000 ± 23,000 |
| Polynuclear cells, % | 14 ± 8 | 11, 33, 35, 44, 50 | 4, 12.5, 15, 18, 24, 35 |
| Lymphocytes, % | 79 ± 21 | 17, 20, 37, 57, 67 | 13, 13, 28, 29, 33, 40 |
| Monocytic cells, % | 7.8 ± 4 | 2.6 ± 3.2 | 1.7 ± 2.3 |
| Erythroid cells: | | | |
|   Proerythroblastic, % | 0 | 1.76 ± 1 | 7 ± 1.7 |
|   Erythroblastic, % | 0 | 1, 5, 18.7, 22, 23 | 16.6, 24, 45, 59, 67, 72 |
|   Total, % | | 2, 6, 18.7, 25.8, 26 | 24, 33, 52, 64.3, 65.5, 77 |
| Myelocytic cells, % | <1 | 7.4 ± 4.3 | 2.0 ± 2.8 |

*Each value is the mean calculated on five mice.
†When the values are too scattered to have a meaning, individual data are given.

TABLE 3

DAILY OUTPUT OF RETICULOCYTES IN PERIPHERAL BLOOD*

|  | Normal mice | Leukemic mice | |
|---|---|---|---|
| Time after virus injection, days | 0 | 14 | 30 |
| Mean spleen weight, mg | 106 ± 14 | 860 ± 49 | 2500 ± 100 |
| Hematocrit, % | 47 ± 1 | 41.7 ± 3 | 57 ± 3 |
| Number of erythrocytes, $10^9$/ml | 8.7 ± 0.4 | 8.6 ± 0.8 | 9.7 ± 0.8 |
| Blood volume, ml | 1.44 ± 0.13 | 1.5 ± 0.2 | 2.1 ± 0.4 |
| Total number of erythrocytes, $10^9$ | 12.5 | 12.9 | 19.9 |
| Reticulocytes, % | 3.8 ± 0.5 | 14.1 ± 4 | 29 ± 6 |
| Total number of reticulocytes (x $10^9$)(A) | 0.4 | 1.2 | 5.8 |
| Mean life-span of reticulocytes in peripheral blood (B), days | 1.25 | 1.5 | 1.5 |
| Daily production rate of reticulocytes in peripheral blood = (A/B) (x$10^9$) | 0.33 | 0.81 | 3.1 |

*Each value is the mean calculated on 10 mice.

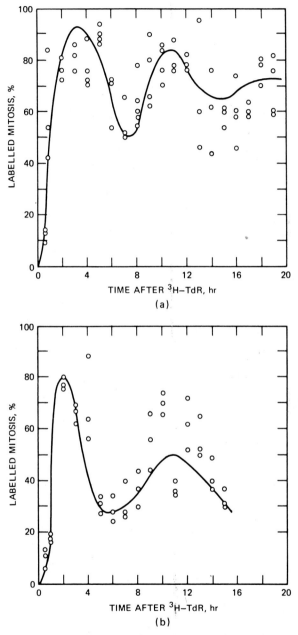

Fig. 5   Curves of labelled mitosis of leukemic spleen cells optimalized with a mathematical model. (a) Exponential growth phase (7 to 21 days after injection of virus) of the disease. (b) Terminal stage (21 to 30 days after injection of virus) of the disease. The $^3$H—TdR (2.5 $\mu$Ci/g) was injected at time 0.

Mitotic phase, $T_m = 0.5 \pm 0.00$ hr.
Presynthetic phase, $T_{G_1} = 0.6 \pm 1.09$ hr.
3. Growth fraction (GF) has been estimated by the formula[12]

$$GF = \frac{LI}{T_s/T_c}$$

$$= \frac{0.45}{5.4/7.6}$$

where LI is labelling index calculated on spleen imprints 1 hr after $^3H-TdR$ injections.

4. The potential doubling time $(T_{d_{pot}})$ of the leukemic spleen is calculated by the formula[13]

$$T_{d_{pot}} = \lambda \frac{T_s}{T_c} = 0.7 \frac{5.4}{0.45} = 8.4 \text{ hr}$$

5. The experimental doubling time $(T_d)$ of the leukemic spleen being then 144 hr as calculated on Fig. 3, the cell loss[13] may be estimated as

$$1 - \frac{T_{d_{pot}}}{T_d} = 1 - \frac{8.4}{144} = 0.94$$

## Labelling Index of the Spleen, Leukemic Cells of the Liver, and Nucleated Cells of the Peripheral Blood

As shown in Table 4, labelling indexes after a single injection of $^3H-TdR$ are not significantly different when calculated on spleen imprints, smears, or histological sections. Therefore, further studies were based on imprint examination. One-half hour after injection of the radioactive marker, 45% of leukemic spleen cells and 65% of leukemic cells of the liver were labelled (Fig. 6). These values increased, reaching 70% for spleen cells and 75% for leukemic cells of the liver. The index for leukemic cells in the spleen did not decrease during the 25 hr of observation, and that for leukemic cells of the liver decreased only after 15 hr, reaching about 50% at 20 hr. The modal number of grains per cell is 32.5 half an hour after injection of $^3H-TdR$, 15.0 at 18 hr, and 12 at 48 hr (Fig. 7).

When several injections of $^3H-TdR$ are given, 90% of leukemic spleen cells and 93% of leukemic liver cells are labelled within 7 hr after the first injection; this percentage does not decrease during a period of 15 hr (Fig. 8).

In contrast, less than 10% of erythroblastic cells and 5% of all nucleated cells are labelled in the peripheral blood 1 hr after $^3H-TdR$ injection (Fig. 9). These values increase slightly reaching only 25% for erythroblastic cells at 15 hr.

TABLE 4

LABELLING INDEXES DETERMINED ON
IMPRINTS, HISTOLOGICAL SECTIONS, AND
SMEARS OF LEUKEMIC SPLEENS*

| Mean spleen weight, mg | Imprints | Histological sections | Smears |
|---|---|---|---|
| 1300 ± 125 | 42.2 ± 3.1 | 38.0 ± 3.0 | 40.5 ± 2.9 |

*Each value is the mean calculated on four DBA/2 mice 20 days after injection of 50 $SD_{50}$ of Friend virus. The labelling index is determined on 2000 cells for each mouse.

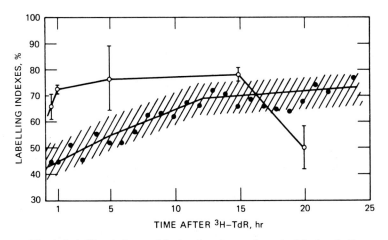

Fig. 6  Labelling indexes of leukemic spleen cells and of leukemic liver cells after a pulse of 2.5 μCi/g of $^3$H—TdR. •, leukemic spleen cells. ○, leukemic liver cells.

## Study of the Terminal Phase of the Disease

### Duration of the Mean Mitotic Cycle of Spleen Cells

Half an hour after a single injection of $^3$H—TdR, 30% of leukemic spleen cells are labelled.

The following parameters have been calculated as described earlier, from the curve of labelled mitoses for the terminal phase of the disease (Fig. 5):

1. Duration of the mean mitotic cycle and of its various phases:

$$T_c = 7.5 \text{ hr} \qquad T_{G_2} = 1.36 \pm 0.54 \text{ hr}$$
$$T_s = 2.91 \pm 2.19 \text{ hr} \qquad T_m = 0.25 \pm 0.00 \text{ hr}$$
$$T_{G_1} = 2.98 \pm 2.18 \text{ hr}$$

2. Growth fraction:

$$GF = \frac{LI}{T_s/T_c} = \frac{0.30}{2.9/7.5} = 0.78$$

3. Potential doubling time:

$$T_{d_{pot}} = \frac{T_s}{T_c} = 0.7\frac{2.9}{0.3} = 6.76$$

4. Cell loss: the experimental doubling time ($T_d$) being then 432 hr, the cell loss is estimated as

$$1 - \frac{T_{d_{pot}}}{T_d} = 1 - \frac{6.76}{432} = 0.98$$

## DISCUSSION

The cell-cycle duration has been studied in a heterogeneous population of splenic cells. Nevertheless, since a leukemic spleen at the stages of the disease that we studied contains at least 80% erythroblastic cells, it is probable that our results, using the percentage of labelled mitosis (PLM) curves,[10] are valid for Friend leukemic cells.

Our data (Table 5) show that Friend disease is characterized by an intense and massive proliferation of hyperbasophilic proerythroblasts in the spleen. This cellular proliferation is characterized by a short cell cycle (7.5 hr) and a growth fraction of 64% during the exponential phase and 77.6% during the terminal phase of the disease, which means that most leukemic cells are in active stages of the cycle.

Because comparable values of the cell-cycle duration have been described for medullary blasts of normal mice,[14] we may assume that viral transformation does not modify this parameter significantly. However, the characteristics of the cell proliferation of the spleen differ markedly from most of the known experimental models. It has been shown that in many neoplastic processes the late slowing down of cellular proliferation is associated either with a lengthening of the cell cycle in the case of ascites[15] and transplanted leukemias[16] or with a reduction of the growth fraction in solid tumors.[17-24] It seems striking that the proliferation of Friend erythroblasts does not slow down at the terminal phase of the disease, when the spleen weight is no longer increasing. From this study it is impossible to conclude whether this phenomenon is linked with the viral transformation.

A comparison of the measured growth rate of the spleen with the rate of cell proliferation has shown that 95% of the cells produced in the spleen are lost.

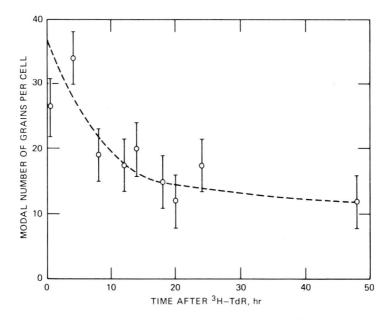

**Fig. 7** Evolution of the modal number of grains per cell in leukemic spleens after a pulse of $^3$H—TdR (2.5 μCi/g).

This important cell loss could be due (1) to the migration of cells from the spleen with or without differentiation or (2) to cell death. Since there is not an important invasion of the liver during the exponential-growth phase of the disease and since relatively few erythroblastic cells are circulating in the blood where they seem unable to multiply, migration of living cells out of the spleen is not quantitatively important.

After quantification of the daily splenic production of cells (3 × 10$^9$ cells for a spleen weighing 1 g) and of the daily output of reticulocytes (10$^9$), it can be estimated that differentiation accounts for only $\frac{1}{3}$ of the cell loss. Therefore, cell death should represent approximately $\frac{2}{3}$ of the splenic cell production at the stage of the disease studied here. Friend leukemia therefore is not a cumulative disease, but a proliferative one.

Comparable cell losses have been reported in many solid experimental[17] and human[13,18] tumors, but it was not always possible to make a distinction between the loss due to cellular differentiation and that due to true cell death. From this point of view, the Friend leukemia model represents a privileged model.

In addition to this important cell lysis, we have noticed a particularly slow decrease of the mean number of grains in labelled cells following a single injection of $^3$H—TdR. The possibility of high reutilization of $^3$H—TdR related to a massive cellular lysis is at present under study.

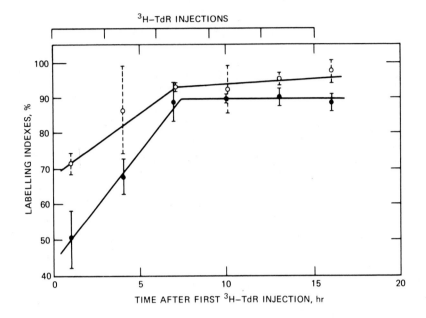

Fig. 8  Labelling indexes of leukemic spleen cells and of leukemic liver cells during the exponential stage of the disease. Every 3 hr for 15 hr 1 $\mu$Ci/g of $^3$H—TdR was injected. •, leukemic spleen cells. ○, leukemic liver cells.

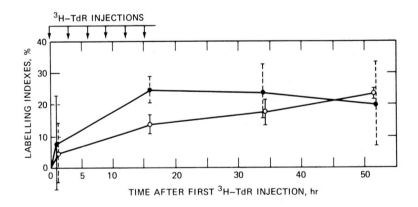

Fig. 9  Labelling indexes of nucleated cells and of erythroblastic cells (proerythroblastic and erythroblastic) in the peripheral blood during the exponential stage of the disease. Every 3 hr for 15 hr 1 $\mu$Ci/g of $^3$H—TdR was injected. •, erythroblastic and proerythroblastic cells. ○, nucleated cells.

TABLE 5

PARAMETERS OF CELL PROLIFERATION IN
FRIEND-VIRUS-INDUCED LEUKEMIA DURING EXPONENTIAL
GROWTH AND AT THE TERMINAL STAGE
OF THE DISEASE*

|  | Exponential phase | Terminal phase |
|---|---|---|
| Time after virus injection, days | 14 | 28 |
| Mean spleen weight, mg | 860 + 49 | 2090 + 181 |
| Duration of: |  |  |
| $T_c$, hr | 7.6 | 7.5 |
| $T_s$, hr | 5.4 | 2.91 |
| $T_{G_2}$, hr | (1.14) | (2.19) |
|  | 1.10 | 1.36 |
| $T_m$, hr | (1.29) | (0.54) |
|  | 0.5 | 0.25 |
| $T_{G_1}$, hr | (0.00) | (0.00) |
|  | 0.60 | 2.98 |
|  | (1.09) | (2.18) |
| Labelled cells 1 hr | 45 | 30 |
| after $^3H-TdR$ injection, % | (1.5) | (1.4) |
| Growth fraction, % | 64 | 77.6 |
| Doubling time of the leukemic spleen, hr |  |  |
| Potential | 8.40 | 6.76 |
| Experimental | 144 | 432 |
| Cell loss, % | 94.2 | 97.9 |

*Each value is the mean calculated on four DBA/2 mice. The mean
values for the duration of the various phases of the mitotic cycle and the
standard deviations (in parentheses) were determined with the aid of a
computer.

# REFERENCES

1. F. Zajdela, Contribution à l'étude de la cellule de Friend, *Bull. Cancer,* **49**: 351-373 (1962).
2. E. A. Mirand, T. C. Prentice, J. C. Hoffman, and J. T. Grace, Effect of Friend Virus in Swiss and DBA/I Mice on $^{59}$Fe Uptake, *Proc. Soc. Exp. Biol. Med.,* **106**: 423-426 (1961).
3. P. E. Tambourin and F. Wendling, Malignant Transformation and Erythroid Differentiation by Polycythemia-Inducing Friend Virus, *Nature (London) New Biol.,* **234**:230-233 (1971).
4. P. E. Tambourin, O. Gallien-Lartigue, F. Wendling and D. Huaulme, Erythrocyte Production in Mice Infected by the Polycythemia-Inducing Friend Virus or by the Anemia Inducing Friend Virus, *Brit. J. Haematol.,* **24**: 505-518 (1973).
5. E. A. Mirand, Murine Viral Induced Polycythemia, *Ann. N. Y. Acad. Sci.,* **149**(Article 1): 486-496 (1968).

6. P. E. Tambourin, F. Wendling, N. Barat, and F. Zajdela, Influence de différents facteurs d'homéostase érythropoïetiques sur l'évolution de la leucémie de Friend, *Nouv. Rev. Fr. Hematol.,* **9**: 461-484 (1969).

7. W. P. Rowe and I. Brodsky, A Graded Response Assay For Friend Leukemia Virus, *J. Nat. Cancer Inst.,* **23**: 1239-1248 (1959).

8. C. L. Paxson and L. H. Smith, Blood Volume in the Mouse, *Exp. Hematol.,* **17**: 42-47 (1968).

9. A. Ganzoni, R. S. Hillman, and C. A. Finch, Maturation of the Reticulocyte, *Brit. J. Haematol.,* **16**: 119-135 (1969).

10. M. Quastler and F. G. Sherman, Cell Population Kinetics in the Intestinal Epithelium of the Mouse, *Exp. Cell Res.,* **17**: 420-438 (1959).

11. A. J. Valleron, J. Y. Mary, and E. Frindel, Méthodes d'analyses sur ordinateur des courbes de mitoses marquées, *Biomedecine,* **18**: 118-129 (1973).

12. M. L. Mendelsohn, Autoradiographic Analysis of Cell Proliferation in Spontaneous Breast Cancer of C3H Mouse. III. The Growth Fraction, *J. Nat. Cancer Inst.,* **28**: 1015-1029 (1962).

13. G. C. Steel, Cell Loss from Experimental Tumours, *Cell Tissue Kinet.,* **1**: 193-207 (1968).

14. E. Frindel, M. Tubiana,, and F. Vassort, Generation Cycle of Mouse Bone Marrow, *Nature,* **214**: 1017-1018 (1967).

15. E. Frindel and M. Tubiana, Durée du cycle cellulaire au cours de la croissance d'une ascite experimentale de la souris C3H, *C.R. Acad. Sci. (Paris),* **265**: 829-832 (1967).

16. C. Choquet, N. Chavaudra, and E. P. Malaise, The Influence of Allogeneic Inhibition and Tumour Age on the Kinetics of L 1210 Leukemia In Vivo, *Eur. J. Cancer,* **6**: 373-378 (1970).

17. E. Frindel, F. Vassort, E. Malaise, H. Croizat, and M. Tubiana, Etude des paramètres de la prolifération cellulaire dans une tumeur expérimentale poussant sous forme solide ou ascitique, *Bull. Cancer,* **55**: 9-20 (1968).

18. V. Iversen, O. H. Iversen, A. Z. Bluming, J. L. Ziegler, and S. Kyalwasi, Cell Kinetics of African Cases of Burkitt Lymphoma, *Eur. J. Cancer,* **8**: 305-308 (1972).

19. C. Friend, Cell Free Transmission in Adult Swiss Mice of a Disease Having the Character of a Leukemia, *J. Exp. Med.,* **105**: 307-318 (1957).

20. F. Wendling, Institut du Radium, Faculté des Sciences, Orsay, France, personal communication.

21. C. Jasmin, C. Rosenfeld, J. Chomette, and C. Piton, Action de l'actinomycine D sur la maladie de Friend, *Rev. Fr. Etud. Clin. Biol.,* **13**: 292-296 (1968).

22. F. Wendling, P. Tambourin, N. Barat, and F. Zajdela, Différences de sensibilité vis-à-vis de l'actinomycine D du tissu pathologique induit par le virus de Friend et du tissu érythropoïetique normal, *C.R. Acad. Sci. (Paris),* **268**: 2222-2225 (1969).

23. N. Reissman and K. Ito, Selective Eradication of Erythropoiesis by Actinomycine D as the Result of Interference with Hormonally Controlled Effector Pathway of Cell Differentiation, *Blood,* **28**: 201-212 (1966).

24. A. F. Hermens, Variations in the Cell Kinetics and the Growth Rate in an Experimental Tumour During Natural Growth and After Irradiation, pp. 145-151, Publication of the Radiobiological Institute of the Organization for Health Research TNO, Rijswijk, the Netherlands, 1973.

# THE CELL CYCLE IN MALIGNANT
# AND NORMAL TISSUES

MORTIMER L. MENDELSOHN
Biomedical Division, Lawrence Livermore Laboratory, University of California,
Livermore, California

## ABSTRACT

Methods for studying cellular proliferation in tumors and normal tissues are reviewed, with emphasis on frequency of labelled mitoses, growth fraction, cell loss, and the turnover of nonproliferating cells. Attention is also paid to methods based on measurement of DNA content of individual cells, including flow microfluorimetry, cytophotometry, and the combination of cytophotometry and autoradiography. Finally, selected cell-cycle measurements from 50 examples of normal tissues, tumors, ascites cell tumors, and tissue cultures are surveyed. Tumors, tissue cultures, and many normal tissues have remarkably similar cell cycles in which transit through the DNA synthetic period ($T_S$) is linearly related to mean cell-cycle time. Several normal epithelial tissues do not show this but instead have a short $T_S$ and a widely ranging long cell-cycle time. It is hypothesized that the cells in these epithelial tissues are under external control and spend much of their intermitotic time in $G_0$. All normal tissues tend to have a shorter $T_{G_2}$ than tumors or tissue cultures. The cell cycle of ascites cell tumors is consistently and strikingly different from that of other tumors, normal tissues, and tissue cultures.

There are three general reasons for attempting an analysis of the kinetics of cell proliferation:

1. To learn about the normal processes of cell division, growth, and growth controls.

2. To understand the dynamics of a disease process.

3. To use kinetics for therapeutic purposes.

Applying these arguments to the tumor field, we intensely want to learn about normal growth control and the abdication of control that leads to cancer. We wish to understand the process of tumor growth and how growth relates to cell of origin, to tumor type, to microarchitecture, to blood supply, to size, to location in the body, to malignant progression, and to many other factors. And finally, since so much of radiation and chemical therapy of cancer relates to the cell cycle, we very much want to optimize therapeutic ratios on the basis of kinetic information about the tumor and the relevant host tissues.

Some of these quests require no more than a labelling index; others demand such precision of estimation of multiple kinetic parameters that they are beyond current feasibility. Some experiments need be done only once but under conditions that invite complexity, overelaboration, and expense; others are needed repeatedly and perhaps on a large proportion of cancer patients and hence require simplicity, economy, and safety. Some involve more mathematics than biology, more engineering than chemistry, and more physics than pathology.

Much has been written about this subject, and there are many excellent reviews culminating in recent years in articles by Lala[1] and Tubiana,[2] in the thesis by Hermens,[3] and in the book *The Cell Cycle and Cancer* edited by Baserga.[4] In this paper I am relying on this prior comprehensiveness and am concentrating on several old and some new aspects of kinetic analysis. I have also used a selected collection of kinetic analyses to summarize and compare the cell-cycle characteristics of tumor and nontumor cells.

## FREQUENCY OF LABELLED MITOSES METHOD

The method of frequency of labelled mitoses (FLM) remains the cornerstone of a thorough kinetic analysis. The FLM method is cumbersome, biased toward short cycles, occasionally ambiguous, and prohibitive in most clinical situations; but it is the only method that gives the transit times ($T_{G_2}$, $T_s$, $T_{G_1}$, $T_m$, and $T_c$) and coefficients of variation of transit time ($CV_{G_2}$, $CV_s$, etc.) of all four phases and of the total cell cycle.

Many of the approaches to extracting parameters by hand from an FLM curve are summarized in Fig. 1. All these suffer from serious drawbacks, particularly the general one that FLM curves are seldom as simple as they seem. One example of the misleading character of FLM curves is shown in Fig. 2. The human observer intuitively takes the peaks of the FLM curve as markers for the interval between cycles, but the peaks of the individual isocyclic waves from which this FLM curve has been synthesized clearly precede the composite peaks by an increasingly large interval. This particular effect is due to the progressive broadening of the isocyclic waves. It and other interpretive aspects have been discussed in several papers on the FLM method by Mendelsohn and Takahashi[5] and by Steel.[6]

Beginning with Barrett[7] and now extending to examples in many laboratories (Steel and Hanes,[8] Barrett,[9] MacDonald,[10] Brockwell, Trucco, and Fry,[11] Hartman and Pedersen,[12] Gilbert,[13] Simon, Stroot, and Weiss,[14] Takahashi, Hogg, and Mendelsohn,[15] and Ashihara[16]), robust analyses of FLM data can now be done by digital computer. These methods generally assume a

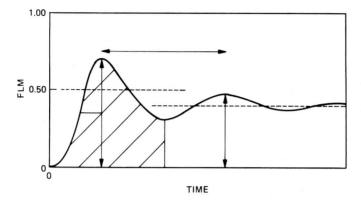

Fig. 1 Hand-oriented methods of analysis of FLM curves: 50% intercept, half-height intercept, area under the first wave, plateau after dampening, peak-to-peak interval, and rate of decay of peak height.[5]

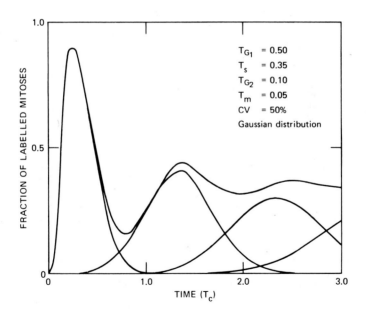

Fig. 2 A synthetic FLM curve and its constitutive isocyclic curves. The isocyclic curves show unambiguously the position in time of successive cycles of cells. (From M. L. Mendelsohn and M. Takahashi, A Critical Evaluation of the Fraction of Labeled Mitoses Method as Applied to the Analysis of Tumor and Other Cell Cycles, in *The Cell Cycle and Cancer*, p. 62, Marcel Dekker, Inc., New York, 1971.)

basic trapezoidal foundation for the average progression of the cohort of labelled cells. They then convolute the trapezoid with one or another dispersion function to simulate the increasing desynchronization of labelled vs. unlabelled cells with time. For example, Barrett's model[7,9] is based on a log normal dispersion, Hartman's early model[12] on a Gaussian dispersion, and Takahashi's[15] on a gamma distribution. Bimodal distributions, heterogeneous mixtures, and correlated behavior from one phase to the next can be modeled and may even be justified biologically; but, given the limited information content of FLM curves, such extensions of the analysis have yet to be justified in actual practice.

Figure 3 shows a typical application of our fitting method[15] to preliminary data from mouse duodenal-crypt cells.[17] The best-fitting synthetic FLM curve is calculated much like a linear regression, by finding the curve with the smallest sum of squared deviations from all points. The parameters of this best-fitting curve are taken as the definitive solution, including T and CV for all four phases and for the total cycle. Such machine analysis eliminates intuitive errors—at least to the extent that the underlying model is a reasonable proximity to reality—but it does not solve all the problems. It cannot correct for underexposure or overexposure of autoradiographs, for biased counting, or for

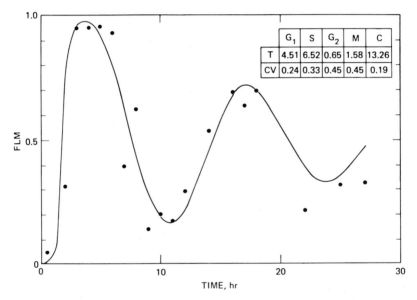

|    | $G_1$ | S    | $G_2$ | M    | C     |
|----|-------|------|-------|------|-------|
| T  | 4.51  | 6.52 | 0.65  | 1.58 | 13.26 |
| CV | 0.24  | 0.33 | 0.45  | 0.45 | 0.19  |

Fig. 3   The cell cycle of duodenal-crypt cells of the mouse.[17] These FLM data are typical of cells with short relatively invariant cycles. The solid line is the best-fitting synthetic FLM curve as judged by least-squares deviations to all data points.[15] The parameters of this synthetic curve are shown in the inset. The consistent deviation of the three terminal points may be due to autoradiographic underexposure and is one example of the kinds of disparity that can appear between the data and the model.[6]

reutilization of label. And most importantly the extracted parameters are inadequately assessed by the present methods. MacDonald's use[10] of $\chi^2$ and our own analysis of variance based on the mean deviation from regression[15] give a general measure of the quality of regression but do not assess the confidence limits for particular transit times or dispersions. Overly sparse data points, uneven distribution of points, variability from animal to animal or from culture to culture, and binomial variation of the FLM values all limit the information content of the FLM curve and contribute to the fuzziness of the kinetic estimates.

## GROWTH FRACTION AND CELL LOSS

Net growth of tumor cells is a resultant of three factors: (1) productive properties of the cell cycle, (2) the proportion of cells committed to the cycle or the growth fraction, and (3) the rate of cell loss from the tumor. As shown in the kineticist's minimal model of tumor growth[18] in Fig. 4, these factors can be formulated in terms of proliferating (P) cells, nonproliferating (Q) cells, and cells that are being lost (L). The reality of tumor growth is certainly more complex than this model, including such additional factors as clonogenicity, clonal diversity, differentiation of subpopulations, vascular and architectural stroma,

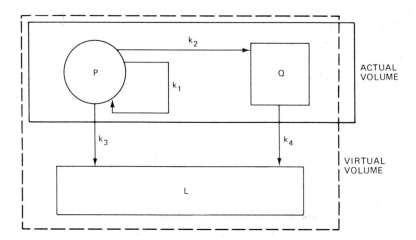

Fig. 4  A minimally complex model of tumor growth. The four rate constants define the net flow among the three cellular compartments. Virtual and actual growth can be cellular growth or total growth, depending on whether or not the noncellular fraction of volume has been estimated. (From M. L. Mendelsohn and L. A. Dethlefsen, Cell Kinetics of Breast Cancer: The Turnover of Nonproliferating Cells, in *Recent Results in Cancer Research, Breast Cancer: A Challenging Problem*, pp. 74, Springer-Verlag, New York, 1973.)

and acellular debris. But either we lack the methods to discern these extra details or they can be analyzed only in isolated situations. As matters stand we can barely resolve the simple model.

Growth fraction [P/(P + Q)] is measured by the disparity between the labelling index predicted from the cell cycle and the observed labelling index either after pulse labelling[19] or after multiple or continuous labelling.[8] Growth fraction and the cell cycle combine to give the cellular production rate, which is the growth rate of virtual cellular volume (P + Q + L). Actual cellular volume or actual growth rate is based on sequential gross measurements of tumor size, and the difference between virtual and actual cellular volume is ascribable to cell loss.

Cell loss can take a variety of forms[20] including death of P cells during the mitotic process, programmed destruction as a result of differentiation, and tissue necrosis. It is increasingly clear that cell loss is a major activity in most tumors and hence that tumor kinetics involves extensive turnover of cells as well as net growth. Of particular relevance to the chemotherapist is the turnover in what to him is the relatively inaccessible Q-cell compartment.

Recently, we have shown how Q-cell turnover can be estimated from labelling indexes that are taken in conjunction with cell-cycle analysis and measurement of the growth fraction.[18] The method is based on the time-dependent relationship between $LI_{obs}(t)$, the measured labelling index for the tumor as a whole, and $LI_{exp}(t)$, the expected labelling index for the P cells. The latter, which is computed from the FLM-based parameters of the cell cycle, describes the slightly oscillating index of labelling of P cells which is expected after a pulse label. Initially the Q cells are unlabelled; but, as the Q-cell compartment expands with subsequent growth, the new Q cells have the expected labelling index. Thus $LI_{obs}(t)$ gradually approaches $LI_{exp}(t)$. This process of progressive dilution of the fraction of initially unlabelled Q cells is described by

$$\frac{Q(0)}{P(t) + Q(t)} = \left[ 1 - \frac{LI_{obs}(t)}{LI_{exp}(t)} \right]$$

When there is no cell loss in the Q-cell compartment, the dilution of unlabelled Q cells and the decay of $1 - [LI_{obs}(t)/LI_{exp}(t)]$ mirror the increase of actual cellular volume. When Q and P cells have the same probability of being lost, the dilution process mirrors the increase of virtual cellular volume. And finally when loss occurs preferentially among Q cells, $1 - [LI_{obs}(t)/LI_{exp}(t)]$ decays faster than virtual volume increases. These relationships are summarized in Fig. 5. Regardless of which pattern is being followed, the extrapolation of $1 - [LI_{obs}(t)/LI_{exp}(t)]$ back to the moment of labelling gives the growth fraction. This is a particularly robust way to estimate the growth fraction because the labelling indexes of all samples are used.

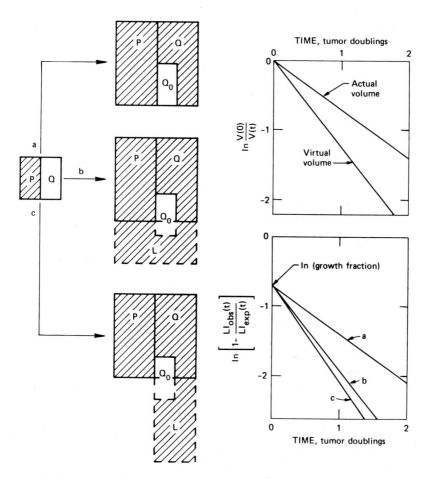

Fig. 5    Three modes of Q-cell loss and their effect on the relationship between the observed and expected labelling index. The block diagram on the left shows a tumor at the moment of flash-labelling. The diagrams in the center show the subsequent growth of the P, Q, and L compartments based on (a) no Q cell loss, (b) equiprobable loss of P and Q cells, and (c) preferential Q-cell loss. The shaded area represents the cells with the expected P-cell labelling index, and the clear area represents the initially unlabelled Q cells. The upper graph shows the inverse of virtual and actual tumor growth, and the lower graph shows the decaying proportion of unlabelled Q cells as expressed by the expected and observed labelling indexes. When the two graphs are constructed from actual data, the mode of Q-cell loss can be inferred from the slope of the one line based on labelling indexes relative to the two lines based on volume. Also, the intercept at zero time of the labelling-index function gives a composite estimate of the growth fraction.[18]

We have applied these methods to three transplantable mouse mammary tumors and have found wide differences in their behavior.[18] For example, two of the tumor types showed preferential loss of Q cells, whereas one showed equiprobable loss of P and Q cells. The half-times of Q cells for the three tumors were 1.2, 7.6, and 12 days. This Q-cell behavior correlates loosely with the microscopic properties of the tumor lines, but the salient result of the study was the great divergence of kinetic behavior in three tumors that have a common genetic, etiologic, and histologic origin.

Again, it should be emphasized that these methods are difficult to the point of being unsuitable for most clinical applications. Volumetric measurements should extend over the better part of a doubling time; samples for FLM analysis should be taken over $1\frac{1}{2}$ cycles or more, should number at least 10, and should be an unbiased representation of the entire tumor; and the labelling procedure must be reliably done. Other methods are considerably less demanding, and, although they do not provide a complete answer, they give the information needed for some applications.

## OTHER METHODS

Double-labelling can be carried out with two isotopes, generally with $^{14}$C- and $^{3}$H-labelled thymidine or with two widely differing doses of a single tracer.[1] The labelling procedure can be done in vivo, in vitro, or by a mixture of both. With this method a single tumor sample can give a reliable estimate of both $T_s$ and the cellular production rate.

Several samples taken at various times after an effective metaphase arrest can provide estimates of production rate and $T_m$.

The labelling index after pulse labelling, multiple labelling, or continuous labelling gives a straightforward estimate of the population at risk under the corresponding schedules of S-phase-specific chemotherapeutic agents.[21] However, these indexes do not measure any kinetic parameter directly, and, in particular, in contrast to several statements in the literature, the saturation labelling index after continuous labelling is not a direct measure of growth fraction.

Grain-count halving of labelled cells is related to the doubling time, but, in the presence of cell loss, it is influenced much like the decay of unlabelled cells and hence is a complex reflection of both actual and virtual doubling time. When limited to mitotic cells, grain-count halving measures the effective generation time of proliferating cells.

## CYTOPHOTOMETRY

The cytophotometric measurement of cells subjected to the Feulgen reaction or to some other DNA stain gives an estimate of the DNA content of individual cells. In well-behaved populations, cells in $G_1$ have the diploid or 2C DNA content, cells in $G_2$ have the 4C DNA content, and cells in S have intermediate DNA contents. Cytophotometrically measured interphase cells can be identified as being from one of these three compartments, but, since there is no time parameter in this approach, one gets the proportion of cells in each compartment and not the transit time. Also this method cannot distinguish arrested from cycling cells, and the analysis can be confounded by polyploidy and heteroploidy. Vendrely[22] has written an excellent review of this subject through 1969.

The recent advent of flow microfluorimeters[23,24] (FMF) may well revolutionize such analyses. These devices sense cells in suspension, measuring the fluorescent response to dyes that have reacted specifically with the DNA or with other cell constituents. Accuracies of a few percent have been achieved at rates of 1000 cells per second. A typical result of an FMF run on the DNA per cell of a proliferating population is shown in Fig. 6.

In conjunction with the initial technical development and cellular application of the FMF at Los Alamos Scientific Laboratory,[23,24] Dean and Jett[25] have developed a computer program to partition DNA histograms into $G_1$, S, and $G_2$ subcompartments. Recently, Gray of Lawrence Livermore Laboratory used their program to analyze synthetic FMF histograms.[26] Gray generates the histograms (1) by predefining a population of $G_1$ and $G_2$ cells with 2C and 4C

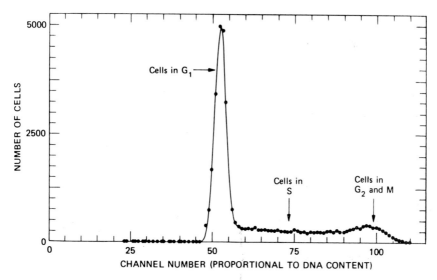

Fig. 6  An FMF curve showing the distribution of DNA contents of CHO cells growing exponentially in suspension culture. A coefficient of variation (CV) of 3.27 was used on the basis of the width of the $G_1$ peak. These measurements were made by Van Dilla and Gray at the Lawrence Livermore Laboratory. Acriflavine Feulgen stain was used.

DNA contents, (2) by assuming an exponential age distribution of S cells and intermediate DNA contents based on a constant rate of DNA synthesis, and (3) by convoluting the idealized error-free histogram with a Gaussian spread function at an assigned coefficient of variation. The curves in Fig. 7 were generated by his method. They have identical partitioning of $G_1$, $G_2$, and S cells, but differ in their coefficients of variation as shown. Table 1 summarizes the ability of the program of Dean and Jett[25] to extract the underlying parameters even in situations in which the bimodality of the curve is buried in the variability.

The DNA histograms from tissues and tumors often contain more structure than the preceding analysis implies. For example, Fig. 8 shows a recent DNA curve taken from mouse liver on the FMF at Livermore. This curve demonstrates a peak near the origin due to cell fragments, a strikingly low coefficient of variation of 4C, polyploid parenchymal cells, the expectedly low (to zero) incidence of cells in S for this nonproliferating population, and a clear-cut double peak in the diploid region. The double peak probably represents Kupfer cells or lymphocytes for the lower peak and parenchymal cells for the upper peak. We believe this to be a demonstration of the effect of chromatin compaction on the staining of DNA similar to the effects (of 10 to 15%) that have been demonstrated previously in leukocytes, liver, and other tissues by conventional cytophotometry.[27] Such deviations in the stoichiometry of DNA stains will obviously complicate histogram analysis, but they also open the interesting possibility of developing reagents to mark specific states of the chromatin and

## TABLE 1

### EXTRACTION OF CELL-CYCLE PARAMETERS FROM SYNTHETIC DISTRIBUTIONS OF DNA CONTENT*

| CV of synthetic distribution, % | Estimated proportion† of cells in | | | Estimated CV of | |
|---|---|---|---|---|---|
| | $G_1$ | $G_2$ | S | $G_1$ peak, % | $G_2$ peak, % |
| 3.0 | 0.63 | 0.16 | 0.21 | 3.0 | 3.0 |
| 5.0 | 0.63 | 0.16 | 0.21 | 5.0 | 5.0 |
| 7.5 | 0.63 | 0 16 | 0 21 | 7.5 | 7.5 |
| 10.0 | 0.63 | 0.16 | 0.21 | 10.0 | 10.0 |
| 12.5 | 0.63 | 0.16 | 0.21 | 12.5 | 12.6 |
| 15.0 | 0.63 | 0.19 | 0.18 | 15.0 | 15.4 |
| 20.0 | 0.62 | 0.10 | 0.28 | 20.0 | 19.1 |

*Parameters were extracted by the method of Dean and Jett[25] applied to distributions of DNA content synthesized by the method of Gray.[26]

†Actual proportions of cells in these phases were $G_1$, 0.6291; $G_2$, 0.1564; and S, 0.2145.

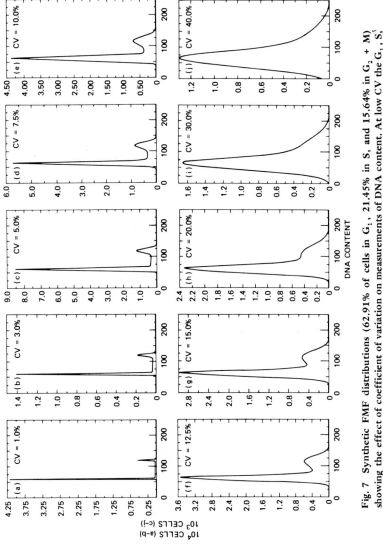

**Fig. 7** Synthetic FMF distributions (62.91% of cells in $G_1$, 21.45% in S, and 15.64% in $G_2$ + M) showing the effect of coefficient of variation on measurements of DNA content. At low CV the $G_1$, S, and $G_2$ phases of the cell cycle are well shown by the distributions of DNA content; but beyond CV = 10% the S phase is obscured, and beyond CV = 30% the bimodality and hence the distinction between $G_1$ and $G_2$ disappear.

hence to distinguish cells by their degree or type of differentiation and perhaps by their phase of the cycle.

As already mentioned, we cannot discriminate between cycling and noncycling cells on the basis of DNA content alone. This distinction can be made by supplementing conventional cytophotometry with DNA labelling and autoradiography of the same cells. Some recent data by Yanishevsky et al.[28] on cultured WI-38 cells illustrate the advantages and disadvantages of this technique. In these experiments the cultures were exposed to tritiated thymidine for 48 hr; thus essentially all cycling cells were labelled. The monolayers were then fixed, Feulgen stained, and photographed at low magnification for subsequent identification of about 100 individual cells. The DNA content of the cells was measured on a scanning cytophotometer;[29] then the slide was autoradiographed, and the cells were reidentified and scored for label.

Figure 9 shows the results from a relatively young culture. The labelled cells have the characteristic histogram of a proliferating population. They have been partitioned into their respective phases, and those in $G_1$ and $G_2$ are shown in the middle panel. The unlabelled cells are in a single peak having the identical mean as the $G_1$ labelled cells but almost twice the coefficient of variation. One

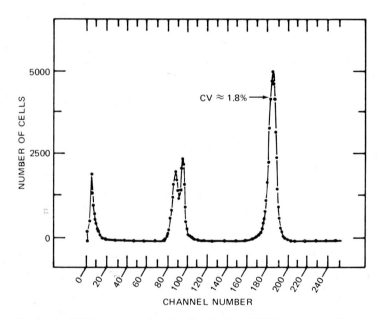

Fig. 8 An FMF curve showing the distribution of DNA contents of mouse liver cells stained with acriflavine Feulgen. The peak near the origin is an artifact due to cell fragments. The double peak in channels 80 to 100 represents diploid cells, presumably with parenchymal liver cells on the right and Kupfer cells and lymphocytes on the left. The peak at channel 185 is due to tetraploid parenchymal cells. There are no cells in S.

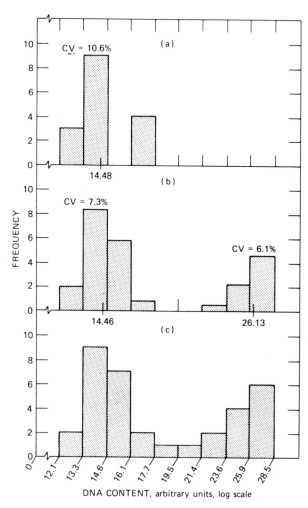

Fig. 9  A CYDAC histogram showing the distribution of DNA content of unlabelled (a) and labelled (b and c) young WI-38 cells.[28] DNA content was measured directly from the slide by CYDAC,[29] a scanning cytophotometer, and the cells were subsequently autoradiographed to show those which had synthesized DNA during the 48-hr period prior to fixation. In c labelled cells ($G_1$, $G_2$, and S) have a distribution of DNA content of a typical proliferating population. The distribution, mean, and CV of labelled cells ($G_1$ and $G_2$) after stripping out the cells in S are shown in b. The data suggest that cells leave the cycle in $G_1$ with an increased variability of DNA content that may reflect unequal partitioning at the prior mitosis.

possible explanation for this increased variability with an unchanged mean is that the out-of-cycle cells are arrested in $G_1$ because of asymmetrical partitioning of their DNA at the prior mitosis.

A similar analysis in an older culture is shown in Fig. 10. The cycling cells have now become polyploid; the noncycling cells have increased in frequency and range from 2C to 4C in DNA content. The 4C peak of noncycling cells could represent $G_2$ arrest or tetraploid cells arrested in $G_1$. Likewise, the nonlabelled cells with intermediate DNA content could be arrested in S or could be from the tails of the 2C or 4C peaks.

Obviously these histograms based on a hundred cells are much noisier and hence much more difficult to interpret than those from hundreds of thousands of cells measured on an FMF. But there is no way at present to get the ancillary

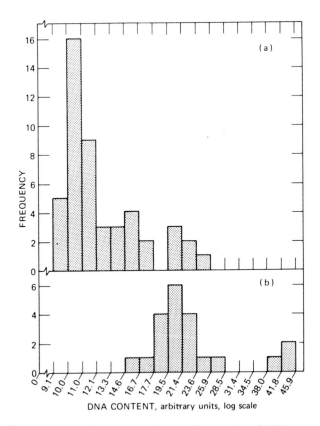

Fig. 10 A CYDAC histogram showing the distribution of DNA content of unlabelled (a) and labelled (b) aging WI-38 cells.[28] The conditions were the same as in Fig. 9 except for the difference in passage number of the cultures. With increasing age the cycling cells have become polyploid, variability of the peaks has increased, a larger fraction of the cells is out of cycle, and it is no longer clear at what point the unlabelled cells left the cycle.

autoradiographic information from an FMF. What is needed is a fluorescent stain to label nuclei in DNA synthesis, a fluorescent version of the PDP procedure of Nelson and Schiffer[30] to label cells in cycle, or a way to identify silver grains in the FMF. Alternatively, current developments in cell sorters by Steinkamp, Romero, and Van Dilla[31] and by Hulett et al.[32] may provide the answer. These devices are able to separate the FMF-measured cells on the basis of DNA content, size, or other parameters. It seems highly likely that scintillation counting could then be used to measure single or multiple radioactive labels in the isolated cells. The equivalent or conventional single or double labelling would thus be combined into the DNA histograms, opening up exciting new approaches to kinetic analysis. The approach is similar to that of cell separation by centrifugation[33] but with the added advantage of considerably improved resolution and multidimensional sorting based on several simultaneously measured cell parameters.

## SURVEY OF KINETIC MEASUREMENTS

Kinetic studies vary enormously in scope, technique, and credibility; many of the older surveys in the literature have indiscriminately lumped these into all-inclusive, noncritical masses of data. Recently Steel[6] reviewed his own experience, limiting himself to a subset of tumors that were analyzed by the method of Steel and Hanes.[8] In a similar attempt to generate a reliable compilation, I have assembled over 50 analyses of tumor and nontumor cells, using only those with well-executed FLM data analyzed by one of the machine methods. Twenty-two of the analyses were done by our method[15] on data from many sources, twenty-four were done by the method of Steel and Hanes,[8] and a few were analyzed by Brockwell, Trucco, and Fry[11] and by Dombernowsky and Hartmann.[34] The survey is illustrative, not comprehensive, and in this preliminary presentation I have not identified the specific primary sources. In anticipation of a more inclusive detailed presentation, I would encourage anyone with appropriate data who needs machine analysis to take advantage of our program or one of the other available programs and to publish or send me the FLM data and the results.

The data are plotted as a function of $T_c$ and are organized into four categories: normal tissue, tumor, ascites tumor, and tissue culture. The values shown are mean transit times, and no attempt is made to correct for fine differences, such as the inclusion or exclusion of $T_m$ in $T_{G_1}$ or $T_{G_2}$.

The relationship between $T_{G_1}$ and $T_c$ is given in Fig. 11. As expected, these two parameters of the cell cycle are closely correlated. For the most part they are well described by a monotonically curving line whose origin is at $T_{G_1} = 0$, $T_c = 10$ hr. Ascites tumors generally lie below the line (i.e., have relatively short $T_{G_1}$), and several normal tissues lie above the line. Otherwise, normal tissues, tumors, and tissue cultures all follow the same relationship.

MENDELSOHN

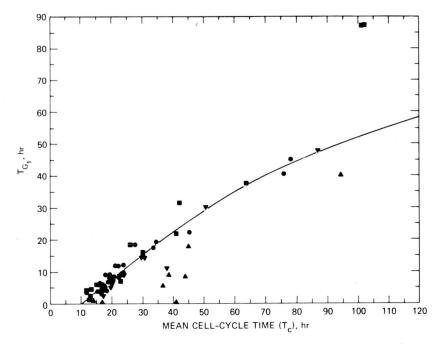

Fig. 11   Mean transit times through $T_{G_1}$ as a function of $T_C$ for four types of cell populations. The points represent data selected from many sources on the basis of computer analysis of good FLM measurements. ▲, ascites tumor. ●, tumor. ■, normal tissue. ▼, tissue culture.

Figure 12 describes $T_S$ as a function of $T_C$. The clear-cut relationship between the parameters for tumors, tissue cultures, and most normal tissues is described by the line, $T_S = 4.0 + 0.3\ T_C$, in hours. Ascites tumors lie well above the line. Several normal tissues lie along a roughly horizontal region at a $T_S$ of 5 to 10 hr; these are mouse skin,[35] corneal epithelium,[11] uterine epithelium,[36] and mouse colon.[8,37] Most striking are the FLM data from mouse skin, shown in Fig. 13.

Several general conclusions are suggested by these data. Ascites cells are clearly a thing apart from other tumors, normal tissues, and tissue cultures. Why this is so remains unclear, but, until the relationships are better understood, this favorite system of the cancer kineticist must be considered a special case, not to be generalized to other tumors. All but the ascites cells and a few normal tissues show a strikingly well behaved, common relationship between $T_C$ and $T_{G_1}$ and between $T_C$ and $T_S$. The linear relationship between $T_C$ and $T_S$ is of particular interest, in part because of the early hypothesis that $T_S$ is a constant and in part because a proportionate effect on $T_S$ largely rules out the speculation that cell cycles are lengthened simply by the insertion of $G_0$ sojourns in the midst of $G_1$ or $G_2$ (Epifanova and Terskikh[38] and many others). The data suggest an

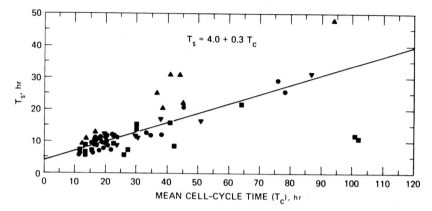

Fig. 12   Mean transit times through S as a function of $T_C$. The equation for a straight line describes the data for all tumors and tissue cultures and many normal tissues. Ascites cells lie above the line, and several normal epithelia lie horizontally below the line. ▲, ascites tumor. ●, tumor. ■, normal tissue. ▼, tissue culture.

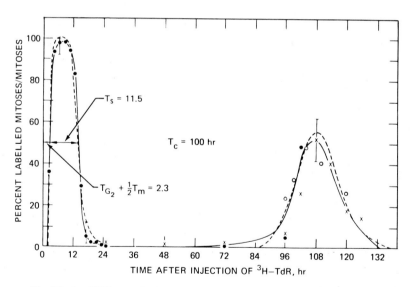

Fig. 13   An FLM experiment on unplucked mouse skin. The bars represent 95% confidence limits, and the symbols refer to three different experiments carried out over a 3-year period. This to my knowledge is the most extreme example of a long cell cycle coupled to a small coefficient of variation and a short $T_S$. [From M. A. H. Hegazy and J. F. Fowler, Cell Population Kinetics of Plucked and Unplucked Mouse Skin. I. Unirradiated Skin, *Cell Tissue Kinet.*, 6: 27 (1973).]

alternate hypothesis; namely, when cells are continuously committed to the cell cycle, their velocities of transit are subject to internal constraints that are shared by $G_1$ and S. But, when cells are being triggered into cycle externally, the control is generally in $G_1$, and therefore the cells generate FLM curves with artificially prolonged $T_{G_1}$ and normal and hence relatively short $T_S$. This describes the behavior of the horizontally placed normal tissues and suggests that all these epithelia have a relatively short but nonetheless real $G_0$ type of cycle. That only these few in vivo normal tissues show this property is the post hoc reason for suggesting external vs. internal control of such cell cycles; it will be an interesting test of the hypothesis to see if this holds up in the future. Meanwhile to the extent that the linearity in Fig. 12 prevails in tumors and some normal tissues, $T_S$ can be used to estimate $T_c$ at a considerable reduction in effort and a considerable increase in clinical applicability.

Figure 14 shows the relationship between $T_c$ and its coefficient of variation ($CV_c$). Ascites cells display a roughly linear regression, suggesting an increment of 10% in $CV_c$ for every 20 hr of $T_c$. The remaining points are so scattered that one cannot identify either a clear regression on $T_c$ or differences among the categories of cells. The two normal tissues with the 100-hr $T_c$ have very different $CV_c$. The mouse skin point lies at 7.9%, and, recalling that this was supposedly a population with a $G_0$ sojourn, one now must explain this very small variability between cycles. Perhaps we are seeing a cell population entrained by some external factor that is itself cyclic, such as the controls that produce waves of hair growth in rodent skin. Why the local cells do not randomize between cycles

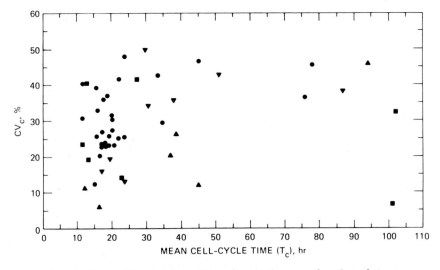

**Fig. 14** The coefficient of variation of cycle time as a function of $T_c$. ▲, ascites tumor. ●, tumor. ■, normal tissue. ▼, tissue culture.

remains a mystery and evokes such far-fetched hypotheses as synchronization of interconnected cells or a rigidly controlled duration of $G_0$.

Finally the relation between $T_{G_2}$ and $T_c$ is shown in Fig. 15. There is a general increase of $T_{G_2}$ with increasing $T_c$; the magnitude of the effect is roughly proportional to the corresponding increase of $T_s$. But the most striking thing about these data is the stratification of $T_{G_2}$ by cell type, as originally suggested by Baserga and Wiebel.[39] Normal tissues have the shortest $T_{G_2}$. They lie in the 1-to-2-hr range except for one point at $T_{G_2}$ = 4.6 hr, $T_c$ = 23 hr, which is from embryonic rat cartilage and gives an atypical FLM curve.[40] Tumors come next with intermediate $T_{G_2}$, and finally there is a wide scattering of large values for ascites tumors and tissue cultures.

To date, $T_{G_2}$ is the only parameter of the cell cycle that differs in normal and tumor cells. This difference has been known for 4 years, but, so far as I am aware, its explanation and its applicability to therapy remain obscure. In $G_2$, the premitotic organizational stage, spindle protein is synthesized, chromosomes are beginning to condense, and many blocks to progression are known to exist. It may be coincidental, but the three systems (tumors, ascites cells, and tissue cultures) with prolongation of $G_2$ also have a high incidence of mitotic abnormality, chromosomal instability, and aneuploidy. Perhaps a slowing of $G_2$ traverse and mitotic instability are closely linked outcomes and are both manifestations of inadequate tissue-culture technique and degeneracy of the tumor milieu. In cancer therapy this might be used constructively by focusing attention on agents which slow, block, or are lethal to $G_2$ cells. In tissue culture

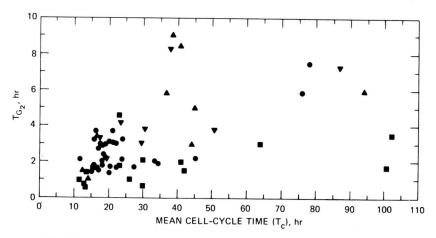

Fig. 15 Mean transit time through $G_2$ as a function of $T_c$. With one exception, normal tissues have the lowest transit times, tumors are intermediate, and ascites tumors and tissue-culture cells have the longest transit times. ▲, ascites tumor. ●, tumor. ■, normal tissue. ▼, tissue culture.

the measurement of $T_{G_2}$ may serve as an additional indication of the quality of the growth conditions.

## CONCLUSION

What then do we know about tumor kinetics? Well, after 15 years of cell-cycle analysis, we now know that most solid tumors behave more like renewal tissues than like exponentially growing populations; we know that some tumors show maturation arrest whereas others have overcommitted themselves to growth at the stem cell or some very early stage and yet can differentiate normally. We know that tumor cell transit times (except for $T_{G_2}$) are surprisingly similar to those of normal cells and are rarely shorter than those of rapidly renewing normal tissues; we know that the variability of tumor cell cycles is similar to that of normal cell cycles; and we have indications that some of the cell-cycle controls are similar in the two systems. We still know very little about how these controls work in normal and abnormal cell cycles, about why ascites tumors behave uniquely, or about the answer to the central question of why tumors enlarge while normal tissues hold to their steady state. We have several general concepts of therapy, such as the use of cycle-specific and phase-specific agents, recruitment into cycle by nonspecific cell killing, and the timing of treatment in terms of the stem-cell kinetics of crucial normal tissues. But we lack finely tuned therapies for specific tumors, and we are far from having the kinetic methods or kinetic insights to provide even a foothold for such approaches in human patients. Clearly we have come a long way, but we still have very far to go.

## ACKNOWLEDGMENTS

The work described in this paper was performed under the auspices of the U. S. Atomic Energy Commission with the support of the U. S. Public Health Service grant 5 R01 14533.

## REFERENCES

1. P. K. Lala, Methods in Cancer Research, Vol. 6, pp. 3-95, Academic Press, Inc., New York, 1971.
2. M. Tubiana, The Kinetics of Tumour Cell Proliferation and Radiotherapy, *Brit. J. Radiol.,* **44**: 325-347 (1971).
3. A. F. Hermens, *Variations in the Cell Kinetics and the Growth Rate in an Experimental Tumour During Natural Growth and After Irradiation,* Uitgeverij Waltman, Delft, Netherlands, 1973.
4. R. Baserga (Ed.), *The Cell Cycle and Cancer,* Vol. 1, Marcel Dekker, Inc., New York, 1971.

5. M. L. Mendelsohn and M. Takahashi, A Critical Evaluation of the Fraction of Labeled Mitoses Method as Applied to the Analysis of Tumor and Other Cell Cycles, in *The Cell Cycle and Cancer*, pp. 55-95, Marcel Dekker, Inc., New York, 1971.

6. G. G. Steel, The Cell Cycle in Tumours: An Examination of Data Gained by the Technique of Labelled Mitoses, *Cell Tissue Kinet.*, **5**: 87-100 (1972).

7. J. C. Barrett, A Mathematical Model of the Mitotic Cycle and Its Application to the Interpretation of Percentage Labelled Mitoses Data, *J. Nat. Cancer Inst.*, **37**: 443-450 (1966).

8. G. G. Steel and S. Hanes, The Technique of Labelled Mitoses: Analysis by Automatic Curve-fitting, *Cell Tissue Kinet.*, **4**: 93-105 (1971).

9. J. C. Barrett, Optimized Parameters for the Mitotic Cycle, *Cell Tissue Kinet.*, **3**: 349-353 (1970).

10. P. D. M. MacDonald, Statistical Inference from the Fraction Labelled Mitoses Curve, *Biometrika*, **57**: 489-503 (1970).

11. P. J. Brockwell, E. Trucco, and R. J. M. Fry, The Determination of Cell-Cycle Parameters from Measurements of the Fraction of Labeled Mitoses, *Bull. Math. Biophys.*, **34**: 1-12 (1972).

12. N. R. Hartmann and T. Pedersen, Analysis of the Kinetics of Granulosa Cell Populations in the Mouse Ovary, *Cell Tissue Kinet.*, **3**: 1-11 (1970).

13. C. W. Gilbert, The Labelled Mitoses Curve and the Estimation of the Parameters of the Cell Cycle, *Cell Tissue Kinet.*, **5**: 53-63 (1972).

14. R. M. Simon, M. T. Stroot, and G. H. Weiss, Numerical Inversion of Laplace Transforms with Application to Percentage Labeled Mitoses Experiments, *Comput. Biomed. Res.*, **5**: 596-607 (1972).

15. M. Takahashi, J. D. Hogg, Jr., and M. L. Mendelsohn, The Automatic Analysis of FLM Curves, *Cell Tissue Kinet.*, **4**: 505-518 (1971).

16. T. Ashihara, Computer Optimization of the Fraction of Labelled Mitoses Analysis Using the Fast Fourier Transform, *Cell Tissue Kinet.*, **6**: 447-453 (1973).

17. L. A. Dethlefsen and R. M. Riley, Hydroxyurea Effects in the C3H Mouse. I. Duodenal Crypt Cell Kinetics, *Cell Tissue Kinet.*, **6**: 3-16 (1973).

18. M. L. Mendelsohn and L. A. Dethlefsen, Cell Kinetics of Breast Cancer: The Turnover of Nonproliferating Cells, in *Recent Results in Cancer Research, Breast Cancer: A Challenging Problem*, pp. 73-86, Springer-Verlag, New York, 1973.

19. M. L. Mendelsohn, Autoradiographic Analysis of Cell Proliferation in Spontaneous Breast Cancer of the C3H Mouse. III. The Growth Fraction, *J. Nat. Cancer Inst.*, **28**: 1015-1029 (1962).

20. E. H. Cooper, The Biology of Cell Death in Tumours, *Cell Tissue Kinet.*, **6**: 87-95 (1973).

21. H. E. Skipper and S. Perry, Kinetics of Normal and Leukemic Leukocyte Populations and Relevance to Chemotherapy, *Cancer Res.*, **30**: 1883-1897 (1970).

22. C. Vendrely, Cytophotometry and Histochemistry of the Cell Cycle, in *The Cell Cycle and Cancer*, pp 227-268, Marcel Dekker, Inc., New York, 1971.

23. M. A. Van Dilla, T. T. Trujillo, P. F. Mullaney, and J. R. Coulter, Cell Microfluorometry: A Method for Rapid Fluorescence Measurement, *Science*, **163**: 1213-1214 (1969).

24. P. M. Kraemer, L. L. Deaven, H. A. Crissman, and M. A. Van Dilla, DNA Constancy Despite Variability in Chromosome Number, in *Advances in Cell and Molecular Biology*, Vol. 2, pp. 47-108, Academic Press, Inc., New York, 1972.

25. P. N. Dean and J. H. Jett, Mathematical Analysis of DNA Distributions Derived from Flow Microfluorimetry, *J. Cell Biol.*, **60**: 523-527 (1974).

26. J. Gray, Lawrence Livermore Laboratory, Livermore, California, personal communication, 1973.

27. B. H. Mayall, Deoxyribonucleic Acid Cytophotometry of Stained Human Leukocytes I. Differences Among Cell Types, *J. Histochem. Cytochem.*, **4**: 249-257 (1969).

28. R. Yanishevsky, M. L. Mendelsohn, B. H. Mayall, and V. J. Cristofalo, Cytophotometric and Autoradiographic Studies of Dividing and Nondividing Human Diploid Cells in Culture, *In Vitro*, **8**: 428 (1973).

29. B. H. Mayall and M. L. Mendelsohn, Deoxyribonucleic Acid Cytophotometry of Stained Human Leukocytes II. The Mechanical Scanner of CYDAC, the Theory of Scanning Photometry and the Magnitude of Residual Errors, *J. Histochem. Cytochem.*, **18**: 383-407 (1970).

30. J. S. R. Nelson and L. M. Schiffer, Autoradiographic Detection of DNA Polymerase Containing Nuclei in Sarcoma 180 Ascites Cells, *Cell Tissue Kinet.*, **6**: 45-54 (1973).

31. J. A. Steinkamp, A. Romero, and M. A. Van Dilla, Multiparameter Cell Sorting: Identification of Human Leukocytes by Acridine Orange Fluorescence, *Acta Cytol.*, **17**: 113-117 (1973).

32. H. R. Hulett, W. A. Bonner, R. G. Sweet, and L. A. Herzenberg, Development and Application of a Rapid Cell Sorter, *Clin. Chem.*, **19**: 813-816 (1973).

33. M. Omine and S. Perry, Use of Cell Separation at 1 g for Cytokinetic Studies in Spontaneous AKR Leukemia, *J. Nat. Cancer Inst.*, **48**: 697-704 (1972).

34. P. Dombernowsky and N. R. Hartmann, Analysis of Variations in the Cell Population Kinetics with Tumor Age in the L1210 Ascites Tumor, *Cancer Res.*, **32**: 2452-2458 (1972).

35. M. A. H. Hegazy and J. F. Fowler, Cell Population Kinetics of Plucked and Unplucked Mouse Skin. I. Unirradiated Skin, *Cell Tissue Kinet.*, **6**: 17-33 (1973).

36. O. I. Epifanova, Effects of Hormones on the Cell Cycle, in *The Cell Cycle and Cancer*, pp. 145-190, Marcel Dekker, Inc., New York, 1971.

37. M. Lipkin and H. Quastler, Cell Population Kinetics in the Colon of the Mouse, *J. Clin. Invest.*, **41**: 141-146 (1962).

38. O. I. Epifanova and V. V. Terskikh, On the Resting Periods in the Cell Life Cycle, *Cell Tissue Kinet.*, **2**: 75-93 (1969).

39. R. Baserga and F. Wiebel, The Cell Cycle of Mammalian Cells, *Int. Rev. Exp. Pathol.*, **7**: 1-30 (1969).

40. B. Dixon, Cartilage Cell Proliferation in the Tail-Vertebrae of New-Born Rats, *Cell Tissue Kinet.*, **4**: 21-30 (1971).

# THEORETICAL ASPECTS
# OF GROWTH FRACTION IN A $G_0$ MODEL

F. J. BURNS
Institute of Environmental Medicine, New York University Medical Center, New York,
New York

## ABSTRACT

In a model of the cell cycle previously presented, the proliferating cells (P cells) were
subdivided into a $G_0$ phase from which cells were released randomly at a rate consistent
with the proliferation rate of the tissue as a whole and a C phase. The C phase received the
cells released from the $G_0$ phase and was of uniform duration consisting of various
subphases including the S phase and the $G_2$ phase. The model in this paper introduces a rate
constant that describes the conversion of P cells into nonproliferating cells (Q cells). The
presence of Q cells requires that the growth fraction (GF) be less than 1. Cell loss was
assumed to occur either uniformly from all the cells in the population (P cells and Q cells)
or solely from the Q population. Expressions for the frequency-of-labelled-mitosis (FLM)
curves, percentage of cells in the S phase, and the age distribution functions were derived in
terms of GF, the proliferation rate, $K_p$, the loss rate, $K_L$, and the durations of the various C
subphases. The results indicate that the ratio of the percentage of cells in the S phase to the
plateau level of the damped FLM curve is GF/2. The model is fitted to experimental FLM
curves of normal tissue and a variety of tumors with diverse growth and cell-loss
characteristics.

The $G_0$ concept has been interpreted in various ways; however, there seems to
be general agreement on the basic idea that $G_0$ cells are fertile cells that have not
yet embarked on the pathway to division.[1-5] In addition to $G_0$ cells, there may
be infertile cells that have lost the potential for cell division. The latter cells have
been designated Q cells,[6] and their existence implies that the fertile fraction, or
growth fraction (GF), is less than unity.[7] The spinous layer of stratified
squamous epithelium is an excellent example of a population of Q cells.

In the classical theory of cell kinetics, the cell cycle starts when the cells are
born at the end of mitosis. Immediately the cells begin to progress by means of
an unknown mechanism through the various phases designated $G_1$, S, and $G_2$,
and the cycle ends with the completion of the next mitosis. The time in each

phase is assumed to have a distinct numerical value, although in practice variability occurs which requires that phase times be represented by some type of distribution function.[8,9] The degree of variability is usually inferred from the degree of damping in successive waves of the frequency-of-labelled-mitoses (FLM) curve.

In the $G_0$ model, variability in phase time is deliberately introduced by specifying that the triggering mechanism which releases the $G_0$ cells into the division pathway is random in the sense that all $G_0$ cells are equivalent and subject to the same transition probability. The existence of a phase involving random triggering tends to desynchronize the cells; and, if the mean residence time in $G_0$ is long in comparison to the length of the remainder of the cycle, the desynchronization is sufficient to cause nearly complete damping of the FLM curve in a single cycle. Hence, no second peak occurs in the FLM curve; instead, a constant plateau value is eventually reached and maintained.

## DESCRIPTION OF THE MODEL

In this paper the effect of introducing Q cells into the $G_0$ model is considered. The basic assumptions underlying the present model are depicted in Fig. 1. The proliferating compartment (P) consists of cells in $G_0$ and cells in what is designated here as the C phase, which receives the cells released from $G_0$. The rate constant for the $G_0$ to C transition is $\gamma$. In the C phase the cells are assumed to progress in accordance with a mechanism that results in a uniform phase duration, T. The subphases of the C phase are also of uniform duration and are as follows: the S phase (duration, $T_s$), the $G_2$ phase (duration, $T_2$), mitosis (duration negligible), and possibly a presynthetic phase designated in the

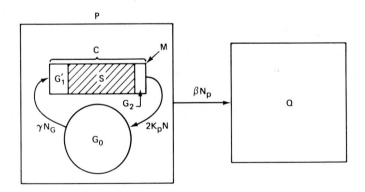

Fig. 1   The elements of the $G_0$ model. Two separate cell loss modes are considered: (1) loss from all cells and (2) loss from the Q compartment only. The transitions from P to Q and from $G_0$ to C are assumed to be random.

diagram as $G_1'$. The Q cells can only be produced by transfer from the P compartment, which occurs with a rate constant $\beta$. All P cells are assumed to be equally subject to the Q transformation. The overall rate of cell production is $K_p N$, where N is total cell number and $K_p$ is a constant.

Two separate modes of cell loss are considered (1) all cells (P and Q) are equally subject to random loss and (2) loss occurs only from the Q population. The latter mode may be applicable to normal stratified squamous epithelium, whereas the former may be applicable to some tumors.

The following rate equations can be written for cell loss mode 1:

$$\frac{dN_C}{dt} = \gamma N_G - K_p N - (\beta + K_L) N_C \tag{1}$$

$$\frac{dN_G}{dt} = 2 K_p N - (\gamma + \beta + K_L) N_G \tag{2}$$

$$\frac{dN_Q}{dt} = \beta N_G + \beta N_C - K_L N_Q \tag{3}$$

where $N_G$, $N_C$, and $N_Q$ are the number of cells in $G_0$, C, and Q, respectively, and $K_L$ is the rate constant for cell loss. Similar equations can be written for cell loss mode 2 with the difference that $K_L$ is set equal to zero in Eqs. 1 and 2 and $N_Q$ is replaced by N in Eq. 3.

The terms in Eqs. 1 to 3 are derived from the flow of cells across the various phase boundaries (Fig. 1). For example, the first term on the right of Eq. 1 represents the rate of flow of cells into the C phase from the $G_0$ phase, the second term is the rate of flow out of the C phase at mitosis, and the third term represents the combined loss rate associated with loss from the population and conversion to the Q phase. The assumption that the flow rate in the C phase is uniform imposes the condition that the efflux of cells through mitosis at time t equals the product of the influx at time T earlier and the probability of remaining in the C phase for time T; i.e., $K_p N = \gamma N_G (t - T) e^{-(K_L + \beta)T}$.

Equations 1 to 3 are easily solved if it is assumed that the cell population is either growing exponentially (exponential constant, K) or is in a steady state (K = 0) and that the proportion of cells in the various compartments is constant. For cell loss mode 1, the foregoing assumptions give the following expressions:

$$\gamma = \frac{K_p + \beta}{2 e^{-K_p + \beta T} - 1} \tag{4}$$

$$GF = \frac{K_p}{K_p + \beta} \tag{5}$$

where $K_p = K + K_L$ and $GF = N_p/N$. For cell loss mode 2, similar expressions are obtained except K replaces $K_p$ in Eq. 4 and in the denominator of Eq. 5.

Age distribution functions, $a(t)$, can be derived[10] for each phase by multiplying the rate that cells enter the phase by the probability of remaining there for time t. For the $G_0$, C, and Q phases, the functions for mode 1 are, respectively:

$$a_G(t) = 2K_p \, e^{-(\gamma + K_p + \beta)t} \tag{6}$$

$$a_C(t) = K_p \, e^{(K_p + \beta)T} \, e^{-(K_p + \beta)t} \qquad \text{(for } t \leqslant T) \tag{7}$$

$$a_Q(t) = \frac{\beta K_p}{K_p + \beta} \, e^{-K_p t} \tag{8}$$

The comparable distribution functions for mode 2 differ only slightly from the mode 1 expressions: K replaces $K_p$ in the exponent of Eqs. 6 and 7 and in the denominator of the coefficient in Eq. 8, and $K_p \beta/(\beta - K_L)$ replaces $K_p$ in the exponent of Eq. 8.

From Eq. 6 the mean duration of $G_0$ can be calculated, and the result is:

$$\bar{t}_G = \frac{1}{\gamma + \beta + K_p} \tag{9}$$

By integration of Eq. 7 within the limits $t = T - T_2 - T_s$ to $t = T - T_2$, the proportion of cells in the S phase, i.e., the pulse labelling index (LI), is obtained:

$$LI = \frac{K_p}{K_p + \beta} \, [e^{(K_p + \beta)(T_2 + T_s)} - e^{(K_p + \beta)T_2}] \tag{10}$$

which reduces, when $(K_p + \beta)T_s \ll 1$, to the more familiar form,

$$LI = K_p T_s \tag{10a}$$

Equation 10a applies also to cell loss mode 2.

The form of the FLM curve can be derived from the movement of a labelled cohort of cells through the cycle.[2] The desynchronization introduced by the $G_0$ phase causes a rapid damping of the FLM curve to a constant or plateau value (P) given by

$$P = \frac{T_s}{T_C} \tag{11}$$

where $T_C$ is the mean duration of the cycle.[11,12] Equation 11 refers only to the proliferating population; therefore, its validity is independent of the presence of

Q cells. The mean duration of the cycle is the sum of the mean duration of the $G_0$ phase and the duration of the C phase; i.e.,

$$T_C = \bar{\tau}_G + T \tag{12}$$

which can be rewritten to give $\bar{\tau}_G$ as follows:

$$\bar{\tau}_G = \frac{T_s}{P} - T \tag{13}$$

Since the terms on the right of Eq. 13 are experimentally measurable, Eq. 13 can be used to determine $\bar{\tau}_G$.

A theoretical FLM curve for the $G_0$ model is shown in Fig. 2. In principle, $T_s$ is determined from the width of the first peak, and T is measured from the beginning of the first peak to the start of the next rise, as indicated in Fig. 2.

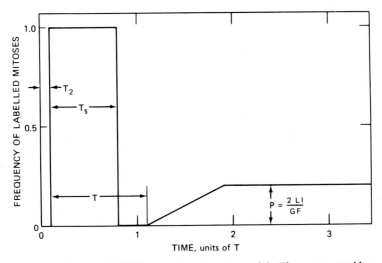

Fig. 2 A theoretical FLM curve for the $G_0$ model. The curve provides experimental estimates of $T_2$, $T_s$, T, and P, as indicated.

The values for the various parameters of the curve shown in Fig. 2 are as follows: $T_s = 0.7T$, $T_2 = 0.1T$, $P = 0.2$, $T = 20$ hr, and $LI = 5\%$. If the condition that $\bar{\tau}_G \gg T$ or, in terms of measurable quantities, $PT/T_s \ll 1$, is fulfilled, it can be shown from Eqs. 4, 9, and 10a that

$$P = \frac{2LI}{GF} \tag{14}$$

which is valid for both modes of cell loss considered here and is the equation used by Mendelsohn to determine GF in tumors.[7] For example, in Fig. 2, $\bar{t}_G = 60$ hr and GF = 0.5. If the condition $\bar{t}_G \gg T$ is not fulfilled, Eq. 5 in conjunction with Eqs. 4, 9, and 10a must be used to calculate GF.

## APPLICATION OF THE MODEL TO EXPERIMENTAL DATA

From published FLM curves for 16 tumors and 2 normal tissues (Refs. 2, 5, 13, and 14), $T_s$, T, and P values were determined and used in Eq. 13 to calculate $\bar{t}_G$. Values for GF were then calculated. The results of both calculations are shown in Table 1. For the entries indicated with an asterisk, the LI values were high enough that it was necessary to use the exact expression for LI (Eq. 10) in the calculation. The experimental data are in columns 1 to 4, and the calculated results are shown in columns 5 to 7.

TABLE 1

EXPERIMENTAL AND DERIVED PARAMETERS OF
THE $G_0$ MODEL

| | $T_s$, hr | T, hr | P | LI, % | $\bar{t}_G$, hr | GF | $\bar{t}_G/T_C$ |
|---|---|---|---|---|---|---|---|
| **Tumors:** | | | | | | | |
| Epidermoid epithelioma | 12 | 15 | 0.25 | 8 | 33 | 0.59 | 0.69 |
| B-16 melanoma | 5 | 10 | 0.17 | 25 | 19 | 2.12* | 0.66 |
| Melanoma b | 21 | 23 | 0.33 | 5 | 41 | 0.26 | 0.64 |
| Melanoma a | 14 | 15 | 0.33 | 23 | 27 | 1.04* | 0.63 |
| DMBA mammary carcinoma | 9 | 10 | 0.33 | 10 | 17 | 0.53 | 0.63 |
| Acute leukemia a | 26 | 30 | 0.33 | | 49 | | 0.62 |
| Acute leukemia b | 30 | 36 | 0.33 | | 54 | | 0.60 |
| BICR ($A_2$) | 10 | 27 | 0.18 | 3.5 | 29 | 0.31 | 0.52 |
| BA 1112 | 10 | 13 | 0.44 | 20 | 10 | 0.70 | 0.43 |
| MCA sarcoma | 22 | 30 | 0.44 | 4.8 | 20 | 0.22 | 0.40 |
| BICR (M1) | 8 | 13 | 0.42 | 34.2 | 6 | 1.03* | 0.32 |
| RIB 5 | 8 | 10 | 0.55 | 30 | 4.5 | 0.71* | 0.31 |
| BICR ($A_{10}$) | 10 | 11 | 0.62 | 9.3 | 5 | 0.22 | 0.31 |
| Circulating leukemia | 16 | 40 | 0.28 | | 17 | | 0.30 |
| C3H mammary | 10 | 20 | 0.36 | 16 | 8 | 0.64 | 0.29 |
| DEA hamster cheek pouch | 6 | 8 | 0.55 | 25 | 3 | 0.59* | 0.27 |
| **Normal tissue:** | | | | | | | |
| Hamster cheek epithelium | 8.6 | 60 | 0.04 | 2 | 155 | 1.00 | 0.72 |
| Intestinal crypt | 6.5 | 10.5 | 0.60 | 35 | 0.3 | 0.99* | 0.03 |

Only one tumor has an obviously unacceptable value for GF or $\bar{\tau}_G$. The B-16 melanoma has a GF value of 2.12, which is significantly in excess of the maximum possible 1.00 and indicates the model is completely inapplicable to this particular tumor. Excluding the B-16 melanoma, 7 of 15 tumors have mean $G_0$ durations greater than one-half the total cycle time. In order of decreasing ratios, they are: (1) epidermoid epithelioma, (2) melanoma b, (3) melanoma a, (4) DMBA mammary carcinoma, (5) acute leukemia a, (6) acute leukemia b, and (7) BICR $A_2$.

Of the 6 autochthonous human tumors analyzed, 5 appear on the preceding list, whereas only 1 of the 5 transplantable tumors appears. None of the 7 tumors on the list show clear evidence of a second peak in the FLM curve, which is consistent with the greater damping to be expected for longer $G_0$ duration.

Growth-fraction values varied greatly from tumor to tumor. Of 12 tumors with measurable GF values, 5 were greater than 0.66, and 4 were below 0.33. There was no obvious correlation between GF and $\bar{\tau}_G/\bar{\tau}_C$ values.

Two normal tissues, intestinal crypt and hamster cheek-pouch epithelium, appear in Table 1. The intestinal-crypt epithelium is not expected to have a $G_0$ phase, because the cycle time is short and damping in the FLM curve is not pronounced. The apparent lack of a $G_0$ phase is confirmed by the $\bar{\tau}_G$ value of 0.3 hr, which means that, if a $G_0$ exists, it does not comprise more than about 3% of the total cycle.

On the other hand, the hamster cheek-pouch epithelium might be expected to have a $G_0$ phase. It is proliferating relatively slowly, and no evidence for a second peak in the FLM curve has been found. In fact, the hamster cheek-pouch FLM plateau is so low that determination of T is difficult. Nevertheless the calculation indicates the possibility that the $G_0$-phase duration could be as much as 72% of the cycle time. As expected, GF values were about 1.00 for both normal tissues.

## DISCUSSION

None of the experimental FLM curves, except that for normal hamster cheek-pouch epithelium, go to zero after the first peak as the theory requires if $T > T_s + T_2$. Part of the explanation for the lack of zero values may be variability in $T_s$ and T. On the other hand, only 3 of the 18 FLM curves analyzed have $T/T_s$ values greater than 2. Of the 3, 1 (cheek-pouch epithelium) goes to zero, and the other 2 (circulating leukemic cells and BICR $A_2$) show reasonably distinct dips before reaching plateau levels, suggesting zero intervals masked by variability.

None of the foregoing proves that a $G_0$ phase exists or that the various assumptions made concerning Q cells and cell loss are correct. At least one tumor was found where the experimental results were completely inconsistent with the model. However in some tumors and in one of the normal tissues, the present analysis indicates that the simultaneous presence of $G_0$ cells and Q cells provides a reasonable interpretation of the experimental data.

It has been suggested that the $G_0$ phase is involved in controlling the rate of cell division by means of a mechanism that varies the $\gamma$ value.[2] If so, the relatively long $G_0$ durations found for autochthonous (especially human) tumors provide hope that such tumors retain a residual responsiveness to normal control mechanisms. The biology of tumor growth may, of course, be more complex than this relatively simple model would allow; however, its simplicity is a virtue until the complexities are fully known.

## ACKNOWLEDGMENTS

The investigation reported here was supported by the U. S. Atomic Energy Commission contract AT(11-1)3380 and is part of a center program supported by the National Institute of Environmental Health Sciences, grant ES 00260.

## REFERENCES

1. L. G. Lajtha, On the Concept of the Cell Cycle, *J. Cell. Comp. Physiol.,* **60**, Suppl. 1: 143 (1960).

2. F. J. Burns and I. F. Tannock, On the Existence of a $G_0$-Phase in the Cell Cycle, *Cell Tissue Kinet.,* **3**: 321-334 (1970).

3. J. A. Smith and L. Martin, Do Cells Cycle? *Proc. Nat. Acad. Sci. U. S. A.,* **70**: 1263-1267 (1973).

4. J. M. Brown and R. Oliver, A New Method of Estimating the Cell Cycle Time in Epithelial Tissues of Long Generation Time, *Cell Tissue Kinet.,* **1**: 11-21 (1968).

5. M. F. Rajewsky, Proliferative Parameters of Mammalian Cell Systems and Their Role in Tumor Growth and Carcinogenesis, *Z. Krebsforsch.,* **78**: 12-30 (1970).

6. G. G. Steel, The Cell Cycle in Tumors: An Examination of Data Gained By the Technizue of Labelled Mitoses, *Cell Tissue Kinet.,* **5**: 87-100 (1972).

7. M. L. Mendelsohn, The Growth Fraction: A New Concept Applied to Tumours, *Science,* **132**: 1496 (1960).

8. J. C. Barrett, A Mathematical Model of the Mitotic Cycle and Its Application to the Interpretation of Percentage Labelled Mitosis Data, *J. Nat. Cancer Inst.,* **37**: 443 (1966).

9. M. Takahashi, Theoretical Basis for Cell Cycle Analysis. I. Labelled Mitosis Wave Method, *J. Theor. Biol.,* **13**: 202 (1966).

10. H. A. Johnson, Some Problems Associated with the Histological Study of Cell Proliferation Kinetics, *Cytologia,* **26**: 32 (1961).

11. E. Trucco and P. J. Brockwell, Percentage Labelled Mitosis Curves in Exponentially Growing Cell Populations, *J. Theoret. Biol.,* **20**: 321 (1968).

12. E. Trucco, personal communication, Argonne National Laboratory, 1970.

13. A. B. Cairnie, L. F. Lamerton, and G. G. Steel, Cell Proliferation Studies in the Intestinal Epithelium of the Rat, *Exp. Cell Res.,* **39**: 528-538 (1965).

14. G. G. Steel, K. Adams, and J. C. Barrett, Analysis of the Cell Population Kinetics of Transplanted Tumours of Widely Differing Growth Rate, *Brit. J. Cancer,* **20**: 784-800 (1966).

# CELL KINETICS OF HUMAN SOLID TUMORS FOLLOWING CONTINUOUS INFUSION OF $^3$H – TDR

JOSE J. TERZ and H. PABLO CURUTCHET
Division of Surgical Oncology, Medical College of Virginia, Health Sciences
Division of Virginia Commonwealth University, Richmond, Virginia

## ABSTRACT

The cell proliferation kinetics of four human solid tumors was analyzed following the administration of tritiated thymidine ($^3$H–TdR) in vivo. Four patients (epidermoid carcinoma of the maxillary antrum, recurrent epidermoid carcinoma of the neck, metastatic carcinoma of the pancreas, and carcinoma of the breast) received a continuous infusion of 2 mCi a day of $^3$H–TdR from 6 to 20 days. Biopsies were obtained during and after the infusion period. In each case the mitotic index, labelling index, percent of labelled mitosis, and median grain count were determined. The duration of the cell cycle ranged between 18 hr (epidermoid carcinoma of the neck) to 6 days (adenocarcinoma of the pancreas). The size of the proliferating tumor-cell population rose to 30% at 6 days and to 60% in 20 days. Ninety percent of the mitoses were labelled at 20 days. In one patient a simultaneous analysis of the cell kinetics of the normal tissue and tumor counterpart was performed. These studies suggest that a significant segment of the tumor-cell population (40%) does not divide (prolonged $G_1$ or $G_0$) at least for 20 days.

With the administration of tritiated thymidine ($^3$H–TdR) in a continuous infusion, significant information has been obtained on the size and behavior of the human leukemia-cell population.[1,2] Similar information on human solid tumors may lead to a better understanding of their tumor cell kinetics as well as more rational therapeutic planning. With this objective we have performed a series of studies on human solid tumors in vivo following a continuous infusion of $^3$H–TdR. This paper describes the preliminary findings on four patients.

## PATIENT SELECTION AND METHODS

Each of the four patients had lesions accessible for repeated biopsy, and their disease was beyond control by any available curative and palliative therapeutic modality. Each patient received a continuous intravenous infusion of $^3$H—TdR (specific activity, 6.7 mCi/mmole) for a period ranging from 6 to 20 days at a rate of 2 mCi per day, administered through a constant infusion pump. Biopsies were obtained at different intervals during and after the infusion of $^3$H—TdR and processed as described in a previous report.[3] The exposure time ranged between 6 to 14 weeks. After this period the slides were developed and stained with Toluidine Blue.

Cells with three or more grains were considered labelled. The labelling index (LI) and mitotic index (MI) were determined by counting 2000 cells per slide. The median grain count (MGC) was determined by counting 200 to 400 cells per slide. The labelled mitotic index (LMI) was determined by counting 100 mitoses.

The reported generation time ($T_c$) was determined by the median grain count halving time of the labelled cells following the end of the infusion.[2]

## RESULTS

*Case 1: carcinoma of the breast.* A 59-year-old female had extensive carcinoma of the left breast involving the chest wall with metastasis to regional nodes and bones. The patient received radiation therapy and chemotherapy and, at the time of this study, was receiving testosterone without apparent benefit. This patient received a continuous infusion of $^3$H—TdR for 17 days (Fig. 1). The LI rose from 10.7% on the 4th infusion day to 65% on the 17th day. Following discontinuation of the infusion, the LI fell to 3% in 14 days. The LMI rose from 24% (on the 4th day) to 76% on the 17th day. This was followed by a rapid dilution of LMI to 1% on the 14th day postinfusion. The MI ranged between 4% and 5% during the study. The MGC reached its peak on the 17th day (15 grains/cell), and the duration of the cell cycle was estimated as 18 hr.

*Case 2: carcinoma of the pancreas.* A 65-year-old female had metastatic carcinoma to the bones, lungs, and skin. A thorough work-up failed to reveal a primary site. This patient received multiple courses of chemotherapy as well as radiation therapy to symptomatic bone metastases with only temporary relief. She expired 16 months following her initial diagnosis, and at autopsy a primary carcinoma of the body and tail of the pancreas was found. This patient was infused for 11 days (Fig. 2). At the end of this period, the LI reached 34% and the LMI reached 63%. Following the discontinuation of the $^3$H—TdR infusion, the LI and LMI reached 8.0% and 26.0%, respectively, on the 10th postinfusion day (Fig. 2). The MI ranged between 1% and 2.9%. The duration of the cell cycle was estimated as 120 hr.

*Case 3: epidermoid carcinoma of the oropharynx.* A 53-year-old male developed recurrent carcinoma of the neck 2 years following radical surgery for carcinoma of the tongue. He received radiation therapy and chemotherapy with only temporary regression of the tumor. This patient was infused for 6 days only (Fig. 3). The LI and LMI reached 33.4% and 51.4%, respectively, at the end

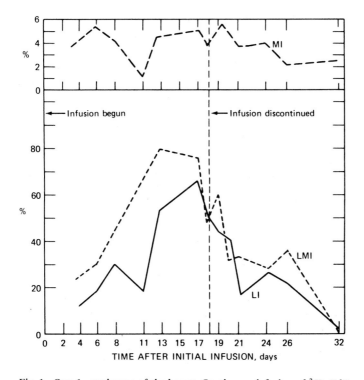

Fig. 1 Case 1: carcinoma of the breast. Continuous infusion of $^3$H−TdR.

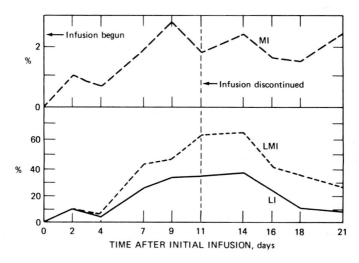

Fig. 2 Case 2: metastatic pancreatic carcinoma. Continuous infusion of $^3$H−TdR.

of the infusion and fell to 19% and 6.6%, respectively, 4 days after interruption of the $^3$H–TdR. The cell cycle is calculated as 18 hr.

   *Case 4: recurrent carcinoma of the maxillary antrum.* A 66-year-old male had extensive recurrent carcinoma of the maxillary antrum after radical surgery and radiation therapy. This patient was infused for 21 days, and biopsies were

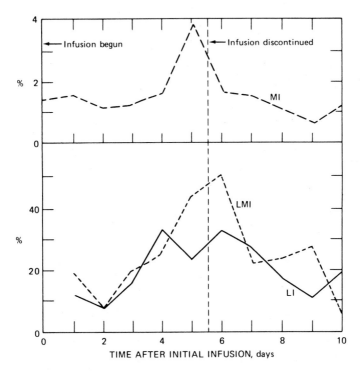

**Fig. 3   Case 3: recurrent carcinoma of head and neck. Continuous infusion of** $^3$**H–TdR.**

obtained from the tumor and normal adjacent mucosa (Figs. 4 and 5). In the tumor the LI rose to 50% on the 7th day and remained essentially unchanged during the infusion period, but 95% of the mitoses were labelled by the end of the infusion. These values fell to 8% and 50%, respectively, on the 3rd day postinfusion. In the normal mucosa 75% of the cells in interphase and 96% of the mitoses were labelled on the 5th day. These indexes did not significantly change throughout the infusion period but fell rapidly after discontinuation of the infusion. The MI was similar in the tumor and in the normal mucosa. The duration of the cell cycle, as determined by halving the MGC, was 19.2 hr in tumor and normal tissues.

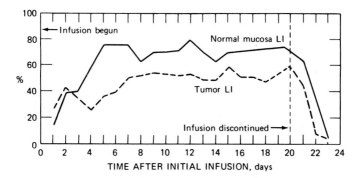

Fig. 4 Case 4: carcinoma of maxillary antrum. Labelling index of normal mucosa and tumor following continuous infusion of $^3$H–TdR.

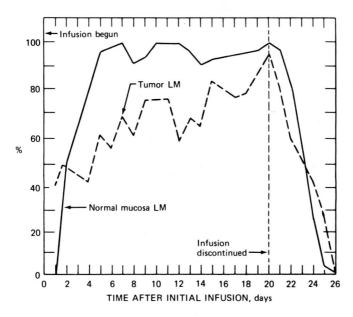

Fig. 5 Case 4: carcinoma of maxillary antrum. Labelled mitosis of normal mucosa and tumor following continuous infusion of $^3$H–TdR.

## COMMENTS

Previous studies in human leukemia have demonstrated well the dynamics of this tumor-cell population. Following continuous infusion of $^3$H–TdR, 100% of the cells in mitosis are labelled within 4 days. The labelling of the cells in interphase will progress in linear fashion, and, at the end of the infusion period,

90% have entered DNA synthesis. These findings demonstrate that practically all components of the tumor-cell population will eventually enter in cycle over a period of at least 20 days.[1,2]

Our preliminary findings on solid tumors do not seem to quite conform with this behavior. At 10 days only 50% of the total cell population is labelled, and this figure does not exceed the 70% mark at 20 days. In Case 4 the LI remained essentially unchanged between the 10th and 20th days of infusion. The following interpretations are possible: (1) the tumor cell population has a large nonproliferative pool, (2) a significant part of this population has a cell cycle longer than the period of infusion with a prolonged $G_1$ or entering $G_0$, or (3) the isotope did not uniformly reach all cells in DNA synthesis.

The analysis of the LM curve shows a progressive rise in the number of labelled cells, but a significant number of mitoses still remained unlabelled during and at the end of infusion. This controversial finding could be explained by the following possibilities:

1. Insufficient exposure time was allowed; however, duplicate sets of slides exposed beyond 16 weeks failed to show any significant difference in the LMI or MGC.

2. Biopsies obtained from peripheral areas with inadequate blood supply and poor oxygenation may result in low LMI. Tannock and Steel[4] have demonstrated in animals and Shirakawa et al.[5] in humans that there is no significant difference in the LMI of tumor-cell populations sampled from the periphery of tumor or from hypoxic tissue as compared with the values obtained from areas close to capillaries or well oxygenated tumor.

3. Inadequate doses of isotopes. We have administered 2 mCi per 24 hr. Clarkson[1] and Shirakawa et al.[5] have used up to 4 mCi per 24 hr. This may be an acceptable explanation. The nonuniform distribution of blood supply in human solid tumors may well result in an unequal uptake of $^3H-TdR$ in different areas. A loading dose of $^3H-TdR$ at initiation of the study and a higher daily concentration of the isotope may result in an early saturation of cells entering DNA synthesis. The fact that the biopsies of normal mucosa showed a prompt labelling of all mitotic figures (Fig. 5) may indicate that, in the presence of normal proliferating tissue with uniform blood supply, the isotope concentration of 2 mCi per 24 hr is adequate.

4. Cells are arrested in $G_2$. This is the only biological assumption that can be made on the basis of the work of Gelfant.[6] However, all technical objections previously discussed must be investigated before this conclusion is accepted.

The duration of the cell cycle for epidermoid carcinoma of the oropharynx and that for carcinoma of the breast do not differ significantly from those reported[3] following a single injection of $^3H-TdR$. A generation time of 120 hr found in the carcinoma of the pancreas is one of the longest reported for this type of tumor and may well confirm the clinical behavior of this tumor. In this patient the primary tumor remained clinically occult throughout the course of the disease, suggesting a prolonged doubling time.

This paper supports the feasibility and importance of the study of the kinetics of human solid tumors with a continuous infusion of $^3$H–TdR and also suggests that solid tumors may have a large nonproliferative pool and that some tumors have a large cell subpopulation with a cycle longer than 20 days. It has again been demonstrated that a normal cell population and its tumor counterpart have similar kinetic behavior.

## ACKNOWLEDGMENTS

The research reported in this paper was supported by Public Health Service grants 1R01 CA11189 and RR-65 from the General Clinical Research Centers Program of the Division of Research Resources, National Institutes of Health.

## REFERENCES

1. B. Clarkson, J. Fried, A. Strife, et al., Studies of Cellular Proliferation in Human Leukemia. III. Behavior of Leukemic Cells in Three Adults with Acute Leukemia Given Continuous Infusions of $^3$H-Thymidine for 8 or 10 Days, *Cancer,* **25**: 1237–1259 (1970).
2. B. Clarkson, J. Fried, and M. Ogawa, Magnitude of Proliferating Fraction and Rate of Proliferation of Populations of Leukemic Cells in Man, in *Recent Results in Cancer Research—Normal and Malignant Cell Growth,* pp. 175–185, Springer-Verlag New York, Inc., New York, 1969.
3. J. Terz, P. Curutchet, and W. Lawrence, Jr., Analysis of the Cell Kinetics of Human Solid Tumors, *Cancer,* **28**: 1100–1110 (1971).
4. I. Tannock and G. Steel, Tumor Growth and Cell Kinetics in Chronically Hypoxic Animals, *J. Nat. Cancer Inst.,* **45**: 123–133 (1970).
5. S. Shirakawa, J. Luce, I. Tannock, and E. Frei III, Cell Proliferation in Human Melanoma, *J. Clin. Invest.,* **49**: 1188–1199 (1970).
6. S. Gelfant, Patterns of Epidermal Cell Division. I. Genetic Behavior of the $G_1$-Cell Population, *Exp. Cell Res.,* **32**: 521-528 (1963).

# TIME-LAPSE CINEMATOGRAPHY OF SYNCHRONIZED CMP HUMAN TUMOR CELLS IN CULTURE

FREDERICK H. KASTEN

Department of Anatomy, Louisiana State University Medical Center, New Orleans, Louisiana

## ABSTRACT

Human epithelial cancer cells from an established cell line (CMP) were synchronized with a sequential double thymidine blockade (2.5 mmolar) and followed in the living state by phase-contrast, time-lapse cinematography. Excess thymidine causes an increase in cell and nuclear size, mitotic inhibition, the production of small, dense nucleoli, and violent activities of the cell membranes. The membrane effects include the development of attachment fibers that undergo rapid and vigorous movements plus zeiosis, or boiling of the cell membrane. The synchronized cell cycle is characterized by a gradual increase in nucleolar size and activity during the S phase, cellular elongation with increased membrane activity and zeiosis in the $G_2$ phase, a highly synchronized mitotic burst of 70% or more of the population at 10 to 11 hr, and the development of $G_1$-phase cells that are mobile, display active membranes with pinocytosis, and produce reversible attachment fibers or microspikes from the cell membrane. Film abstracts are presented from the original 16-mm movie.

A thorough investigation of the morphologic and molecular events that take place during the cancer-cell cycle requires a variety of experimental approaches. The ones I will discuss involve time-lapse cinematography of cultured cells to document the cellular changes during and following treatment with excess thymidine to induce synchronization.

The cells used were of the CMP cell line,[1,2] an established human epithelial cancer line derived in 1964 from a biopsy of a metastatic adenocarcinoma from Charles M. Pomerat. It seems appropriate to acknowledge an indebtedness to him not only for his self-sacrificing attitude, which prompted him to insist that part of his tumor biopsy be used for cell cultivation, but also for his introducing me to the living cell in vitro. I first became acquainted with Dr. Pomerat's work at a special lecture he gave when I was an undergraduate biology student at the University of Houston in 1949. Fourteen years later I became actively involved in tissue-culture research as a colleague of Pomerat's at the Pasadena Foundation for Medical Research.

With regard to the use of thymidine to induce cell synchrony, workers have shown that it blocks DNA synthesis,[3,4] and, following release of the thymidine blockade—in practice, carried out as a sequential double thymidine sequence,[5,6] the cells begin the DNA synthetic phase. In this paper I will review some morphologic features (phase contrast) of these tumor cells while in thymidine and in the synchronized cell cycle which follows. The manuscript is based on a 16-mm film, "Dynamic Activities of the Synchronized Mammalian Cell Cycle—A Time-Lapse Study." The results presented here represent some of the highlights of the film. Abstracts from the film will demonstrate that 2.5 mmolar thymidine induces a number of cellular disturbances that are demonstrable in living cells[7]:

1. A rapid increase in cell and nucleus size.

2. Inhibition of mitosis.

3. Development of thin extensions of the cell membrane (attachment fibers), which undergo unusually rapid and vigorous movements.

4. Zeiosis, or "boiling" of the cell membrane.

5. Production of small, dense nucleoli.

The cell cycle that follows the double thymidine synchronizing technique has the following characteristics:

1. A gradual increase in the size and activity of nucleoli from the early to late S phase.

2. Elongation of cells, increased membrane activity, and zeiosis in the $G_2$ phase.

3. A highly synchronized mitotic burst of more than 70% of the population at approximately 10 to 11 hr.

4. Production of $G_1$-phase cells that are mobile, have active membranes, display pinocytosis, and produce reversible attachment fibers or microspikes from the cell membrane.

## MATERIAL AND METHODS

The CMP cells are grown in Rose chambers and synchronized by a sequential double blockage with thymidine as described previously.[8] Briefly, the technique involves treatment of exponentially growing cells for 24 hr with 2.5 mmolar thymidine (thymidine-1). At the end of this time, the blockage is released by washing the cells in balanced salt solution (BSS) and incubating them in normal medium for 15 hr (postwash-1). A second thymidine blockage is imposed for 24 hr (thymidine-2). At the end of this time, cells are washed with BSS and placed in normal medium (postwash-2), at which time DNA synthesis ensues.[9] Randomly growing cells are used as controls. The phase-contrast and cinematographic equipment and techniques are described elsewhere.[10-12] Briefly, all photomicrographs were taken of CMP cells in Rose chambers at 37°C with phase-contrast optics. Figures 1 to 4, 6 to 8, and 10 are abstracts from 16-mm film records. The original 16-mm film was copied onto 35-mm negatives, which were then printed to a 5- by 7-in. size. Figure 10 was photographed directly on 4- by 5-in. film. Figures 2, 3, and 6 are derived from films taken with double-microscope units outfitted to photograph each image on half a single 16-mm film frame. Analysis of the 16-mm film records has been facilitated by a photo-optical data analyser. The photomicrographs shown are largely abstracts derived from the movie presented at the symposium.

## RESULTS

### Control Cells

Untreated CMP cells grow as flattened epithelial cells, which may form small colonies and tend to merge. The individual cells contain a large, prominent nucleus with several dense nucleoli, many cytoplasmic granules, occasional filamentous mitochondria, and active cell membranes that can form ruffled folds or thin filamentous extensions (Figs. 1 to 3). Occasionally, giant cells are observed which are mono- or multinucleated. The cell-cycle time is approximately 28 hr, according to growth curves and analyses of film records where cells are followed from one mitosis to the next.

### Effects of Thymidine

When excess thymidine is added to cells, the first change observed is an increase in cell and nucleus size. This change becomes apparent in the first few hours. Figure 2 illustrates the uniform, round appearance of nuclei in thymidine medium and their tendency to be slightly larger than nuclei in control cells. Cells that happen to be in mitosis when thymidine is added invariably complete division. After a few hours there are no further mitoses. This inhibition of mitotic entry is especially dramatic when viewed side-by-side with randomly growing cells.

Of special interest to "nucleologists" are certain dynamic changes in nucleoli. Recorded on film are some examples of nucleolar divisions as well as fusions, observed particularly in thymidine-treated cultures. Since similar phenomena are occasionally seen in untreated cells, it could not be proved from this work that there is a causal relation to the presence of thymidine. These film sequences were shown in the original film but will not be considered further in this paper. However, it should be noted that thymidine-blocked cells exhibit unusually small nucleoli with dense zones at their margins after prolonged exposure to the metabolite.

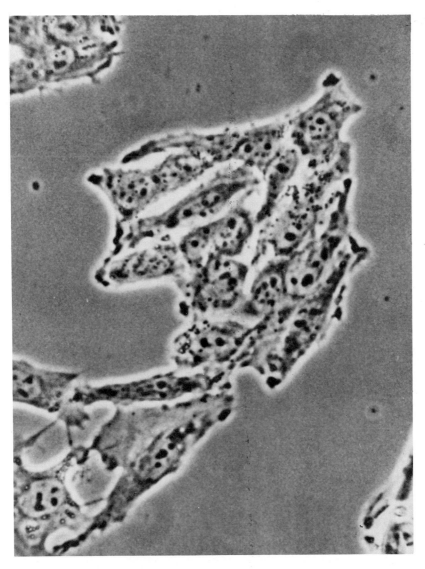

Fig. 1 Field of untreated CMP cells at 36 hr in vitro. 25x obj., no ocular, 1 frame/min taking rate.

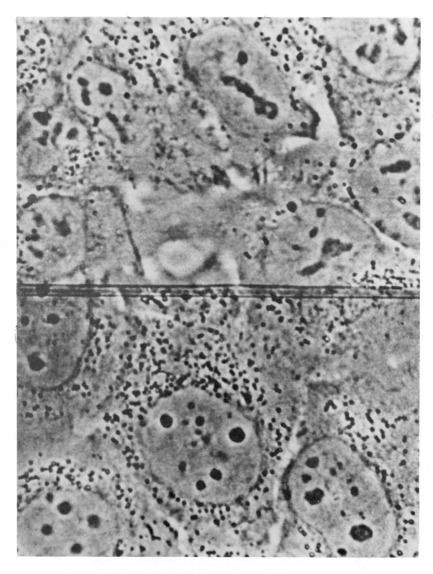

Fig. 2   Upper-field: control cells. Lower-field: cells after 24 hr in thymidine-2. Note that treated cells have slightly enlarged nuclei and dense nucleoli. 40× obj., 6× ocular, 2 frames/min taking rate.

A number of multinucleated giant cells are seen in the thymidine-2 medium, but their significance is uncertain since normal cultures also contain some giant cells. One of the most striking cellular effects of thymidine is on the activity of cell membranes. Two distinct responses are detected in living cells. One is the formation of multiple fibrous extensions of the cell membrane, which are referred to as attachment fibers, microspikes, intercellular bridges, or microvilli. I prefer to use the term attachment fibers or microspikes, since most of the other terms have been used by electron microscopists to describe specialized structures not ordinarily visible by light microscopy in living cells. Attachment fibers develop with great rapidity from the cell membranes of many kinds of cultured cells and may disappear as quickly. The fibers are of varying length and tend to be less than 0.5 $\mu$m in width. They attach at their tips—which are often enlarged—to other cells or to the surface of the substrate on which the cells are growing. In thymidine, large numbers of attachment fibers form, which appear knotty and under tension. They exhibit unusually vigorous and rapid to-and-fro movements. This highly energetic activity is best appreciated in the original movie sequence. However, an isolated example of this activity is shown in the film abstract of Fig. 3, which was photographed simultaneously with untreated cells on a double-microscope apparatus.

A second membrane response to thymidine is an energetic blebbing, or boiling of cell membranes (zeiosis). An example is shown in Fig. 4. The single film abstract demonstrates the phase-dense membrane ruffles, although it does not produce the total visual impact of the boiling phenomenon. This activity is commonly seen in cultured cells at the onset of and during mitosis. In the presence of thymidine, boiling is induced in cells that never advance into mitosis.

## Synchronized Cells

A mild synchrony is induced by thymidine-1 pretreatment, but this is not adequate for our needs. The second thymidine block causes a much better degree of synchrony, judging from both the 95+% of cells labelled with radioactive thymidine soon after release of the second block (Fig. 5) and the mitotic burst that occurs later.

The S phase encompasses the first 8 hr in the postwash-2 medium. These cells are slightly larger than many control cells and display small, dense multiple nucleoli (Fig. 6). In the second part of the S phase, nucleoli become larger. In one film sequence a nucleolus hypertrophies and produces a nucleolar cap. In the period immediately preceding mitosis ($G_2$), the cells become more active in terms of their movements and membrane activity. The cells develop a narrow, elongated appearance, in contrast to the broad, flattened shape seen in the S phase. Another feature of $G_2$-phase cells is boiling at the cell membranes. Examples of typical cells in $G_2$ are shown in Figs. 7 and 8.

The mitotic burst usually occurs in this cell line at about 10 to 11 hr postwash. As cells enter mitosis, they become spherical and fall away from the

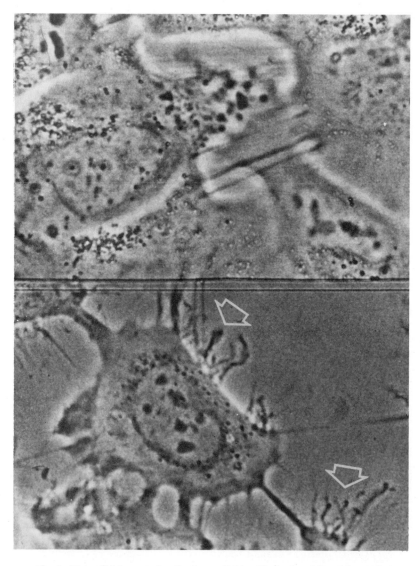

Fig. 3    Upper-field: control cells. Lower-field: cells in thymidine-2 for 10 hr.
Arrows mark attachment fibers in violent activity. 40× obj., 6× ocular,
2 frames/min taking rate.

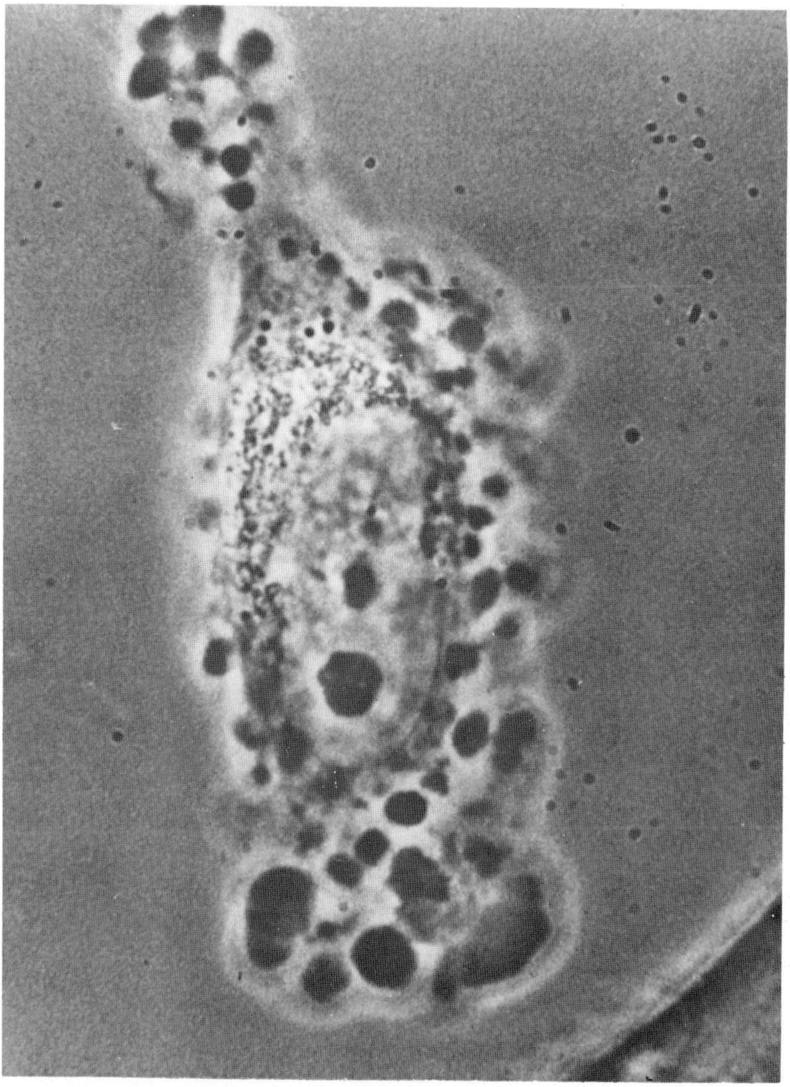

Fig. 4   Single cell after 24 hr in thymidine-2. Cell membrane shows zeiosis, or boiling. 100x obj., 6x ocular, 4 frames/min taking rate.

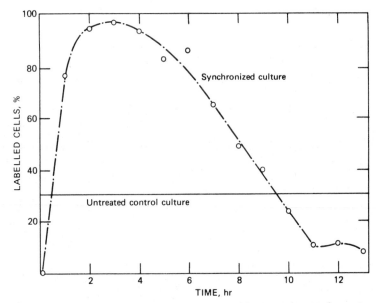

Fig. 5  Percentage of synchronized CMP tumor cells labelled with $^3$H—TdR
for 1 hr in normal medium after final blockage in 2.5 mmolar unlabelled
thymidine. Time 0 hr occurs 1 hr after blocked cells are placed in normal
medium. The unusually high level of synchrony is especially well demonstrated in the early- and mid-S phase (0 to 5 hr) by the rapid and almost 100%
labelling rate. During the G$_2$ (8 to 10 hr) and M (10 to 11.5 hr) phases,
synchrony drops to 85 to 90%. [From F. H. Kasten and F. F. Strasser, Amino
Acid Incorporation Patterns During the Cell Cycle of Synchronized Human
Tumor Cells, in *The Nucleolus, Its Structure and Function*, W. S. Vincent and
O. L. Miller, Jr. (Eds.), National Cancer Institute Monograph 23, p. 356,
1966.]

glass substrate. The number of isolated round cells outlined by halos with
phase-contrast optics is an indicator of mitotic activity in fresh cultures. The
mitotic burst involves as much as 70% of the entire population at any one time
when cover-slip preparations are fixed and stained at regular intervals. Since
some dividing cells are preferentially lost during fixation, the division rate is
probably greater than 70%. Large numbers of dividing cells can be collected at
the mitotic burst (thymidine-spray technique)[13,14] and studied directly or used
to initiate a G$_1$-synchronized population. An example of cells isolated in
metaphase is shown in Fig. 9.

Following mitosis, membranes appear around the cell margins. These
G$_1$-phase cells start out as relatively small and narrow elements, with new
membranes appearing primarily at the ends of each cell. In the first several hours
after daughter cells form, they are quite mobile and move actively over the glass
surface. Their membranes exhibit the heightened activity that accompanies

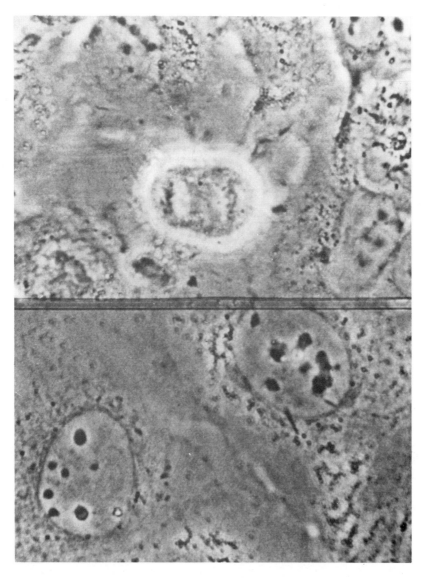

Fig. 6  Upper-field: control cells with a single cell in mitosis. Lower-field: cells in S phase (7 hr postwash). 40× obj., 6× ocular, 2 frames/min taking rate.

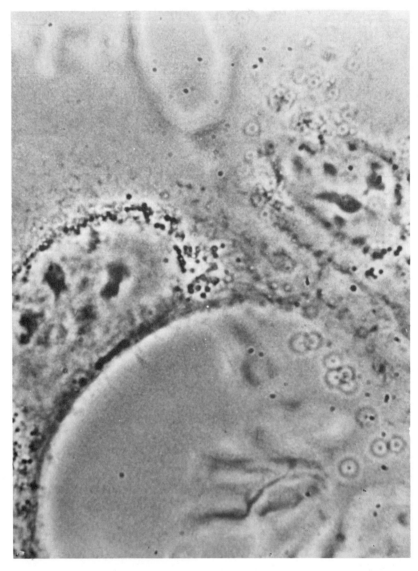

Fig. 7  The $G_2$-phase cells at 10 hr postwash. Note membrane activity. 100x obj., 6x ocular, 4 frames/min taking rate.

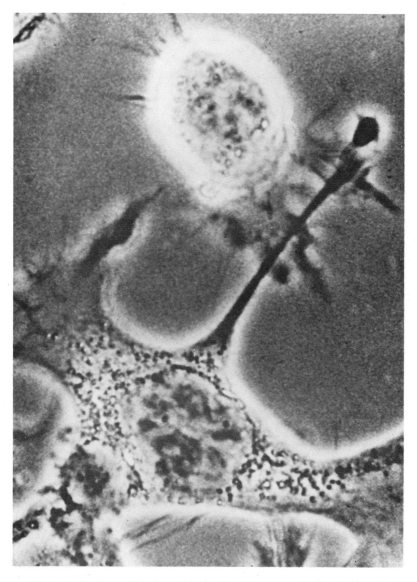

Fig. 8  A $G_2$-phase cell and one in mitosis at 9 hr postwash. Premitotic cells tend to elongate prior to rounding up. 100x obj., 6x ocular, 2 frames/min taking rate.

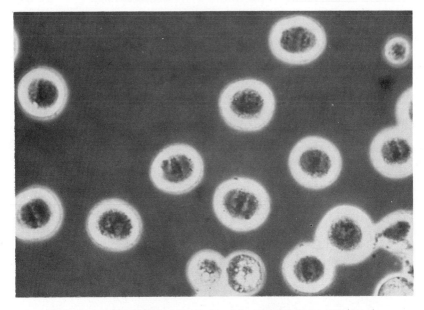

Fig. 9  Field of metaphase cells isolated from thymidine-synchronized
cells at mitotic burst (11 hr postwash) by spraying glass surface with medium.
40x obj., 1.25x Optovar (Zeiss), 590x final magnification.

pinocytosis. In addition, numerous microspikes appear and disappear rapidly
from the broad undulating membrane surface (Fig. 10), similar to what is seen in
the $G_2$ phase and during thymidine treatment.

## DISCUSSION

A variety of techniques have been developed to induce synchrony of
mammalian cells in culture. The technique employed here uses an inhibitor,
thymidine, which acts on cells in the DNA synthesis phase. The mechanism
involves the production of a high level of thymidine triphosphate. This produces
an inhibition of components in the pathway to deoxycytidine triphosphate, an
essential precursor of DNA.[4] The inhibition is reversed by washing the cells or
by adding deoxycytidine or serum, which apparently contains sufficient
deoxycytidine to reverse the block.

There has been some discussion in the literature about what happens to
other cell processes during and after thymidine inhibition of DNA synthesis (see
the discussion by Mitchison[15]). While cell multiplication decreases or ceases, it
has also been reported that mitotic abnormalities occur and chromosomes are
damaged.[16,17] Other workers have found that the thymidine treatment induces

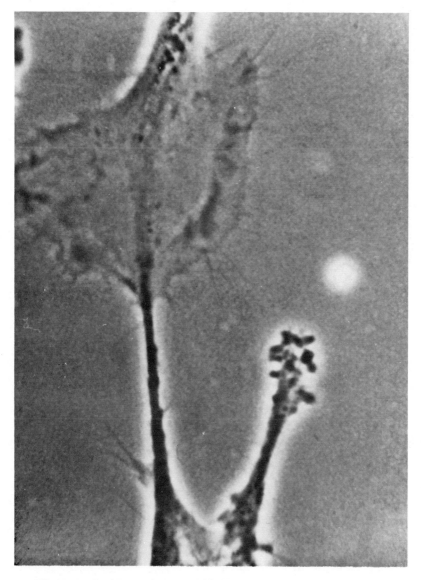

Fig. 10  Interesting membrane activities in $G_1$-phase cells. Upper-cell shows broad undulating surface with fine microspikes. Lower-cell displays zeiotic blebs. 100× obj., 6× ocular, 2 frames/min taking rate.

altered time periods in the subsequent cell cycle.[16,18,19] This does not seem to be the case for the CMP cells, at least with respect to the time taken to traverse S, $G_2$, and M. There is evidence that protein synthesis continues in the presence of excess thymidine,[20,21] but there is some disagreement about whether RNA synthesis goes on unabated[21] or is depressed.[8,22] In any case, there is some kind of unbalanced growth. The film records indicate that excess thymidine causes cells to be slightly enlarged, perhaps as a result of protein synthesis. These enlarged cells are present at the beginning of the S phase when the block is removed. Of interest to us is whether or not the synchronized S phase is altered as a consequence of continued protein and possible RNA synthesis. It seems unlikely that the S phase is abnormal because the time to traverse $S + G_2$ is about 9 to 10 hr and the mitotic burst occurs when expected, i.e., 10 to 11 hr. Also, nuclear DNA content is doubled during the 8-hr period following release of the block, according to cytophotometric measurements of Feulgen-stained cells.[23] It is therefore concluded that synchronous CMP cell cultures made by double-thymidine blockages are not distorted with respect to the S phase or with premitotic events. Mitchison has discussed the fact that "... there are two dissociable cycles in the growing cell—the DNA-division cycle and the growth cycle." He emphasizes the need to analyze the effects of specific inhibitors on both cycles, which are independent of each other.

Although excess thymidine exerts its primary effect on DNA synthesis, the observations on living cells indicate that this natural metabolite has a marked influence on cell membranes. It is shown that thymidine induces a violent boiling at the cell surface as well as the formation of attachment fibers, which likewise undergo vigorous movements. It is not known whether these membrane responses result from direct effects of the compound or are mediated indirectly through biochemical alterations elsewhere in the cell. At the concentration used (2.5 mmolar), there was no cell death detected. Attention is directed to the general review of thymidine metabolism by Cleaver.[24]

With regard to the induced synchrony, the film records indicate that the nucleolus undergoes a hypertrophy in the late S phase. In parallel experiments on these cells, it was shown by autoradiography that significant changes in DNA and RNA metabolism occur in the intranucleolar and perinucleolar regions during the S phase.[9] It would be surprising if some of these macromolecular events were not accompanied by visible changes. For example, in one sequence a nucleolus is observed to extrude a cap of medium-dense material that remains attached to the organelle. Since the cell is in the late S phase, it is unlikely that the nucleolar extrusion is caused by thymidine. It should be noted, however, that nucleolar segregation occurs following administration of various anti-metabolites and antibiotics.[25] Is it possible that the nucleolar extrusion observed here is a normal phenomenon which takes place during a very brief part of the cell cycle and has been previously overlooked in randomly growing cultures? More examples of such nucleolar segregation in normal cultures need to be found to pursue this idea further.

The one other main point that bears mentioning is the fact that cell membranes undergo dynamic changes during the cell cycle. As mentioned earlier, the membranes are sensitive to thymidine. The repertoire of visible responses by membranes is limited; hence, some of the same membrane responses observed in excess thymidine are seen at discrete times during the cell cycle ($G_2$, early $G_1$). Hand in hand with these surface membrane changes are accompanying phenomena, such as changes in cell shape and pinocytosis. In support of these observations of increased membrane activity during $G_1$ and $G_2$ is a report based on scanning electron microscope studies of cultured cells.[26] It was shown that during $G_1$, cells display numerous microvilli, blebs, and ruffles; only the ruffles persist in the S phase. During $G_2$ microvilli increase in number. Kraemer[27] has suggested that throughout the cell cycle there occur conformational or terminal complex changes of sialoglycolipids or sialoglycopeptides on the cell surface. These sialic acid components are thought to chelate calcium ions at the surface, thereby altering the surface charge. For fuller discussions of cell-membrane and cell-surface changes during the cell cycle, see some recent reviews.[15,28]

Any method of inducing cell synchrony which disturbs normal metabolism needs to be examined carefully. The excess-thymidine technique produces a variety of physiologic disturbances, but these seem to be reversed following removal of the metabolite. Judging from the results presented plus other autoradiographic studies, it is considered that there occurs an essentially normal cell cycle (S, $G_2$, M, early $G_1$) following double thymidine synchronization of CMP cells.

## ACKNOWLEDGMENTS

The research for this paper was supported by U. S. Public Health Service research grants CA-12067 from the National Cancer Institute and NS-09524 from the National Institute of Neurologic Diseases and Stroke, grant HL-15103 (Specialized Center of Research) from the National Heart and Lung Institute, and Training Grant 5-T01-DE-0024 from the National Institute of Dental Research. The assistance of Fredy Strasser, Barry Morgan, and Diane Thouron is acknowledged.

## REFERENCES

1. R. J. Bovis and F. H. Kasten, Preliminary Observations of CMP Cells, a New Human Tumor Epithelial Cell Line, *J. Ultrastruct. Res.,* **13**: 567 (1965).
2. Y. Ohnuki, T. Okigaki, and F. H. Kasten, A New Human Tumor Epithelial Cell Line (CMP-Cell Line), *In Vitro,* Vol. 4, p. 153, Williams & Wilkins Company, Baltimore, Md., 1969.
3. N. Xeros, Deoxyriboside Control and Synchronization of Mitosis, *Nature,* **194**: 682-683 (1962).

4. G. A. Gentry, P. A. Morse, and V. R. Potter, Pyrimidine Metabolism in Tissue Cultures Derived from Rat Hepatomas. III. Relationship of Thymidine to the Metabolism of Other Pyrimidine Nucleosides in Suspension Cultures Derived from the Novikoff Hepatoma, *Cancer Res.*, **25**: 517-524 (1965).

5. D. Bootsma, L. Budke, and O. Vos, Studies on Synchronous Division of Tissue Culture Cells Initiated by Excess Thymidine, *Exp. Cell Res.*, **33**: 301-309 (1964).

6. D. F. Peterson and E. C. Anderson, Quantity Production of Synchronized Mammalian Cells in Suspension Culture, *Nature*, **203**:642-643 (1964).

7. F. H. Kasten and F. F. Strasser, Dynamic Activities of the Synchronized Mammalian Cell Cycle: A Time-Lapse Study, *J. Cell Biol.*, **35**: 150A (1967).

8. F. H. Kasten, F. F. Strasser, and M. Turner, Nucleolar and Cytoplasmic Ribonucleic Acid Inhibition by Excess Thymidine, *Nature*, **207**: 161-164 (1965).

9. F. H. Kasten and F. F. Strasser, Nucleic Acid Synthetic Patterns in Synchronized Mammalian Cells, *Nature*, **211**: 135-140 (1966).

10. C. G. Lefeber, Modular Design for Time-Lapse Cinemicrography, in *Cinemicrography in Cell Biology*, G. G. Rose, (Ed.), pp. 3-26, Academic Press, Inc., New York, 1963.

11. F. H. Kasten, C. M. Pomerat, and I. Rappaport, Cinematography, Phase-Contrast and Fluorescence Microscopy of Human Thyroid Tumors in Tissue Culture with Observations of Virus-Like Lesions, *Texas Rep. Biol. Med., Suppl. 1*, **23**: 337-370 (1965).

12. F. H. Kasten, Rat Myocardial Cells *in vitro*: Mitosis and Differentiated Properties, in *Symposium on Functional Differentiated Culture Systems*, F. H. Kasten (Ed.), *In Vitro*, Vol. 8, pp. 128-149, Williams & Wilkins Company, Baltimore, Md., 1972.

13. F. H. Kasten, Demonstration of Isolated Synchronized Populations of Mitotic Cells, *J. Ultrastruct. Res.*, **21**: 167-168 (1967).

14. F. H. Kasten, Use of a Thymidine-Spray Technique to Yield Highly Synchronized, Isolated Cell Populations in Mitosis, *J. Cell Biol.*, **35**: 153A (1967).

15. J. M. Mitchison, *The Biology of the Cell Cycle*, pp. 26-33, Cambridge University Press, New York, 1971.

16. H. Firket and P. Mahieu, Synchronisme des divisions induit dans des cellules HeLa par un excès de thymidine. Etude des perturbations éventuelles du cycle cellulaire, *Exp. Cell Res.*, **45**: 11-22(1966).

17. S-J. Yang, G. M. Hahn, and M. A. Bagshaw, Chromosome Aberrations Induced by Thymidine, *Exp. Cell Res.*, **42**: 130-135 (1966).

18. G. Galavazi, H. Schenk, and D. Bootsma, Synchronization of Mammalian Cells *in vitro* by Inhibition of DNA Synthesis. 1. Optimal Condition, *Exp. Cell Res.*, **41**: 428-437 (1966).

19. R. A. Tobey, E. C. Anderson, and D. F. Peterson, The Effect of Thymidine on the Duration of G1 in Chinese Hamster Cells, *J. Cell Biol.*, **35**: 53-59 (1967).

20. J. H. Kim, S. H. Kim, and M. L. Eidinoff, Cell Viability and Nucleic Acid Metabolism After Exposure of HeLa Cells to Excess Thymidine and Deoxyadenosine, *Biochem. Pharmacol.*, **14**: 1821-1829 (1965).

21. G. P. Studzinski and W. C. Lambert, Thymidine as a Synchronizing Agent. 1. Nucleic Acid and Protein Formation in Synchronous HeLa Cultures Treated with Excess Thymidine, *J. Cell Physiol.*, **73**: 109-118 (1969).

22. R. B. Painter, R. M. Drew, and R. E. Rasmussen, Limitations in the Use of Carbon-Labelled and Tritium-Labelled Thymidine in Cell Culture Studies, *Radiat. Res.*, **21**: 355-366 (1964).

23. F. H. Kasten, The Potential of Quantitative Cytochemistry in Tumor and Virus Research, in *Introduction to Quantitative Cytochemistry-II*, G. L. Wied and G. F. Bahr (Eds.), pp. 263-296, Academic Press, Inc., New York, 1970.

24. J. E. Cleaver, *Thymidine Metabolism and Cell Kinetics*, pp. 93-96, Wiley-Interscience, Inc., New York, 1967.

25. W. E. Bernhard and N. Granboulan, Electron Microscopy of the Nucleolus in Vertebrate Cells, in *The Nucleus*, A. J. Dalton and F. Haguenau (Eds.), Vol. 3, pp. 81-149, Academic Press, Inc., New York, 1968.
26. K. Porter, D. Prescott, and J. Frye, Changes in Surface Morphology of Chinese Hamster Ovary Cells During the Cell Cycle, *J. Cell Biol.*, **57**: 815-836 (1973).
27. P. M. Kraemer, Configuration Change of Surface Silic Acid During Mitosis, *J. Cell Biol.*, **33**: 197-200 (1967).
28. R. A. Tobey, D. F. Petersen, and E. C. Anderson, Biochemistry of G2 and Mitosis, in *The Cell Cycle and Cancer*, R. Baserga (Ed.), pp. 309-353, Marcel Dekker, Inc., New York, 1971.

# INVESTIGATION OF FETAL ANTIGEN
# IN CHICKENS WITH AMV-INDUCED LEUKEMIA

BOB G. SANDERS,* RAY L. TEPLITZ,† ANNA M. BRODETSKY,‡ HENRY FUNG,‡ and
KAY L. WILEY*
*The University of Texas, Zoology Department, Austin, Texas, †Department of
Cytogenetics, City of Hope Medical Center, Duarte, California, and ‡Department
of Microbiology, California State College, Long Beach, California

## ABSTRACT

A red-blood-cell fetal antigen is present on the hemopoietic cells of chickens, especially the red blood cells, at pre- and posthatching. The antigen is lost with development but reappears on the peripheral red blood cells of chickens with AMV-induced leukemia. A genic repression—derepression hypothesis was postulated to account for the disappearance and subsequent reappearance of the fetal antigen. A second fetal—adult marker, hemoglobin, was used to investigate the genic repression—derepression hypothesis. Adult leukemic chickens were found to express the fetal antigen on their red blood cells; however, only adult hemoglobin was present in these cells. The fetal antigen was found to be expressed on the membranes of red-blood-cell precursors in the bone marrow of all chickens, including adult nonleukemic chickens. The expression of the fetal antigens on the membranes of red-blood-cell precursors raised the possibility that the reappearance of the fetal antigen on the red blood cells of adult leukemic chickens may not involve genic repression—derepression but may involve instead either (1) release of preerythrocytes that were blocked in the process of differentiation or maturation such that the cells continued to express the fetal antigen or (2) release of preerythrocytes expressing the fetal antigen into the peripheral blood owing to the progression of the leukemic condition. Both of these hypotheses are attractive in leukemia studies since additional red-blood-cell markers may be useful in detecting and monitoring leukemia in the early stages.

The genic expression of fetal products in tumors of adult animals, especially man, has attracted considerable attention over the past few years. The reason for this interest is that embryonic cells have several characteristics of tumorous cells, i.e., rapid cell division, high nuclear—cytoplasmic ratio and high RNA content. Further, the reexpression of an embryonic or fetal gene product on the cell membrane of tumors of adult animals might not induce an immune response toward the aberrant cells. The tumorous animal might be expected to exhibit immune tolerance to an antigen that had been expressed previously in early embryonic or fetal development. Thus, an understanding of fetal tumor antigens is of utmost importance.

Fetal tumor antigenic systems have been studied in several vertebrates, including man,[1-4] hamsters, and mice.[5-8] The most thoroughly studied system of fetal tumor antigens is the carcinoembryonic antigen (CEA) originally reported by Gold[3] in humans in which an antigen is present in early embryonic development, disappears with development, and reappears with the onset of carcinoma of the colon in adults. Carcinoembryonic antigen is somewhat more complex than originally thought since it has been found in varying levels in individuals having no evidence of carcinoma. Fetal tumor antigenic studies in several laboratories have been concerned with the characterization of CEA,[1,4] with the perfection of sensitive assays for measuring the occurrence of the antigen, and with use of these assays for early detection and monitoring of the progress of tumors before and after treatment.[2]

Unfortunately, little information is presently available on the cell type(s) involved in producing fetal antigens in animals bearing tumors or on the genetic mechanism(s) responsible for the reappearance of a fetal antigen. The chicken fetal leukemia antigen system is proposed as a model to investigate fetal-leukemia antigens.

In the chicken fetal leukemia antigen system, an antigen localized to peripheral red blood cells was found present at the time of hatching, disappeared with chick development,[9,10] and reappeared on the peripheral red-blood-cell membranes of adult chickens with AMV-induced leukemia,[11] thus rendering the chicken fetal leukemia antigen system a viable model for investigating regulatory control of fetal leukemic antigens.

This study is a continuation of earlier studies[9,10] with a primary objective of investigating a gene repression—derepression hypothesis to explain the appearance of a fetal antigen in adult leukemic chickens. The fetal leukemia antigen and fetal adult hemoglobin differences were used to investigate the repression—derepression hypothesis. Evidence is presented to demonstrate that proerythrocytes in the bone marrow of normal adult chickens possess the fetal antigen. A cell differentiation or cell maturation blockage hypothesis will be offered as a possible alternative hypothesis to explain the reappearance of the fetal antigen in adult leukemic chickens.

## MATERIALS AND METHODS

Details of the techniques employed are given in earlier papers.[9,10] Randomly bred white rock chickens were used throughout the study. Antisera were produced in rabbits against the red blood cells of 1-day-old chicks. The chicks were bled by heart puncture, and blood was collected in Alsevers solution. The cells were washed three times in 0.75% saline. The rabbits were given biweekly intravenous injections of 0.1 to 0.5 ml of a 20% suspension of red blood cells for a total of seven injections. One week after the last injection, the rabbits were bled for antisera. The antisera were made monospecific for the young-chicken (1 to 6 weeks old) red-blood-cell antigens by adsorption of the antisera with washed, packed red blood cells from adult chickens. The adsorbed antisera reacted with red blood cells from embryonic chicks and young chickens (1 to 6 weeks old) but did not react with the red blood cells of adult chickens (120 days old or older).

The agglutination and hemolytic assays described in Refs. 9 and 10 were used to determine the presence or absence of the fetal antigen in various ages of chickens as well as in adult chickens with AMV-induced leukemia.

Acute myeloblastotic leukemia was induced in chickens with the BAI strain A of avian myeloblastosis virus (AMV) using a procedure described by Baluda.[12] One-day-old chicks were inoculated intraperitoneally (i.p.) with a single injection of approximately $1.0 \times 10^6$ infective units of AMV. Peripheral blood smears stained with Giemsa were examined at weekly intervals to monitor the onset and progress of leukemia. Red blood cells were examined at weekly intervals by agglutination and/or hemolytic assays to determine the disappearance of the fetal antigen and its subsequent reappearance on the red blood cells of adult leukemic chickens.

Acrylamide gel electrophoresis of hemoglobin was performed on the red blood cells obtained from different aged chickens. Hemoglobin samples were prepared as follows: Red blood cells in anticoagulant were collected by heart puncture from chickens of various ages; the cells were washed three times, lysed with an equal volume of distilled water, and centrifuged at 16,000 rpm for 10 min to remove the cellular debris. The acrylamide gel electrophoresis techniques for determining fetal–adult hemoglobin differences and for monitoring the hemoglobin type present in adult leukemic chickens have been described.[13]

Bone-marrow samples were taken from 3-, 30-, 120-, and 180-day-old chickens. The chickens were killed by exsanguination, the rib bones were removed, and the bones were flushed with Tyrode's balanced salt solution using a syringe and needle. The bone-marrow cells were washed three times in Tyrode's solution, and the red-colored cells that packed on the bottom of the centrifuge tube during centrifuge were made into a 2% suspension in 0.75% saline; these cells were then tested by agglutination for the presence of the fetal antigen. Inhibition assays were performed to determine the degree of specificity by adsorbing the antisera specific for young-chicken red blood cells with packed red blood cells obtained from the bone marrow. The adsorbed antisera were then assayed by agglutination for the presence of antibodies specific to the fetal antigen using a 2% suspension of red blood cells from a 3-day-old chicken. Non-bone-marrow-adsorbed antisera and red blood cells from a 3-day-old chicken served as the positive control. Acrylamide gel techniques were used to determine the electrophoretic properties of hemoglobin of bone-marrow cells.

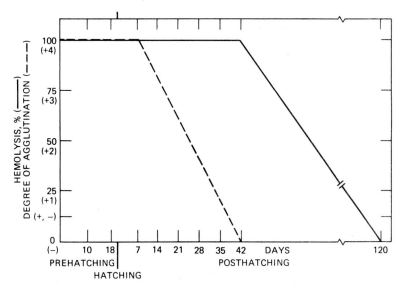

**Fig. 1** Presence of the fetal antigen on the red blood cells of different-aged chickens.

## RESULTS

By means of the adsorbed antisera specific for the red blood cells of young chickens used in the agglutination and hemolytic assays, the peripheral blood of chickens at various ages was assayed for the presence of the fetal antigen. The disappearance of the fetal antigen from the peripheral red blood cells is depicted in Fig. 1. The less sensitive agglutination assay shows the red blood cells of chickens to possess the fetal antigen at 10 days prehatching and up to 6 weeks posthatching. Red blood cells from embryos younger than 10 days were not assayed. At approximately 2 weeks posthatching, the degree of reactivity (as denoted by +4, +3, +2, +1) begins to decrease rapidly, and at 42 days posthatching the chickens were classified as negative for the fetal antigen. However, the more sensitive hemolytic assay demonstrated that the disappearance of the fetal antigen from the cells and the appearance of cells not expressing the antigen was a gradual process. All red blood cells expressed the antigen from 10 days prehatching until 40 days posthatching; at approximately 40 days posthatching, a small number of cells not expressing the antigen could be detected, and at 120 days posthatching the chicken red blood cells were adult-like; i.e., no cells possessing the fetal antigen could be detected.

Table 1 shows the effects of AMV-induced leukemia on the reappearance of the fetal antigen in chickens that received an inoculation with AMV at 1 day posthatching. The onset of leukemia in the chickens was variable. However, several chickens inoculated at 1 day posthatching expressed clinical symptoms of

TABLE 1

REAPPEARANCE OF THE FETAL ANTIGEN IN CHICKENS
WITH AMV-INDUCED LEUKEMIA

| Age of chickens, days | No. of chickens studied | No. of chickens giving a positive agglutination reaction | Degree of agglutination reaction (+4,−) | RBC agglutinated, % |
|---|---|---|---|---|
| 3 | 35 | 35/35 | +4 | 100 |
| 180 (nonleukemic) | 20 | 0/20 | Neg. | 0 |
| 180 (leukemic) | 33 | 10/33 | +2,+1 | 5−20 |

leukemia after 120 days (the fetal antigen was absent from the normal red-blood-cell membranes by this time). Such leukemic chickens were shown to reacquire the red-blood-cell fetal antigen as adults. Red blood cells from normal young chickens (1 to 40 days old) possess the fetal antigen; adult chickens (120 days old or older) do not normally express the fetal antigen on their red blood cells. However, adult (120 days old or older) chickens with AMV-induced leukemia reexpressed the fetal antigen in varying degrees. First, as measured by the agglutination assay, only one-third of the chickens (10/33) expressed the antigen, although all chickens (33) were shown to have clinical symptoms of leukemia and died shortly thereafter from the disease. Second, the degree of reactivity of red blood cells from leukemic adult chickens was extremely weak; i.e., a +2 reaction was the highest reaction recorded. Third, a large number of the red blood cells (80 to 95%) were not agglutinated by the antibody reagent. Thus, these studies on the reappearance of the fetal antigen on the peripheral red blood cells obtained from leukemic chickens demonstrated that some of the red blood cells in the peripheral blood possess the antigen. Counts of the number of cells agglutinated in relation to those not agglutinated indicated that individual chickens exhibited 5 to 20% agglutination of their red blood cells; the remainder of the cells remained free floating as individual cells. The hemolytic assay was used with blood samples from six of the adult chickens previously shown by the agglutination assay to possess the fetal antigen (Table 2). Data from the hemolytic assay were in agreement with the agglutination-assay data in that only a portion (5 to 25%) of the adult leukemic chicken red blood cells possessed the antigen. It should be pointed out that the chickens died soon after the antigen was found on their red blood cells. Thus, the serological studies demonstrated that a fetal antigen on the membrane of red blood cells obtained from young chickens did reappear on the peripheral red blood cells obtained from adult chickens with AMV-induced leukemia.

Hemoglobin was used as a second red-blood-cell marker in the study. Adult–fetal hemoglobin differences have been reported in several verte-brates.[14-16] Embryonic hemoglobin has been demonstrated in turkey and partridge,[17] in white Peking duck,[18] and in the house sparrow.[19] There is

TABLE 2

PRESENCE OF THE FETAL ANTIGEN AS MEASURED
BY THE HEMOLYTIC ASSAY

| Age of chickens, days | No. of chickens studied | No. of chickens expressing fetal antigen | Degree of reaction (hemolysis), % |
|---|---|---|---|
| 3 | 10 | 10/10 | 100 |
| 180 (nonleukemic) | 10 | 0/10 | 0 |
| 180 (leukemic) | 6 | 6/6 | 5−25 |

TABLE 3

HEMOGLOBIN PATTERNS OF DIFFERENT-AGED CHICKENS
AND OF CHICKENS WITH AMV-INDUCED LEUKEMIA*

| Prehatching | | | | Hatching | | Posthatching | | |
| 2 day | 5 day | 7 day | 8 day | 20 day | 14 day | 180 day (adult) | 180 day (leukemic adult) |
|---|---|---|---|---|---|---|---|
| $E_3$ | $E_3$ | $E_3$ | $E_3$ | $E_3$ | | | |
| | | | $A_1$ | $A_1$ | $A_1$ | $A_1$ | $A_1$ |
| $E_4$ | $E_4$ | $E_4$ | | | | | |
| | $A_2$ | $A_2$ | $A_2$ | $A_2$ | $A_2$ | $A_2$ | $A_2$ |
| | | | | $E_6$ | $E_6$ | $E_6$ | $E_6$ |

*E, embryonic. A, adult.

controversy over whether embryonic hemoglobins are present in chickens; however, several investigators have presented evidence in the form of multiple bands to demonstrate fetal−adult hemoglobin difference.[16,17,20-26] Data obtained from acrylamide gel electrophoresis of hemoglobin from chickens at various ages of embryonic development are shown in Table 3. Hemoglobin from 2-day embryos possessed two major bands, designated $E_3$ and $E_4$ (designations taken from a paper by Schalekamp et al.,[25] in which major and minor hemoglobin bands were described). A minor hemoglobin band ($E_6$) was detected in 14-day embryos and persisted throughout adulthood. Hemoglobin $E_3$ was detectable in 2-day chick embryo red blood cells and was present up to 20 days posthatching. Hemoglobin $E_4$ was detectable in 2-day embryos and was present up to the 7th day of embryonic development. The first adult hemoglobin (designated $A_2$) was detectable at 5 days of embryonic development and was present throughout adult life. The second adult hemoglobin ($A_1$) was detectable at the 8th day of embryonic development and was present throughout the life of the adult chicken. Thus, by electrophoretic means we can detect five hemoglobin

TABLE 4

DETECTION OF FETAL ANTIGENS AND HEMOGLOBIN PATTERNS OF
BONE-MARROW RED BLOOD CELLS FROM DIFFERENT-AGED CHICKENS

| Age of chickens, days | Agglutination of RBC | Assay after adsorption | Hemoglobin patterns |
|---|---|---|---|
| 3 | +4 | – | $E_3, E_4$ |
| 20 | +2 | – | $E_3, E_6, A_1, A_2$ |
| 120 | +2 | – | $E_6, A_1, A_2$ |
| 180 | +2 | – | $E_6, A_1, A_2$ |

patterns from the peripheral blood of chickens: $E_3, E_4$ ; $E_3, E_4, A_2$ ; $E_3, A_1, A_2$ ; $E_3, E_6, A_1, A_2$ ; and $E_6, A_1, A_2$.

Hemoglobins from chickens with AMV-induced leukemia exhibited three hemoglobin bands that were electrophoretically identical to hemoglobins $E_6, A_1$, and $A_2$. Further, the hemoglobin obtained from the lysis of red blood cells possessing the fetal antigen contained only hemoglobins $E_6$, $A_1$, and $A_2$. Attempts to examine the hemoglobin patterns of individual red blood cells have not been successful in our laboratory. Therefore, the possibility of the presence of fetal hemoglobin cannot be eliminated.

An examination of the bone marrow of chickens of different ages by means of the agglutination assay demonstrated that the bone-marrow red blood cells possess the fetal antigen (Table 4). The age of the chicken did not influence the number of cells agglutinated or the degree of agglutination, since hemopoietic cells from the bone marrow of adult chickens agglutinated similarly to those of younger chickens. Adsorption of antibodies specific for the fetal antigen with bone-marrow cells from chickens of different ages rendered the antisera nonreactive when assayed with young-chicken red blood test cells, showing that the proerythrocytes in the bone marrow or some other cell type(s) contained the fetal antigen. Further, acrylamide gel electrophoresis of hemoglobin from preerythrocytes obtained from the bone marrow of adult chickens showed only the adult hemoglobin pattern.

## DISCUSSION

The chicken studies have demonstrated a fetal antigen on the red blood cells which is present at pre- and posthatching, disappears with aging,[9,10] and reappears in chickens with AMV-induced leukemia.[11] Antisera prepared against AMV do not react with the embryonic cells nor with the red blood cells of chickens with AMV-induced leukemia.[11] These studies indicated that the fetal antigen was not a component of the virus. A question arises as to how AMV might affect the erythroid cell line since AMV induces myeloblastotic leukemia and supposedly does not directly involve the erythroid cell line. One hypothesis is that the myeloid and erythroid cells originate from the same stem cells. Thus, viral infection and/or viral transformation infecting cells of either the myeloid or the erythroid cells line could lead to the expression of fetal antigens on the red blood cells of adult leukemic chickens. A model for this is seen in human chronic granulocytic leukemia in which red and white precursors both contain the Philadelphia chromosome.[27,28] As a working hypothesis, the loss and subsequent reappearance of the antigen on the membrane of red blood cells was postulated to be the result of gene repression—derepression. Several aspects of the study did not support the repression—derepression hypothesis. First, the appearance of the fetal antigen in leukemic chickens was highly variable; i.e., some leukemic chickens did not express the fetal antigen on their peripheral red blood cells; other leukemic chickens were variable in the expression of the antigen (5 to 25% of the red blood cells expressed the antigen). Assuming a repression—derepression hypothesis to be correct, one would explain the data by postulating that only a small number of stem cells were influenced by the virus; therefore, one would not expect to obtain large numbers of red blood cells expressing the fetal antigen. However, not detecting the antigen on the peripheral red blood cells until shortly before the time that the leukemic conditions became evident is difficult to correlate with a repression—derepression hypothesis. Unfortunately, the animals died soon after detection of the fetal antigen and, therefore, were not studied over an extended period to determine if the number of red blood cells expressing the fetal antigen increased with time.

The fetal—adult hemoglobin electrophoretic differences were investigated to further explore the repression—derepression hypothesis. The assumption was that if the red blood cells from leukemic chickens were truly embryonic, then perhaps other gene-controlled fetal markers might also be expressed. The data showed that only adult hemoglobin was present in the red blood cells of adult leukemic chickens. Therefore, the red blood cells expressing the fetal antigen were not fetal cells in regard to the expression of fetal hemoglobin. However, all fetal genes may not be depressed in unison. Hence, additional embryonic—adult markers are necessary for a more complete examination of this possibility. Horton, Chernoff, and Meadows[29] reported an erythroleukemia patient with reduced amounts of $A_2$ adult hemoglobin but having about 60% fetal hemoglobin. They further point out that the hemoglobin profile of other types of leukemia may vary widely and that the red blood cells in certain individuals with leukemia may be more closely related to fetal than to adult.

Finding the fetal antigen on red-blood-cell precursors in the bone marrow of normal adult chickens suggested that mechanism(s) other than repression—derepression may account for the appearance of the fetal antigen on the peripheral red blood cells of adult leukemic chickens. According to Lucas[30] the bone marrow of the adult chicken has an abundance of mature erythrocytes.

The following cells of the erythrocyte series are found in the bone marrow of adult chickens: large early erythroblasts, erythroblasts, late erythroblasts, early polychromatic erythrocytes, mid-polychromatic erythrocytes, late polychromatic erythrocytes, and normal mature erythrocytes. The late polychromatic erythrocytes and mature erythrocytes contain hemoglobin.[30] Thus, one may postulate that the fetal antigen is present on the membranes of late polychromatic erythrocytes and mature erythrocytes and that under leukemic conditions these cells are released into the peripheral blood. In adult leukemic chickens, an interruption of the mechanism(s) regulating release of cells from the bone marrow could result in the emergence of red blood cells still expressing the fetal antigen into the peripheral blood. Under normal conditions in adult chickens, the gene(s) controlling the expression of the fetal antigen on the membranes of red blood cells would be repressed before or during the release of the red blood cells into the peripheral blood. Further, the abundance of mature erythrocytes in adult bone marrow is not found in the bone marrow of embryonic chickens.[30] Thus, in the embryo and in the young chicken, morphologically mature erythrocytes of the bone marrow may be released into the blood stream while still expressing the fetal antigen. As the animal develops, the cells are retained in the bone marrow until the gene expressing the fetal antigen is repressed.

Antigens of normal tissue that are expressed at some stage in differentiation have been referred to as phase-specific antigens.[7] Although a blockage in differentiation could explain the chicken fetal antigen data, a genetic mechanism may not be necessary to explain the reappearance of the fetal antigen on the peripheral red blood cells. The progression of the leukemic state could force preerythrocytes into the peripheral blood. These two hypotheses, cell differentiation blockage and/or premature cell release, seem to be the most plausible. Another possible explanation is that the fetal antigen is made in white blood cells and is adsorbed onto the red-blood-cell membrane. Additional red-blood-cell markers may prove useful for early detection of leukemic conditions and for monitoring the progress of the tumor.

## ACKNOWLEDGMENT

The research for this paper was supported by National Institutes of Health grant CA12851.

## REFERENCES

1. J. E. Coligan, J. T. Lautewschleger, Marianne L. Egan, and C. W. Todd, *Immunochemistry*, 9: 377-386 (1972).
2. M. L. Egan, J. T. Lautewschleger, J. E. Coligan, and C. W. Todd, Radioimmune Assay of Carcinoembryonic Antigen, *Immunochemistry*, 9: 289-299 (1972).

3. P. Gold and S. O. Freeman, Specific Carcinoembryonic Antigens of the Human Digestive System, *J. Exp. Med.,* **122**: 467-481 (1965).

4. J. Krupey, P. Gold, and S. O. Freeman, Purification and Characterization of Carcinoembryonic Antigens of the Human Digestive System, *Nature,* **215**: 67-68 (1967).

5. J. H. Coggin and K. R. Ambrose, A Rapid In Vivo Assay for SV40 Tumor Immunity in Hamsters, *Proc. Soc. Exp. Biol. Med.,* **138**: 246-252 (1969).

6. J. H. Coggin, K. R. Ambrose, and N. G. Anderson, Fetal Antigen Capable of Inducing Transplantation Immunity Against SV40 Hamster Tumor Cells, *J. Immunol.,* **105**: 524-526 (1970).

7. J. H. Coggin, S. G. Harwood, and N. G. Anderson, Radiation-Enhanced Oncogenesis by SV40, *Proc. Soc. Exp. Biol. Med.,* **134**(4): 1109-1111 (1971).

8. R. Duff and F. Rapp, Reaction of Serum from Pregnant Hamsters with Surface of Cells Transformed by SV40, *J. Immunol.,* **105**: 549-561 (1970).

9. B. G. Sanders, Developmental Suppression of Fowl Red Blood Cell Antigens, *Genetics,* **52**: 471 (1965).

10. B. G. Sanders, Developmental Disappearance of a Fowl Red Blood Cell Antigen, *J. Exp. Zool.,* **167**(2): 165-177 (1968).

11. R. L. Teplitz, B. G. Sanders, A. M. Brodetsky, H. Fung, and K. L. Wiley, Fetal-Leukemic Antigen of Chicken Blood Cells, *Cancer Res.,* **34**: 1049-1053 (1974).

12. M. Baluda, The Role of the Bursa-Dependent Lymphoid Tissue in Oncogene by Avian Myeloblastosis Virus, *Virology,* **32**: 428-437 (1967).

13. J. Travis and B. G. Sanders, Haptoglobin Evolution: Polymeric Forms of HP in the Bovidae and Cervidae Families, *J. Exp. Zool.,* **180**: 141-148 (1972).

14. V. M. Ingram, *The Hemoglobins in Genetics and Evolution,* Columbia University Press, New York, 1963.

15. C. Manwell, Comparative Physiology: Blood Pigments, *Annu. Rev. Physiol.,* **22**: 191-244 (1960).

16. C. Manwell, C. M. A. Baker, J. D. Rolansky, and M. Foght, Molecular Genetics of Avian Proteins. II. Control Genes and Structural Genes for Embryonic and Adult Hemoglobins, *Proc. Nat. Acad. Sci. U. S. A.,* **49**: 496-503 (1963).

17. C. Manwell, C. M. A. Baker, and T. W. Betz, Ontogeny of Haemoglobin in the Chicken, *J. Embryol. Exp. Morphol.,* **16**: 65-81 (1966).

18. T. A. Borgese and J. F. Bertles, Hemoglobin Heterogeneity: Embryonic Hemoglobin in the Duckling and Its Disappearance in the Adult, *Science,* **148**(3669): 509-511 (1965).

19. F. M. Bush and J. I. Townsend, Ontogeny of Hemoglobin in the House Sparrow, *J. Embryol. Exp. Morphol.,* **25**: 33-45 (1971).

20. V. D'Amelio and A. M. Salvo, The Serological Specificity of Chicken Hemoglobin Fractions, *Z. Naturforsch.,* **146**: 455-457 (1959).

21. V. D'Amelio and A. M. Salvo, Further Studies on the Embryonic Chick Hemoglobin. An Electrophoretic and Immunoelectrophoretic Analysis, *Acta Embryol. Morphol. Exp.,* **4**: 250-259 (1961).

22. V. D'Amelio, The Globins of Adult and Embryonic Chick Hemoglobin, *Biochim. Biophys. Acta,* **127**: 59-65 (1966).

23. C. R. Denmark and K. W. Washburn, Hemoglobin Types in Chick Embryos with Different Adult Hemoglobin Genotypes, *Poultry Sci.,* **48**: 464-474 (1969).

24. K. Hashimoto and F. H. Wilt, The Heterogeneity of Chicken Hemoglobin, *Proc. Nat. Acad. Sci. U. S. A.,* **56**: 1477-1484 (1966).

25. M. Schalekamp, M. Schalekamp, D. V. Goor, and R. Slingerland, Re-Evaluation of the Presence of Multiple Haemoglobins During the Ontogenesis of the Chicken, *J. Embryol. Exp. Morphol.,* **28**: 681-713 (1972).

26. D. Schurch, J. Godet, V. Nigon, and J. P. Blanchet, Electrophorese des hemoglobines de poulet sur gel de polyacrylamide, *Experientia,* **24**: 548-549 (1968).

27. J. Trujillo and S. Ohno, Chromosomal Alteration of Erythropoietic Cells in Chronic Myeloleukemia, *Acta Haematol.*, **29**: 311-316 (1963).
28. J. Whang, E. Frei, III, J. H. Tjio, P. P. Carbone, and G. Brecher, The Distribution of the Philadelphia (Ph) Chromosome in Patients with Chronic Myelogenous Leukemia, *Blood,* **22**: 664-673 (1973).
29. B. F. Horton, A. I. Chernoff, and R. W. Meadows, The Hemoglobin Profile and Erythroleukemia, *Cancer,* **26**: 904-910 (1970).
30. A. M. Lucas, and C. Jamroz, *Atlas of Avian Hematology,* Agriculture Monograph 25, U. S. Department of Agriculture, Washington, 1961.

# CELL-CYCLE VARIATIONS IN ONCOGENIC TRANSFORMATION IN SYNCHRONIZED MOUSE EMBRYO CELLS IN CULTURE

JOHN S. BERTRAM* and CHARLES HEIDELBERGER†
McArdle Laboratory for Cancer Research, University of Wisconsin,
Madison, Wisconsin

## ABSTRACT

Malignant transformation has been induced by $N$-methyl-$N'$-nitro-$N$-nitrosoguanidine (MNNG) in the C3H/10T1/2 CL8 line of mouse-embryo fibroblasts synchronized by three different procedures. Treatment of cells at various times after release from arginine or isoleucine deficiency or from postconfluence inhibition of cell division resulted in a maximum transformation frequency in cells treated between 4 hr prior to S phase and the $G_1$/S boundary. No differences have been detected in either the rate of binding of tritiated MNNG to logarithmic phase cells in comparison to cells blocked in $G_1$ of the cycle or in the extent and stability with time of binding to cells in the sensitive and insensitive phases of the cell cycle.

For many years work at the McArdle Laboratory for Cancer Research has been directed at elucidating the mechanism of action of the oncogenic hydrocarbons. Because investigations in vivo impose severe limitations on the experimental procedures that may be attempted, recent work has used cultured fibroblasts originally obtained from C3H mouse prostates.[1] More recently we have developed a new fibroblastic cell line, designated C3H/10T1/2 CL8 and derived from C3H mouse embryos, which is highly sensitive to postconfluence inhibition of cell division[2] and in which morphologically transformed foci are produced in a quantitative manner in response to oncogenic hydrocarbons. These foci are malignantly transformed because the cells produce sarcomas on injection into X-irradiated syngeneic mice.[3] This paper describes the production of cell-cycle synchrony in C3H/10T1/2 CL8 cells and the cell-cycle dependency of malignant

---

*Present address: Department of Experimental Therapeutics, J. T. Grace, Jr., Cancer Drug Center, Roswell Park Memorial Institute, Buffalo, N. Y.

†American Cancer Society Professor of Oncology.

transformation in response to $N$-methyl-$N'$-nitro-$N$-nitrosoguanidine (MNNG).[4] Also described are preliminary investigations of binding of MNNG to these cells.

## MATERIALS AND METHODS

### Cell Cultures

Stock cultures were maintained in Eagle's basal medium supplemented with 10% fetal-calf serum.[2] Cells for the synchrony and transformation studies were grown in roller bottles to a state of postconfluence inhibition of cell division.

### Synchrony

Synchrony was induced (1) by amino acid deficiency. Cells were harvested and plated ($10^5$ cells/dish) in arginine- or isoleucine-deficient medium supplemented with 10% dialyzed fetal-calf serum. After 48 hr they were released from the block by replacement of deficient medium with complete medium. Synchrony was also achieved (2) by release from postconfluence inhibition of cell division. Confluent cultures were trypsinized and plated ($10^5$ cells/dish) in complete medium. In both cases progression through the cell cycle was monitored by measuring the incorporation of tritiated thymidine ($^3$H–TdR) into acid-insoluble material and by cell counts.

### Transformation Studies

At various times after release from the cell-cycle block, replicate cultures were treated with 4 $\mu$g/ml of MNNG in acetone (Fig. 1). After about 3 weeks dishes were fixed, stained, and scored for malignantly transformed and total surviving colonies (Fig. 2). The morphological criteria and the verification of malignant transformation have been described.[3]

### Tritiated MNNG Binding Studies

MNNG$-$Me$[^3$H] , 73.5 mCi/mmole, was used throughout. Incorporation into acid-insoluble material was measured in replicate culture dishes by lysing cells with sodium dodecyl sulfate, precipitating macromolecules with 10% trichloroacetic acid, and filtrating the macromolecules on glass fiber disks. These disks were assayed for radioactivity by liquid scintillation counting.[5]

## RESULTS

Initiation of DNA synthesis after restoration of the deficient amino acid began after a 4-hr delay in both arginine- and isoleucine-deprived cells (Figs. 3 and 4). Cell division occurred between 10 and 14 hr after release in the isoleucine blocked cells (Fig. 4). These results confirm previous work in Chinese

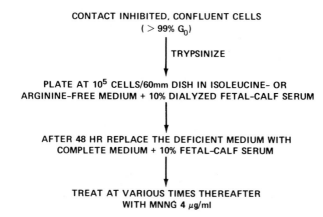

CONTACT INHIBITED, CONFLUENT CELLS
( > 99% $G_0$ )

TRYPSINIZE

PLATE AT $10^5$ CELLS/60mm DISH IN ISOLEUCINE- OR
ARGININE-FREE MEDIUM + 10% DIALYZED FETAL-CALF SERUM

AFTER 48 HR REPLACE THE DEFICIENT MEDIUM WITH
COMPLETE MEDIUM + 10% FETAL-CALF SERUM

TREAT AT VARIOUS TIMES THEREAFTER
WITH MNNG 4 μg/ml

Fig. 1 Protocol for induction of synchrony in C3H/10T1/2 CL8 cells by deprivation of arginine or isoleucine.

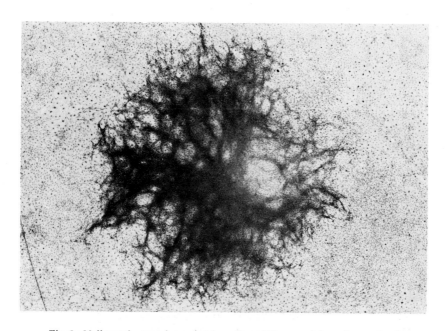

Fig. 2 Malignantly transformed colony in a dish treated 3 weeks previously with 4 μg/ml of MNNG. (Giemsa stain; magnification, 7x.)

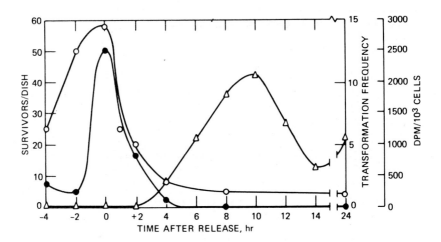

Fig. 3  Effects of 4 $\mu$g/ml of MNNG on cells synchronized by arginine deprivation. •, transformation frequency. ○, survivors per dish. △, incorporation of $^3$H—TdR into non-MNNG treated controls.[4]

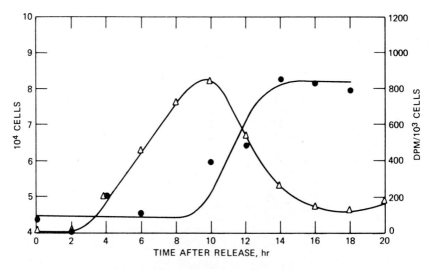

Fig. 4  Synchrony induced by releasing cells from 48-hr isoleucine deprivation. •, number of cells. △, incorporation of $^3$H—TdR.[4]

hamster cells deprived of isoleucine[6] and indicate that amino acid deficiency blocks cells in late $G_1$, approximately 4 hr from S phase. When cells were treated with MNNG at various times prior to, at the time of, or after release of the cell-cycle block, pronounced differences in transformation frequency (TF) were observed. The TF is here defined as the percentage of malignantly transformed colonies to the number of surviving colonies at each time point. In arginine-deprived cells the peak of TF occurred at the time of release of the block (Fig. 3); lesser values of TF were obtained in cells treated 4 hr prior to release of the block. In cells treated after release of the block, the TF declined progressively and reached a low level at 4 hr, when DNA synthesis was just beginning. The peak of TF observed in isoleucine-deprived cells was located 4 hr after release from the block; a second small peak was located just before the onset of the next round of DNA synthesis (Fig. 5). The reasons for these apparent differences in location of the sensitive phase for malignant transformation between the two synchronization procedures are not known. However, Chinese hamster cells are known to react differently to the effects of deprivation of these two essential amino acids.[6-8]

Cells released from postconfluence inhibition of cell division entered S phase after 12 to 14 hr and began to divide 20 hr after release (Fig. 6). Similar values

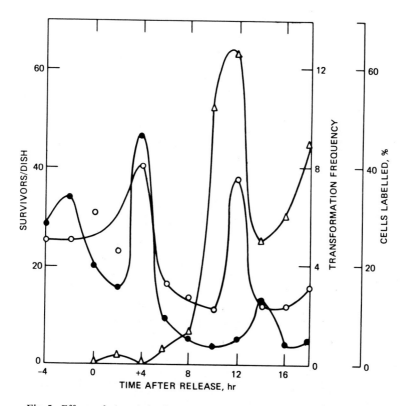

Fig. 5  Effect of 4 µg/ml of MNNG on cells synchronized by isoleucine deprivation. ●, transformation frequency. ○, survivors per dish. △, percent of cells labelled.[4]

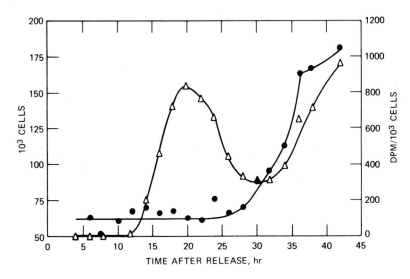

Fig. 6  Synchrony induced by releasing cells from postconfluence inhibition of cell division. •, number of cells. △, incorporation of $^3H-TdR$.[4]

have been published for 3T3 cells.[9] The peak in TF occurred between 8 and 14 hr after release, with a second peak of approximately equal magnitude located just prior to the next round of DNA synthesis (Fig. 7). This second peak is believed to represent the sensitive phase in the next cell-division cycle. These results, using three synchronization procedures, clearly demonstrate the cell-cycle phase specificity of malignant transformation induced by MNNG and locate the sensitive phase somewhere between 4 hr prior to S and the $G_1/S$ boundary. We are unable at present to locate the sensitive phase with greater accuracy than this since the half-life of MNNG under these culture conditions is 90 min and since there are some uncertainties about the exact position of the cells in the cycle.

We are currently investigating several possible explanations for this cell-cycle specificity. Lawley and Thatcher[10] have shown in hamster cells that the extent of MNNG-induced methylation of cellular macromolecules can vary according to the growth state of the cell cultures. Some preliminary experiments have been carried out in which the rate and the extent of methylation of cellular macromolecules have been measured in cells at various stages of the cell cycle.

The relationship between concentration of tritiated MNNG and binding to cellular macromolecules over a 4-hr treatment period in logarithmically growing cells is plotted in Fig. 8. The amount of MNNG ranges from nontoxic to the highly toxic concentrations that are required for malignant transformation. It is possible that the initial nonlinear portion of the curve is due to competition for MNNG or its activated derivative from nucleophiles present in the culture medium.

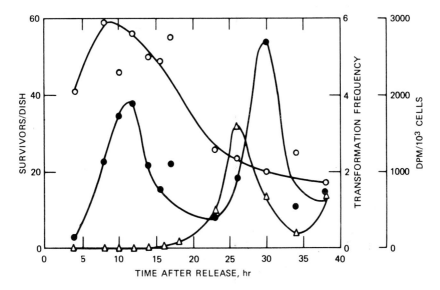

**Fig. 7**  Effect of 4 µg/ml of MNNG on cells released from postconfluence inhibition of cell division. ●, transformation frequency. ○, survivors. △, incorporation of $^3$H—TdR.[4]

The rate of binding of 4 µg/ml of tritiated MNNG was investigated next. No differences in the initial binding to cellular macromolecules over a 90-min period were found in cells blocked in $G_1$ by 48-hr arginine deprivation or in an equal number of cells in the logarithmic-growth phase (Fig. 9). However, the extent of binding to the logarithmically growing cells began to decrease after the initial 90-min period, which corresponds to the half-life of MNNG in the culture medium.[5]

Although no differences in initial rate of uptake could be demonstrated in logarithmic-growth phase cells vs. cells blocked in $G_1$ phase, it was possible that the binding during phases s⁻ ɪsitive and insensitive to malignant transformation might differ. Thus, we treated cells blocked by arginine deprivation with tritiated MNNG (4 µg/ml or 0.5 µg/ml) at various times prior to, at, and after restoration of arginine. Replicate cultures were treated for 2 hr or for 4 hr and then harvested, and the incorporation of tritium into acid-insoluble material was measured. No major differences were found in the radioactivity bound to cultures in the sensitive phase of the cell cycle (zero hours after release) or in cultures treated at insensitive phases (−4 or +4 hr after release) (Fig. 10).

These studies are being extended to examine the extent and stability with time of the alkylation of specific sites in cells treated in different stages of the cell cycle. We are also examining, in collaboration with A. R. Peterson (McArdle Laboratory), the rate of production and of rejoining of single-strand breaks in DNA induced by MNNG treatment at various stages of the cell cycle.

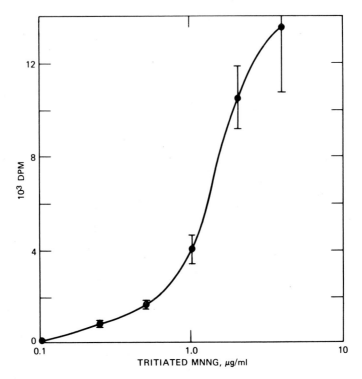

Fig. 8 Dose—response characteristics of the binding of tritiated MNNG to cellular macromolecules. Mean ± S. E.[5]

Little is known of the events immediately preceding DNA synthesis, which corresponds to the sensitive phase for malignant transformation induced by MNNG, except that protein synthesis is required for the transition from $G_1$ to S phase.[11,12] The most attractive interpretation for these results is phase specificity in the competence of cells to respond to the premalignant lesion or to repair premalignant damage. It is of interest that both MNNG-induced mutation in Paramecia[13] and X-ray induced lethality in Chinese hamster cells[14] show phase-specific variations, with maxima at the $G_1$/S boundary. Finally it should be noted that not all chemicals induce transformation at the same stage of the cell cycle; cytosine arabinoside, in particular, has been shown to be S-phase specific.[15]

## ACKNOWLEDGMENTS

The research for this paper was supported in part by grants BC-2C from the American Cancer Society and CA 07175 from the National Cancer Institute, National Institutes of Health.

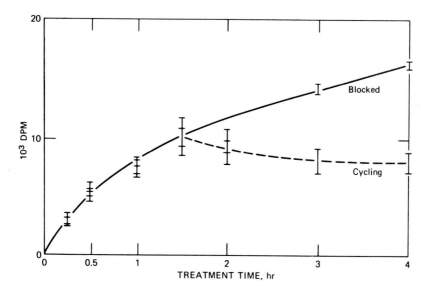

Fig. 9  Rate of binding of tritiated MNNG to cellular macromolecules in cells blocked in $G_1$ of the cell cycle by arginine deprivation (solid line) and in logarithmic-growth-phase cells (broken line). Mean ± S. E.[5]

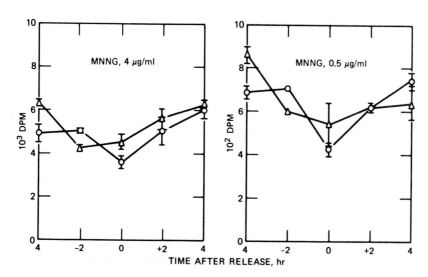

Fig. 10  Binding of tritiated MNNG to cellular macromolecules in cells treated at various times of the cell cycle. Mean ± S. E. △, binding after 2-hr treatment. ○, binding after 4-hr treatment.[5]

# REFERENCES

1. T. T. Chen and C. Heidelberger, *J. Nat. Cancer Inst.*, **42**: 915-925 (1969).
2. C. A. Reznikoff, D. W. Brankow, and C. Heidelberger, *Cancer Res.*, **33**: 3231 (1973).
3. C. A. Reznikoff, J. S. Bertram, D. W. Brankow, and C. Heidelberger, *Cancer Res.*, **33**: 3239 (1973).
4. J. S. Bertram and C. Heidelberger, *Cancer Res.*, **34**: 526 (1974).
5. J. S. Bertram and C. Heidelberger, submitted to *Cancer Res.*
6. R. A. Tobey and K. D. Ley, *Cancer Res.*, **31**: 46-51 (1971).
7. L. P. Everhart, *Exp. Cell Res.*, **74**: 311-318 (1972).
8. J. J. Freed and S. A. Schatz, *Exp. Cell Res.*, **55**: 393-409 (1969).
9. K. Nilausen and H. Green, *Exp. Cell Res.*, **40**: 166-168 (1965).
10. P. D. Lawley and C. J. Thatcher, *Biochem. J.*, **116**: 693-707 (1970).
11. D. P. Highfield and W. C. Dewey, *Exp. Cell Res.*, **75**: 314-320 (1972).
12. Y. Fujiwara, *Cancer Res.*, **32**: 2089-2095 (1972).
13. R. F. Kimball, *Mutat. Res.*, **9**: 261-271 (1970).
14. J. B. Little and G. M. Hahn, *Int. J. Radiat. Biol.*, **23**: 401-407 (1973).
15. W. F. Benedict, P. A. Jones, M. S. Baker, and J. S. Bertram, Proceedings of the XI International Cancer Congress, Florence Italy, October 20–26, 1974, in press.

# NEOPLASTIC DISEASE
# OF YAQUINA BAY BIVALVE MOLLUSKS

MICHAEL C. MIX
Department of General Science, Oregon State University, Corvallis, Oregon

## ABSTRACT

A cellular proliferative disorder that superficially resembles mammalian leukemia has been found in several species of pelecypod mollusks from Yaquina Bay, Oreg. This paper reviews the history of the disease, its cytomorphological and histopathological characteristics, molluscan oncoloy, and cell renewal and describes current research on the neoplastic disease of bivalve mollusks.

A disease with several serious implications and ramifications, the so-called neoplastic disease of Yaquina Bay bivalve mollusks (hereafter referred to as the neoplastic disease), has been found in several species of economically important shellfish in Yaquina Bay, Oreg.

This paper describes a comparatively new and expanding area of study—invertebrate oncology, or, to be more specific, molluscan oncology.

## HISTORY AND DESCRIPTION OF THE NEOPLASTIC DISEASE

### History

Yaquina Bay is a typical Oregon estuary. The bay is 22.5 km long and 0.16 to 1.6 km wide and is relatively free of industrial development or onshore human habitation except downbay near the town of Newport. It supports three commercial oyster companies all located approximately 10 km upbay from its confluence with the Pacific Ocean. In addition to the commercial enterprises, the bay is extremely popular with recreational or personal-use shellfishermen, who exploit a wide variety of clam species the year around.

Two races of *Crassostrea gigas* (the Pacific oyster and the Kumamoto oyster) and *Ostrea lurida* (the native or Olympia oyster) are raised by commercial oyster growers. Typically, *C. gigas* seed or spat (small, young oysters) are imported from Japan, allowed to grow 1 to 3 years on the commercial beds, and are harvested and sold, generally to local or regional establishments. All oyster companies raise *C. gigas,* and two of them market only this species. Native populations of *O. lurida,* confined primarily to the commercial growing areas, produce spat, usually during late spring or early summer spawning periods although sporadic spawning may occur through the summer. Currently, only one oyster company raises *O. lurida* commercially; a second company recently ceased marketing this oyster because of a continuing population decline of the species on its beds and the high production costs associated with its processing.

It has been thought for many years that significant mortalities of *O. lurida* occur annually (usually during the winter) in Yaquina Bay, but no systematic investigation of either mortality rates or the causes of mortality was conducted prior to 1962. Lack of documentation of these mortalities and criticism of the experimental design of recent studies on mortality have been the subjects of controversy among various individuals directly involved (e.g., oyster growers, scientists, and personnel from the Oregon Fish Commission). To illustrate this problem, I will cite results of extensive discussions on *O. lurida* mortality that I have had with the two oyster growers whose companies have raised *O. lurida* since the late 1800s; both are third-generation oystermen. Both agree that until the 1930s *O. lurida* was abundant on all oyster beds and that since then the populations have declined. The reasons for the decline are not known although infectious diseases, overexploitation, and the neoplastic disease have been offered as potential explanations. With regard to winter mortality, one of the growers (who still markets the oyster) claims his oysters do not and have not suffered this mortality, whereas the other, located almost directly across the bay, feels that his oysters are subjected to this mortality almost every year.

In 1962 Albert K. Sparks and his graduate students from the College of Fisheries, University of Washington, began investigating both *O. lurida* and *C. gigas* as part of a study (hereafter referred to as the UW study) in Washington, Oregon, and California on the distribution and pathological effects of a parasitic copepod, *Mytilicola orientalis.* The emphasis of this study was later changed to a general investigation of mortality rates and possible causes of mortalities from all pathological causes. Subsequently the (then) Bureau of Commercial Fisheries (BCF) began support of a mortality investigation by the Oregon Fish Commission in which stations were set up in various areas of Yaquina Bay and other bays in Oregon. In the BCF study both living and gaping (moribund oysters no longer capable of closing their shells)oysters (*C. gigas* and *O. lurida*) were collected and fixed by the Oregon Fish Commission and sent to the College of Fisheries for processing and diagnosis. One slide from each oyster was retained by the College of Fisheries, another was sent to the BCF Biological Laboratory, Oxford, Md., for confirmatory diagnosis, and a third was returned to the Oregon Fish Commission for their collection.

In the UW study a small float station was anchored off the dock of the Oregon Oyster Company. Pacific oysters were placed in two of the compartments, and native oysters and bay mussels (*Mytilus edulis*) were placed together in the last compartment of each basket. One hundred and fifty Pacific oysters and 100 each of the native oysters and bay mussels were placed in each basket. The float was constructed in such a way that the baskets of shellfish were under 0.5 to 0.8 m of water. Pacific oysters from the 1962 Japanese seed shipment and native oysters tonged from commercial beds were used for the original stocking of the station. Bay mussels were collected from pilings at the Oregon Oyster Company. Groups of native oysters were a composite of several age classes approximately 1 to 2 cm in shell length. Result [1] from both studies which are possibly related to the neoplastic disease are:

1. Pacific oysters in Yaquina Bay are subject to unusually low mortalities during the first 2 or 3 years in the area (<10%), low salinities during winter freshets being the principal cause of mortality.

2. There appeared to be presumptive evidence that a *Hexamita* species may cause mortalities of *O. lurida* in Yaquina Bay, although *Hexamita* may be a secondary invader of moribund oysters.

3. Peculiar cells originally thought to be a possible protozoan pathogen were frequently found in *O. lurida* from Yaquina Bay. The appearance of these cells seemed to correlate with mortality patterns in *O. lurida*, and the UW group thought the cells were a significant cause of high mortalities in this species in the area around the Oregon Oyster Company.

4. By 1969 Sparks and C. A. Farley of the BCF Biological Laboratory felt that the "peculiar" cells were apparently abnormal leucocytes and that the disorders represented a "leukemic" neoplasm of *O. lurida*. It was conceded that the possibility of parasitic involvement would not be completely eliminated.

5. Native oysters were consistently subjected to heavy mortalities, and replacement populations (100 oysters) were usually necessary after 1 to 1.5 years. A sharp mortality peak occurred shortly after the oysters were placed in the float in 1963 (30% within 3 months), and a steady mortality pattern was maintained until January 1965, when there was an abrupt peak in mortality rates. Since these oysters were transferred from a subtidal location to the float, it is possible that the early mortalities may have been due to handling or more probably to difficulties of the population in adjusting to the new environment. The sharp increase in mortalities in January 1965 may well have been caused by the reduction of salinity caused by flooding of the entire estuary. When a new population was introduced into the float in March 1965, there was again a sharp initial mortality, followed by a steady die-off until the end of 1967. Mortalities were generally heavier, however, during the fall, winter, and early spring months. It was the UW group's belief, based on examination of histological populations, that the major cause of mortality was the presumed neoplastic disease.

In conjunction with these studies, Farley[2] and Farley and Sparks[3] published descriptions of the neoplastic disease in *Mytilus edulis* and *O. lurida* from Yaquina Bay, Oreg., and *Crassostrea virginica* (American oyster) from eastern U. S. bays (locations were not given).

Goner,[4] in studies on reproductive cycles in Yaquina Bay bivalves, followed histological changes in the gonads of clams, mussels, and oysters (*Adula californica, Mytilus edulis, Mya arenaria, Macoma nasuta, Macoma irus,* and *O. lurida*). After consulting with personnel at the BCF Biological Laboratory, he felt that the neoplastic disease was present in some of his *O. lurida, Mytilus edulis, Macoma irus,* and *M. nasuta* samples.

No further studies were conducted on the neoplastic disease until 1972.

## Description of the Neoplastic Disease

Some investigators[3,5] feel that there is more than one type of "leukemoid" neoplasia in bivalves not only from Yaquina Bay but in several bays and estuaries throughout the United States (see Farley and Sparks[3] and Sparks[5] for reviews). However, many of the neoplastic diseases have been found in only a very small number of animals; thus, there is a limited amount of information available. Because of this and because most workers now seem to agree on cell and tissue characteristics which typify the Yaquina Bay neoplastic disease, this paper will be confined to descriptions given by Farley[2] for *M. edulis;* by Farley and Sparks[3] for the "vesicular type" in *O. lurida, M. edulis,* and *C. virginica;* and by Sparks.[5]

Bivalves affected by the neoplastic disease frequently exhibit one or more nonspecific gross signs, including poor condition, pale digestive diverticula, and mantle recession—all signs indicative of starvation.

The following were listed by Farley[2] as cellular characteristics of the neoplastic disease in mussels:

1. Morbid anatomical changes consisting of focal and diffuse collections of unusually large, generally round or ovoid cells of mesenchymal origin, possibly representing atypical hemocytes (leucocytes) (Figs. 1 to 4).

2. Nuclei of atypical cells two to four times larger than those of normal hemocytes.

3. Binucleate cells suggesting asynchronous division were common.

4. Nuclear chromatin was finely reticulated, and one to five nucleoli were usually observed in interphase nuclei.

5. Atypical cells collected mainly in the vesicular connective tissue (Leydig tissue) and in hemolymph sinuses of muscle and mantle tissues.

6. Dividing cells within the atypical aggregates appeared to contain excessive numbers of chromosomes, probably in polyploid ranges.

7. Tripolar and tetrapolar (mitotic) figures were observed as well as division figures showing displaced groups of chromosomes.

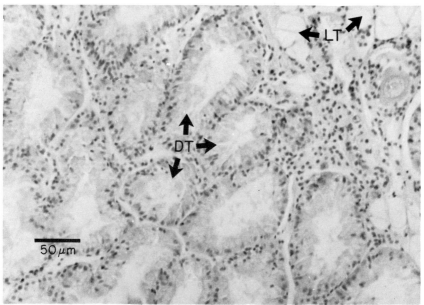

Fig. 1   Normal tissue of *Mytilus edulis*. DT, digestive tubules. LT, Leydig tissue. Small nuclei scattered throughout the connective tissue are leucocyte (hemocyte) nuclei.

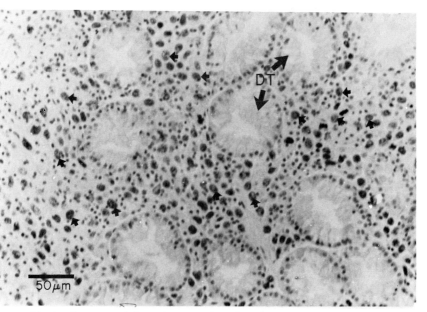

Fig. 2   Tissue containing a large number of neoplastic cells (small arrows). DT, digestive tubules.

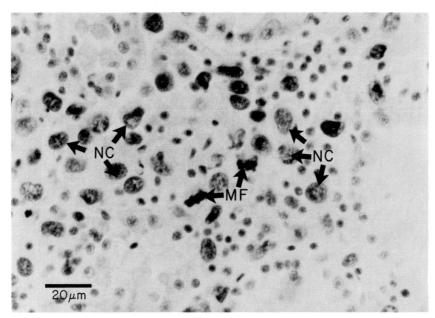

**Fig. 3** Tissue containing a large number of neoplastic cells. NC, neoplastic cells. MF, mitotic figures.

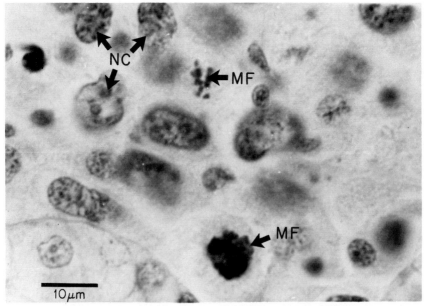

**Fig. 4** Neoplastic cells. NC, neoplastic cells. MF, mitotic figures.

Farley and Sparks[3] listed these characteristics for the disease (vesicular type) in *O. lurida, M. edulis,* and *C. virginica:* enlarged cells and nuclei two to four times the size of normal leucocytes and nuclei, irregular nuclear shapes and generally irregular (or variable) contours, binucleate cells (multinucleate cells are found rarely), increased density of chromatin, multiple nucleoli, pycnosis and nuclear lysis in advanced lesions, and presence of tripolar figures and polyploidy. They also indicated that there was some evidence that these neoplastic cells in *O. lurida* were dedifferentiated vesicular connective-tissue cells (Leydig cells) although they did not explain what this evidence was. They differentiated between vesicular-type neoplastic cells and hemocyte-type neoplastic cells. It seems that the vesicular type is now accepted as the neoplastic disease of bivalve mollusks in Yaquina Bay.

Histologically, these disorders are characterized by diffuse collections of abnormal, mitotically active cells, which invade and replace the Leydig tissue. Collections are sometimes evident first in the hemolymph vessels and sinuses and can be found commonly in the muscle and byssal tissues of mussels. Invasion of epithelia is uncommon but has been observed in *O. lurida* from Yaquina Bay.[3]

Farley and Sparks[3] state that in both *M. edulis* and *O. lurida* a peak prevalence of 12% occurred in December. Advanced cases were most common in the early winter (December), and both species showed apparent indications of mortality during this period.

## MOLLUSCAN NEOPLASIA AND CELL RENEWAL

Basically, problems and challenges associated with the neoplastic disease are related to the paucity of knowledge about normal and abnormal molluscan cellular processes, particularly cellular renewal, kinetics, and differentiation. It is evident that complete answers and solutions to problems related to the neoplastic disease must await an accretion of facts and descriptions of such cell processes. To facilitate subsequent discussion, I will briefly review two areas of molluscan research that are consociated to the problems posed by the neoplastic disease: neoplasia and cell renewal in mollusks. Clearly, a third topic, immunity, could be included, but it is beyond my competence. For reviews of cellular immunity in invertebrates, see Stauber,[6] Feng,[7] Tripp,[8] Salt,[9] Sindermann,[10] and Cheng and Rifkin.[11] For descriptions of invertebrate cellular defense mechanisms, see Sparks.[5]

### Molluscan Neoplasia

In spite of the relative plethora of published descriptions of molluscan, primarily pelecypod, neoplasms during the past decade (see Pauley[12] and Sparks[5] for reviews), most of the tumors or abnormal cell growths have only been described grossly and/or histologically after examination and analysis of (often improperly) fixed tissues. This is not surprising when one realizes that the majority of molluscan tumors have been found after shucking (removal of the animal from the shell) or during routine slide reading of tissue sections in conjunction with various studies or research programs unrelated to studies of neoplasia. Thus, since normal survival is not compatible with shell removal, it has not been possible to conduct more detailed and sophisticated analyses of cells or tissues associated with a tumor. It has been pointed out that what is observed in a relatively superficial morphological inspection of neoplasia with the light microscope is a very limited spectrum of cellular manifestations.[13] Therefore, extreme caution must be exercised when evaluating abnormal growths analyzed exclusively with this instrument.

Aside from this, there is a rather more serious problem—that of definitely classifying abnormal growths as being neoplastic. As Pauley[12] points out, the scarcity of information about neoplasms of mollusks and other invertebrates makes the distinction between neoplasia, hyperplasia, and response to injury or infection difficult to determine confidently because there are no trenchant established criteria to diagnose neoplasia in these animals.

The typical molluscan tumor is characterized by a polyp-like growth that contains relatively normal, recognizable cell types.[5] With few exceptions[2,3,14] mitotic figures, normal or abnormal, are scarce; therefore, it is assumed that growth is relatively slow. It has seldom been possible to ascertain whether growth of the tumor has stopped or retrogressed or whether it will progress, or already has progressed, to fatal termination.[5]

Virtually all discussions or analyses of invertebrate neoplasia dwell on the absence of definitive criteria for identification or classification of unusual cell growths or proliferations as neoplastic and malignant. A brief review of the salient points raised in connection with invertebrate neoplasia and an examination of criteria suggested by various researchers for evaluating abnormal growths illustrate the confusion and problems that currently exist in invertebrate oncology.

Scharrer and Lochhead[15] thought that invertebrate tumors were the result of abnormal cell proliferation. Further, they suggested that the terminology used in mammalian pathology should not be applied to the invertebrates until their comparative relationships are better understood, a suggestion often unheeded in papers on invertebrate tumors even though most invertebrate pathologists seem to agree in principle that such terms should be avoided.

Pauley[12] lists several criteria that could possibly be used in evaluating abnormal molluscan cell or tissue growth. These include the presence of any gross swelling or lump; expansion of a growth into normal tissues; infiltration, invasion, or replacement of normal tissues by atypical cell types or abnormal arrangements of cells as revealed by histological examination; the presence of mitotic figures within a suspect growth; and metastasis from a primary lesion. Pauley[12] feels that all these conditions, except metastasis, have been found in various tumors reported in oysters. Several papers have subsequently been published that describe invasive proliferative disorders of bivalve mollusks (Refs. 2, 3, 14, 16, and 17); however, it is not clear whether actual metastasis has occurred in these animals.

Sparks[5] explains that according to currently accepted medical usage the definition of a tumor is now virtually restricted to neoplasia characterized by autotomy or growth of cells or tissues independent from the normal laws of growth of the organism and that growth of the tumorous tissue not only is independent and excess of the normal tissue but persists at the same rate and pattern after termination of the stimulus that initiated the accelerated growth. However, he concedes that since the vast majority of invertebrate tumors are found in nature, it is usually impossible to determine whether the proliferation of tissue would persist at the same rate and in the same pattern if the stimulus initiating the proliferation were removed.

Dawe,[18] in a paper on invertebrate oncology, thought that opinion was still sharply divided concerning the authenticity of neoplasms in invertebrate phyla but that many accepted the universality of neoplasms among all metazoan animals. Good and Finstad,[19] for instance, in a challenge to participants of the National Cancer Institute symposium on neoplasms and related disorders of invertebrate and lower vertebrate animals held in 1969, proposed that malignancies in invertebrates lacking an immunologic system represented an essential incongruity and that the difficulties in finding or producing true malignant processes in invertebrates were a function of this incongruity. They also contended that true malignant adaptations do not occur or rarely occur among most invertebrates. Dawe also indicated that the available hard facts concerning anomalies of growth and form in invertebrates are few—a condition that still exists—and that a great deal of thoughtful work needs to be done before the significance of what is known can be clearly understood.

In recognition of the problems plaguing invertebrate pathologists, Dawe[18] tabulated a list of parameters he hoped would stimulate biologists to characterize neoplastic diseases or related disorders. These parameters are grouped under four major headings with several subdivisions and include macroanatomical characteristics [e.g., anatomic location, size, consistency, and invasion (gross)], microanatomical characteristics (e.g., lethality, responsiveness, growth rate, and progression), and microbiological characteristics (e.g., in vivo: transmissibility by infections agents, antigenic profile, and cell kinetics and in vitro: nutritional requirements, cloning efficiency, and gain or loss of antigens). It is indicative of our present nescience that, of the 65 parameters Dawe listed and including every molluscan tumor ever described, only 10 to 15 of the parameters have been described in detail.

Perhaps, in the final analysis, it is the invertebrate pathologists' lack of knowledge about normal molluscan cell renewal and kinetics that poses the greatest difficulty in evaluating neoplasia in animals of this phylum. Abnormal cell proliferation, the presence of mitotic figures within a suspected growth, and growth of cells or tissues independent from the normal laws of the organism were mentioned as potential evaluative criteria of neoplasia in invertebrates. Yet, to date, there have been, to my knowledge, only three studies[20-22] that attempt to analyze normal cell renewal systems and/or cell kinetics of any molluscan tissue except those associated with gametogenesis. As recently as 10 years ago, a paper was published with the central thesis that somatic mitosis in oysters (*Crassostrea virginica*) was rarely observed and that the paper constituted the first written report of epithelial mitosis in oysters! Although somatic mitoses may be rarely observed in *C. virginica*, such is certainly not the case for the two other commercial oyster species (*C. gigas* and *Ostrea lurida*) grown in the United States. It is usually possible to observe mitotic figures in all digestive tissues (stomach, gut, and digestive diverticula), gills, mantle, and blood cells in most histological sections. It seems unfortunate that a recent reviewer cited this paper and implied that the lack of mitoses was a general characteristic of molluscan tissues.

Yet, in spite of myriad problems and deficiencies, molluscan pathologists are gradually accumulating what will hopefully some day constitute a sufficient number of samples and examples to enable us to characterize neoplasia in this most fascinating group of animals. As Dawe[18] indicated,

> There exists a gap phylogenetically viewed in our knowledge of neoplasms and related disorders among the animals proximal to the fishes in time of evolutionary origin. If this gap is not soon filled, the advantages offered by study of these animals cannot accrue to cancer research until long after the time when they might have been exploited to the fullest.

## Molluscan Cell Renewal

Researchers have only recently become interested in normal cell kinetics and cell renewal systems in mollusks of commercial importance. Unfortunately, there have been few successful attempts to use autoradiography and tritiated thymidine ($^3$H–TdR) in studying cell renewal in mollusks.

Some work has been done with spermatogenesis in mollusks, but most of these studies did not use autoradiography. Beeman[23-25] has used autoradiographic techniques ($^3$H–TdR with a specific activity of 2.0 Ci/mmole and exposure times of 15 to 82 days) to study spermatogenesis, sperm storage and exchange, and stomach-tooth renewal in the sea hare (*Phyllaplysia taylori*).

During preliminary studies Cheney[20] obtained virtually no cell labelling in the Pacific oyster, *Crassostrea gigas*, or the blue mussel, *Mytilus edulis*, although he subsequently used $^3$H–TdR (3.0 Ci/mmole and exposure times of 2 to 3 weeks) to study the morphology, morphogenesis, and reactive responses of Manila clam (*Tapes semidecussata*) blood cells. The reason for this failure in *C. gigas* and *M. edulis* is not entirely clear since it is possible to observe numerous mitoses in several tissues of these animals. Cheney[20] and Mix[26] have speculated that *C. gigas* may have a relatively long period of DNA synthesis and slow cell turnover times.

Mix[21,26] and Mix and Sparks[27-29] have published a series of papers on the histopathological effects of gamma irradiation on various tissues of *C. gigas* and on tissue repair and cell renewal systems in the digestive tubules, gut, and gills. These studies comprise the bulk of what is known about cell renewal in bivalve mollusks. However, unless cells can be labelled and traced, little can be definitively stated about cell renewal systems and nothing can be said about the parameters of the cell cycle.

Mix and Tomasovic[30] used a very high specific activity $^3$H–TdR and the freshwater mussel, *Margaritifera margaritifera*. In preliminary studies clams weighing approximately 30 g each (excluding shell weight) were injected with 30 $\mu$Ci of $^3$H–TdR (1.0 $\mu$Ci/g; specific activity, 50.3 Ci/mmole; concentration, 30 $\mu$Ci/ml). The significant findings of this work include

1. Labelling was observed in all tissues studied—gut, stomach, digestive tubules, gills, and blood cells.

2. Labelled cells were first found 4 hr after injection.

3. Injections into the pericardial sinus or visceral mass were both effective means of introducing $^3$H–TdR.

4. It was necessary to expose the slides for only 3 to 5 days compared to exposure times of 15 days to 6 months in other studies of cell renewal in mollusks using low-specific-activity $^3$H–TdR.

Use of high-specific-activity $^3$H–TdR may hold great promise for elucidating molluscan cell renewal systems and cellular kinetics. Mix and Tomasovic,[30] however, pointed out some potential problems. High specific activity and high concentrations necessarily mean an increased radiation dose to cells and tissues, and such doses may alter normal cell renewal and cell kinetics. They also stated that because of relatively large radiation doses, there could be increased production of secondary products that would result in extraneous labelling although this did not occur in a recent study.[22]

Tomasovic and Mix,[22] in what may be the first detailed study of a molluscan cell renewal system, used high-specific-activity $^3$H–TdR (50.3 Ci/mmole and 56 Ci/mmole) and autoradiographic techniques to study cell renewal in the gill epithelium of the freshwater mussel *Margaritifera margaritifera*. This system is remarkably similar to that of the mammalian small intestine, and, surprisingly, the minimum transit time from the dividing transient population in the gill furrow to the gill ridge tip may be no more than 24 hr. Again, it must be emphasized that much work remains to be done to evaluate the usefulness of high-specific-activity $^3$H–TdR in molluscan work. Nevertheless, I feel that these studies represent a substantial beginning in our attempts to more fully understand normal cell renewal and cellular kinetics in mollusks.

Virtually nothing is known about cellular differentiation or dedifferentiation in mollusks. Establishment of molluscan cell lines would be of great help; however, attempts made with molluscan cell and tissue culture have been few and are concerned with a small number of species. There have been three trends in the development of molluscan tissue culture: the production of organ cultures, the culture of cells of those mollusks that are intermediate hosts for parasites or viruses, and the study of certain problems of cellular physiology proper to those species.[31]

To date, only maintenance culturing has been achieved and no molluscan cell lines yet exist. However, the National Institutes of Health has recently awarded grants to three west coast investigators who are attempting to establish such a cell line from tissues of the freshwater gastropod *Biomphalaria glabrata*.[32]

# CURRENT RESEARCH

To my knowledge, I am the only investigator currently conducting an on-going study of the neoplastic disease in Yaquina Bay. At least one individual (Goner[4]) is analyzing slides of various Yaquina Bay bivalves made during previous studies (unrelated to the neoplastic disease) to determine the existence and incidence of the disease in other shellfish populations.

Last year (1972) I received funds from the National Oceanic and Atmospheric Administration Sea Grant to establish a research program that will hopefully supply information for analyzing the effects of the neoplastic disease on at least one commercially important bivalve, *Ostrea lurida,* and to gather data that may provide clues relative to its etiology. For further clarification specific objectives of the study are listed:

1. To determine if the neoplastic disease occurs in native and imported oyster populations in Yaquina Bay.

2. To determine if there are differences in the occurrence and incidence of the disease in native and imported *O. lurida* raised in Yaquina Bay.

3. To determine if the disease occurs in imported populations in all areas of the bay.

4. To determine if there is a seasonality in the occurrence of the disease and if there is any correlation with location in the bay.

5. To determine if the disease causes mortality.

6. To further characterize the histopathology of the disease at the light-microscopic and ultramicroscopic levels.

7. To determine with autoradiography if cellular dedifferentiation does occur and, further, to determine the origin of the neoplastic cell. In addition, all other pathological conditions are being described, analyzed, and cataloged.

In June 1972, 19,500 *O. lurida* spat (2 months old) were obtained commercially; the age of all oysters was known as well as the source of the parental stock, also obtained commercially. Oysters were placed in trays located at six sites in Yaquina Bay, one site in Alsea Bay, and one site on the Olympia Oyster Company grounds. Sites in Yaquina Bay are located at the Marine Science Center boat dock (1.30 km upbay from the U. S. Highway 101 bridge); the location where some of Farley's samples apparently came from, Sawyer's Landing (5.13 km); the Fish Commission raft (7.66 km), a second apparent source of Farley's samples; the Oregon Oyster Company (9.80 km) (two trays, one on the bottom and the second suspended 1 to 1.5 m below the surface at the identical site used during the UW study); and the Oysterville Oyster Company (9.05 km). Sampling of 10 oysters from each Yaquina Bay site and from Alsea Bay began in October 1972 and has been continued on a monthly basis since that time. Oysters from Puget Sound are sampled quarterly. Twenty wild adult *O. lurida* from the commercial beds in Yaquina Bay and Puget Sound are also sampled quarterly. Beginning in October 1973, the sample size was doubled at sites on commercial oyster grounds, and 10 *Mytilus edulis* have been sampled from each of four locations in Yaquina Bay: on-bottom at the Oregon Oyster Company and the Marine Science Center boat dock and off-bottom (1 to 1.5 m below the surface) at both these locations. Also, the *O. lurida* populations were reduced in September to 500 oysters per tray to obtain more precise mortality data.

Each oyster is routinely fixed in Davidson's solution (formalin—acetic acid—alcohol—glycerin, modified with seawater), sectioned, and stained with Harris' hematoxylin and eosin, Heidenhain's iron-hematoxylin, or modified Gomoris' trichrome. Live material is also routinely examined by phase contrast microscopy and is stained with various vital and supravital stains.

Results of the first year, after analysis of approximately 700 oysters (samples through June 1973), are:

1. No oysters were found with histopathological symptoms of the neoplastic disease, nor were the large cells characteristic of the disease observed in any oyster.

2. There was no significant mortality at any location that could not be accounted for. There were significant mortalities caused by crab predation at two sites (Marine Science Center and Oysterville), and silting occasionally caused mortality; but, because of the initial large populations, this was not considered detrimental to the study.

3. A haplosporidian disease organism was discovered in samples from Alsea Bay and from all sites in Yaquina Bay except those maintained at the commercial oyster grounds.[33] This is the first report of a haplosporidian disease of *O. lurida* and perhaps of any *Ostrea* species.

The relevance and relationship, if any, of these findings to the neoplastic disease are discussed in the next section.

## UNANSWERED QUESTIONS

Except for descriptions based on observations with the light microscope of cellular and histological modifications manifested by the neoplastic disease, our ignorance of this abnormal condition is almost complete. I have listed four basic questions for which there are no complete answers.

*Is the neoplastic disease related to pelecypod epizootics, and, if so, in which bivalve populations and in which bays or estuaries does it occur?* Table 1

TABLE 1

SPECIES IN WHICH THE NEOPLASTIC DISEASE HAS BEEN
OBSERVED AND INCIDENCE OF THE DISEASE

| Species | Location* | Incidence, % | Numerical data† | Refs. |
|---------|-----------|--------------|-----------------|-------|
| *Mytilus edulis* | YB | 7 | 3/43 | Farley[2] |
| | YB | 12 | 7/57 | Farley[2] |
| | YB | 12 | None‡ | Farley and Sparks[3] |
| | YB | 5 | None | Goner[4] |
| *Ostrea lurida* | YB | 12 | None | Farley and Sparks[3] |
| | YB | 5 | None | Goner[4] |
| *Crassostrea virginica* | ECW | None given | None | Farley and Sparks[3] |
| *Macoma irus* | YB | 5 | None | Goner[4] |
| *Macoma nasuta* | YB | 5 | None | Goner[4] |

*YB, Yaquina Bay. ECW, east coast waters.
†Number with disease/total number.
‡Assumed to be the highest of the two values in Farley's earlier paper.[17]

summarizes the pertinent information necessary to analyze this question. Because of the notable absence of numerical data, it seems somewhat premature to conclude that this disease causes or represents an epizootic condition. Also, Farley's data[2,17] is based on only two samples, one collected in September 1968 and the other in February 1969. Clearly, this is an insufficient amount of information on which to determine incidence. Thus, the scanty evidence that is available suggests that approximately 5 to 10% of several localized populations of Yaquina Bay bivalves may have the neoplastic disease although it is unclear when during the year or where in the bay it occurs. The report that the disease has been found in *C. virginica* somewhere in east coast bays included no numerical data or bay locations.

*Does the neoplastic disease cause significant mortality in Yaquina Bay bivalve populations?* As discussed earlier, this question has caused controversy and confusion, primarily owing to lack of documentation. Farley[17] felt that the disease caused mortality in *M. edulis;* and Farley and Sparks[3] and Sparks et al.,[1] on the basis of mortality figures accumulated during the UW study, thought that the major cause of mortality of *O. lurida* was the neoplastic disease. Because of the abrupt mortality peaks that occurred whenever new (100 oysters) populations were transferred from the oyster grounds to the float, however, Sparks et al.[1] speculated that death might have been caused by handling or by difficulties the population had in adjusting to the new environment. Also, greatly reduced salinities, a frequent occurrence during the Oregon winters, may have contributed to the mortalities. The latter explanation should be seriously explored since I have found (Mix, unpublished research) that the freshwater which flows over the saltwater wedge during winter was always uniformly deeper than 1 m from the surface of the water over the oyster grounds. Thus, the oysters used in the UW study were positioned in the water column where they were subject to maximum influence by winter freshets. No natural populations of O. lurida or any commercially raised O. lurida are found anywhere except on the bottom of the bay. Thus, a great deal of caution should be used in extrapolating mortality data from the UW study to natural populations of O. lurida. The fact that I did not observe the disease or any mortality in O. lurida during the first year of my study should not yet be considered evidence as to whether mortality of this species does or does not occur. Goner[4] thought that the disease did not occur until oysters were 2 years old. Also, the UW study used O. lurida that were at least in their second year of life.

No other information (aside from my conversations with commercial oystermen discussed earlier) is available which would contribute to answering this question.

*What are the possible causes of the neoplastic disease?* It is difficult to even form hypotheses because of the paucity of factual data. Nevertheless, it is possible to fit some of the available information into a discussion of potential causes:

1. It has been maintained that this condition does not represent a neoplastic disease but is a normal host response to an unknown insult. It can only be said that every competent invertebrate pathologist who has examined the slides considers this condition abnormal. It is usually considered to be one of the most abnormal syndromes we have seen in a mollusk.

2. It is an abnormal cellular manifestation to an infectious disease organism. Sparks[3] stated that the seasonal nature of the onset of these abnormalities is characteristic of virtually all known oyster epizootics of parasitic causation. He added that no protistan of known pathogenicity has been associated with the diseased oysters. Apparently, the UW group did not find *Hexamita* in O. lurida with the neoplastic disease. The recent finding[33] of a haplosporidian disease of O. lurida from Yaquina Bay does not contradict the latter statement since oysters with the haplosporidian have not been found in locations used by the UW study. Also, it is unlikely that the presence of this organism would have escaped detection by these investigators. Nothing is known about viral or bacterial diseases of Yaquina Bay shellfish.

3. It is an abnormal cellular manifestation of some physical or chemical environmental factor. The only information that may provide clues is that the disease apparently occurs during the winter months and that oysters in the UW study and mussels in Farley's studies were held or collected in the upper 1 m of the water column. Excepting the possible influence of low-salinity water, there are no known factors consistent with this information which provide any additional insight.

4. The abnormal cells are themselves parasites of the shellfish. Farley and Sparks[3] dismissed this possibility with the statement, "their morphology and

mitotic activity are, however, unlike any known parasitic forms, but are strongly suggestive of molluscan cells." I feel that they do not resemble any type of molluscan cell I have seen; however, they certainly do not resemble any conventional disease organisms. Obviously a great deal remains to be done in this area.

5. There may be a genetic factor that causes the neoplastic disease. The fact that it has been reported in five species (four in Yaquina Bay) makes this unlikely. The current investigation using natural and imported oysters may help determine if this is a plausible explanation.

*Is the neoplastic disease infectious?* A cursory examination of the available data might lead one to conclude that it is, since in previous studies several animals from a single clustered population had the disease. However, if it is infectious, this raises many perplexing questions. For example, since it has been found at the mouth of the bay and 10 km upbay and has been found in several species and thus would be assumed to be caused by a nonspecific agent, why is it not found in all species in all parts of the bay? [Not one Pacific oyster (*C. gigas*) held in the same float as *O. lurida* in the UW study was found with the disease.] Since Yaquina Bay shellfish have historically been introduced into other west coast bays and since water circulation would likely transmit the infectious agent to other bays, why has the disease not been found in other bivalves in other bays? What is the significance of finding *C. virginica* on the east coast with the disease?

There are many other questions that remain unanswered and other factors that could be considered. However, they must await further, more definitive research. If this paper has made more scientists aware of the problem and fresh ideas are forthcoming, it will have served its purpose.

## ADDENDUM

Results of the second year of research, after tissue analysis of approximately 800 additional oysters (samples through June 1974) and laboratory studies using $^3$H–TdR are:

1. Three feral adult *O. lurida* were found with histopathological symptoms and the large cells characteristic of the neoplastic disease.

2. Two of the three oysters were fortuitously labelled with $^3$H–TdR. This is the first time that cells associated with an invertebrate proliferative disorder resembling cancer have been labelled. Results will be published in a forthcoming paper.

3. Based on careful studies, it now seems clear that winter mortalities of *O. lurida* and *M. edulis* living in the top 2 m of the water column, 10 km upbay from Newport, are caused by continuous low salinities. Decreased salinities (0 to 5%) occurred in the surface waters (0 to 2 m) during the first heavy rains in December 1973 and continued through the first of March 1974. There were 100% mortalities of all shellfish in the top 1.5 m of the water column whereas

less than 1% mortality occurred in similar bivalves located directly below (3 to 6 m) the animals affected by low salinities. There was no evidence that the neoplastic disease contributed to the winter mortalities.

## ACKNOWLEDGMENTS

The author extends his appreciation to C. Austin Farley, John Harshbarger and the Registry of Tumors in Lower Animals (Museum of Natural History, Smithsonian Institution) for permission to examine slides relevant to my studies; to Keith King, Steve Tomasovic, and James Pribble for technical assistance; to Robert Olson and Kenneth Chew for valuable suggestions; and to Albert K. Sparks for permission to include results from an unpublished manuscript.

The research for this paper was supported in part by the National Oceanic and Atmospheric Administration (maintained by the U. S. Department of Commerce) Institutional Sea Grant 04-3-158-4.

## REFERENCES

1. A. K. Sparks, K. K. Chew, E. R. Jones, and D. W. Weitkamp, Oyster Mortalities and Associated Symbionts and Pathological Conditions in Oregon, unpublished manuscript, 1969.
2. C. A. Farley, Sarcomatoid Proliferative Disease in a Wild Population of Edible Mussels (*Mytilus edulis*), *J. Nat. Cancer Inst.*, 4: 509-516 (1969).
3. C. A. Farley and A. K. Sparks, Proliferative Diseases of Hemocytes, Endothelial Cells, and Connective Tissue Cells in Mollusks, *Bibl. Haematol.*, 36: 610-619 (1970).
4. J. J. Goner, Sea Grant Memorandum, Marine Science Center, Oregon State University, personal communication, Newport, Oreg., 1971.
5. A. K. Sparks, *Invertebrate Pathology. Noncommunicable Diseases*, Academic Press, Inc., New York, 1972.
6. L. A. Stauber, Immunity in Invertebrates, with Special Reference to the Oyster, *Proc. Nat. Shellfish. Ass.*, 50: 7-20 (1961).
7. S. Y. Feng, Responses of Molluscs to Foreign Bodies, with Special Reference to the Oyster, *Fed. Proc. Fed. Amer. Soc. Exp. Biol.*, 26: 1685-1692 (1967).
8. M. R. Tripp, General Mechanisms and Principles of Invertebrate Immunity, in *Immunity to Parasitic Animals*, Vol. 1, G. J. Jackson, R. Herman, and I. Singer (Eds.), pp. 111-128, Appleton-Century-Crofts, Inc., New York, 1969.
9. G. Salt, *The Cellular Defense Reactions of Insects*, Cambridge Monographs in Experimental Biology, Vol. 16, Cambridge University Press, New York, 1970.
10. C. J. Sindermann, *The Principal Diseases of Marine Fish and Shellfish*, Academic Press, Inc., New York, 1970.
11. T. C. Cheng and E. Rifkin, *Cellular Reactions in Marine Mollusks in Response to Helminth Parasites*, American Fisheries Society, Special Publication, No. 5, pp. 443-496, 1970.
12. G. B. Pauley, A Critical Review of Neoplasia and Tumor-Like Lesions in Mollusks, *Nat. Cancer Inst. Monogr.*, 31: 509-539 (1969).
13. L. P. Merkow, M. Slifkin, and M. Pardo, Biological and Morphological Evaluation of Neoplastic Growth, in *Environment and Cancer*, Twenty-fourth Annual Symposium on

Fundamental Cancer Research, Houston, Texas, 1971, pp. 256-285, The Williams & Wilkins Company, Baltimore, Md., 1972.

14. P. H. Wolf, Neoplastic Growth in Two Sydney Rock Oysters, *Crassostrea commercialis*, *Nat. Cancer Inst. Monogr.*, **31**: 563-573 (1969).

15. B. Scharrer and M. S. Lochhead, Tumors in the Invertebrates: A Review, *Cancer Res.*, **10**: 403-419 (1950).

16. J. A. Couch, An Unusual Lesion in the Mantle of the American Oyster *(Crassostrea virginica)*, *Nat. Cancer Inst. Monogr.*, **31**: 557-562 (1969).

17. C. A. Farley, Probable Neoplastic Disease of the Hematopoietic Systems in Oysters (*Crassostrea virginica* and *Crassostrea gigas*), *Nat. Cancer Inst. Monogr.*, **31**: 541-555 (1969).

18. C. J. Dawe, Phylogeny and Oncology, *Nat. Cancer Inst. Monogr.*, **31**: 1-39 (1969).

19. R. A. Good and J. Finstad, Essential Relationship Between the Lymphoid System, Immunity and Malignancy, *Nat. Cancer Inst. Monogr.*, **31**: 41-58 (1969).

20. D. P. Cheney, The Morphology, Morphogenesis, and Reactive Responses of [3]H— Thymidine Labeled Leucocytes in the Manila Clam, *Tapes semidecussata* (Reeve), Ph. D. Thesis, University of Washington, Seattle, Wash., 1969.

21. M. C. Mix, Cell Renewal Systems in the Gut of the Oyster, *Crassostrea gigas* (Mollusca: Bivalvia), *Veliger*, **14**: 202-203 (1971).

22. S. P. Tomasovic and M. C. Mix, Cell Renewal in the Gill of the Freshwater Mussel, *Margaritifera margaritifera*: An Autoradiographic Study Using High Specific Activity Tritiated Thymidine, *J. Cell Sci.*, **14**: 561-570 (1974).

23. R. D. Beeman, An Autoradiographic Demonstration of Stomach Tooth Renewal in *Phyllaplysia taylori* Dall, 1900 (Gastropoda: Opisthobranchia), *Biol. Bull.*, **136**: 141-146 (1969).

24. R. D. Beeman, An Autoradiographic and Phase Contrast Study of Spermatogenesis in the Anaspidean Opisthobranch *Phyllaplasia taylori* Dall, 1900, *Arch. de Zool. Exptl. and Gen.*, **111**: 5-22 (1970).

25. R. D. Beeman, An Autoradiographic Study of Sperm Exchange and Storage in the Sea Hare, *Phyllaplasia taylori*, a Hermaphroditic Gastropod (Opisthobranchia: Anaspidea), *J. Exp. Zool.*, **175**: 125-132 (1970).

26. M. C. Mix, Chronic Histopathological Degeneration of Selected Tissues in the Pacific Oyster, *Crassostrea gigas*, Following Acute γ-Irradiation and Its Relation to Mitotic Inhibition, *Radiat. Res.*, **49**: 176-189 (1972).

27. M. C. Mix and A. K. Sparks, Studies on the Histopathological Effects of Ionizing Radiation on the Oyster, *Crassostrea gigas*. I. The Degenerative Phase Involving Digestive Diverticula, Stomach and Gut, *J. Invertebr. Pathol.*, **16**: 14-37 (1970).

28. M. C. Mix and A. K. Sparks, Repair of Digestive Tubule Tissue of the Pacific Oyster, *Crassostrea gigas*, Damaged by Ionizing Radiation, *J. Invertebr. Pathol.*, **17**: 172-177 (1971).

29. M. C. Mix and A. K. Sparks, Histopathological Effects of Various Doses of Ionizing Radiation on the Gonad of the Oyster, *Crassostrea gigas*, *Proc. Nat. Shellfish. Ass.*, **61**: 64-70 (1971).

30. M. C. Mix and S. P. Tomasovic, The Use of High Specific Activity Tritiated Thymidine and Autoradiography for Studying Molluscan Cells, *J. Invertebr. Pathol.*, **21**: 318-320 (1973).

31. O. Flandre, Cell Culture of Mollusks, in *Invertebrate Tissue Culture*, Vol. 1, C. Vago (Ed.), pp. 361-383, Academic Press, Inc., New York, 1971.

32. C. Bayne, Department of Zoology, Oregon State University, personal communication, 1973.

33. M. C. Mix and V. Sprague, Occurrence of a Haplosporidian in Native Oysters *(Ostrea lurida)* from Yaquina Bay and Alsea Bay, Oregon, *J. Invertebr. Pathol.*, **23**: 252-254 (1974).

# CELL KINETICS AND TUMOR THERAPY: AN OVERVIEW

FREDERICK A. VALERIOTE

Section of Cancer Biology, Division of Radiation Oncology, Mallinckrodt Institute of Radiology, Washington University School of Medicine, St. Louis, Missouri

## ABSTRACT

Although information on the cell-population kinetics of tumors is extremely important in the rational design of cancer chemotherapy schedules, it is but one of a number of important factors that must be considered. These factors relate to the drug, the tumor, and the host themselves as well as to the interactive areas for each of these three important variables. Each of the approximately two dozen factors that must be included in any scientific design of chemotherapy schedules is considered, and those relating directly to cell-population kinetics are expanded upon. The importance of each of these factors, as well as their implications in therapy and the necessity of any further research in these areas, is discussed. The purpose of this review is to place cell-cycle analysis in tumor therapy in proper perspective.

Researchers in cancer chemotherapy face a number of frustrations beyond the complexity and intractability of the disease itself. There is, for example, our inability to fulfill the rising hopes of the public for a quick cancer "cure." There is the lack of appreciation of our work sometimes demonstrated by clinicians, whose questions about treatment schedules and combinations we cannot always answer and who tend to think of us as remote from the needs of actual patients. Most frustrating to us, however, despite the attitudes of clinicians, is our inability to apply our findings directly to the relief of those suffering from cancer, for example, in the design of chemotherapy schedules for maximum benefits with minimum side effects.

Despite these frustrations the experimentalist is an important part of the struggle against cancer. Our model systems have provided important concepts, such as the proliferative dependence of the cytotoxicity of chemotherapeutic agents; the classification of phase-specific and cycle-specific agents; the relationship between tumor growth, clonogenic cells, growth fraction, and cell loss; and the existence of immune surveillance, all of which we expect will help directly in the design of therapy. Cooperation between clinician and researcher makes it possible to design models to fit particular situations and to apply clinically the results of experiments with those models. A good example of this procedure is seen in the development of a more appropriate model— spontaneous AKR lymphoma—for dealing with the various factors, including the sensitivity to steroids, important in treating acute lymphocytic leukemia in humans. Where treatment schedules developed with transplantable leukemias are not translatable to specific solid tumors, appropriate models must be developed. Furthermore, the experimentalist is able to suggest and develop such techniques as culturing human tumor cells, determining cell-population kinetic data in vivo, and establishing mathematical models to define and answer the biological questions important to the construction of a scientific therapeutic base. It seems logical, then, on the basis of the urgency of our joint effort, to encourage cooperation and communication between clinicians and researchers in such key areas as modeling and protocol design.

A few years ago researchers felt that an understanding of cell kinetics would serve as the Rosetta stone for cancer chemotherapy. However, although an increasing number of clinicians have been encouraged to pursue this theme, the basic researcher's optimism concerning its potential has faded. In its place immunotherapy and antiviral therapy have become the centers of attention. I still believe that the cell kineticist has an important role to play in providing therapeutically relevant information, as will become obvious in this review.

A point I wish to emphasize is that the scope of cell kinetics is much broader than consideration of the distribution of generation times. The discipline includes those data plus a variety of other kinetic parameters describing both normal and tumor tissues, including dose— and time—survival curves to anticancer agents, rates of movement of cells between functionally different cell compartments, the effect of anticancer agents on the size of and interrelationships among these cell compartments, the responses of cells as a function of their proliferative states, and the effect of anticancer agents on cell progression through the cell cycle. From this perspective, I see cell kinetics as a complex discipline that is presently in its infancy. However, I do not intend to define all the parameters important to therapy design as branches of cell kinetics. Drug resistance, the biochemistry of the tumor, the mechanism of action of the drug, the existence of anatomical sanctuaries, and a host of other factors not in the realm of cell kinetics must be considered prior to or during therapy.

One major reason for our present inability to translate biological information into definitive protocol designs is that we have yet to quantitate for human malignancies many critical parameters concerning the drug, the tumor, and the host. These factors, which must be considered in designing chemotherapy schedules, are illustrated in Fig. 1. I will discuss each factor and its therapeutic importance, present available data pertinent to the application of that factor in schedule design, and, finally, suggest further experimentation that seems

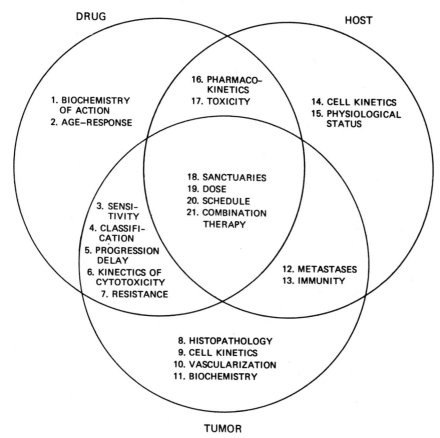

**DRUG**

1. BIOCHEMISTRY
   OF ACTION
2. AGE–RESPONSE

**HOST**

16. PHARMACO-
    KINETICS
17. TOXICITY

14. CELL KINETICS
15. PHYSIOLOGICAL
    STATUS

18. SANCTUARIES
19. DOSE
20. SCHEDULE
21. COMBINATION
    THERAPY

3. SENSI-
   TIVITY
4. CLASSIFI-
   CATION
5. PROGRESSION
   DELAY
6. KINECTICS OF
   CYTOTOXICITY
7. RESISTANCE

12. METASTASES
13. IMMUNITY

8. HISTOPATHOLOGY
9. CELL KINETICS
10. VASCULARIZATION
11. BIOCHEMISTRY

**TUMOR**

Fig. 1 The factors concerning drug, tumor, and host which must be understood for optimal chemotherapy scheduling.

required. In the process I will try to develop a view of the proper role or cell kinetics in both research and therapy.

## DRUG

### Biochemistry of Action

The biochemistry of action of anticancer agents provides us with knowledge of the interaction of these drugs with cellular constituents. A complete understanding of the mechanism of their action at the biochemical level should define the mechanism of their lethal and nonlethal effects on normal and malignant cells. This biochemical information provides one of the foundation stones for predicting therapeutic response or interpreting results, especially with regard to combination chemotherapy. For example, it is difficult to theorize on the cellular response to a drug such as cytosine arabinoside or to predict the outcome of the combination of the drug with other agents if we do not know whether its cytotoxicity results from inhibition of DNA polymerase or from incorporation into polynucleotides. The same holds true for any nonlethal effects it may produce, such as progression delay. This is well illustrated by the efforts of a number of investigators who have attempted to use known biochemical effects of each agent to predict drug combinations that might yield synergistic killing of malignant cells[1] and have thereby provided important concepts and information to the area of combination chemotherapy. Obviously, exact knowledge of drug biochemistry is a prerequisite for such predictions. In addition, an understanding of the mechanism of lethality should provide us with information necessary for the selection and synthesis of more effective agents.

This is a vigorously studied area in oncology, and a voluminous amount of data is available on the biochemical action of most clinically useful anticancer agents.[2,3] Nevertheless, much more information is required, especially that which can be correlated with the cellular effects of the agents. Implicit in such investigation is the importance of a thorough understanding of cell physiology and the prerequisite necessity of intensive research in cell and molecular biology.

## Age—Response

The degree of lethality of most anticancer agents depends strongly on the phase of the cell cycle; this relationship is referred to as age—response. It is worthwhile for therapeutic purposes to divide anticancer agents into two groups in terms of age—response as illustrated in Fig. 2. In the phase specific group, cell killing is all or none. In this example only those cells in DNA synthesis, or the S phase, are killed. In reality, though experimental age—response curves for phase-specific agents do not demonstrate such absolute differences in phase specificity, such approximation simplifies schedule design and is more valid than experiments would indicate.[4] One technical problem is the acquisition of pure populations of cells in each of the phases of the cell cycle. Because so-called synchronized populations are contaminated to some degree by cells in other phases, the question of how phase specific a number of agents are remains unanswered. The second group of agents kill cells in all phases of the cell cycle (Fig. 2); however, they likely demonstrate some phase-dependent differential cytotoxicity.

Age—response information, especially for the phase-specific agents, is essential for a scientific approach to drug scheduling. We presently apply age—response results obtained experimentally both in vivo and in vitro directly to the treatment of human tumors. Further, it is likely that the results are applicable to normal cells in cycle. Thus, if cytosine arabinoside kills cells in the S phase of the cell cycle for the few experimental cell populations studied, it seems reasonable to expect and predict that it will so affect all proliferating cells

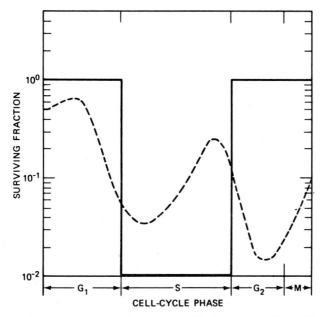

Fig. 2   Age—response curves for phase-specific (——) and cycle-specific (- - -) agents.

against which it demonstrates cytotoxicity. Although much age—response information has been accumulated,[5,6] more information on other cell types is essential, and more-detailed experiments on the effects of different dose levels and exposure times must be conducted.

## DRUG—TUMOR

### Sensitivity

The sensitivity of a tumor to a given anticancer agent refers specifically to the agent's ability to kill malignant cells. This parameter can be obtained roughly for human tumors by determining a given agent's effectiveness in terms of clinical response. The fact that this is one of the more easily obtained parameters is demonstrated by its being the basis of phase-2 clinical studies for anticancer agents and thus the first consideration in the clinical design of chemotherapy.[7] Unfortunately, the techniques used to evaluate tumor sensitivity at the clinical level are quite gross, especially for solid tumors. Furthermore, the doses and schedules employed can be important determinants in the response of various kinds of tumors. As will be discussed later, an agent might be quite effective against proliferating tumor cells, but, if a tumor has only a small fraction of malignant cells in cycle at the time of initial treatment, it may appear resistant

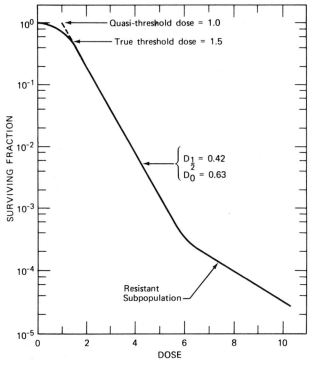

Fig. 3 A dose—survival curve. Dose is in arbitrary units, and survival is normalized to an untreated control. The different aspects of the curve are explained in the text.

to the drug. Thus, the drug could be termed ineffective although it might be an effective agent, in combination, if the tumor cells were first recruited into cell cycle.

An important observation, yet to be explained, is that individual tumors can respond quite differently to a given anticancer agent even though the tumors are classified as being of identical histological type. The possibility of heterogeneity within a single tumor has been demonstrated in that different clones of cells derived from a single tumor can have different sensitivities to a given agent.[8] Thus a number of drugs active against specific histological tumor types are required.

Experimentally, the sensitivity of a tumor to the agent can be defined in terms of the cell dose—survival curve. A number of important elements in a dose—survival curve are shown in Fig. 3. First, the slope of the dose—survival curve, usually defined in terms of $D_0$ or $D_{1/2}$, is generally taken as an index of the sensitivity of the tumor to the drug and allows an estimate of the dose required to reach a given survival level.

Second, the shoulder portion of the curve defines a minimum, or threshold, dose necessary to approach an exponential rate of cell killing. In Fig. 3 there are two indications of this dose, the quasi-threshold dose (as defined in radiobiology) and the true beginning of the exponential portion of the curve. It is the latter to which I will be referring. Obviously, if an effective single dose of drug is to be given, then it must be greater than the threshold level. For fractionated therapy, unless the sublethal damage is not repaired (i.e., the shoulder region is not reproduced after each fraction), the dose per fraction for an optimal protocol must be greater than the threshold level. The importance of knowing the extent of this shoulder region has been discussed briefly in reference to radiotherapy,[9] but no attention has been paid to its importance in chemotherapy. Repair phenomena are known for some of the agents, especially the alkylating agents.[10] Assuming the accumulated sublethal damage is repaired between fractions, Fig. 4 illustrates the outcome of four different fractionation schedules using the dose—survival curve illustrated in Fig. 3 but neglecting the resistant subpopulation. It can be seen that as a consequence of the shoulder region the outcome varies drastically depending on the dose per fraction used. A number of experimental tumors have been demonstrated to have broad shoulders to anticancer agents in vivo.[11]

Finally, any change in the slope of the curve allows one to determine if there are subpopulations of resistant cells and to measure their proportion in the tumor population.[12,13]

Present attempts to culture human tumor cells both in vitro and in vivo so that the effects of anticancer agents on the proliferative capacity of these cells can be assessed by quantitative cellular dose—survival curves are among the most important areas being pursued in cancer biology.[14,15] Hopefully, new techniques will allow us to construct dose—survival curves for an individual's tumor and to use this information to choose the proper drug and the appropriate dose.

## Classification

The first classification of the action of anticancer agents based on the shapes of the dose—survival curves was performed by Berry;[16] later a more extensive classification was carried out by Bruce, Meeker, and Valeriote.[17] Two types of dose—survival curves were found (Fig. 5).

With one group of agents there is a decrease in survival with increasing dose until a plateau is reached after which there is little if any increase in cell killing with increasing dose. The agents that give this shape of dose—survival curve are phase-specific agents (or cell-cycle phase-specific agents). Included in this group are hydroxyurea, cytosine arabinoside, and vinblastine. One would theoretically expect such dose—survival curves for agents with discrete age—response functions given a population of cells distributed around the cell cycle. Figure 5 shows experimental results for phase-specific agents given either as a single dose or as multiple doses over a 24-hr period. As expected for drugs that are

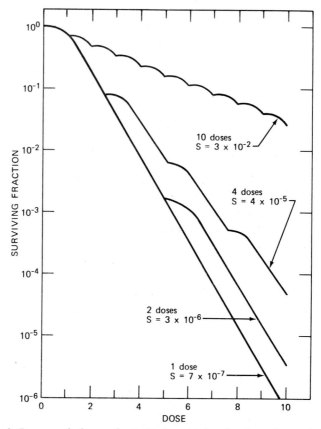

Fig. 4 Dose—survival curve for 1-, 2-, 4-, or 10-dose fractions of an anticancer agent. Dose is in arbitrary units. Survival levels for a constant total dose are indicated as they would exist at the end of the course of therapy.

metabolized rapidly in vivo, such as hydroxyurea, only the cells in the sensitive S phase are killed by a single dose. If the agent remains for an extended time following its administration, one would expect a greater degree of cell killing as cells entered the sensitive phase in the presence of the drug. The survival curve for single doses of cytosine arabinoside demonstrates this effect.

Multiple doses of phase-specific agents, with proper spacing, would be expected to yield a higher degree of cell killing than an equivalent single dose. The effect of such dose fractionation is shown for vinblastine and cytosine arabinoside in Fig. 5, and the importance of the interval is shown dramatically in Fig. 6. Figure 6 shows the results of varying the interval between the administration of two equal doses of cytosine arabinoside. An optimal interval is found which likely depends not only on the phase specificity of the agent but also on the extent of progression delay and distribution of cell-cycle phase

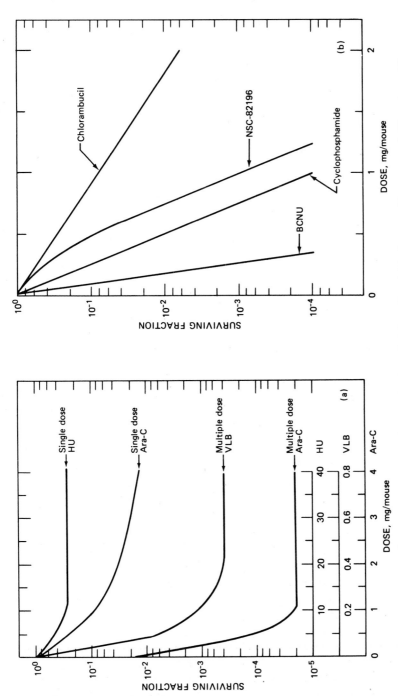

**Fig. 5** Dose—survival curves for leukemic cells following the in vivo administration of (a) phase-specific agents and (b) cycle-specific agents. HU, hydroxyurea. Ara-C, cytosine arabinoside. VLB, vinblastine. BCNU, 1,3-bis(2-chloroethyl)-1-nitrosourea. NSC-82196, 5-[3,3-bis(2-chloroethyl)-1-triazeno] imidazole-4-carboxamide. Data taken from Refs. 11, 17, 18, and unpublished data.

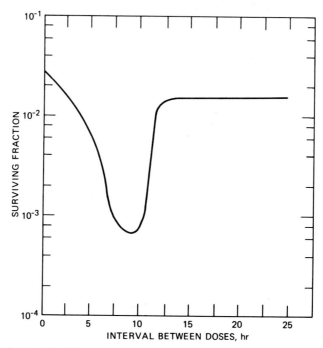

**Fig. 6** Survival of leukemic cells as a function of the interval between the administration of two doses of 1 mg each of cytosine arabinoside per mouse.

transit times. Our lack of precise knowledge of these parameters for human tumors makes it difficult to extrapolate from mouse to man at the present time. The main reason that the survival plateau is at different levels for different drugs is probably a consequence of progression delay, discussed later, for which there is some experimental evidence.[19] For optimal therapeutic effect with phase-specific agents, doses that yield a cell kill to at least the plateau level should be administered. Extensive, if not complete, killing of cells in the sensitive phase would be ensured. Obviously, to realize killing of all tumor cells by phase-specific agents, the drug must be maintained at cytotoxic levels for extended periods.

The second group of agents defined produced exponential dose—survival curves (Fig. 5). These agents have been termed cycle-specific agents since they are often more effective on proliferating (in-cycle) than on nonproliferating (out-of-cycle) cells. Fractionation scheduling, which might be necessary for phase-specific agents, is not as important for these agents since they can kill cells in all phases of the cell cycle. One should simply administer doses greater than the threshold dose so that the efficiency of tumor-cell killing is high. The dose, however, should not be greater than the level at which the survivors are predominantly drug-resistant cells since only increased killing of normal cells

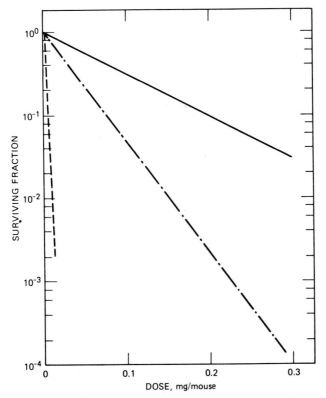

**Fig. 7** Dose—survival curves for normal hematopoietic stem cells (—), a transplanted leukemia (— · —), and a transplanted plasmacytoma (- - -) to melphalan administered in vivo. Data taken from Refs. 17 and 21.

would then be obtained. The dose restriction due to killing of normal cell populations will be discussed later. An important property of this class of agents is that cell killing is first order; that is, for a constant dose increment, the same fractional reduction in cell number will be realized irrespective of the cell-population size. This well-known concept in radiobiology was introduced into cancer chemotherapy by Skipper's group.[20]

In extrapolating this information to the clinic, I believe we can feel confident that drugs in the two different classes act similarly on human tumor cells.

Experimental studies indicate that the differential response of normal and tumor tissue to a given agent vary significantly according to tumor types. An example of this is shown in Fig. 7 for an experimental plasmacytoma and a transplanted leukemia treated with melphalan. The limiting normal tissue studied in both cases was the hematopoietic stem-cell population. Although the

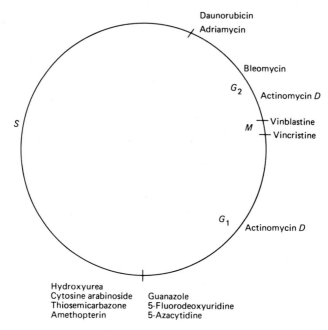

**Fig. 8** Locus of action of a number of anticancer agents for inhibition of cell progression.

difference in sensitivity between the transplanted leukemia and the normal cell population is small, there is a large differential sensitivity for the plasmacytoma. Human plasmocytomas are known clinically to be much more sensitive to melphalan than are leukemias. Data such as these demonstrate the usefulness of quantifiable experimental systems for therapeutic design in human neoplasia and also illustrate the necessity of employing experimental systems that closely mimic the human tumor to which the results are to be applied. Since each type of cancer must at this stage be considered separately, a large number of model systems (using experimental animal tumors as well as human tumors) must be developed. The effects of anticancer agents on them should then be assayed at the cellular level.

## Progression Delay

Progression delay is another important factor in the design of therapy schedules, though as yet very little information is available.[22] It is known[23] that a number of the anticancer agents inhibit cells in their progression from one phase of the cell cycle to another (Fig. 8). For example, vinblastine inhibits passage of cells from $G_2$ through mitosis, actinomycin D inhibits cells in their movement from $G_1$ into S and through $G_2$ to mitosis, and cytosine arabinoside and amethopterin inhibit cells from moving past the $G_1/S$ boundary.

An important aspect of progression delay is the relationship between the concentration of the anticancer agent and the degree of blockage of the cells. For cytosine arabinoside the concentration of drug required to block the progression of cells from $G_1$ into S is approximately one-tenth the dose required to kill cells in S. It is likely to be generally true that blocking doses are lower than cytotoxic doses, which implies that, following the administration of cytotoxic doses of these drugs, the surviving cell population will exhibit progression delay. Although it seems likely that the positions of blocks in progression are similar for different proliferating cell populations and thus in vitro data can be extrapolated to the clinic, the kinetics of these progression delays for a number of different cell lines and drug doses both in vivo and in vitro might be different and should be studied.

In regard to combination chemotherapy, cell-progression blockage has been considered as a tool for synchronizing malignant cells so that a second agent would be more effective.[24,25] Obviously such an approach requires extensive knowledge of the kinetics of the block. A phase-specific agent often blocks cells from progressing into the portion of the cell cycle in which it is cytotoxic. Since such an agent is often administered in a fractionated schedule, sufficient time must be allowed for the release of all or a significant proportion of the block before the second fraction is given. Some scheduling of anticancer agents with allowance for progression delay[26] has been attempted in humans, and much more such scheduling will need to be done in the future.

The biochemical mechanisms of a few of these blocks are partially understood, but little is known for most agents. Further, the relationship of these blocks to the phenomenon of unbalanced growth,[27] as well as the kinetics of the blocks and the resulting cytotoxicity, needs to be investigated. In addition, to define optimum therapy schedules, we need information about the dose dependency of progression delay, the duration of the block following drug removal, and the effect of the block on the subsequent transit time of the cells through other phases of cell cycle.

## Kinetics of Cytotoxicity

The time course of cell killing by a given drug, as well as the extent, is important to any schedule design. Figure 9 shows three different kinetics of cytotoxicity observed in vivo for malignant cells following drug administration. For large doses of cyclophosphamide, cell killing is complete within 1 or 2 hr. Such an effect is characteristic of many alkylating agents. Actinomycin D, on the other hand, demonstrates an extended cell killing following administration of a single dose of drug. This extended killing may reflect not only effective levels of drug remaining in contact with the cells but also the active drug remaining in the cell and exerting its lethal effect some time later as the cell passes into a drug-sensitive phase. Finally, as shown by cytosine arabinoside, there is an immediate killing of cells in the sensitive S phase, followed some time later by further killing, possibly of cells blocked in the cell cycle and undergoing unbalanced growth. It is expected that most phase-specific agents will demonstrate this latter form of cytotoxic kinetics.

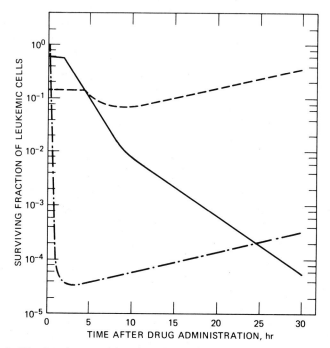

Fig. 9  Kinetics of cytotoxicity of a number of anticancer agents. - - -, 1 mg of cytosine arabinoside per mouse. —, 10 μg of actinomycin D per mouse. — · —, 2 mg cyclophosphamide per mouse. Data are from Ref. 28 and unpublished results.

The therapeutic importance of the kinetics of cytotoxicity can be appreciated for fractionated schedules since this information bears on when a second drug should be administered and is therefore essential in defining and predicting the effects of drug combinations. Further, reversing agents must be so administered that they do not reverse a large portion of malignant cell killing. Finally, if we knew exactly the kinetics of the cytotoxicity of malignant and normal cell populations, much of the modeling to be discussed here would be superfluous.

That we know so little about the molecular biology of cell lethality while such knowledge is important in predicting or understanding drug effects on cell populations indicates that this area deserves intensive study.

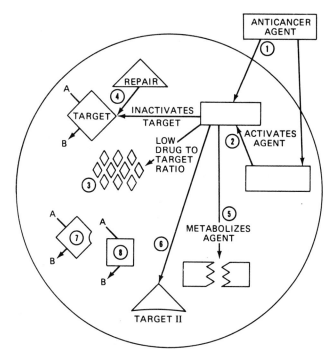

Fig. 10 Mechanisms of cellular drug resistance: (1) Modification of plasma membrane to arrest drug transport. (2) Decreased activity or loss of the enzyme that converts the parent drug into an active form. (3) Increased intracellular concentration of target macromolecules. The ratio of drug to target molecules becomes low; so sufficient numbers of active target macromolecules persist for survival of the cell. (4) Increased activity of the repair system such that the cell is more able to recover from the drug-induced lesion. (5) Increased activity of the enzyme(s) that metabolizes the anticancer agent. (6) Synthesis of a number of macromolecules with which the drug can bind. (7) Modification of the structure of the target so that it is no longer able to bind the drug. (8) Increased activity or de novo synthesis of another macromolecule that can carry out the function of the target macromolecule and is unaffected by the drug.

## Resistance

A final factor that must be considered with regard to drug–tumor interaction is the development of drug resistance, the mechanisms[29] of which are described briefly in Fig. 10. Understanding the biochemical mode of action of agents not only indicates likely mechanisms of resistance but also provides for logical choices of additional agents to destroy the resistant cells. The mechanisms of resistance can also suggest the mechanism(s) of cell lethality for a given drug. The clinical importance of drug resistance is well documented and is a major reason for the transfer of a patient from one drug to another. In fact, one of the clinical bases for combination drug therapy is to prevent the selection of drug-resistant mutants. As we define the different possible modes of resistance experimentally, the assays we develop can also be used to detect and define drug resistance in patients.

It was indicated earlier that dose—survival curves might provide information on the existence of resistant subpopulations. An example of this process is shown in Fig. 11 where a cyclophosphamide-resistant leukemic cell population is demonstrable. This information can be used to optimize the scheduling of agents. In this case doses greater than that corresponding to the change in slope should not be administered, since the remaining cells are drug resistant and there is little increased killing of them although a proportional increase in toxicity to the host will occur. Further, an understanding of the physiological basis for this resistance would aid in defining curative therapy.[31] One approach to this problem which has been tested experimentally[32] is the use of membrane-active agents which increase the permeability of the cell membrane and as a result allow more of the anticancer agents to enter. Also, the resistance mechanism itself might be employed to allow a greater incorporation of some other drug. For example, if the resistance mechanism is the activation of an alternate metabolic pathway, suitable cytotoxic precursors for this new pathway might be effective. It seems likely, however, that as scheduling in combination chemo-therapy becomes more effective, as we accumulate knowledge on agents that are not cross resistant, and as new anticancer agents are developed, drug resistance will no longer be a limit to therapy.

# TUMOR

## Histopathology

Tumor histopathology is an important parameter in that it allows the investigator to classify a tumor cell population. Since cancer should be thought of as a class of diseases, as metabolic diseases are considered a class of diseases, each of the distinct tumor entities should be dealt with separately in terms of biology and, possibly, of therapy. For example, bronchogeneic carcinoma may be classified into a number of distinct tumors, such as oat-cell carcinoma and squamous-cell carcinoma, and their present therapy schedules are quite different. Clinically, these distinctions provide a basis for comparison of results between investigators. Although the morphological classification of cancer is well defined,[33] the biology and specific therapy are not.

## Cell Kinetics

In the past, extensive knowledge of the kinetics of the different tumor cell populations was thought likely to become a major focus for the development of

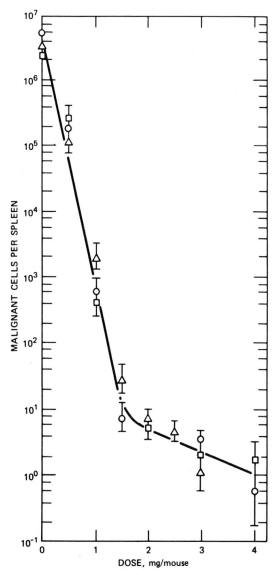

Fig. 11 Dose—survival curve of a murine leukemia following administration of cyclophosphamide. Different symbols represent different experiments. Errors are ±1 S.E. Data from Ref. 30.

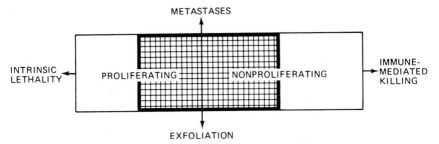

Fig. 12  Cell-compartment model for a solid tumor. Clonogenic cells are bounded by the thick line. Arrows indicate mechanisms of cell loss from the tumor.

successful protocols for the treatment of human tumors. Recently, however, because of the limited translation of available information into actual drug scheduling, this idea has come into disrepute. This seems ill-deserved since little information on cell kinetics is available for human tumors, and indeed little is known for most experimental tumors.

Figure 12 illustrates a solid-tumor model in which I have defined a number of subpopulations of cells. Clonogenic cells, contained within the shaded rectangle, can be either proliferating or nonproliferating and are defined as having unlimited proliferative capacity. Similarly, nonclonogenic cells can be either proliferating or nonproliferating.

In designing drug schedules, one needs the distribution of cell-cycle phase transit times specifically for the proliferating clonogenic cells. The distribution is expecially important when phase-specific agents are used, since optimal cell killing depends on maintaining the cytotoxic levels of the agent for a period of time during which a large proportion of the cells pass into the sensitive phase without inducing progression delay. Information on cell-cycle transit times and their distributions has been obtained for a wide variety of experimental tumors and for some human tumors.[34,35] There seems to be a large variation in the distribution of cell-cycle phase transit times between different tumors; so one cannot dictate one specific optimal time interval over which therapy with phase-specific agents should be given. As a first approximation, therapy could be scheduled for a period equal to the mean generation time. The duration of therapy will more likely depend on the kinetics of killing of normal cells as discussed in a later section. One must distinguish between generation and doubling time; tumors can have long doubling times and yet contain proliferating clonogenic cells that have short generation times. It is the generation time that is important in the scheduling of phase-specific anticancer agents.

Unfortunately, present techniques used to determine generation-time distributions have several limitations. First, it is assumed that the proliferating cells constitute a homogeneous population. It is quite possible that 90% of the proliferating cells in a tumor have only limited proliferative capacity (i.e., are not clonogenic); yet, at present, their distribution of phase transit times would be the basis for therapy. We therefore require techniques to distinguish specifically the proliferating clonogenic cells from other proliferating cells since therapy must be determined by the distribution of the proliferating clonogenic cells.

Second, although the distribution of generation times of 90% of a proliferating cell population can be determined quite accurately, the remaining 10% are assumed by the form of the distribution to which the data are fit. This tail of the distribution is of extreme importance in the design of therapy using phase-specific agents, though at present it is beyond determination.

With regard to the relationship of cycle-specific drugs and proliferating cells, a point made by Steel[35] needs experimental clarification: does a cell that has a long generation time, on the tail of the (log normal) distribution, respond like all other proliferating cells to these agents, or is it more like the $G_0$ cell?

The nonproliferating clonogenic cells are generally referred to as $G_0$ cells. Such cells have the capacity to become proliferating cells. Optimal therapy for a tumor with a $G_0$ cell population would likely require recruitment of these cells into a proliferative state where they can be killed more effectively by anticancer agents. The $G_0$ population could be of such a small size that recruitment might not be necessary if significant killing could be obtained with nontoxic doses of drugs that give exponential dose—survival curves. It seems likely that for most solid tumors, however, the $G_0$ population will be of a significant size. Thus, the kinetics of movement of cells between the $G_0$ and proliferating state as a function of both tumor growth and time following therapy is an important consideration, but it is little investigated. The $G_0$ cells have been discussed frequently with regard to optimal schedule design, but in only a few cases have they been isolated and quantified in experimental tumors.[36] Recently, Schabel has designed and tested therapy for an experimental tumor in which a significant fraction of the clonogenic cells are nonproliferating.[37] A cycle-specific agent is first given, leading to the recruitment of the $G_0$ cells, after which phase-specific agents can be effectively employed. With the exception of studies on the small lymphocyte in acute leukemia,[38] little information exists to indicate a $G_0$ population in human tumors.

It is essential that we know more about the mechanisms that control the transition of cells between the proliferating and nonproliferating states at the biochemical and cellular levels. There are a number of normal cell populations, such as hematopoietic stem cells and lymphocytes, which contain a significant fraction of $G_0$ cells capable of being stimulated to move into cell cycle. These cell populations are likely useful as general models for $G_0$ cells, and their response to anticancer agents might be readily applied to malignant cell populations.

The importance of clonogenic cells cannot be overstressed. A major factor that is determined by their doubling time is the interval of time between drug courses. This interval must be less than the time taken for the clonogenic cells to repopulate to their pretreatment level. Only in this way will the population of clonogenic cells eventually be destroyed.

One reason why some tumors are more sensitive to anticancer agents may be that fewer clonogenic cells need to be destroyed. For example, experimental transplanted leukemias have been shown to have a high proportion of clonogenic cells, and thus only a few cells produce a tumor "take," whereas other tumors might require many orders of magnitude more cells to produce a take.[39] The importance of knowing the fraction of clonogenic cells in a tumor is that it defines explicitly the number of cells which must be destroyed in order to cure the host. An important therapeutic conclusion to this discussion is that cycle-specific rather than phase-specific agents should be used clinically whenever possible so as not to necessitate the rather extensive kinetic data required for the effective scheduling of phase-specific drugs.

One physiologically defined cell population comprises the nutritionally deficient cells. These cells may or may not be in cell cycle and exist under low oxygen or low substrate concentrations as a result of their large distances, in cellular terms, from a capillary. The only kinetics that have been studied for this cell population are for hypoxic cells in tumors and deal with their relationship to radiation sensitivity. Nutritionally deficient cells are discussed in more detail in the following section. Such cells might be expected to have a modified sensitivity to many of the anticancer agents; however, this has not yet been demonstrated.

In some tumors one finds a population of differentiated cells (defined by morphological or functional characteristics) which are out of cell cycle and generally considered to lack the ability to reenter the cell cycle. They are thus of no importance in the therapeutic design of anticancer agents.

One parameter that is often obtained for experimental tumors and for some human tumors is the growth fraction. However, this parameter measures the fraction of proliferating cells and, unfortunately, neither distinguishes the physiological state of the nonproliferating cells nor separates the clonogenic from nonclonogenic cells.

Also shown in Fig. 12 are mechanisms by which cells are lost from the primary tumor. These include exfoliation, in which cells are lost from the host; immune-mediated killing of tumor cells, which is discussed in the section on immunity; intrinsic lethality, which refers to lethal factors, such as chromosomal imbalance; and metastasis from the primary tumor, which is discussed in a later section.

We have little information that all these subpopulations of cells exist in experimental tumors and essentially no information for human tumors. Knowledge of the fraction of the cell population which exists in each of these different compartments, as well as knowledge of the kinetics of their interrelationship, is the second most important piece of cellular information in the design of rational therapeutic schedules. Further, it seems that the populations and their interrelationships might change with tumor size and therapy and that any such changes might drastically modify subsequent treatment. An example of this is the change in the fraction of hypoxic cells following irradiation of solid tumors.[40] The fact that the kinetics of reoxygenation vary from one tumor to another makes one suspect that a similar diversity of response might exist, for example, for the rate of movement of $G_0$ cells into cell cycle following treatment. It has been shown that the generation time, phase transit times, growth fraction, and cell loss factor can change following chemotherapy.[41,42] Several concepts essential for a scientific approach to chemotherapy have been developed from tumor-cell kinetic studies. However, more-precise cellular techniques must be developed and much more data must be obtained from human tumors before this area will become a major factor in protocol design.

## Vascularization

The pattern of vascularity in a tumor might be expected to modify drastically tumor response to anticancer agents in two distinct ways. First, vascularity plays the major role in determining the proportion of cells in the different clonogenic cell populations. In poorly vascularized tumors, one might expect a large proportion of nutritionally deficient and possibly $G_0$ cells. This area has been little worked, with the notable exception of the study by Tannock,[43] who has shown a decreasing growth fraction with increasing distance from the capillary. With irradiation the oxygenation of the tumor is modified so as to make subsequent courses more effective. Fractionated courses of chemotherapy might yield results similar to those caused by the fractionated irradiation of solid tumors. Proliferating cells close to the capillaries might be preferentially destroyed by the drug, lysed, and removed, after which $G_0$ cells might be triggered into cell cycle. Thus cells remote from a capillary could be exposed to higher drug concentrations as a result of the removal of intervening killed cells.

Second, the existence of the remote cells is one of the reasons for administering large doses of given anticancer agents so that cytotoxic levels are reached. Large doses might be most important in poorly vascularized tumors, such as sarcomas, as compared to the well-vascularized carcinomas.

## Biochemistry

The biochemical pathways within the tumor affect not only its sensitivity to a particular drug but also the mechanism of cytotoxic response. Hall and his colleagues[44,45] have shown for a number of anticancer agents that both the uptake and the conversion of drugs to their active form are major determinants of their lethal effect and serve also as predictors of their clinical usefulness. Of

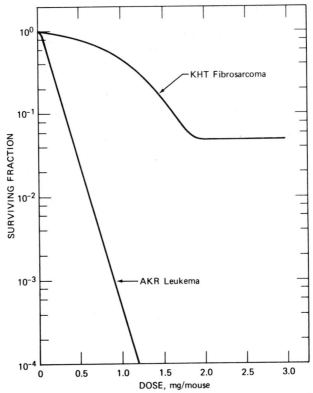

**Fig. 13  Dose—survival curves for two different transplantable tumors following in vivo administration of 5-FU.**

obvious therapeutic importance for a given drug is the fact that, if the tumor lacks either the transport function or activating enzymes, administration will yield only host toxicity. An example of this factor applicable to the design of therapy has recently been shown for daunorubicin, which requires a specific reductase for its activation. The activity of this enzyme in the patient's leukocytes correlates extremely well with the patient's drug response.[46] It might be worthwhile to screen tumor cells for required enzymes before deciding on the drugs to be employed.

A second example of the role of tumor biochemistry is shown for the drug 5-fluorouracil (5-FU), which can be metabolized to either 5-FUdR or to 5-FUR. The 5-FUdR interferes with DNA synthesis and is a phase-specific agent, whereas 5-FUR is incorporated into RNA and might be expected to kill cells throughout the cell cycle. The dose—survival curves for 5-FU are quite different for two different experimental transplantable tumors and might be reflecting such a difference in the cellular metabolism of the agent (Fig. 13). This example points out again the importance of knowing whether or not an agent is phase specific before scheduling its administration.

The biochemical profile of cancer cells is thus an important parameter both in selecting the drugs to be employed and in scheduling their use. Further, knowledge of tumor biochemistry might allow for the development of more effective anticancer drugs.

## HOST–TUMOR

### Metastases

The very existence of metastases is one of the main requisites for the use of anticancer agents in contrast to radiotherapy or surgery. A high probability of metastases for a given tumor or a high incidence of nonlocal failure following surgery or radiotherapy would also be a definite indication for the concomitant use of chemotherapy. Solid tumors demonstrate an increased doubling time with increasing tumor size; this has been explained in terms of an increased fraction of nonproliferating clonogenic cells, an increased cell-cycle time, or an increased loss of cells. Metastatic tumors are likely in an early state of development and might be extremely sensitive to many anticancer agents since they can be expected to contain few nonproliferating clonogenic cells. The expected relationship between tumor size and sensitivity to phase-specific agents has been demonostrated;[47] it indicates the importance of initiating chemotherapy as soon as possible. Thus the significance of defining the tumor cell compartments in terms of size or age of the tumor is clear.[48]

### Immunity

It is now widely felt that the host develops some immunity against a growing tumor, the cytotoxic component being mediated by the cellular arm of the immune system. The humoral arm is thought to produce a blocking antibody that interferes with cell-mediated cytotoxicity. Whether anticancer agents are beneficial or detrimental to the tumor-directed cytotoxic immunity is not known. Therapeutically, one wants to administer those agents which are tumoricidal but do not compromise any active host immunity. It would also be to the therapist's advantage to obtain at the same time a selective inhibition of blocking antibody synthesis. The literature on immunotherapy either alone or in combination with other modes of therapy for both experimental and human tumors is voluminous and beyond the scope of this discussion.

The action of anticancer agents on the immune system is poorly understood despite the availability of a number of quantitative assays for B cells, T cells, and macrophages. A classification of this action has been attempted;[49] however, much more work is needed to delineate the cellular components of the immune system, their biological functions, and their interrelationships before adequate explanation, classification, or exploitation can be developed.

An added sense of urgency in delineating the effects of drugs on the immune system arises from the large number of deaths in cancer patients resulting from opportunistic infections.[50] Hopefully, new schedules will minimize any compromising of the immunologic status of the patient and combine both better detection and therapeutic procedures to end this type of failure.

## HOST

### Cell Kinetics

The tissues of the host that often limit the aggressiveness of chemotherapy are those which have a population of proliferating cells, such as those found in the gastrointestinal tract and bone marrow. The destruction of a significant proportion of these cells will lead to irreversible host toxicity. As in the case of tumors, a determination of the cell-cycle parameters and the existence and kinetic interrelationships of possible subpopulations of cells are important considerations. Figure 14 provides a simple cellular compartmental description of the gastrointestinal tract and bone marrow. A small fraction of the stem cells are normally proliferating as are the majority of those cells in the amplification compartment. Few functional cells are proliferating. The most pertinent cell populations with regard to chemotherapy are the cells in the stem and amplification compartments. We need to know the fraction of stem cells in the nonproliferative state and the kinetics of their movement in and out of this $G_0$ state both under normal conditions and following any perturbation. In this respect studies of stem-cell control mechanisms are useful not only in understanding the biology of the system but also in indicating possible approaches to manipulating the size and physiological state of these cell compartments and of the differentiated descendants.

### Physiological Status

The physiological status of the patient will also determine the intensity of the therapy to be employed. For example, a patient treated previously may not have recovered sufficiently to tolerate a full course of therapy. Further, any impairment of the major organs that metabolize or excrete the drugs must be considered as must other factors, such as age, nutritional status, and psychiatric status. The decisions that are made in this area are inevitably more empirical than scientific.

## DRUG–HOST

### Pharmacokinetics

By pharmacokinetics I mean the change in effective anticancer activity in the serum as a function of time following drug administration. It is not so much the

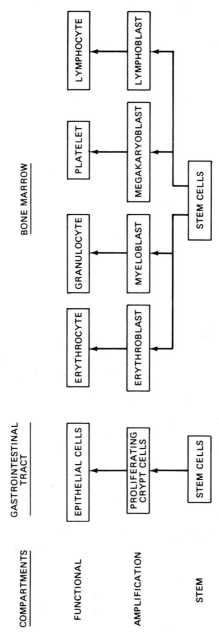

**Fig. 14** Cell-compartment model for the gastrointestinal mucosa and bone marrow.

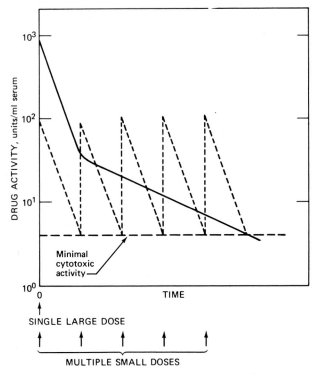

**Fig. 15** Serum activity of an anticancer agent administered either as a single large dose (——) or as multiple small doses (- - -). Minimal cytotoxic activity is that level below which there is no lethal effect on the malignant cells.

shape of the drug disappearance curve that is important here but rather the duration of time over which cytotoxic drug levels are maintained. The sensitivity of the tumor to the drug gives one an estimate of the drug level required for effective treatment; the pharmacokinetics of the drug indicates its dose and the frequency of administration required to maintain cytotoxic levels. For example, as shown in Fig. 15, cytotoxic levels of a phase-specific drug can be maintained in either of two different ways. First, a large initial dose will produce effective levels for an extended period of time. Second, smaller doses of the drug could be administered at intervals of time sufficient to ensure that the serum level never falls below the minimal cytotoxic concentration and repeated often enough that the desired fraction of cells passes through the sensitive phase during treatment. For some drugs, such as vinblastine, a large initial dose is possible since the biological half-life of the drug in the host is fairly long.[51] For other agents, such as hydroxyurea, whose half-life is short, fractionated schedules must be employed for the drug to be effective. For phase-specific agents that block cells in their progression through the cell cycle, a third scheme is necessary. Sufficient time between drug administrations must be allowed so that the drug activity becomes less than the blocking concentration and cells can again pass through cell cycle. The interval must obviously be short enough that no cells pass through the sensitive phase.

Although complex models of drug disposition have been developed,[52] it is unfortunate that in animals and in man many of the studies have been carried out using radioactive compounds or assaying the serum for the chemical species itself. These assays may not determine the most important parameter, which is the activity of these agents in terms of destruction of the proliferative capacity of malignant cells.[51,53] The importance of drug disposition on the kinetics of drug action is well known for agents other than anticancer drugs;[54] its implication in cancer chemotherapy was indicated in Fig. 9. Further, the localization of drug in vivo might be a prognosticator of effectiveness as shown for bleomycin for skin cancer and the possibility of actinomycin D for salivary tumors.[55] Different routes of administration are known to affect tumor response; however, the time—activity relationship should take this into account and reflect any differences. An example of the importance of route of administration is shown for oral thioguanine where maximum concentration is not reached until many hours after administration. As will be seen later for drug combinations, the time of maximum activity of two drugs in relation to each other can drastically affect the fraction of malignant cells killed. Thus, if the therapist is trying to schedule agents given by different routes, the pharmacokinetics of the agents must be known for optimal treatment.

One concept discussed in pharmacokinetics is the C x T relationship,[56] which states that the degree of cell killing following exposure to an agent is proportional to its concentration multiplied by the time over which the exposure occurs. For agents that produce exponential dose—survival curves, one can consider the lethal mechanism as being similar to that of radiation, where there is a target being inactivated. In that case the C x T equation is both mathematically predicted and logically expected. However, for agents that are phase specific, this equation does not necessarily hold, since the kinetics of cell killing are a function of the distribution of generation times. Further, should the agent induce progression delay, the relationship of drug concentration and exposure time to cell killing becomes more complex.

For many drugs the intracellular concentration of their active species is the cytotoxic determinant and is a function of the biochemistry of the cell itself as it depends on transport properties and intracellular mechanism of drug activation and inactivation. Further, many anticancer agents are metabolized by the host to active or inactive species. For example, the drug cyclophosphamide must be activated by the liver before it will destroy the proliferative capacity of cells. Compounds such as steroids or phenobarbital modify this activation and must be taken into consideration in the therapy.

## Toxicity

In considering the toxicity of anticancer agents on normal host tissue, one must deal with cell-renewal systems as distinct from all other tissues. As indicated previously, the stem-cell populations of the bone marrow and gastrointestinal tract represent the most important group of cells destroyed by anticancer agents. It has been estimated that the destruction of more than 99.9% of the hematopoietic or intestinal stem cell-population is fatal to the host.[57,58] To cure a tumor-bearing host, on the other hand, one must often reduce the survival of the malignant cell population to a level of about $10^{-10}$. Obviously then, for effective therapy a drug must be quite selective for the tumor cells. This represented the basis for the work of Bruce and his colleagues,[59] in which the sensitivity of malignant cells (a transplanted lymphoma) was compared to that of the hematopoietic stem-cell population (Fig. 16). Exponential dose–survival curves were found for both cell populations exposed to many anticancer agents; however, the differential killing varied greatly among the cycle-specific agents. Cyclophosphamide was found to be the most efficacious both from comparison of the slopes of these two cell populations[59] and from animal survival time and survival frequency.[60] In responding to phase-specific agents, the rapidly proliferating tumor cells showed a marked difference in survival when compared to the normal stem cells, the majority of which are nonproliferating. It seems essential that such comparisons be accomplished in appropriate experimental model systems or, if possible, for human normal and tumor cell populations as one component of a rational chemotherapy.

To date, cellular assays of the effect of anticancer agents on normal cell populations have been restricted to the hematopoietic system. Because of the susceptibility of the gastrointestinal tract to many anticancer drugs, this tissue is important to study with quantitative assays. Possibly, the technique developed by Withers[61] permitting gastrointestinal stem-cell quantitation could be applied to this problem. Also, it is important to understand and be able to predict the effect on the immune system, and, as indicated previously, cellular assays for its components are available.

Since a stem-cell population has a capacity for self-renewal, repopulation can occur. If the sensitivity of the stem cells to the anticancer agents and the rate of repopulation following drug administration were known, the optimal drug and fractionation-interval dosage could be determined. Although it is not possible at the present time to assay directly the effects of agents on human hematopoietic stem cells, an assay is available for a class of hematopoietic cells[62] that is important in granulopoiesis and might be considered as an indicator of drug effects on the stem-cell population. Few data are available in this area,[63] though, and it is clear that more must be accumulated. In addition, vigorous efforts to culture stem cells are necessary.

An important problem that must be considered here is whether rapidly proliferating stem cells are more sensitive to anticancer agents than nonprolif-

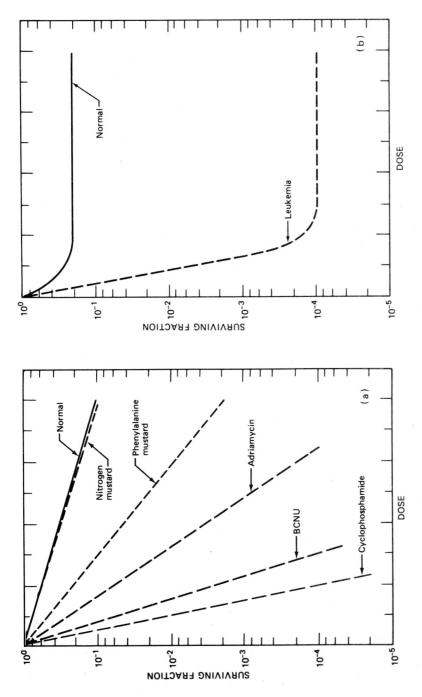

Fig. 16  Dose—survival curves of normal hematopoietic stem cells (——) and a transplanted leukemia (- - -) exposed to (a) cycle-specific and (b) phase-specific agents.

erating or $G_0$ stem cells. For phase-specific agents[64] it should be obvious that the proliferating stem cells are more sensitive since they pass through phases of the cell cycle during which these particular agents express their lethality. As for those agents which produce exponential dose—survival curves, the proliferating cells are usually more sensitive than the nonproliferating cells and in some cases, are as sensitive as some tumor-cell populations.[65,66] For either class of agent, the drug should not be given while stem cells are proliferating, and the interval of time between treatments should be sufficient to permit the majority of stem cells to revert to the $G_0$ state. An early example of this effect was demonstrated in tumor-bearing mice receiving amethopterin and folinic acid.[67] Optimal therapy resulted when the reversing agent was administered after a significant fraction of the leukemic cells were killed by the amethopterin but before a significant fraction of the hematopoietic stem cells were recruited into cell cycle and were destroyed by the drug. More research is necessary to determine the prevalence of this phenomena and the mechanisms responsible for it. Cell culture may serve as an appropriate model since the cells can be put into a number of nonproliferating states.

It is therefore important to know the time following drug administration at which the stem cells become proliferative, or, more precisely, the kinetics of entry of these stem cells into cell cycle following their destruction or the destruction of their proliferating descendents, or both. Since the stem cells proliferate to replenish destroyed descendents as well as their own population, it becomes important to know how the extent of destruction of the progeny affects the kinetics of the surviving stem cells.

Unlike tumor cell populations where the sensitivity to the anticancer agent may vary from one tumor type to another, the response of normal cell populations should be quite similar from one patient to another. That some differences might occur is demonstrated by the different recovery kinetics of peripheral blood elements and stem cells when exposed to nitrosoureas, radiation, or myleran compared to other anticancer agents.[68] The number of leukocytes in the peripheral blood has been used to measure the extent and duration of toxicity and thus to predict the time for safe administration of subsequent courses of therapy.[69] It has been shown experimentally[68] that when leukocytes are repopulating the host, the stem-cell compartment is almost fully repopulated. Quantitation of both lethal and nonlethal cellular effects of anticancer agents is an important and unexplored field.

With regard to nonrenewing tissues, it is known, for example, that Vinca alkaloids lead to neural toxicity, daunorubicin to cardiac toxicity, and bleomycin to renal toxicity. The mechanisms of these toxicities are not known, although they are crucial to an understanding of dose limitations for these agents. Although the anticancer agents that affect the cell-renewal population can be administered repeatedly since cellular repopulation occurs, the total dose of such agents as daunorubicin is limited, as is the total dose of X-radiation for nonrenewing tissues.

## Sanctuaries

One reason for the failure of chemotherapy is that tumor cells exist in regions of the host into which drugs pass with difficulty. The classic example of such a sanctuary is the meninges of the brain. Leukemic cells can infiltrate the meninges and proliferate there, but most anticancer drugs cannot enter the area in high concentrations.[70] This limitation is circumvented by modifying therapy so that effective levels are reached in these sites. For meningeal leukemia the administration of intrathecal drugs or of drugs that cross the blood—brain barrier and irradiation of the tumor-bearing areas are often effective.

It is important to know of the existence of these anatomical sanctuaries for different tumors and the relationship between cells invading these areas and the progression of the disease. It is also vital to know whether the kinetics of the tumor are different in such sanctuaries than in other parts of the body. Good tumor models, representative of such situations, would be of great help in designing therapy schedules.

## Dose

For a given drug employed against a given tumor, the best dose will depend on the dose—survival curve for the particular tumor cells, the dose—effect curve for normal cell populations in the host, and the pharmacokinetics of the drug. The aim is to ensure that effective levels are maintained for the required time interval.

## Schedule

The schedule of drug administration is then the major consideration that involves all the previously defined parameters to determine the number of dose fractions to be given and the method by which the drug is to be administered, whether single or fractionated injections or infusions. The importance of drug scheduling was demonstrated quite early by Goldin for methotrexate[71] and later by Skipper for cytosine arabinoside.[72] Although little effect was produced by daily fractions, good results and in some cases cures were obtained by administering these phase-specific agents every few hours for one to two generation times. The examination of a number of different schedules[73] is now an integral part of the drug screening program of the National Cancer Institute. Figure 17 conceptualizes the data from Skipper's group. Each drug administration kills a constant fraction of the malignant cell population, 90% in this example, and, depending on the schedule employed, a number of different outcomes can be obtained. If the drug is not given at the proper intervals, the tumor will increase in size between dose fractions and finally kill the host. Optimal therapy can be described simply as leading to the destruction of all malignant cells and so providing cure. For both phase- and cycle-specific agents, it is important to know the growth fraction of the tumor and, more specifically,

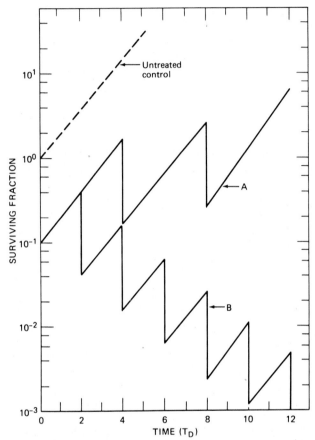

**Fig. 17**   Survival of malignant cells following two different courses of therapy.
Curve A, improper intervals. Curve B, proper intervals. The abscissa is in terms
of the doubling time, $T_D$, of the clonogenic cells.

the traction of clonogenic cells in cell cycle. For tumors having low growth
fractions, aggressive therapy should not be used initially. Rather, the aim should
be to kill only the proliferating cells. Subsequent courses of therapy can then be
designed to eradicate the initially nonproliferating clonogenic cells as they enter
cell cycle. Most human solid tumors likely have low growth fractions, and
investigators are now examining comparable model tumors in animals.[74,75]

In fact, depending on these factors, quite different schedules must be used.
If the tumor demonstrates a broad shoulder in the dose—survival curve and the
normal stem cells are highly proliferative dependent in their response to the
drug, then high-dose intermittent therapy is demanded. On the other hand, if
there is no shoulder, the growth fraction is small, and the normal stem cells
demonstrate little proliferative dependence to a given drug, then small daily

doses would be appropriate. Because of the differences in the predicted therapy resulting from variations in the factors we have considered, it is little wonder that we have seen only the beginnings of the translation of experimental chemotherapy into clinical trials.

## Combination Therapy

If more than one drug is to be administered, a number of factors must be reconsidered. The biology of combination therapy is extensive, and only a few examples will be given here. First, the surgical removal of a tumor prior to chemotherapy has an excellent rationale in that not only is a sizeable tumor cell population removed from the host but, possibly more important, the malignant cells so removed are likely to be quite resistant to chemotherapy. Chemotherapy, either preoperative or postoperative, has a powerful role to play in the treatment of tumors such as breast cancer where, for the majority of patients, removal of the primary tumor is not curative. In fact, the surgical intervention itself can cause the spread of tumor cells. In the case of chemotherapy adjuvant to surgery, the question of how the cell kinetics of wound healing will be affected by the drugs must be considered.

Postoperative radiotherapy can be useful in destroying residual tumor cells but is usually ineffective on metastases. Preoperative radiotherapy is likely to produce a better result than preoperative chemotherapy for solid tumors owing to the greater effect of radiation on nonproliferating clonogenic cells. Whether the agent is a drug or radiation, the purposes of preoperative therapy are first to reduce the number of malignant cells substantially, and thus reduce possibility of metastases, and second to reduce the size of the tumor so as to make surgery possible.

Let us now examine some examples of combination chemotherapy. If two phase-specific agents that kill cells in the same phase of the cell cycle are to be administered, it would not be reasonable from what has been shown in this review to administer these two agents simultaneously. The best procedure would involve administering one of the agents, waiting a sufficient time to allow the remaining viable cells to pass into a sensitive phase, and then giving the second agent. A prerequisite of this approach is exact knowledge of the extent of any progression delay. Data are available for some drug combinations; Fig. 18 presents two examples of combined S-phase specific agents, cytosine arabinoside with 6-thioguanine and cytosine arabinoside with methotrexate. With the former combination, the expected schedule dependency is shown; however, for the latter combination synergism rather than nonadditivity is found when the agents are given together. A striking cellular aspect of the latter combination is shown in Fig. 19. In addition to the increased killing observed immediately, a second mode of cell killing becomes prominent later. The biochemistry of this second phase of cell killing is not known and points up the difficulties involved in basing predictions on limited data.

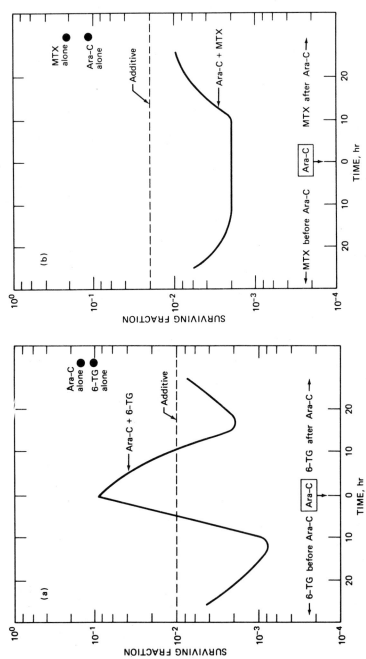

**Fig. 18** Survival of leukemic cells following the administration of cytosine arabinoside (Ara-C) combined with either (a) 6-Thioguanine (6-TG) or (b) Methotrexate (MTX) in vivo. One drug is administered, and, at the time indicated on the abscissa, the second agent is given. The expected additive level (---) is the product of the survival levels of the individual agents used alone. Data from unpublished experiments.

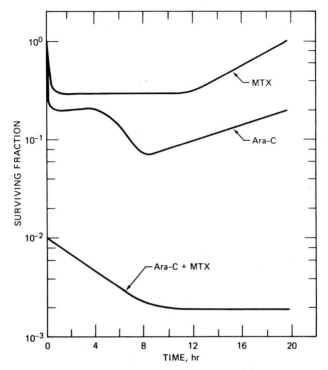

**Fig. 19** Survival of leukemic cells following the administration of a single dose of 1 mg of cytosine arabinoside (Ara-C), 1 mg of methotrexate (MTX), or 1 mg of Ara-C + 1 mg of MTX to leukemia-bearing mice. A 2-min interval existed between the Ara-C and MTX administrations when the combination was given.

A combination treatment that is likely important for solid tumors has been described by Schabel.[37] The first agent destroyed proliferating clonogenic cells, and the second agent was administered when the nonproliferating clonogenic cells had been recruited into cell cycle.

As a final example, Table 1 summarizes the effects of the combination of amphotericin B and BCNU administered to mice bearing an advanced transplantable leukemia. The mice harbor about $10^9$ clonogenic, syngeneic leukemic cells when treated with a dose of amphotericin B, which, by itself, has little cytotoxic effect, and with a dose of BCNU, which, by itself, decreases cell survival by $10^{-2}$ Why the combination is curative is presently not known and further points up our inability to make predictions on the available information.

It would be incorrect to think that these factors are being discussed only for schedule synthesis in experimental animal tumors. Many clinicians and biologists are attempting to use available information to design better therapies.[75,76] This

**TABLE 1**

EFFECTS OF COMBINATION CHEMOTHERAPY ON MICE WITH
AN ADVANCED TRANSPLANTABLE LEUKEMIA

| Treatment | Fraction of leukemic cells surviving 24 hr after drug administration | Mice surviving at 30 days |
|---|---|---|
| None | $10^0$ | 0/10 |
| 0.5 mg amphotericin B alone | $8 \times 10^{-1}$ | 0/10 |
| 0.2 mg BCNU alone | $5 \times 10^{-2}$ | 0/10 |
| 0.5 mg amphotericin B plus 0.2 mg BCNU | $2 \times 10^{-3}$ | 5/10 |

must be continued and expanded in the future if we are to eradicate human malignancies.

## CONCLUSION

In Fig. 20, I have attempted to correlate the factors I have discussed to indicate their role in decisions about schedule design. The manner in which each affects scheduling has been described in this review.

All these factors need be considered in defining optimal chemotherapy or in providing a scientific basis for chemotherapy. A number of investigators have put some of these factors together in previous reviews.[77-82] It should be clear from this presentation, however, that much of the needed data from human tumors is unavailable. This lack of data is the chief reason for the inability of the biologists to translate presently available information into successful clinical protocols. We need more information in many areas, and we need intensive research aimed at the resolution of technical problems and the elucidation of basic concepts.

## ACKNOWLEDGMENT

The research for this paper was supported by U. S. Public Health Service grant 1PO2CA13053 from the National Cancer Institute.

## REFERENCES

1. A. C. Sartorelli, Approaches to the Combination Chemotherapy of Transplantable Neoplasma, *Progr. Exp. Tumor Res.*, 6: 228-288 (1965).

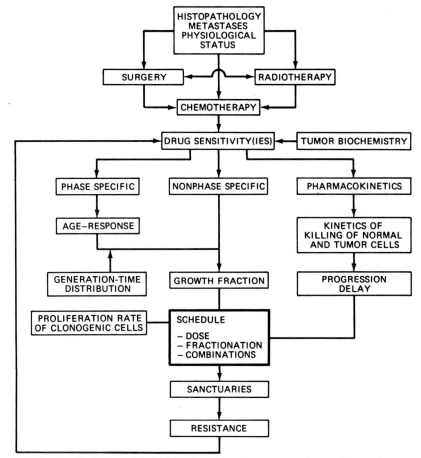

**Fig. 20  Flow diagram indicating the appropriate sequence for considering the different factors important in the scheduling of anticancer agents.**

2. E. S. Greenwald, M. Goldstein, and P. Barland, *Cancer Chemotherapy,* 2nd ed., Medical Examination Publishing Co., Flushing, N.Y., 1973.
3. R. J. Schnitzer and F. Hawking (Eds.), *Experimental Chemotherapy,* Vol. 5, Academic Press, Inc., New York, 1968.
4. P. G. Steward and G. M. Hahn, The Application of Age Response Functions to the Optimization of Treatment Schedules, *Cell Tissue Kinet.,* 4: 279-291 (1971).
5. F. Mauro and H. Madoc-Jones, Age Response of Cultured Mammalian Cells to Cytotoxic Agents, *Cancer Res.,* 30: 1367-1408 (1970).
6. B. K. Bhuyan, L. G. Scheidt, and T. J. Fraser, Cell Cycle Phase Specificity of Antitumor Agents, *Cancer Res.,* 32: 398-497 (1972).
7. S. K. Carter, Study Design Principles for the Clinical Evaluation of New Drugs as Developed by the Chemotherapy Programme of the National Cancer Institute, in *The*

*Design of Clinical Trials in Cancer Therapy*, pp. 242-289, Futura Publishing Co., Brussels, 1973.

8. E. Frei, Combination Cancer Therapy: Presidential Address, *Cancer Res.*, **32**: 2593-2607 (1972).

9. S. Hornsey, The Radiation Response of Human Malignant Melanoma Cells in Vitro and in Vivo, *Cancer Res.*, **32**: 650-651 (1972).

10. W. D. De Wys, A Dose—Response Study of Resistance of Leukemia L1210 to Cyclophosphamide, *J. Nat. Cancer Inst.*, **50**: 783-789 (1973).

11. F. A. Valeriote and S. J. Tolen, Survival of Hematopoietic and Lymphoma Colony-Forming Cells in Vivo Following the Administration of a Variety of Alkylating Agents, *Cancer Res.*, **32**: 470-476 (1972).

12. F. A. Valeriote, W. R. Bruce, and B. E. Meeker, Synergistic Action of Cyclophosphamide and 1,3-Bis(2-Chloroethyl)-1-Nitrosourea on a Transplanted Murine Lymphoma, *J. Nat. Cancer Inst.*, **40**: 935-944 (1968).

13. W. E. Powers and L. J. Tolmach, A Multicomponent X-Ray Survival Curve for Mouse Lymphosarcoma Cells Irradiated in Vivo, *Nature*, **197**: 710-711 (1963).

14. L. Morasca and G. Balconi, Different Sensitivity to Actinomycin D of Biopsies of Human Tumors Cultivated in Vitro, *Eur. J. Cancer*, **9**: 301-304 (1973).

15. P. F. Kruse and M. K. Patterson, Jr., *Tissue Culture: Methods and Applications*, Academic Press, Inc., N.Y., 1973.

16. R. J. Berry, A Comparison of Effects of Some Chemotherapeutic Agents and Those of X-Rays on the Reproductive Capacity of Mammalian Cells, *Nature*, **203**: 1150-1153 (1964).

17. W. R. Bruce, B. E. Meeker, and F. A. Valeriote, Comparison of the Sensitivity of Normal Hematopoietic and Transplanted Lymphoma Colony-Forming Cells to Chemotherapeutic Agents Administered in Vivo, *J. Nat. Cancer Inst.*, **37**: 233-245 (1966).

18. W. R. Bruce, B. E. Meeker, W. E. Powers, and F. A. Valeriote, Comparison of the Dose- and Time-Survival Curves for Normal Hematopoietic and Lymphoma Colony-Forming Cells Exposed to Vinblastine, Vincristine, Arabinosylcytosine and Amethopterin, *J. Nat. Cancer Inst.*, **42**: 1015-1023 (1969).

19. B. K. Bhuyan, T. J. Fraser, L. G. Gray, S. L. Kuentzel, and G. L. Neil, Cell-Kill Kinetics of Several S-Phase-Specific Drugs, *Cancer Res.*, **33**: 888-894 (1973).

20. H. E. Skipper, F. M. Schabel, Jr., and W. S. Wilcox, Experimental Evaluation of Potential Anticancer Agents. XIII. On the Criteria and Kinetics Associated with "Curability" of Experimental Leukemia, *Cancer Chemother. Rep.*, **35**: 1-111 (1964).

21. M. Ogawa, D. E. Bergsagel, and E. A. McCulloch, Differential Effects of Melphalan on Mouse Myelomas (Adj PC-5) and Hematopoietic Stem Cells, *Cancer Res.*, **31**: 2116-2119 (1971).

22. R. A. Tobey and H. A. Crissman, Use of Flow Microfluorometry in Detailed Analysis of Effects of Chemical Agents on Cell Cycle Progression, *Cancer Res.*, **32**: 2726-2732 (1972).

23. G. P. Wheeler, B. J. Bowdon, D. J. Adamson, and M. H. Vail, Comparison of the Effects of Several Inhibitors of the Synthesis of Nucleic Acids upon the Viability and Progression Through the Cell Cycle of Culture H. Ep. No. 2 Cells, *Cancer Res.*, **32**: 2661-2669 (1972).

24. S. Vadlamudi and A. Goldin, Influence of Mitotic Cycle Inhibitors on the Antileukemic Activity of Cytosine Arabinoside (NSC-63878) in Mice Bearing Leukemia L1210, *Cancer Chemother. Rep.*, **55**: 547-555 (1971).

25. W. Sinclair, The Combined Effect of Hydroxyurea and X-Rays on Chinese Hamster Cells in Vitro, *Cancer Res.*, **28**: 198-206 (1968).

26. B. Lampkin, T. Nagao, and A. M. Mauer, Synchronization of the Mitotic Cycle in Acute Leukemia, *Nature*, **222**: 1274-1275 (1969).

27. M. W. Lieberman, DNA Metabolism, Cell Death, and Cancer Chemotherapy, in *The Pathology of Transcription and Translation*, E. Farber (Ed.), pp. 37-53, Marcel Dekker, Inc., New York, 1972.

28. T. Vietti and F. Valeriote, Actinomycin D: Kinetics of Its Lethal Action on a Transplantable Leukemia, *J. Nat. Cancer Inst.*, **46**: 1177-1181 (1971).

29. C. R. Ball, Intracellular Factors Influencing the Response of Tumors to Chemotherapeutic Agents, in *Scientific Basis of Cancer Chemotherapy*, G. Mathé (Ed.), pp. 26-40. Springer-Verlag New York Inc., New York, 1969.

30. F. A. Valeriote, W. R. Bruce, and B. E. Meeker, Synergistic Action of Cyclophosphamide and 1,3-Bis(2-Chloroethyl)-1-Nitrosourea on a Transplanted Murine Lymphoma, *J. Nat. Cancer Inst.*, **40**: 935-944 (1968).

31. F. A. Valeriote and P. Steward, Modeling of Cyclophosphamide Action Against a Transplantable Leukemia, in preparation.

32. H. Riehm and J. L. Biedler, Potentiation of Drug Effect by Tween 80 in Chinese Hamster Cells Resistant to Actinomycin D and Daunomycin, *Cancer Res.*, **32**: 1195-1200 (1972).

33. L. V. Ackerman and J. A. del Regato, *Cancer Diagnosis, Treatment and Prognosis*, 4th ed., C. V. Mosby Co., St. Louis, 1970.

34. F. Gavosto and A. Pileri, Cell Cycle of Cancer Cells in Man, in *The Cell Cycle and Cancer*, R. Baserga (Ed.), pp. 99-128, Marcel Dekker, Inc., New York, 1971.

35. G. G. Steel, The Cell Cycle in Tumors: An Examination of Data Gained by the Technique of Labelled Mitoses, *Cell Tissue Kinet.*, **5**: 87-100 (1972).

36. P. J. Rosen, S. Perry, and F. M. Schabel, Jr., Proliferative Capacity of Leukemic Cells in AKR Leukemia, *J. Nat. Cancer Inst.*, **45**: 1169-1178 (1970).

37. F. M. Schabel, Jr., The Use of Tumor Growth Kinetics in Planning "Curative" Chemotherapy of Advanced Solid Tumors, *Cancer Res.*, **29**: 2384-2389 (1969).

38. E. F. Saunders and A. M. Mauer, Reentry of Nondividing Leukemic Cells into a Proliferative Phase in Acute Childhood Leukemia, *J. Clin. Invest.*, **48**: 1299-1305 (1969).

39. D. E. Bergsagel and F. A. Valeriote, Growth Characteristics of a Mouse Plasma Cell Tumor, *Cancer Res.*, **28**: 2187-2196 (1968).

40. Conference on Time and Dose Relationships in Radiation Biology as Applied to Radiotherapy, Carmel, Calif., Sept. 15-18, 1969, USAEC Report BNL-50203, Brookhaven National Laboratory, 1969.

41. V. T. De Vita, D. A. Bray, F. Bostick, and C. M. Bagley, The Effect of Chemotherapy on the Growth of Leukemia L1210. II. Persistence of a Nitrosourea-Induced Change in the Growth Characteristics of Transplant Generations, *Cell Tissue Kinet.*, **5**: 459-466 (1972).

42. R. E. Johnson, M. Zelen, and N. H. Kemp, Chemotherapeutic Effects on Mammalian Tumor Cells. I. Modification of Leukemia L1210 Growth Kinetics and Karyotype with an Alkylating Agent, *J. Nat. Cancer Inst.*, **34**: 277-290 (1965).

43. I. F. Tannock, The Relation Between Cell Proliferation and Vascular System in a Transplanted Mouse Mammary Tumor, *Brit. J. Cancer*, **22**: 258-273 (1968).

44. D. Kessel and I. Wodinsky, Thymidine Kinase as a Determinant of the Response to 5-Fluoro-2'-Deoxyuridine in Transplantable Murine Leukemias, *Mol. Pharmacol.*, **6**: 251-254 (1970).

45. T. C. Hall, Biochemical Factors Predicting Response to Chemotherapeutic Agents, in *Cancer Chemotherapy II*, I. Brodsky, S. B. Kahn, and J. H. Moyer (Eds.), pp. 93-101, Grune & Stratton, Inc., New York, 1972.

46. D. H. Huffman and N. R. Bachur, Daunorubicin Metabolism in Acute Myelocytic Leukemic, *Blood*, **39**: 637-643 (1972).

47. W. R. Laster, Jr., et al., Success and Failure in the Treatment of Solid Tumors. II. Kinetic Parameters and "Cell Cure" of Moderately Advanced Carcinoma 755, *Cancer Chem. Rep.*, **53**: 169-188 (1969).

48. V. T. De Vita, Cell Kinetics and the Chemotherapy of Cancer, *Cancer Chem. Rep.*, **2**(3): 23-33 (1971).

49. T. Makinodan, G. W. Santos, and R. P. Quinn, Immunosuppressive Drugs, *Pharmacol. Rev.*, **22**: 189-247 (1970).

50. J. Klastersky, Prevention of Infectious Complication and Testing of Antimicrobial Drugs in Cancer Patients, in *The Design of Clinical Trials in Cancer Therapy*, M. Staquet (Ed.), Futura Publishing Co., New York, 1973.

51. F. A. Valeriote and W. R. Bruce, An in Vitro Assay for Growth-Inhibiting Activity of Vinblastine, *J. Nat. Cancer Inst.*, **35**: 851-856 (1965).

52. V. T. Oliverio and D. S. Zaharko, Tissue Distribution of Folate Antagonists, *Ann. N. Y. Acad. Sci.*, **186**: 387-399 (1971).

53. J. Borsa, G. F. Whitmore, F. A. Valeriote, D. Collins, and W. R. Bruce, Studies on the Persistence of Methotrexate, Cytosine Arabinoside, and Leucovorin in Serum of Mice, *J. Nat. Cancer Inst.*, **43**: 235-242 (1969).

54. M. Gibaldi, G. Levy, and H. Weintraub, Drug Disposition and Pharmacologic Effect, *Clin. Pharmacol. Ther.*, **12**: 734-742 (1971).

55. H. S. Schwartz, J. E. Sodergren, and R. Y. Amboye, Actinomycin D: Drug Concentrations and Actions in Mouse Tissues and Tumors, *Cancer Res.*, **28**: 192-197 (1968).

56. H. E. Skipper, The Effects of Chemotherapy on the Kinetics of Leukemic Cell Behaviour, *Cancer Res.*, **25**: 1544-1550 (1965).

57. T. Alper, The Relevance of Experimental Radiobiology to Radiotherapy, *Brit. Med. Bull.*, **29**: 3-6 (1973).

58. E. A. McCulloch, L. Siminovitch, and J. E. Till, Spleen-Colony Formation in Anemic Mice of Genotype WWv, *Science*, **144**: 844-846 (1964).

59. W. R. Bruce and F. Valeriote, Normal and Malignant Stem Cells and Chemotherapy, in *The Proliferation and Spread of Neoplastic Cells*, pp. 409-420, The Williams & Wilkins Company, Baltimore, Md., 1968.

60. W. R. Bruce, F. A. Valeriote, and B. E. Meeker, Survival of Mice Bearing a Transplanted Syngeneic Lymphoma Following Treatment with Cyclophosphamide, 5-Fluorouracil, or 1,3-Bis(2-Chloroethyl)-1-Nitrosourea, *J. Nat. Cancer Inst.*, **39**: 257-266 (1967).

61. H. R. Withers and M. M. Elkind, Microcolony Survival Assay for Cells of Mouse Intestinal Mucosa Exposed to Radiation, *Int. J. Radiat. Biol.*, **17**: 261-267 (1970).

62. J. S. Senn, E. A. McCulloch, and J. E. Till, Comparison of Colony Forming Ability of Normal and Leukemic Human Marrow in Cell Culture, *Lancet*, **2**: 597-598 (1970).

63. C. H. Brown III and P. P. Carbone, Effects of Chemotherapeutic Agents on Normal Bone Marrow Growth in Vitro, *Cancer Res.*, **31**: 185-190 (1971).

64. F. A. Valeriote and W. R. Bruce, Comparison of the Sensitivity of Hematopoietic Colony-Forming Cells in Different Proliferative States to Vinblastine, *J. Nat. Cancer Inst.*, **38**: 393-399 (1967).

65. W. R. Bruce and B. E. Meeker, Comparison of the Sensitivity of Hematopoietic Colony-Forming Cells in Different Proliferative States to 5-Fluorouracil, *J. Nat. Cancer Inst.*, **38**: 401-405 (1967).

66. L. M. Van Putten, P. Lelieveld, and L. K. J. Kram-Idsenga, Cell-Cycle Specificity and Therapeutic Effectiveness of Cytostatic Agents, *Cancer Chemother. Rep.*, **56**: 691-700 (1972).

67. A. Goldin, J. M. Venditti, L. Kline, and N. Mantel, Eradication of Leukemic Cells (L1210) by Methotrexate and Methotrexate Plus Citrovorum Factor, *Nature*, **212**: 1548-1550 (1966).

68. F. A. Valeriote, D. C. Collins, and W. R. Bruce, Hematological Recovery in the Mouse Following Single Doses of Gamma Radiation and Cyclophosphamide, *Radiat. Res.,* **33**: 501-511 (1968).

69. D. E. Bergsagel, G. L. Robertson, and R. Hasselback, Effect of Cyclophosphamide on Advanced Lung Cancer and the Hematological Toxicity of Large, Intermittent Intravenous Doses, *Can. Med. Ass. J.,* **98**: 532-538 (1968).

70. L. E. Broder and S. K. Carter, *Meningeal Leukemia,* Plenum Publishing Corporation, New York, 1972.

71. A. Goldin, J. M. Venditti, S. R. Humphreys, and N. J. Mantel, Modification of Treatment Schedules in the Management of Advanced Mouse Leukemia with Amethopterin, *J. Nat. Cancer Inst.,* **17**: 203-212 (1956).

72. H. E. Skipper, F. M. Schabel, Jr., and W. S. Wilcox, Experimental Evaluation of Potential Anticancer Agents. XXI. Scheduling of Arabinosylcytosine to Take Advantage of Its S-Phase Specificity Against Leukemic Cells, *Cancer Chemother. Rep.,* **51**: 125-141 (1967).

73. J. M. Venditti, Treatment Schedule Dependency of Experimentally Active Antileukemic (L1210) Drugs, *Cancer Chemother. Rep.,* **2**(3): 35-59 (1971).

74. J. Sanberg and A. Goldin, Use of First Generation Transplants of a Slow Growing Solid Tumor for the Evaluation of New Cancer Chemotherapeutic Agents, *Cancer Chemother. Rep.,* **55**: 233-238 (1971).

75. H. E. Skipper, Kinetics of Mammary Tumor Cell Growth and Implications for Therapy, *Cancer,* **28**: 1479-1499 (1971).

76. B. D. Clarkson and J. Fried, Changing Concepts of Treatment in Acute Leukemia, *Med. Clin. N. Amer.,* **55**: 561-600 (1971).

77. G. Mathé, M. Schneider, and L. Schwarzenberg, The Time Factor in Cancer Chemotherapy, *Eur. J. Cancer,* **6**: 23-31 (1970).

78. H. E. Skipper, Kinetic Behavior Versus Response to Chemotherapy, in *Prediction of Response in Cancer Therapy,* NCI Monograph 34, pp. 2-14, Superintendent of Documents, U. S. Government Printing Office, Washington, December 1971.

79. H. E. Skipper et al., Implications of Biochemical, Cytokinetic, Pharmacologic, and Toxicologic Relationships in the Design of Optimal Therapeutic Schedules, *Cancer Chemother. Rep.,* **54**: 431-450 (1970).

80. G. Mathé (Ed.), *Scientific Basis of Cancer Chemotherapy,* Vol. 21, Recent Results in Cancer Research, Springer-Verlag New York Inc., New York, 1969.

81. P. Emmelat, Perspectives in Chemotherapy of Cancer, in *Cancer Chemotherapy,* F. Elkerbout, P. Thomas, and A. Zwaveling (Eds.), pp. 84-104, The Williams & Wilkins Company, Baltimore, Md., 1971.

82. H. E. Skipper, Cancer Chemotherapy Is Many Things, G. H. A. Clowes Memorial Lecture, *Cancer Res.,* **31**: 1173-1180 (1971).

# ON THE CHARACTERIZATION OF THE HUMAN CLONOGENIC CANCER CELL.
# I: ITS NUMBER AND ITS RADIOSENSITIVITY*

J. ROBERT ANDREWS

Radiotherapy Section, Radiology Service, Washington Veterans Administration Hospital, and Department of Radiology, Georgetown University Medical Center, Washington, D. C.

## ABSTRACT

Fundamental to an understanding of the cell cycle and, especially, its implications in cancer is a consideration of the number of cells with unlimited proliferative, that is, clonogenic, capacity and their radiosensitivity. There is no direct method for the quantification of these parameters in human cancers. Human cancer radiotherapy does provide an indirect solution, for such radiotherapy data may be treated in a manner similar to the treatment of in vitro or in vivo radiation dose—cell survival data. That is, the fraction of human cancers not cured or the fraction recurring may be treated as the "surviving fraction" and a dose—response relationship developed. Such a curve permits the assessment of radiosensitivity as a function of $D_0$ and the extrapolation of the curve to zero dose yields a number $N_0 n$, $N_0$ being an approximation of the number of clonogenic cells and n being their mean extrapolation number. Several reported clinical series of squamous- and basal-cell cancers and of Hodgkin's disease are suitable for such treatment. Their analysis suggests $D_0$'s of 200 to 400 rads and $N_0 n$'s of several hundred to several tens of thousands for squamous- and basal-cell carcinomas and a $D_0$ of 150 rads and an $N_0 n$ of 150,000 for Hodgkin's disease. The implications of these findings are developed.

Whatever may be the cause of cancer, it seems evident that a cancer does not manifest itself except through the intermediary of the clonogenic cell, clonogenicity being defined as the capacity for sustained proliferation. Cancer is cured by radiotherapy when no clonogenic cancer cells survive the irradiation. Conversely, cancer recurs when one or more clonogenic cancer cells survive. The

---

*This paper is expanded from material presented at the Conference on the Biological and Clinical Basis of Tumor Radiosensitivity, Rome, Oct. 7-8, 1971, and published in *The Biological and Clinical Basis of Radiosensitivity*, pp. 121-140, Charles C Thomas, Publisher, Springfield, Ill., 1974.

probability of either result is a function of the size of the clonogenic cell population, of the radiation response of that population, and of the radiation dose. Results of human cancer radiotherapy provide data from which something of the radiation response and of the size of the clonogenic cell population can be derived. Such a derivation is based on the following premises:

1. The ratio of cancers not cured, and therefore recurrent or potentially recurrent, to cancers irradiated is a surviving fraction of cancers.

2. The results of human cancer radiotherapy permit, when adequate, the development of this surviving fraction of cancers in the high dose range.

3. This surviving fraction of cancers can be plotted as a function of radiation dose in conformity with commonly understood radiation dose—cell or cell-population survival curves.

4. The terminal portions of such dose—survival curves yield the limiting minimum value of the negative slope of the surviving fraction as a function of dose or, a more commonly understood parameter of the radiation response, the limiting maximum value of $D_0$.

5. Extrapolation of this limiting negative slope to zero dose yields a number $N_0 n$ that characterizes the size, $N_0$, of the clonogenic cell population, assuming the survival of one clonogenic cell at some low level of survival probability, and its mean extrapolation number, n, another parameter of the radiation response. [The parameters $D_0$ and n, which characterize the radiation response, come from the single-hit multitarget model of the relationship of single-cell survival probability as a surviving fraction, SF, to radiation dose, D, where SF = $1 - (1 - e^{-D/D_0})^n$ and $D_0$ is the dose that yields a surviving fraction of 0.37 in the exponential portion of the dose—survival curve. The number, N, of cells surviving from an irradiated population, $N_0$, of clonogenic cells is $N_0(SF)$.

6. The conversion of a radiation dose administered in fractional increments to the equivalent single dose by the application of the Ellis convention is valid. [The Ellis convention[1] assumes a single-dose equivalent, the nominal standard dose (NSD) in terms of the rad-equivalent therapy (ret), to be NSD(ret) = (total dose)/($f^{0.24} t^{0.11}$), where f is the number of fractional increments of dose and t is the overall time in days in which the total dose is administered. The component f is presumed to account for intracellular repair of sublethal injury between fractional doses, and the component t, for the increase in cell numbers due to cell division between doses. The t component may be ignored in applying the convention to tumors of epidermal and epithelial origin because, in general, their proliferation rates are small relative to the time required to complete a definitive course of radiotherapy. In using the Ellis convention, investigators are inconsistent in that they either retain or drop the t component.]

## MATERIALS AND METHODS

The kind and amount of recorded experience with human cancer radiotherapy appropriate for analysis are very limited. The development of a dose—

response relationship requires a range of doses that would yield a range of responses. The ethics of human cancer radiotherapy does not permit this kind of exploration, because each therapeutic attempt must be for the maximum beneficial effect. In fact, only one deliberately determined radiation-dose—cancer-cure response study exists in the human cancer radiotherapy literature.[2] Radiation-dose—cancer-cure response data found to be suitable for analysis, suitability being defined simply as data sufficient to generate a dose—cure relationship, are, besides those of Widmann,[2] those of Hale and Holmes,[3] Shukovsky,[4] Fletcher,[5,6] and Kaplan.[7] The Widmann and the Hale and Holmes data are for single irradiations; the others are for multiple irradiations.

Multiple-dose irradiation data have been transformed to single-dose equivalents by applying the Ellis convention, and, where irradiations were performed with X rays, the tabulated or plotted doses have been increased by 10% over the recorded doses to yield a "cobalt-equivalent" dose.

The opposite of tumor cure is tumor recurrence, which may be cited as a tumor recurrence rate or as an actual or potential surviving fraction of tumors, which, in the reports previously cited, is assumed to be

$$\text{Surviving fraction of tumors} = 1 - \text{cured fraction of tumors}$$

This fraction of tumors recurrent, actual or potential, is plotted, after the corrections previously indicated have been introduced, as surviving fraction vs. radiation dose. Where data are adequate, a typical radiation-dose—cell-survival curve is generated. The mean $D_0$ of the population or of that component of the population represented by the terminal portion of the dose—survival curve can be determined by graphic analysis of the curve. A surviving fraction of 0.05, i.e., an actual or potential tumor recurrence rate of 5%, is equated with a 5% probability of the survival of 1 or more clonogenic cancer cells. The number $N_0 n$ is obtained by extrapolating the terminal exponential portion of the curve from the radiation dose at which the survival, at the 5% probability level, of one clonogenic cell is assumed to zero dose. Figures 1 through 6 are constructed on these principles. Dose is not designated in specific terms of rads, roentgens, or rets because dose is reported quite differently by various investigators and because the terms may be considered equivalent for the argument of this work.

## RESULTS

Figure 1 is constructed from Widmann's data[2] (Table 1), which come from a study deliberately designed to determine the optimal single dose of low-energy X rays for the destruction of cancers of the skin. The responses of 127 skin cancers to various doses were studied. The cancers were described as "moderately flat, none in excess of an estimated 5 mm. elevation above the surrounding skin. The surface areas ranged from 1 to 8 cm. in diameter. The types were evenly divided

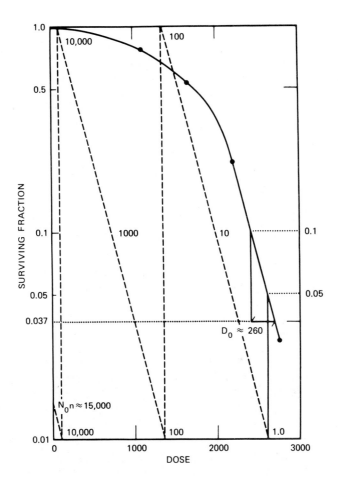

Fig. 1 Surviving fraction vs. dose plotted from the data of Widmann.[2] Figures 1 through 6 are developed similarly. Dose is in terms of the rad, roentgen, or ret, as may be appropriate to the data. Surviving fraction represents the fractional persistence or recurrence of cancer, that is, failure or potential failure of treatment, at the doses or dose-equivalents shown. The term is analogous with that employed in quantitative cellular or tumor experimental radiobiology. $D_0$ is derived graphically in the usual way; it is that dose, or dose-equivalent, which reduces survival probability to 37% (in the figures, from 0.1 to 0.037 surviving fraction) in the exponential portion of the dose—response curve. $N_0 n$ is found by extrapolation from the dose, or dose equivalent, which yields or presumably would yield a 95% cure or control rate, that is, 0.05 surviving fraction, this being considered as consonant with a 5% probability of the survival of one clonogenic cell.

**TABLE 1**

DATA FROM WIDMANN[2] (1941)

| Dose* | Cure rate, % | Fraction cured | Fraction† surviving |
|---|---|---|---|
| 1100 | 23 | 0.23 | 0.77 |
| 1500 | 47 | 0.47 | 0.53 |
| 2000 | 78 | 0.78 | 0.22 |
| 2500 | 97 | 0.97 | 0.03 |

*Doses were single doses of low-energy X rays and were reported in roentgens. The reported doses have been increased by 10% to give a cobalt-equivalent dose.

†Fraction surviving means the fraction of tumors not cured and in which it may be presumed clonogenic cells survive. This fraction is 1 − fraction cured and is plotted as the surviving fraction of tumors in Fig. 1.

between basal- and squamous-cell carcinoma." The range of doses employed and the results attained allow the construction of the curve for radiation dose—tumor recurrence (surviving fraction of tumors) shown in Fig 1. Analysis of the curve in accordance with the principles developed above yields the values, $D_0 \sim 260$ and $N_0 n \sim 15,000$.

Figure 2 and Table 2 present data from Hale and Holmes,[3] who described their study as "an attempt to evaluate the effect that a given number of roentgens, delivered to a carcinoma of the skin, had upon the success or failure of the treatment." A total of 893 lesions received a single irradiation with doses ranging from 1200 to 4000 R of X-radiation (HVL, 1 mm of aluminum to 0.6 mm of copper). All doses used in this study yielded low ($<0.20$) levels of failure, or, as used here, surviving fractions. Thus, as shown in Fig. 2, only the terminal end of the survival curve can be constructed; this, however, is the critical portion for from it can be determined the limiting maximum value of $D_0$ and the extrapolation to $N_0 n$. The data in Table 2 show also that excessively high single doses did not effect more cures but that a saturation value was attained at the dose level of 2650 R with a cure rate of 95%. Derived values of $D_0$ and $N_0 n$ are $D_0 \sim 360$ and $N_0 n \sim 1000$.

Shukovsky[4] studied the radiotherapy results of the treatment of carcinoma of the supraglottic larynx and, with doses reduced to rets, found the dose—response relationships shown in Table 3 and Fig. 3. Values of $D_0$ and $N_0 n$ derived from the analysis of these data are $D_0 \sim 200$ and $N_0 n \sim 70,000$.

The clinical dose—response studies of Fletcher[5,6] are particularly pertinent because of the abundance of the case material and the exhaustive study to which this material has been submitted. Table 4 and Fig. 4 develop the dose—response relationships found in the 1972 study, and Table 5 and Fig. 5, those found in

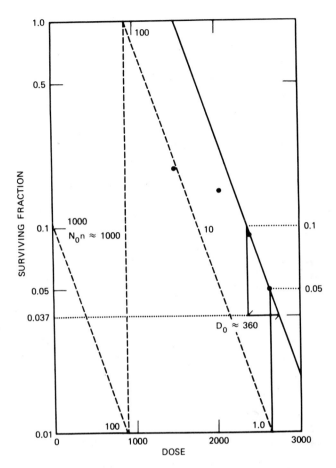

Fig. 2  Surviving fraction vs. dose plotted from the data of Hale and Holmes.[3]

### TABLE 2

### DATA FROM HALE AND HOLMES[3] (1947)

| Number of lesions | Single irradiation | | Mean dose plus 10% for cobalt equivalence* | Failures, % | Surviving fraction of tumors |
| --- | --- | --- | --- | --- | --- |
| | Dose range | Mean dose | | | |
| 153 | 1200–1800 | 1500 | 1650 | 19 | 0.19 |
| 229 | 1900–2200 | 2050 | 2255 | 15 | 0.15 |
| 304 | | 2400 | 2640 | 9 | 0.09 |
| 66 | 2500–2800 | 2650 | 2915 | 5 | 0.05 |
| 111 | 3000–3300 | 3150 | 3465 | 5 | 0.05 |
| 30 | 3500–4000 | 3750 | 4125 | 7 | 0.07 |

*The cobalt-equivalent dose and the surviving fraction of tumors are plotted in Fig. 2, to maximum equivalent dose of 3000.

## TABLE 3

### DATA FROM SHUKOVSKY [4] (1970)*

| Dose, ret | Fraction cured | 1 − fraction cured |
|---|---|---|
| 1700 | 0.15 | 0.85 |
| 1800 | 0.64 | 0.36 |
| 1900 | 0.76 | 0.24 |
| 2000 | 0.85 | 0.15 |

*All values approximate.

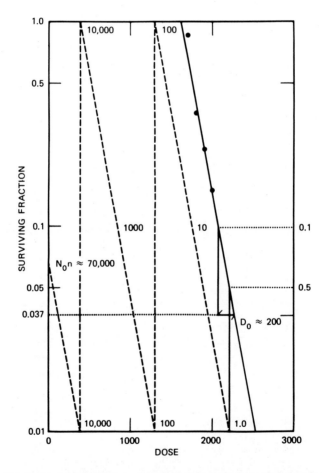

Fig. 3 Surviving fraction vs. dose plotted from the data of Shukovsky.[4]

**TABLE 4**

DATA FROM FLETCHER[5] (1972)*

| Dose, ret | Surviving fraction |
|-----------|--------------------|
| 1560 | 0.33 |
| 1700 | 0.31 |
| 1950 | 0.175 |
| 2300 | 0.075 |
| 2430 | 0.06 |

*Data have been modified by the author according to procedures described in the materials and methods section.

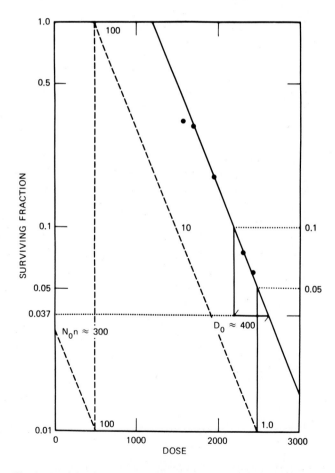

Fig. 4   Surviving fraction vs. dose plotted from the data of Fletcher.[5]

TABLE 5

DATA FROM FLETCHER[6] (1973)

| Doses,*<br>rads | Doses,†<br>rets | Control<br>rate,% | Derived<br>surviving<br>fraction |
|---|---|---|---|
| Adenocarcinoma (Breast) | | | |
| 3250 | 1660 | 65 | 0.35 |
| 4000 | 1950 | 85 | 0.15 |
| 4750 | 2250 | 95 | 0.05 |
| Squamous-Cell Carcinoma (Neck) | | | |
| 3500 | 1750 | 65, 80‡ | 0.35, 0.20‡ |
| 4750 | 2250 | 86 | 0.14 |
| 5000 | 2330 | 92 | 0.08 |
| 5500 | 2470 | 90 | 0.10 |

*Calculated mean doses from Fletcher data; delivery rate: 1000 rads/week.
†As converted by the author.
‡Two data points.

1973. A particular feature of the studies is that they are of subliminal disease. Derived values of $D_0$ and $N_0 n$ are $D_0 \sim 300-400$ and $N_0 n \sim 300-3000$.

The evolution of the radiotherapy of Hodgkin's disease has been in the direction of greater and greater doses to larger and larger volumes of tissue. This has resulted in the accumulation of many data points but with no consistency in their documentation. Kaplan[7,8] has assembled, collated, and analyzed these data, but the deficiencies of their documentation necessitate many assumptions in reducing them to dose—response curves in accordance with the thesis of this paper. The data and their conversions are given in Table 6 and are plotted in Fig. 6. The derived values of $D_0$ and $N_0 n$ for Hodgkin's disease are $D_0 \sim 150$ and $N_0 n \sim 150,000$.

Fletcher's data[6] reveal some important radiation dose—tumor volume relationships for a given response. Conceptually, the larger the tumor volume, the greater, in proportion to the volume, the radiation dose required for a given rate of cure. The mathematics of this concept is straightforward; an increase of the critical clonogenic cell number by, say, a factor of 10 requires an increase of the radiation dose by a factor of 2.3, the natural logarithm of 10, times the $D_0$ dose. The dose—volume relationships for an estimated 90% tumor cure or local control rate for cancers of the tonsil and the supraglottic larynx are shown in Table 7. The data points for the measurable volumes, 4.2, 14, and 65 cm$^3$, are plotted in Fig. 7 with the number of $D_0$'s ($D_0 = 300$, as derived from the Fletcher data of Fig. 5) required for the 90% cure or control rate. The interpretation of

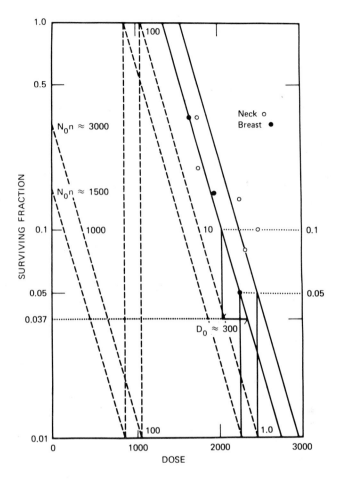

Fig. 5  Surviving fraction vs. dose plotted from the data of Fletcher.[6]

the graphical representation of these dose—tumor volume relationships is that the increase in the number of the critical, or clonogenic, cells of a tumor is not proportional to the increase of its volume. The solid line intersecting the tumor volumes, 4.2, 14, and 65 $cm^3$, lies between $D_0$'s of 6 and 6.66, a difference of only 0.66 $D_0$'s. The broken line is constructed to extend from the tumor volume 4.2 $cm^3$ to a volume 10 times this great, or 42 $cm^3$. These volumes lie between 6 and 8.3 $D_0$'s, a difference of 2.3 $D_0$'s, the difference in the dose required if the increase in volume were due to an increase, by a factor of 10, of the number of critical, or clonogenic, cells. At this 42 $cm^3$ volume the actual increase in the dose required is only 0.55 $D_0$'s (Fig. 7). This suggests that the increase in the number of critical, or clonogenic, cells is only 24% (0.55/2.3 × 100) of the gross increase of the tumor volume. If, in fact, this were not the

## TABLE 6

### DATA FROM KAPLAN[8] (1972)

| Dose, rads | Dose,* rets | Recurrences† % | Recurrent (surviving) fraction |
|---|---|---|---|
| 500 | 400 | 78 | 0.78 |
| 1000 | 675 | 60 | 0.60 |
| 1500 | 909 | 48 | 0.48 |
| 2000 | 1156 | 35 | 0.35 |
| 2500 | 1351 | 26 | 0.26 |
| 3500 | 1750 | 11.5 | 0.115 |
| 4000 | 1951 | 4.4 | 0.044 |
| 4400 | 2095 | 1.3 | 0.013 |

*Conversion based on assumed daily dose of about 200 rads.
†Computed as recurrences/fields at risk × 100.

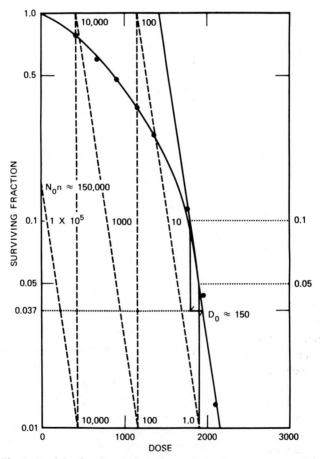

Fig. 6 Surviving fraction vs. dose plotted from the data of Kaplan.[7,8]

**TABLE 7**

**DATA FROM FLETCHER[6] (1973)**
**(DOSE–TUMOR SIZE RELATIONSHIPS FOR AN**
**ESTIMATED 90% TUMOR CONTROL RATE)**

| Tumor diameter, cm | Subliminal | 2 | 2–4 | 4–6 |
|---|---|---|---|---|
| Tumor volume, $cm^3$ | Subliminal | 4.2 | 14 | 65 |
| Dose, rads | 5000 | 6090 | 6800 | 7310 |
| Fractions/weeks | 25/5 | 30/6 | 35/7 | 37/7.5 |
| Ret | 1575 | 1800 | 1900 | 2000 |
| $D_0$'s, ret/300* | 5.25 | 6.0 | 6.33 | 6.66 |

*$D_0 = 300$ (Fig. 5).

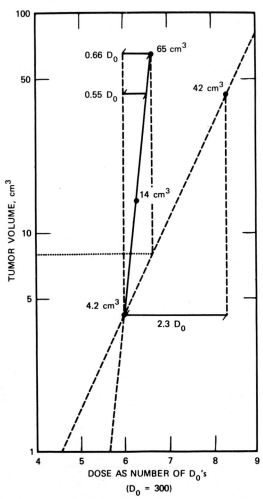

Fig. 7 The dose–volume relationship for 90% cure or control rate of cancers of the tonsil and supraglottic larynx. ——, actual data points. - - - -, projected data points. Data from Fletcher.[6]

case, the dose required for the stated control rate for a 42-cm$^3$ tumor volume would be 2490 ret, a dose generally exceeding human tolerance. [The derivation of this is as follows: Table 7 shows 1800 ret required for the assumed level of cure or control of a tumor volume of 4.2 cm$^3$. With a value of 300 rads assigned to $D_0$, an increase in the clonogenic volume of cells to 10 X 4.2, or 42 cm$^3$, requires an increase of 2.3 X 300, or 690 rads. The dose then required is 1800 + 690, or 2490 ret. This contrasts with the dose, 1800 + (0.55 X 300), or 1965, actually required on the basis of human experience. Or, considered another way, if the volume, 42 cm$^3$, does indeed represent a 10-fold increase in clonogenic cells, then the absolute increase in dose necessary to kill this additional load is 1965 − 1800, or 165 rads. This would yield a $D_0$ value of 165/2.3, or 72 rads, a value of $D_0$ which is exceptionally low and which is not consistent with the values found herein by survival-curve analysis.]

In summary, the results of the analyses of this study suggest 200 to 400 $D_0$'s for carcinomas and 300 to 3000 $N_0n$'s for subliminal disease and up to 70,000 $N_0n$ for overt disease. For Hodgkin's disease the derived values are 150 for $D_0$ and 150,000 for $N_0n$.

## DISCUSSION

The development of numbers in this study is not for the purpose of implying a high degree of quantitative validity to the conclusions drawn, for no confidence limits can be established and the numbers are not subject to experimental verification, but for the purposes (1) of relating the radiosensitivity, in terms of derived values of $D_0$, of human cancers to the radiosensitivity of other mammalian cells, (2) of assessing the number of critical, or clonogenic, cells in human cancers, and (3) of determining the relationship between this number and the volume of a cancer.

In respect of apparent radiosensitivity as related to the oxygen effect, it has been found that in a population of cells which is asynchronous in respect of cell-cycle phasing and heterogeneous in respect of oxygenation the dose—survival curve may be biphasic. This is for the reason that the oxygenated component of the cell population will be selectively depleted at low doses while a relatively greater proportion of hypoxic of anoxic but viable cells will survive to higher doses.[9] Where a population is homogeneous rather than heterogeneous in respect of oxygenation the dose—survival curve will be monophasic with its negative slope or $D_0$ functions, within limiting values, of the degree of oxygenation.[10] Values of $D_0$ for mammalian cells irradiated with low-LET radiations range from 100 to 200 rads for air-equilibrated or oxygenated cells and from 2.5 to 3 times these values at extreme degrees of hypoxia.[11] The values of $D_0$ (200 to 400) derived from this study for carcinomas suggest that what is being displayed in the terminal portions of the dose—survival curves of Figs. 1 through 5 are the terminal portions of biphasic curves, whereas the value of $D_0$ of 150 for

Hodgkin's disease is the terminal portion of a monophasic curve. Such suggestions imply subpopulations of relatively hypoxic and radioresistant clonogenic cells in carcinomas but an oxygenated and fully radiosensitive population in Hodgkin's disease. Whether or not the cells having the $D_0$'s, 200 to 400, derived from this study represent the entire clonogenic cell population or only an hypoxic clonogenic subpopulation is not important from the point of view of the potentiality for cure by radiotherapy, for they do represent the maximum level of radioresistance of the population. If there is a subpopulation of air-equilibrated and radiosensitive cells in the cancer cell population, it already has been destroyed by the radiation doses used in clinical practice.

The number $N_0 n$ cannot be broken down into its components, $N_0$ and n, for there presently exist no means for their determination in the human situation. The assignment of the number 1 as the number of clonogenic cells persisting as the regenerative base at a cancer-cure rate of 95% as the base for back extrapolation to zero dose is arbitrary. Extrapolation to determine a number $N_0 n$ is, however, valid; and, where the clonogenic cell-population number is known, the ratio of $N_0 n$ to the known clonogenic cell-population number gives the value[12] of n. In any event, the value of n is not infinite; and at the most the numbers of clonogenic cells suggested by this study for human cancers are small compared, for example, with the number $10^9$ commonly suggested as the number of cells in a gram of tissue. Those who would choose a fraction other than 0.05 as the conceptual base for the survival of 1 clonogenic cell could gain, simply by inspecting the figures, an impression of the magnitude by which $N_0 n$ would change in relation to another choice. The same consideration obtains for those who may believe that the survival of more than one clonogenic cell is essential for tumor recurrence. In this case $N_0 n$ would be found simply by applying the new number chosen as a multiplication factor to the numbers shown on the figures.

There can be little question about the lack of a direct relationship between an increase of the number of clonogenic cells and an increase of tumor volume, for the considerations of Table 7 and the development of Fig. 7 rest on solid clinical and radiobiological bases.

## CONCLUSIONS

Tentative conclusions that may be drawn from this study are

1. The radiosensitivity of human cancer cells is similar to that of other mammalian cells.

2. The clonogenic cells of human carcinomas are populations or subpopulations of hypoxic and relatively radioresistant cells.

3. These populations or subpopulations are small in relation to cancer volume, and they do not increase in size proportionate to an increase of volume.

4. Hodgkin's disease is a population of cells, also relatively small in relation to tumor volume, at or near the maximum level of radiosensitivity owing to the oxygen effect.

5. Subliminal carcinomas are populations or subpopulations of very small numbers of clonogenic cells that are similar in radiosensitivity to those populations or subpopulations of clonogenic cells of grossly demonstrable cancers.

# REFERENCES

1. F. Ellis, Dose, Time, and Fractionation: A Clinical Hypothesis, *Clin. Radiol.*, **20**: 1-7 (1969).
2. B. P. Widmann, Radiation Therapy in Cancer of the Skin, *Amer. J. Roentgenol., Radium Ther. Nucl. Med.*, **45**: 382-394(1941).
3. C. H. Hale and G. W. Holmes, Carcinoma of the Skin: Influence of Dosage on the Success of Treatment, *Radiology*, **48**: 563-569 (1947).
4. L. J. Shukovsky, Dose, Time, and Volume Relationships in Squamous Cell Carcinoma of the Supraglottic Larynx, *Amer. J. Roentgenol., Radium Ther. Nucl. Med.*, **108**: 27-29 (1970).
5. G. E. Fletcher, Clinical Dose—Response of Subclinical Aggregates of Epithelial Cells, *J. Radiol., Electrol., Med. Nucl.*, **53**: 201-206 (1972).
6. G. E. Fletcher, Clinical Dose—Response Curves of Human Malignant Epithelial Tumours, *Brit. J. Radiol.*, **46**: 1-12 (1973).
7. H. S. Kaplan, Evidence for a Tumoricidal Dose Level in the Radiotherapy of Hodgkin's Disease, *Cancer Res.*, **26**: 1221-1224 (1966).
8. H. S. Kaplan, *Hodgkin's Disease*, Harvard University Press, Cambridge, Mass., 1972.
9. W. E. Powers and L. J. Tolmach, Demonstration of an Anoxic Component in a Mouse Tumor-Cell Population by *in vivo* Assay of Survival Following Irradiation, *Radiology*, **83**: 328-336 (1964).
10. C. J. Koch, J. Kruuv, and H. E. Frey, Variation in Radiation Response of Mammalian Cells as a Function of Oxygen Tension, *Radiat. Res.*, **53**: 33-42 (1973).
11. M. M. Elkind, Cellular Radiobiology and Particle Radiotherapy: Principles, Presumptions, and Pitfalls, in Conference on Particle Accelerators in Radiation Therapy, USAEC Report LA-5180-C, Los Alamos Scientific Laboratory, March 1973.
12. H. R. Withers, J. T. Brennan, and M. M. Elkind, The Response of Stem Cells of Intestinal Mucosa to Irradiation with 14 MeV Neutrons, *Brit. J. Radiol.*, **43**: 796-801 (1970).

# THE KINETICS OF CELL-CYCLE TRANSIT
# AND ITS APPLICATION TO CANCER THERAPY
# WITH PHASE-SPECIFIC AGENTS

PALMER G. STEWARD
Division of Radiation Oncology, Mallinckrodt Institute of Radiology,
Washington University School of Medicine, St. Louis, Missouri

## ABSTRACT

An analytical technique is described for simulating the progression of tumor-cell populations through a cell cycle that includes a $G_0$ phase having an exponential transit-time distribution. The kinetic behavior of a variety of cell populations is simulated, and the significance of this behavior with respect to cancer therapy is examined. The potential role in protocol design of pulse-labelled-mitoses (PLM) data that have been analyzed by computer is examined using the EMT6 tumor as a case study. Computer analysis of the EMT6 tumor PLM data is found to be sufficiently precise to be of potential value in the design of therapeutic protocols for this tumor when S-phase-specific agents are used.

The pulse-labelled-mitosis (PLM) curve is probably the most effective tool available for experimentally determining the kinetics of cells progressing through the cell cycle (hereafter called cell-cycle transit). "Unfolding" the transit-time distributions of the component phases ($G_2$, S, and $G_1$) from a PLM curve requires computer analysis. Takahashi, Hogg, and Mendelsohn[1] have developed a computer program, incorporating a previously developed model of the cell cycle,[2] which automatically analyzes experimental data points of a PLM curve. Steel and Hanes[3] have automated a semiautomatic computer method developed by Barrett[4] that similarly unfolds PLM data. These two programs, which use different models of the cell cycle, do not yield identical phase transit-time distributions from the same experimental PLM data. For example, the experimental PLM data for the EMT6 tumor grown intradermally in mice has been obtained and analyzed by Rockwell, Kallman, and Fajardo,[5] using both computer programs. The means and variances found by these programs for the $G_2$ and S phases are in good agreement. However, the means and variances found for the overall cell cycle and the $G_1$ phase are only in fair agreement.

The question to which this paper addresses itself is: Does the computer analysis of experimental PLM data for the EMT6 tumor define the kinetic behavior of cell-cycle transit to within the limits of precision required for the design of therapy for this tumor when S-phase-specific agents are used? This paper fulfills the stated purpose as follows:

1. The analytical method used to simulate the progression of cells through the cell cycle is described.

2. The kinetic behavior of EMT6 cells as determined by Steel's and by Mendelsohn's* programs are both simulated by this method.

3. The kinetics of a cell population composed of two subpopulations is simulated to be indistinguishable by PLM analysis from the homogeneous population identified by Steel and by Mendelsohn, although each individual subpopulation differs significantly in kinetic behavior from that of the homogeneous EMT6 population.

4. The kinetic behaviors of two additional cell populations are simulated, one with a smaller and one a larger mean and standard deviation than those indicated by Steel's and by Mendelsohn's analyses to be likely for the cell cycle of the EMT6 cells.

5. Therapy on these populations is simulated for two and three doses of an S-phase-specific agent.

## THE ANALYTICAL METHOD

A slightly extended version of a model of the cell cycle developed by Hahn[6,7] was used to simulate cell progression through the cycle (Fig. 1). The cell cycle is divided into N physiological age intervals. The number of age intervals in the $G_1$, S, and $G_2$ phases is $N_{G_1}$, $N_S$, and $N_{G_2}$, respectively. Cells are manipulated so as to simulate aging following each discrete simulated time interval, taken to be $\frac{1}{2}$ hr for the simulations reported here. For example, following each simulated $\frac{1}{2}$-hr interval, the fraction of $G_1$-phase cells that are advanced by 0, 1, or 2 age intervals is $\beta_{G_1}$, $1 - \beta_{G_1} - \alpha_{G_1}$, and $\alpha_{G_1}$, respectively, where $\alpha_{G_1} + \beta_{G_1} \leq 1$. The S- and $G_2$-phase cells are similarly manipulated. The $Nth$ interval contains mitotic cells that are treated as $G_2$-phase cells with the following exception: cells leaving the $Nth$ age interval are doubled in number, and a fraction $f_{N1}$ is placed in the first age interval and a fraction $f_{N0}$ ($f_{N1} + f_{N0} = 1$), in a $G_0$, compartment. Simultaneously, a fraction $f_{01}$ of the

*Although the mathematical and computer methods used in this analysis of PLM data were developed by Takahashi,[1] the computer program incorporating this method was refined and is provided as a service by Mortimer Mendelsohn to those with PLM data requiring analysis. The computer analysis of the EMT6 tumor PLM data used in this paper was provided to Rockwell[5] by Steel and Mendelsohn.

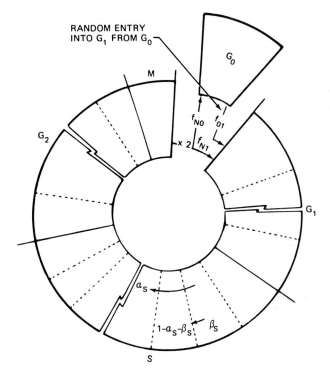

Fig. 1   A diagram of the analytical method.

cells that were in $G_0$ prior to the manipulation are placed in the first age interval. This yields an exponential distribution of transit times through $G_0$ since there is random cell removal from this compartment. It is permissible for $N_{G_1} = 0$; when it does, if $f_{N0} = 1$, it simulates a $G_1$ of one age interval with an exponential transit-time distribution.

# RESULTS

## Application of Method

The PLM data of the EMT6 tumor redrawn from Rockwell, Kallman, and Fajardo[5] are given in Fig. 2 along with the curves fitted to the data by the computer programs of Steel and of Mendelsohn. For Mendelsohn's program the probability density function of the transit times for each phase and for the cell cycle is assumed to be the gamma distribution, and the values for the coefficients of variation are restricted by the condition that they must be the reciprocal square root of some positive integer. Thus, the maximum value for the

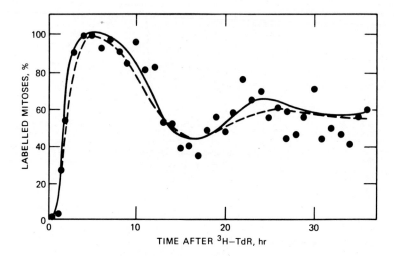

Fig. 2 Percent labelled mitoses in regions with no necrotic features as a function of time after pulse labelling an EMT6 tumor. The pulse labelled mitoses of the cell population were identified by Steel's (—) and by Mendelsohn's (- - - -) analyses of the data points. (Based on Ref. 5.)

coefficient of variation is 1, and in this case the probability density function for the transit time is an exponential. Steel's program assumes the probability density function of the transit times to be log normal. The means, $\mu$, standard deviations, $\sigma$, and coefficients of variation (CV) of the transit-time distributions that correspond to the curves in Fig. 2 are given in Table 1.

Experimental data points of the PLM curve usually have very little scatter as they rise toward the first peak. Since the shape of this initial rise is determined solely by the $G_2$-phase transit-time distribution, the computer programs are expected to provide us with this distribution to a high degree of precision. The scatter in the data points defining the rest of this first peak of the PLM curve is usually not excessive, providing us with the S-phase transit-time distribution to a high degree of confidence as well. Often, however, the data defining successive waves of labelled mitoses are quite scattered, and the reliability of transit-time distributions for the $G_1$ phase, even those obtained by computer analysis, is in question. The approach in this paper is to choose $\alpha$, $\beta$, N, and f for our analytical method such that the cells will progress through the cell cycle in a manner consistent with or deviating in certain prescribed ways from that indicated by the PLM curves of Fig. 2. In this endeavor, the transit-time distributions found by Mendelsohn and by Steel are assumed to be reliable for the $G_2$ and S phases. Therefore, this study is directed primarily at the effects produced by varying those parameters which determine the kinetic behavior of cells in the remainder of the cycle.

**TABLE 1**

TRANSIT-TIME DISTRIBUTION PARAMETERS
DETERMINED FROM ANALYSES BY STEEL AND BY
MENDELSOHN OF THE PLM DATA OF FIG. 2*†

| | Steel | | | Mendelsohn | | |
|---|---|---|---|---|---|---|
| | $\mu$ | $\sigma$ | CV | $\mu$ | $\sigma$ | CV |
| $G_1$ | 7.3 | 10.9 | 1.5 | 8.0 | 8.0 | 1.0 |
| S | 11.9 | 3.6 | 0.30 | 11.9 | 4.5 | 0.38 |
| $G_2$ | 1.9 | 0.7 | 0.37 | 1.7 | 0.76 | 0.45 |
| M | ‡ | ‡ | ‡ | 0.69 | 0.31 | 0.45 |
| C§ | 20.7 | 7.1 | 0.34 | 22.3 | 9.1 | 0.41 |

*Based on Ref. 5.

†Mean, $\mu$; standard deviation, $\sigma$; and coefficient of variation, CV.

‡A mitotic cell is considered to be in either the $G_1$ or the $G_2$ phase.

§Cell cycle.

## Steel Analysis vs. Mendelsohn Analysis

The transit-time distributions found by Mendelsohn and by Steel for the $G_2$ and S phases are shown in Figs. 3 and 4. The points in these figures illustrate the degree to which the analytical method can reproduce these distributions. The corresponding values of the parameters $\alpha$, $\beta$, and N are also indicated. In Mendelsohn's distribution for the $G_2$ phase, mitosis and $G_2$ have been combined so that a single phase with a mean transit time of 2.39 hr and a coefficient of variation of 0.45 is considered.

The transit-time distributions for the cell cycle are similarly illustrated in Fig. 5. The $G_1$-phase transit-time distribution is dependent on the distributions illustrated in Figs. 3 to 5. The parameters determined by the analytical method for the $G_1$ phase and the cell cycle are given in Fig. 5.

As shown in Figs. 4 and 5, Mendelsohn's analysis indicates a higher probability for short transit times for S phase and the cell cycle than is indicated by Steel's analysis and than is simulated by the analytical method. Mendelsohn's model of the cell cycle, which is used in his computer analysis of PLM curves, assumes that the transit-time distributions for each of several age intervals within the cell cycle are exponential. This assumption may give excessive weight to short transit times and suggests a cause for the difficulty in fitting by the analytical method the cell-cycle distribution found by Mendelsohn's program. The fit to Mendelsohn's distribution indicated in Fig. 5 was chosen because, of the more reasonable possible fits, the cell population described by it deviates in

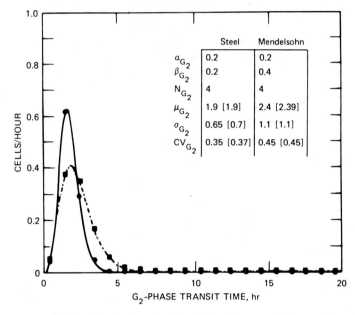

Fig. 3  Probability density function for the $G_2$-phase transit times of the cell population with the PLM curve given in Fig. 2. The distributions obtained by Steel's (——) and Mendelsohn's (— · — ·) analyses are compared with that of the cell populations simulated by our analytical method, which are intended to mimic the behavior of Steel's (●) and Mendelsohn's (■) populations. The parameters used in the analytical method are shown, and the resulting means, standard deviations, and coefficients of variation are compared with those found by Steel and Mendelsohn (taken from Table 1 and enclosed in brackets).

its kinetic behavior maximally from that of the cell population described by the transit-time distributions of Steel. Thus, when therapy is simulated on these cell populations and one tries to determine whether or not the two computer analyses of the PLM curve are sufficiently similar to imply the same optimal therapy protocol, one will be considering a worst case.

## Composite Population

Figure 6 shows that a cell population with a kinetic behavior intermediate between those found by Mendelsohn and by Steel could be a composite of two populations, one cycling at a more rapid rate than the other. The S- and $G_2$-phase parameters for these two populations are given in Table 2 and are chosen to provide transit-time kinetics for these two phases which are intermediate between those found by Steel's and by Mendelsohn's analyses.

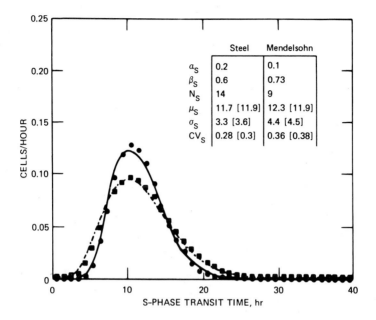

**Fig. 4** Probability density function of the S-phase transit times for the cell population with the PLM curve given in Fig. 2. Curves, points, and table are as described in the legend for Fig. 3.

These two populations differ only in their kinetic behavior during the $G_1$ phase, the parameters for which are given in Fig. 6. Although the cell-cycle transit-time distribution of the composite population has the appearance of that of a single population, the $G_1$ phase clearly shows a two-component transit-time distribution as indicated in the insert in Fig. 6. One component of the population has a mean cycle time of 16.6 hr, the other a mean of 26.5 hr, the composite population being 50% of each.

## Two Limiting Divergent Populations

The effect of allowing the $G_1$-phase transit-time distribution to lie outside the limits suggested by Steel's and by Mendelsohn's analyses has been examined. The cell-cycle transit-time distributions for two of these populations are shown in Fig. 7. The $G_2$-phase and S-phase parameters are given in Table 2, and $G_1$-phase parameters are shown in the figure. The mean and standard deviation of the cell-cycle time distribution for one population (A) are smaller than, and for the other (B) larger than, those found by either Steel or Mendelsohn for the EMT6 cells.

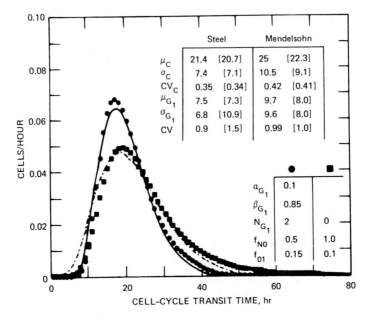

**Fig. 5** Probability density function of cell-cycle transit times for the population with the PLM curve given in Fig. 2. Curves, points, and table are as described in the legend for Fig. 3.

## Simulation of Therapy with S-Phase-Specific Agents

Therapy with S-phase-specific agents was simulated for the populations shown in Figs. 5 to 7 as follows:

1. The cells were advanced through the cell cycle by our analytical method until an equilibrium age—density distribution had been established.

2. The time was initialized to 0 and the population normalized to 1 cell.

3. At hour 1 all S-phase cells were eliminated from the population, simulating the effect of a single dose of an S-phase-specific agent.

4. At hourly intervals thereafter the number of cells, their distribution in the cell cycle (i.e., age distribution), and the number surviving a second dose were determined.

5. Whenever three doses were administered, S-phase cells were first eliminated at hour 1 and again at the time resulting in minimum cell survival; the number of cells surviving a third dose was then recorded at hourly intervals. The results of simulated therapy on the cell populations depicted in Figs. 5, 6, and 7 are shown in Figs. 8, 9, and 10, respectively. For a cell population with the

TABLE 2

## PARAMETERS DEFINING THE $G_2$ AND S PHASES OF AN INTERMEDIATE POPULATION

|  | S | $G_2$ |
|---|---|---|
| $\alpha$ | 0.2 | 0.2 |
| $\beta$ | 0.65 | 0.25 |
| N | 13 | 4 |
| $\mu$ | 11.9 | 2.0 |
| $\sigma$ | 3.6 | 0.75 |
| CV | 0.30 | 0.38 |

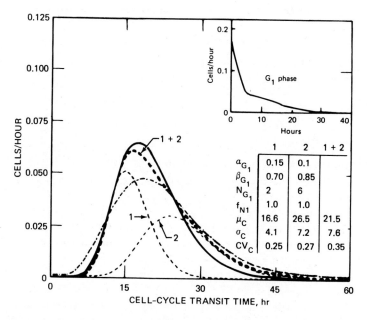

Fig. 6 Probability density function for the cell-cycle transit times of a composite population (- - - -) compared with that found by Steel (——) and by Mendelsohn (— · — ·) in their analyses of the PLM data shown in Fig. 2. The components (1 and 2) of the composite population are also indicated. The figure and Table 2 contain the parameters used in the analytical method, as well as the resulting means, standard deviations, and coefficients of variation for the phase and cycle times. The inset shows the $G_1$-phase transit-time distribution for the composite population. The composite is 50% each of 1 and 2.

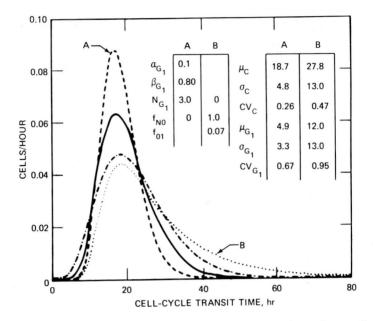

**Fig. 7** Probability density functions for cell-cycle transit times of two cell populations (A and B), each of which differs significantly from that found by the analyses of Steel (——) and Mendelsohn (— · — ·) of the PLM data shown in Fig. 2. The parameters are as described in the legend for Fig. 6.

parameters determined by Steel's program, the time interval between two doses for maximal cell killing appears to be 10 hr (Fig. 8). (This timing neglects all toxic effects of therapy except the lethal action upon S-phase cells; see Discussion.) For the cell population chosen to represent that defined by Mendelsohn's program, the optimal time interval between two administrations is 11 hr. For the composite population (Fig. 9), the optimal time interval is 10 hr (8 hr for one subpopulation, 12 hr for the other). For the two cell populations whose kinetic behaviors are depicted in Fig. 7, the optimal time interval between dose administrations as shown in Fig. 10 is 9 hr for one and 11 hr for the other.

Although the time intervals for optimal dose administrations does not vary greatly from population to population, those populations with the smaller mean generation times and smaller standard deviations have characteristics indicating that the timing for the dose intervals is quite critical. For the faster growing subpopulation of Fig. 9, nearly four times greater cell killing would be achieved were the second dose to be administered 8 hr rather than 11 hr after the first dose. The timing of subsequent dose administrations for the populations with the larger standard deviations is less critical. For these populations there would be little change in the cell survival as the interval between dose administrations varies from 8 to 13 hr.

The optimal time for a subsequent dose as predicted by the model (Figs. 8 to 10) is when the fewest number of cells exist outside the S phase. With this in mind one can clearly visualize the chain of events resulting in the behavior shown in Figs. 8 to 10 by observing the change in the age—density distribution as a function of time following a single dose. Such a set of age—density distributions is illustrated in Fig. 11 for the EMT6 cell population identified by Steel's program. (Its kinetic behavior is illustrated in Figs. 3 to 5.) Here the distribution at 0 hr is the equilibrium age—density distribution; at 1 hr all S-phase cells are eliminated, and in subsequent hours the S phase is refilled by cells entering through $G_1$ from $G_0$ and mitosis. At 12 hr, which, as Fig. 8 indicates, is a nearly optimal time for giving a second dose, a large fraction of the cells is in S phase.

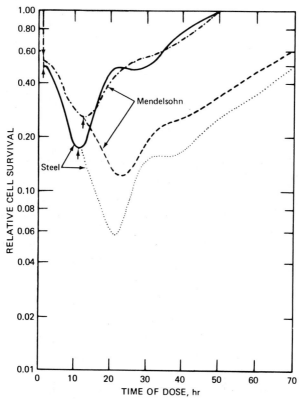

Fig. 8  Number of cells from the populations identified by the analyses by Steel (—) and by Mendelsohn (— · — ·) of the PLM data (Fig. 2) surviving a two-dose protocol from an S-phase-specific agent. The first dose is given at 1 hr, and the second dose, at the abscissa times. The effect of a three-dose protocol is similarly illustrated (- - - - and · · · ·) where the first two doses are given at the times indicated by the arrows.

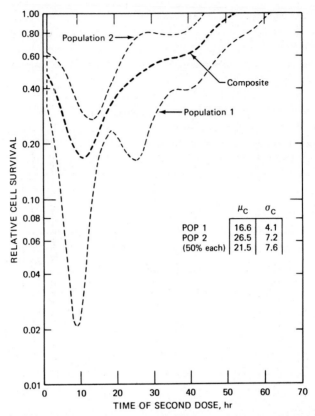

Fig. 9 Number of cells of the composite population of Fig. 6 that survive the second of two doses of an S-phase-specific agent. The first dose is given at hour 1, and the second dose, at the abscissa times. Cell survival in the component populations is also indicated. The means and standard deviations of the cell-cycle transit times for the two component populations as well as the composite population are shown.

## DISCUSSION

The kinetic behavior of cell-cycle transit is only one of many factors that must be considered in protocol design. For example, some of the toxic effects of anticancer agents are manifested by cell-cycle progression delay. In a large cell population, the cells are certain to show a distribution of delay times; so the therapy simulation curves of Figs. 8 to 10 will not simply be displaced along the time axis but will manifest a more general distortion. Dose dependence has been ignored because in the therapy simulations described here the number of S-phase cells surviving is negligible compared to the number of nonsensitive (not in

S-phase) cells. However, cell-cycle progression delay is probably dose dependent; thus not only will Figs. 8 to 10 be distorted along the time axis but this distortion may be dose dependent. Another factor that has not been adequately considered is the time dependence of the concentration of anticancer agents at the tumor site. If cells progress into S phase during the time that the agent is at lethal levels in the patient, one may expect smaller and smaller fractions of these cells entering S phase to be killed as the concentration of the anticancer´agent to which the cells are exposed decreases. A third factor ignored is the perturbation of cell survival caused by the patient's own defense mechanisms to the cancer cells. These responses may themselves be time dependent owing to their

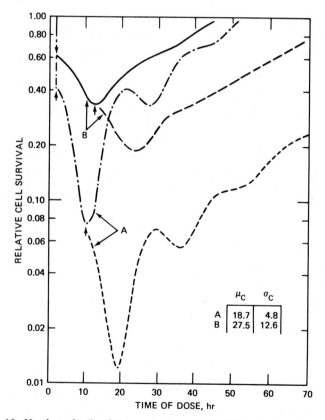

Fig. 10  Number of cells of the populations of Fig. 7 (A and B) surviving the second of two doses of an S-phase-specific agent (— and  — · —) when the first dose is given at hour 1 and the second dose at the abscissa times. The number of cells surviving the third of three doses of this agent (- - -) is illustrated where the first two doses are given at the times indicated by the arrows. Means and standard deviations of the cell-cycle transit times are given.

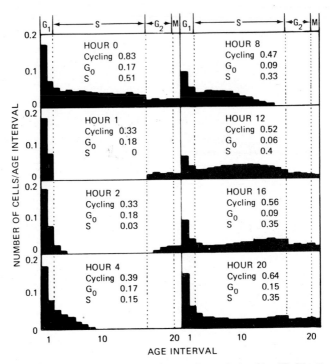

**Fig. 11** Age—density distributions of the cell population identified by Steel's analysis of the PLM data (Fig. 2). At hour 0 the equilibrium age distribution is shown. At hour 1 an S-phase-specific agent is applied, and the subsequent age distributions are shown at the indicated times assuming the transit-time distributions illustrated for our fit of Steel's analysis in Figs. 3 to 5. The number of cells in cycle, in $G_0$, and in S phase is given for each time.

perturbations by the anticancer agents. A fourth factor ignored is the possibility of a time-dependent enhancement of the rate of $G_0$ cells entering the $G_1$ phase (i.e., recruitment of $G_0$ cells into cycle).

We have suggested that the EMT6 cell population described by Steel's and by Mendelsohn's analyses of the PLM data of Fig. 2 is perfectly compatible with a heterogeneous population of two components, one cycling faster than the other. One possible mechanism for the establishment of such a two-component population would be the existence of two possible metabolic modes for each cell, with cells on different sides of an environmental threshold metabolizing by different biochemical pathways. The composite population (Fig. 9) does not differ significantly in its response to a two-dose regimen from that of the homogeneous populations of Fig. 8, although each of the two components behaves quite differently from the other. Thus the possibility of a composite population is not of great therapeutic significance unless there is reason to concentrate therapy more on one component than on the other. On the basis of Fig. 9, for example, one might conclude that it is more difficult to eliminate the slower growing population than the faster growing population; thus one should concentrate his efforts therapeutically on the component which cycles more slowly, expecting the faster cycling component to be eliminated in the process. It is important to realize, however, that for these two components to coexist, a control mechanism, e.g., nutrient deprivation, must be operating to limit the growth of the faster cycling population, since in the absence of such a mechanism the slower growing component would, after sufficient time, become a negligibly small part of the total population. With this in mind, it may be reasonable for one to treat selectively the faster growing population under the assumption that the slower growing population will be induced into more rapid proliferation by subsequent environmental changes. This adds further emphasis to the previous conclusion that when considering therapy design the kinetics of cell-cycle transit must be considered in conjunction with other factors influencing the kinetic behavior of the population.

For these reasons, and probably many others, we do not claim that the results depicted in Figs. 8 to 10 are directly applicable clinically; yet the kinetic behavior of cell-cycle transit is sufficiently complex that a systematic computer analysis is helpful in identifying its significance in cancer therapy. For example, by comparing the curves in Figs. 8 and 10, one can predict the strong possibility that cell killing can be significantly increased by optimal timing of subsequent doses for a population whose cell transit-time distribution has a small mean and a small standard deviation. For populations whose cell transit-time distributions have a large mean and a large standard deviation, it is probably of greatest concern to keep cell proliferation to a minimum between doses, since for these populations the advantage of optimal timing is much less.

For each of the cell populations we have examined, the analytical method predicts an optimal time for the second administration of an S-phase-specific agent, since the cells that were in the $G_2$ and $G_1$ phases during the first administration progress into S phase in approximately half a mean cell-cycle time. This is shown in Fig. 11, where at hours 2, 4, and 8 the wave of cells moving into S phase is clearly visible, and, by hour 12, the age distribution peaks in S phase, and the number of cells in $G_0$ is at a minimum. This is then the optimum time for a subsequent administration if it is to be the final dose given. It was a similar observation that led to the suggestion[8] that doses of phase-specific agents presently administered as a single push could be split in half, the second half dose being administered slightly more than half a cell-cycle time following the first. Approximately one cell-cycle time following the first administration, the second administration would be expected to have minimal effect since by this time the nadir in the age—density distribution created by the first administration would have progressed into S phase again. However, as shown by the age distribution at hour 20, this effect is not as pronounced as one might expect. Although the age distribution in S phase at this time is concave upward, the vacancy in the distribution has nearly disappeared owing to the synchronous cohort's rapid dispersion as implied by the broad transit-time distributions of this cell population (Figs. 3 to 5).

## CONCLUSION

Information on cell kinetics derivable from PLM curves is far from sufficient for protocol design. However, the therapeutic conclusions derivable from Steel's and from Mendelsohn's analyses of the PLM data indicated by Fig. 8 do not differ, and data such as these may play a useful role in protocol design if applied judiciously. Although there is possibly a significantly greater advantage to optimal dose timing for cell populations whose phase transit-time distributions have smaller standard deviations, two cell populations can differ greatly in their kinetic behavior of cell-cycle transit without differing significantly in their optimal timing (Fig. 10). We conclude that the analysis of PLM data by the computer programs of Steel and of Mendelsohn is sufficiently precise to be of potential value in protocol design.

## ACKNOWLEDGMENTS

The contribution of Don P. Ragan, who made his PC12/7 computer available for this analysis, is gratefully acknowledged.

The research for this paper was supported by U. S. Public Health Service grant 1PO2CA13053 from the National Cancer Institute.

## REFERENCES

1. Manabu Takahashi, Joseph D. Hogg, Jr., and Mortimer L. Mendelsohn, The Automatic Analysis of PLM Curves, Cell Tissue Kinet., 4: 505-518 (1971).
2. M. Takahashi, Theoretical Basis for Cell Cycle Analysis. II. Further Studies on Labelled Mitosis Wave Method, J. Theor. Biol., 18: 195-209 (1968).
3. G. G. Steel and S. Hanes, The Techniques of Labelled Mitoses: Analysis by Automatic Curve-Fitting, Cell Tissue Kinet., 4: 93-105 (1971).
4. J. C. Barrett, A Mathematical Model of the Mitotic Cycle and Its Application to the Interpretation of Percentage Labelled Mitoses Data, J. Nat. Cancer Inst., 37: 443-450 (1966).
5. Sara C. Rockwell, Robert F. Kallman, and Luis Felipe Fajardo, Characteristics of a Serially Transplanted Mouse Mammary Tumor and Its Tissue Culture Adapted Derivative, J. Nat. Cancer Inst., 49: 735-749 (1972).
6. G. M. Hahn, State Vector Description of the Proliferation of Mammalian Cells in Tissue Culture. I. Exponential Growth, Biophys. J., 6: 275-290 (1966).
7. G. M. Hahn, A Formalism Describing the Kinetics of Some Mammalian Cell Populations, Math. Biosci., 6: 295-304 (1970).
8. Palmer G. Steward and George M. Hahn, The Application of Age Response Functions to the Optimization of Treatment Schedules, Cell Tissue Kinet., 4: 279-291 (1971).

# EVALUATION OF THE PDP INDEX
# AS A MONITOR OF GROWTH FRACTION
# DURING TUMOR THERAPY

LEWIS M. SCHIFFER,* ARNOLD M. MARKOE,* and JANET S. R. NELSON†
*Cell and Radiation Biology Laboratories, Allegheny General Hospital,
Pittsburgh, Pennsylvania, and †Division of Radiation Oncology,
University Hospital, Seattle, Washington

## ABSTRACT

The rationale of using the PDP (primer—template-available, DNA-dependent DNA polymerase) index as an estimator of growth fraction in unperturbed murine tumors is described.
Evidence is presented to indicate that the PDP index may also be an estimator of growth
fraction in systems perturbed by radiation and chemotherapeutic drugs. Also described are
the responses of the PDP and $^3$H—TdR labelling indexes after sublethal doses of radiation,
BCNU, hydroxyurea, and vincristine in the solid T1699 adenocarcinoma and the solid S-180
sarcoma. This assay procedure has substantive potential in the design of new therapeutic
regimens for murine tumors.

Those of us who use drugs or radiation to treat patients with cancer are
frustrated by the lack of information on the acute effects of these modalities on
tumors. As a result cytotoxic drug scheduling and fractionated forms of
radiation are among the least well studied aspects of treatment. For this reason
also, treatment is usually confined to toxicity of normal tissues rather than to
predicted and defined end points in the tumor itself.

We need one or more tools or techniques to develop some of these areas of
knowledge. Clearly, our present use of tritiated thymidine ($^3$H—TdR) in vivo to
measure cytokinetic parameters is severely limiting in the areas of time, radiation
dose, and multiple tissue sampling. The work discussed in this paper was
designed to overcome some of these difficulties and, hopefully, to provide a
potentially useful tool for the cancer therapist.

The concept of noncycling cells or growth fraction (GF) as defined by
Mendelsohn[1] is important not only from the specific cytokinetic viewpoint but
also as a theory with general usefulness in the therapy of cancer. We know, for
example, that with some exceptions the most radiosensitive cells are in late $G_1$,

$G_2$, and M—all within the proliferating pool of cells. Likewise, many of the successful chemotherapeutic protocols have been designed to use cycle-specific agents that act on cells within the proliferating pool. Other protocols are designed to induce cells from the noncycling state into a vulnerable position within the proliferating pool.

For clinical purposes there are, at present, only two crude, indirect ways of assessing the growth potential of a human tumor-cell population: the mitotic index and the $^3$H–TdR labelling index ($^3$H–TdR LI). The mitotic index has been recognized as a cytokinetic parameter for many years but is little used for prescribing therapy. The $^3$H–TdR LI may be useful in dispersed tumor-cell populations, such as in the leukemias, where it can be obtained in vitro. There are many problems and disadvantages when this technique is used for solid tissue. In vivo $^3$H–TdR procedures can, of course, be accomplished experimentally but have achieved little clinical usefulness because of the factors mentioned previously.

In recent years fluctuation of cellular DNA-dependent DNA polymerase (DDDP) during the mammalian cell cycle has been actively investigated using a cell-free assay system that usually requires the addition of exogenous DNA primer—template. Under these conditions the activity of the cytoplasmic DDDP exhibits marked fluctuation according to position in the cell cycle[2,3] and shows little activity in quiescent or noncycling systems.[2,4] Nuclear DDDP activities, on the other hand, do not change appreciably during the cell cycle[2,3,5] and may remain detectable in quiescent cells.[2] However, if exogenous DNA primer—template is not added in this assay procedure and sole reliance for DNA synthesis is placed on endogenous primer—template being present, nuclear DDDP activity does exhibit considerable fluctuation in synchronized mammalian cell populations.[5] This activity is also discernibly higher in cells from logarithmically growing cultures than in cells from stationary-phase cultures.[5]

These studies, all using a cell-free assay system, measure an average DDDP activity in all cells of the studied cohort and cannot indicate the activity of DDDP in a given cell or the proportion of cells in a population which exhibit DDDP activity. We recently described[6] an in vitro autoradiographic method for qualitatively detecting the presence of DDDP in individual nuclei using the cell's own endogenous nuclear DNA as primer—template. This in vitro assay is called the primer—template-available, DNA-dependent DNA polymerase (PDP) assay. It allows the determination of the fraction of cells in a given population with PDP-positive nuclei, the PDP index.

The fact that nuclei are labelled indicates that they contain DNA polymerase and DNA competent to act as primer—template. Cells other than those in DNA synthesis are forced to label if they contain these constituents. In all experiments performed to date, the PDP index exceeds the $^3$H–TdR LI.

It is appropriate to consider what we believe we are measuring with the PDP index. It is apparent that all cells in DNA synthesis (S) are PDP positive. This information is obtained from S-180 ascites cells synchronized by hydroxyurea. Peripheral blood lymphocytes, which are normally out of cycle, are PDP negative. These same cells stimulated out of cycle by phytohemagglutinin become PDP positive 5 to 11 hr prior to the start of the S phase. Dead cells, measured by S-180 ascites cells heat killed by 45°C temperatures, become PDP negative with a half-time of 30 min. Mitoses are approximately 50% PDP positive, depending on which cell system is used, with prophases almost always positive and with decreasing positivity during mitosis. We have not measured $G_2$ cells directly, but, from the evidence of positive prophase figures, we feel they are generally PDP positive.

Recently we showed[7] that the fraction of cells whose nuclei contain DDDP and DNA capable of acting as primer–template is a close estimate of the fraction of cells in cycle (GF) in murine tumors that have a short $G_1$ phase (Table 1).

TABLE 1

COMPARISON OF MEASURED TUMOR GROWTH FRACTIONS
WITH THE PDP INDEX

| Tumor type | Tumor age, days | Measured growth fraction | PDP index, mean ± 1 S.E.M. |
|---|---|---|---|
| T 1699 solid | 14 | 0.30 | 0.27 ± 0.03 |
| H 2712 solid | 7 | 0.47 | 0.44 ± 0.02 |
| S-180 solid | 5 | 0.62* | 0.51 ± 0.03 |
| Ehrlich ascites | 2 | 0.78 | 0.80 ± 0.02 |
| Ehrlich ascites | 4 | 0.74 | 0.70 ± 0.01 |
| Ehrlich ascites | 6 | 0.60 | 0.61 ± 0.04 |
| Ehrlich ascites | 9 | 0.52 | 0.62 ± 0.01 |
| S-180 ascites | 2 | 0.95 | 0.88 ± 0.01 |
| S-180 ascites | 4 | 0.93 | 0.88 ± 0.02 |

*Value obtained from the literature.[8]

This confirms our estimates of PDP positivity during the various phases of the cell cycle.

Studies in cells with longer $G_1$ phases, such as human tumor cells, are now in progress, but in this paper we present some of our studies on the effects of drugs and radiation on the PDP indexes of solid transplantable murine tumors and on murine ascites tumors.

## MATERIALS AND METHODS

Single-cell suspensions were obtained from the solid, transplantable mammary adenocarcinoma T1699 (JAX) and the solid sarcoma 180 (S-180) by mincing the tumor tissue in culture medium. Cells from the S-180 ascites system were harvested directly from the peritoneum.

These cells were pelleted, washed, and spread onto acid-cleaned slides. The air-dried, unfixed smears were dipped in 0.25% agar and again air dried. This process appears to disrupt the cytoplasmic membrane, leaving only nuclei adhering to the slide. The slides were then subjected to the PDP assay described previously.[6] Briefly, chambers were made by affixing a glass ring to each slide; then 0.5 ml of incubation medium was added. This medium contained $8.3 \times 10^{-5}$ mole each of deoxycytidine-5'-triphosphate, deoxyguanosine-5'-triphosphate, and deoxyadenosine-5'-triphosphate and $10^{-2}$ mole of $MgCl_2$, all in $2 \times 10^{-2} M$ Tris—HCl buffer (pH 7.7 at $25°C$). Before use, the medium was supplemented with 400 mg of Ficoll and 4 $\mu$Ci of tritiated deoxythymidine-5'-triphosphate (specific activity, 17 to 19 Ci/mmole) per milliliter of incubation medium. The slides were incubated at $37°C$ for 45 min. After fixation, rinsing, and dehydration, the slides were autoradiographed with a 1 : 1 dilution of NTB2 liquid emulsion. The results to be discussed were derived from a minimum of three (usually six) animals per point and evaluation of 500 nuclei from each animal for label.

Tritiated thymidine (1 $\mu$Ci/g of body weight) was administered intraperitoneally (i.p.) to different animals 45 min before sacrificing. The tumors were minced in tissue-culture medium and handled as previously described. Five hundred cells were counted for the $^3$H—TdR LI.

The irradiation studies were performed by giving 600 R whole-body X-irradiation. This is below the lethal level at 7 days. Vincristine was administered in a single i.p. dose at 2.5 mg/kg and BCNU was administered in a single i.p. dose at 40 mg/kg. These are approximately $LD_{10}$ dosages. The hydroxyurea was given intraperitoneally in two doses of 2 g/kg each separated by 3 hr. This is also below the $LD_{10}$ for the mouse. The drugs and radiation, then, were administered individually as single, intensive treatments.

## RESULTS AND DISCUSSION

In all the graphs in this paper, the hatched areas represent the normal PDP and $^3$H—TdR LI for tumors of that age. The 0 day for the S-180 tumor is the 5*th* day after implantation, and the 7*th* day represents the 12*th* day after implantation in unperturbed tumors. The width of the hatched area does not represent any significance values. Although we have convincing evidence that the PDP index is a very close estimate of GF in unperturbed systems (Table 1), we have no evidence that this is so in tumors treated with drugs or radiation. Although we believe this may be the situation, we will refer to PDP indexes rather than GF and try to make an argument for the equivalence of these values.

## Effects of Irradiation

In the T1699 system (Fig. 1), the PDP LI does not change until after 3 days postirradiation. However, the PDP LI at 7 days (21 days after implantation) is below the normal for a 21-day unperturbed tumor. The $^3$H—TdR LI, or fraction of cells in S phase, is increased at 2 days after irradiation, is further elevated at 3 days, and returns toward normal at 7 days. If we make the challengeable assumption of no change in S phase duration ($T_s$) during this period of time, the cell-cycle time ($T_c$) is decreased at 3 days after irradiation and is back to normal by 7 days.

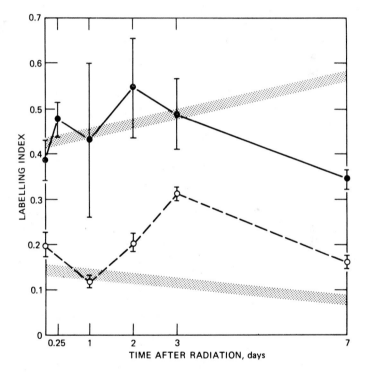

Fig. 1  Effects of 600-R, whole-body, 250-kVp radiation on the 14-day T1699 solid mammary adenocarcinoma. The hatched areas are normal values for unperturbed tumors. ●, PDP. ○, $^3$H—TdR. Ɨ, 1 S.E.M.

In the S-180 system (Fig. 2), the PDP LI is elevated at 2 days after irradiation and remains so throughout the study. At 2 days and thereafter, the $T_c$ is prolonged if one assumes the $T_s$ is unchanged.

Although no direct comparisons are available, these data are consistent with the radiation-response data reported by Denekamp,[9] which showed that carcinomas and sarcomas behaved differently. The volumes of transplanted

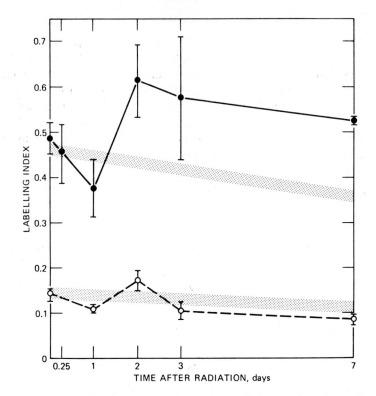

Fig. 2  Effects of 600-R, whole-body, 250-kVp radiation on the 5-day S-180 solid sarcoma. The hatched areas are normal values for unperturbed tumors. •, PDP. ○, ³H—TdR. ⚊, 1 S.E.M.

carcinomas given 1 to 2 krad of radiation decreased slowly but continuously, whereas the sarcomas, on average, stopped growing significantly after 2 or 3 days. We can contribute no cell-loss data, but the reduction in PDP LI for the T1699 after 3 days is compatible with this information. Other studies[10] have shown variable increases in GF in transplanted sarcomas after irradiation, as seen in our S-180 system. Also there is some evidence[11] that $T_c$ decreases shortly after irradiation in carcinomas, as also indicated in our T1699 system.

## Effects of BCNU

There is an increase in the PDP LI in both tumors immediately after the administration of 1,3-bis(2-chloroethyl)-1-nitrosourea (BCNU). In the T1699 tumor (Fig. 3), the increase is striking and is prolonged for 3 days. Following the peak elevation at 1 day, a linear reduction to a very low level at 7 days occurs. The ³H—TdR LI is transiently elevated at 2 days only.

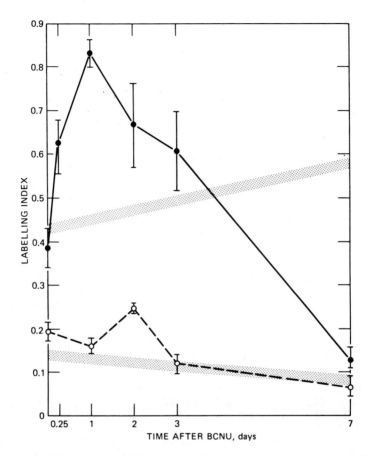

Fig. 3   Effects on the 14-day T1699 solid mammary adenocarcinoma of 40 mg/kg of BCNU given intraperitoneally. The hatched areas are normal values for unperturbed tumors. ●, PDP. ○, $^3$H−TdR. Ī, 1 S.E.M.

In the S-180 tumor (Fig. 4), the increase in PDP LI is short, peaking at 6 hr and again at 7 days. The $^3$H−TdR LI is depressed at 2 days and thereafter.

BCNU, one of the first nitrosoureas to be used clinically, has been found to prolong the S phase as well as the $G_2$ period.[12] There is also some evidence, in the L1210 leukemia, that there is a reduced GF at 7 days after drug administration.[12] Our data for the T1699 solid tumor show a marked reduction in PDP LI 7 days after drug, but, in addition, the data indicate a marked elevation in PDP LI over the first 3 days. One or both of the following theories may explain these results: It has been shown that BCNU is more effective in resting hematopoietic stem cells than in the rapidly proliferating ones.[13] If this holds true for tumor cells as well, a selective kill of noncycling tumor cells should increase the PDP LI. It may also be conceivable that cells are recruited

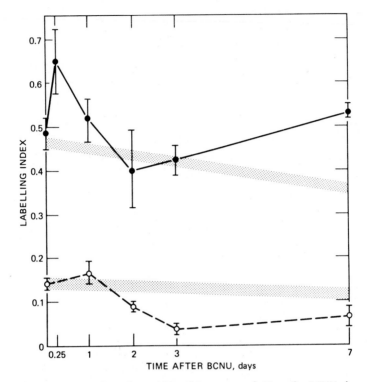

Fig. 4   Effects on the 5-day S-180 solid sarcoma of 40 mg/kg BCNU given intraperitoneally. The hatched areas are normal values for unperturbed tumors. •, PDP. ○, $^3$H–TdR. $\bar{x}$, 1 S.E.M.

out of the noncycling state and into the proliferative fraction, thereby increasing the PDP LI. The latter explanation would seem less likely since the 7-day value of the PDP LI is markedly reduced and most cells seem to be in the noncycling compartment. However, the possibility of a reversion of cells recruited into cycle back into the noncycling compartment cannot be excluded.

Our data on the S-180 tumor are less clear. We see depression of DNA synthesis, like that seen in the L1210, but no depression of the PDP LI. No estimates of $T_c$ are made, because of the known prolongation of $T_s$ by BCNU.

### Effects of Hydroxyurea

The effects of hydroxyurea (HU) are also different in the two systems tested. Hydroxyurea, which either kills or inhibits cells in S phase[14] and prevents cells from advancing through the $G_1$–S interface, has been used as a synchronizing agent. This effect can be clearly observed in Fig. 5 in which HU was given at 0 and 3 hr in the S-180 ascites experimental series. DNA synthesis is immediately suppressed and then rises to 100% at 10 hr. Presumably the surviving cells were held at the $G_1$ –S interface until the drug effect dissipated. These surviving cells are all in the proliferative pool, however, and therefore the PDP LI is also very high. The solid-tumor data are more confusing.

In the T1699 tumor (Fig. 6), the only significant alteration in PDP LI is an increase at 1 and 2 days after drug administration. This is paralleled by a general increase in $^3$H–TdR LI. These data are consistent with the results recently reported by Dethlefsen and Riley.[15] They found an increased GF in transplanted C3H tumors at 24 hr after HU administration.

The S-180 tumor (Fig. 7) shows a transient 6-hr rise in PDP LI followed by a sustained rise at 3 days. In this case the $^3$H–TdR LI was depressed throughout.

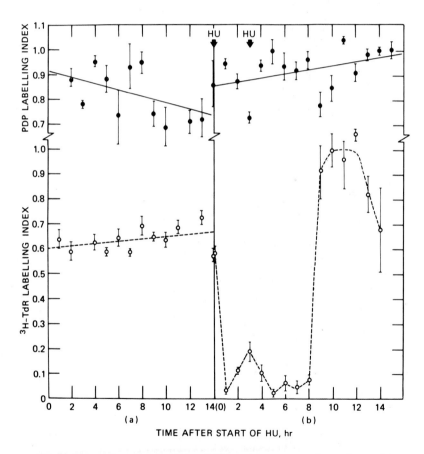

Fig. 5   Acute effects on the 4-day S-180 ascites sarcoma of two doses of 2 g/kg of HU given intraperitoneally. (a) Control. (b) Experimental. The straight lines are linear least-mean-square fits of the actual points. These values have been corrected for viability by the eosin dye technique.

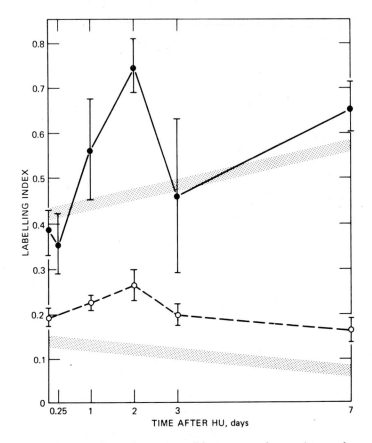

Fig. 6 Effects on the 14-day T1699 solid mammary adenocarcinoma of two doses of 2 g/kg of HU given intraperitoneally. The hatched areas are normal values for unperturbed tumors. •, PDP. ○, $^3$H—TdR. ⫶, 1 S.E.M.

The rises in PDP LI may represent the recruitment of cells from the noncycling state to the proliferative compartment. The variations are, perhaps, indicative of the synchronous effects of the drug. No estimate of $T_c$ is made because of the effects of HU on $T_s$.

### Effects of Vincristine

In the T1699 tumor (Fig. 8), there is a marked 6-hr drop in the PDP LI following administration of vincristine (VCR), which persists through day 2. With the return to normal on day 3, the $^3$H—TdR LI approximately doubles and stays elevated through 7 days.

In a similar fashion, there is an acute drop in the 6-hr PDP LI in the S-180 tumor (Fig. 9). It does not persist, however, and values are essentially normal

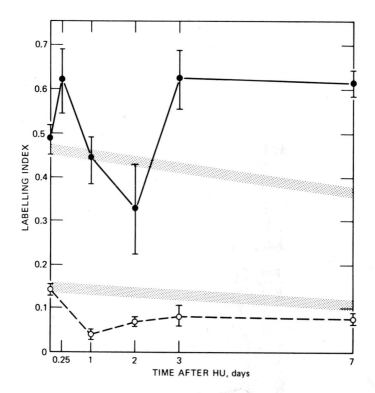

Fig. 7   Effects on the 5-day S-180 solid sarcoma of two doses of 2 g/kg of HU given intraperitoneally. The hatched areas are normal values for unperturbed tumors. ●, PDP. ○, $^3$H—TdR. ⌶, 1 S.E.M.

until a marked rise in the PDP LI by day 7. The $^3$H—TdR LI does not vary significantly from normal.

If the only effect of VCR is to prevent cells from getting through metaphase, and thereby to increase the number of metaphase figures, we would expect to see a decrease in the PDP LI due to the reduced incidence of PDP positivity in mitotic figures. However, the PDP LI is reduced even at 2 days, and this may substantiate the recent findings[16,17] that VCR also blocks the movement of noncycling cells into the proliferating pool. The large increase in the PDP LI of the S-180 tumor cells at 7 days is inexplicable except, perhaps, on the basis of partial synchrony.

## CONCLUSION

These studies demonstrate that chemotherapeutic agents and X-irradiation can cause a variation in the PDP LI. The PDP assay can, therefore, act as a

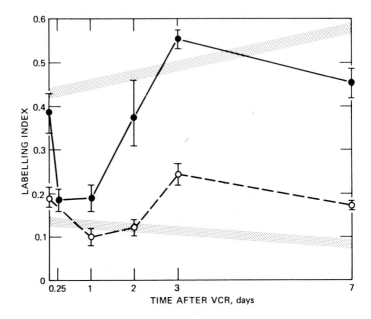

Fig. 8 Effects on the 14-day T1699 solid mammary adenocarcinoma of 2.5 mg/kg of VCR given intraperitoneally. The hatched areas are normal values for unperturbed tumors. ●, PDP. ○, $^3$H—TdR. ⊥, 1 S.E.M.

responding modality for studying tumor-cell kinetics. Most of the results presented here are explicable by our present knowledge of cytokinetics, although some are not. It is our thesis that the PDP index not only estimates the GF of unperturbed tumor systems but also can do the same for therapeutically perturbed systems. The PDP assay has the great advantage that it is an *in vitro* test, it can be used on biopsy specimens, and it is potentially convertible to a rapid assay. Of cytokinetic importance, the PDP LI gives values that are applicable to the tumor at the time of biopsy and do not represent median values obtained during protracted $^3$H—TdR studies.

## ACKNOWLEDGMENTS

We gratefully acknowledge the assistance of Dolores Migliorato, Linda Fisher, and Barbara Diletusso.

The research for this paper was supported in part by a Clinical Radiation Therapy Research Center grant CA10438, a Radiation Biology and Cancer Research training grant CA05224 from the National Cancer Institute, and a General Research Support grant (RR5709) from the National Institutes of Health.

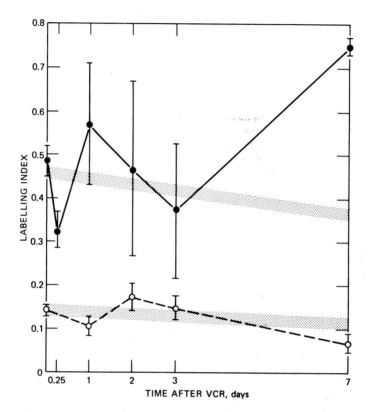

**Fig. 9**   Effects on the 5-day S-180 solid sarcoma of 2.5 mg/kg of VCR given intraperitoneally. The hatched areas are normal values for unperturbed tumors. •, PDP. ○, $^3$H—TdR. ⌶, 1 S.E.M.

# REFERENCES

1. M. L. Mendelsohn, Autoradiographic Analysis of Cell Proliferation in Spontaneous Breast Cancer of C3H Mouse. III. The Growth Fraction, *J. Nat. Cancer Inst.*, **28**: 1015-1029 (1962).
2. L. S. Chang, McK. Brown, and F. J. Bollum, Induction of DNA Polymerase in Mouse L Cells, *J. Mol. Biol.*, **74**: 1-8 (1973).
3. J. G. Lindsay, S. Berryman, and R. L. P. Adams, Characteristics of Deoxyribonucleic Acid Polymerase Activity in Nuclear and Supernatant Fractions of Cultured Mouse Cells, *Biochem. J.*, **119**: 839-848 (1970).
4. Y. Rabinowitz, I. S. McCluskey, P. Wong, and B. A. Wilkite, DNA Polymerase Activity of Cultured Normal and Leukemia Lymphocytes: Response to Phytohemagglutinin, *Exp. Cell Res.*, **57**: 257-262 (1969).
5. D. L. Friedman and G. C. Mueller, A Nuclear System for DNA Replication from Synchronized Hela Cells, *Biochim. Biophys. Acta*, **161**: 455-468 (1968).
6. J. S. R. Nelson and L. M. Schiffer, Autoradiographic Detection of DNA Polymerase Containing Nuclei in Sarcoma 180 Ascites Cells, *Cell Tissue Kinet.*, **6**: 45-54 (1973).

7. A. Markoe, L. Schiffer, and J. Nelson, In-Vitro Estimation of Tumor Growth Fraction, *Clin. Res.*, **21**: 650 (1973).

8. L. Simpson-Herren and H. H. Lloyd, Kinetic Parameters and Growth Curves for Experimental Tumor Systems, *Cancer Chemother. Rep.*, **54**: 143-174 (1970).

9. J. Denekamp, The Relationship Between the "Cell Loss Factor" and the Immediate Response to Radiation in Animal Tumors, *Eur. J. Cancer*, **8**: 335-340 (1972).

10. J. Denekamp and R. H. Thomlinson, The Cell Proliferation Kinetics of Four Experimental Tumors After Acute Irradiation, *Cancer Res.*, **31**: 1279-1284 (1971).

11. H. A. Van Peperzeel, Effects of Single Doses of Radiation on Lung Metastases in Man and Experimental Animals, *Eur. J. Cancer*, **8**: 665-675 (1972).

12. R. C. Young and V. T. DeVita, The Effect of Chemotherapy on the Growth Characteristics and Cellular Kinetics of Leukemia L1210, *Cancer Res.*, **30**: 1789-1794 (1970).

13. L. M. Van Putten, P. Lelieveld, and L. K. J. Kram-Idsenga, Cell-Cycle Specificity and Therapeutic Effectiveness of Cytostatic Agents, *Cancer Chemother. Rep.*, **46**: 691-700 (1972).

14. E. Farber and R. Baserga, Differential Effects of Hydroxyurea on Survival of Proliferating Cells in Vivo, *Cancer Res.*, **29**: 136-139 (1969).

15. L. A. Dethlefsen and R. M. Riley, Hydroxyurea Effects on the C3H Mouse. II. Mammary Tumor Cell Kinetics, *Cell Tissue Kinet.*, **6**: 173-184(1973).

16. B. C. Lampkin, N. B. McWilliams, and A. M. Mauer, Cell Kinetics and Chemotherapy in Acute Leukemia, *Seminars Hematol.*, **9**: 211-223 (1972).

17. N. B. McWilliams, A. M. Mauer, and B. C. Lampkin, Dose Dependent Vincristine Effects, *Clin. Res.*, **19**: 494 (1971).

# COMBINATION CHEMOTHERAPY AND IMMUNOTHERAPY OF TRANSPLANTABLE MURINE LEUKEMIA

G. M. KOLLMORGEN,* J. J. KILLION,* W. A. SANSING,* and J. C. BUNDREN†
*Oklahoma Medical Research Foundation and the Department of Radiological Sciences, Oklahoma University Health Sciences Center, Oklahoma City, Oklahoma, and †Cancer Research Laboratory, Phillips University, Enid, Oklahoma

## ABSTRACT

A series of experiments was done to determine if chemotherapy followed by active immunotherapy could be used to induce complete remission of ascitic tumors in mice. All studies were done using the leukemic L1210 tumor cells grown in $BDF_1$ males. Chemotherapy consisted in using cyclophosphamide, thioguanine, or cytosine arabinoside in combination with cis-platinous diamminodichloride. The estimated number of cells that survived chemotherapy was determined by treating tumor-bearing mice (about $10^8$ tumor cells at time of treatment) with the preceding agents. Following chemotherapy, mice were given active immunotherapy, which consisted of injecting neuraminidase-treated cells (specific) and/or Bacillus Calmette-Guerin (BCG) (nonspecific). Tumor cells used for immunization were grown in culture and were either drug sensitive or drug resistant. The time interval between chemotherapy and immunotherapy varied from 0 to 72 hr. Results indicate that the addition of BCG to either drug-sensitive or drug-resistant cells increased the number of surviving mice. Drug-resistant cells treated with Vibrio cholerae neuraminidase were more effective than drug-sensitive cells treated with VCN. The optimal time for treatment occurred between 12 to 36 hr after chemotherapy. Mice that were cured developed tumor-specific immunity, which was evaluated 60 days after immunotherapy.

A number of recent studies have linked the oncological process to the immunological status of the host.[1-5] These studies indicate clearly that immunosuppression and immunodeficiency in animals and man increase susceptibility to neoplastic diseases. They do not, however, necessarily suggest that all neoplastic diseases are the consequence of an abnormal immune system. In fact, progressive tumor growth may occur in spite of immune competence or the retention of the potential to produce a favorable host response against its tumor.[6,7]

In light of other studies, host response seems likely to be, at least in part, dependent on the characteristics of the tumor-cell membrane.[8-10] For example, tumor cells treated with *Vibrio cholerae* neuraminidase (VCN) prior to injection elicit a different host response from that elicited by untreated cells. Whereas untreated cells grow progressively and ultimately cause death of the host, VCN-treated cells induce tumor-specific immunity.[10-12] Tumor remission has also been reported after tumor-bearing animals were immunized with VCN-treated cells.[6,7,13] Since treated cells caused tumor remission and induced tumor-specific immunity, host response to treated cells must have also been directed against untreated cells.

Rejection of growing tumors after immunization with VCN-treated tumor cells is severely limited by tumor size.[6,14] Although small tumors can be rejected, large tumors may undergo only a temporary reduction in rate of growth.

Even though active immunotherapy may not be effective against large tumors when used alone, it may induce remission of residual tumor after tumor burden has been minimized with other modalities. Ideally, surgery, radiotherapy, and chemotherapy used alone or in combination would minimize tumor burden before initiation of active immunotherapy. This modality, if effective, not only could cause remission of residual tumor but also could induce tumor-specific immunity. Retention of the ability to produce an effective immune response is, of course, essential for the success of active immunotherapy. Consequently, a series of experiments was designed to determine the efficacy of combination chemotherapy and immunotherapy in $BDF_1$ mice bearing the ascitic L1210 leukemic tumor. This tumor–host system was chosen for the following reasons:

1. A single viable tumor cell grows progressively and causes death of the host.[15]

2. This tumor grows well in vitro and in vivo (as either an ascitic or solid subcutaneous tumor).

3. This tumor is one of three standard tumors used to screen potentially useful chemotherapeutic agents.[16]

4. The effectiveness of a variety of chemotherapeutic agents has been reported for this tumor grown in several strains of mice.[17]

## MATERIALS AND METHODS

### Tumor–Host System

L1210 leukemic cells were grown in the peritoneal cavity of $BDF_1$ mice as an ascitic tumor. Cells transferred from donor to recipient were harvested during log growth to ensure the maximum number of cells in the proliferative pool and a minimal amount of bloody exudate in the peritoneal cavity. At time of transfer, the donor was killed (cervical dislocation), and cells and ascitic fluid were washed from the peritoneal cavity with 0.9% NaCl solution (normal saline).

After centrifugation, cells were resuspended in and washed with 1% ammonium oxalate to remove red cells. Tumor cells were then resuspended, counted, and diluted in normal saline. The desired number of cells were injected into recipients using a volume of 0.2 ml. Tumor-bearing mice were checked four times daily for deaths, and autopsies were done when necessary to determine the cause of death.

## Chemotherapeutic Agents

Chemical agents were dissolved immediately before use and injected into the peritoneal cavity of tumor-bearing mice. Chemotherapy (treatment with cyclophosphamide, thioguanine, or cytosine arabinoside) was initiated when tumors contained an estimated $10^8$ cells. Cyclophosphamide (100 mg/kg) and thioguanine (10 mg/kg) were given as a single injection. Cytosine arabinoside (10 mg/kg) was given as eight injections at 3-hr intervals. Treatment with *cis*-platinous diamminodichloride (PDD) was begun 4 hr after treatment with other drugs and proceeded as follows: after cyclophosphamide, daily doses of 3 mg/kg for 4 days; after thioguanine, daily doses of 2 mg/kg for 4 days, and after cytosine arabinoside, a single dose of 5 mg/kg. Agents, dosages, and schedules of treatment were based on reports of other investigators who considered tolerance doses of normal tissues and the most desirable route and sequence of administration.[18]

## Cultured cells

L1210 leukemic cells were grown in suspension culture using Fischer's medium supplemented with 10% heat-inactivated fetal calf serum and antibiotics (50 units/ml of penicillin and 50 μg/ml each of streptomycin and kanamycin). Cells were grown at $37°C$, and the pH was maintained at about 7.0 with 8% $CO_2$ in air. Stock cultures were maintained in log growth with necessary dilutions and checked periodically for contamination. Thioguanine ($5.95 \times 10^{-5}$ molar) and PDD ($6.66 \times 10^{-6}$ molar) were added at the same time to cells in log growth. Cell counts were done with hemocytometers. Cell viability was determined with trypan blue (final concentration 0.08%). Both drug-resistant and drug-sensitive cells were harvested for neuraminidase treatment during log growth. After centrifugation, cells were washed once with normal saline before exposure to the enzyme.

## Treatment with Neuraminidase

Cells grown either in vivo or in vitro were washed in normal saline immediately before exposure to *Vibrio cholerae* neuraminidase. Cells were stirred slowly during exposure to VCN for 1 hr at $37°C$. The final mixture contained equal parts (by volume) of neuraminidase (1 unit/$10^6$ cells) and acetate buffer (pH, 5.6). After treatment, cells were centrifuged, washed, and diluted with normal saline; adjusted to a concentration of $5.0 \times 10^7$/ml; and frozen without preservative in ampules at $-90°C$. In some cases, heat-inactivated ($65°C$ for 30 min) neuraminidase was used. Before injection, cells were thawed at $37°C$ and in some cases mixed with *Bacillus Calmette-Guerin* (BCG) before injection. Some mice were given only 1 mg of BCG, some mice were given $10^7$ VCN-treated cells, and some mice were given both. All injections were made into the peritoneal cavity. The time interval between chemotherapy and immuno-therapy varied from 0 to 72 hr. Sixty days after immunotherapy some surviving mice were challenged with $10^2$ to $10^7$ untreated cells from the peritoneal cavity of donors to determine the extent of immunity. Some mice were challenged with L5178Y cells to determine the specificity of immunity.

## RESULTS

Leukemic L1210 cells were grown in the peritoneal cavity of $BDF_1$ mice as an ascitic tumor. Initial studies were designed to determine the relationship between the number of cells injected and the median survival time of the host. As shown in Fig. 1, median survival time ranged from $6.7 \pm 0.6$ days after an injection of $10^7$ cells to $16.5 \pm 1.3$ days after an injection of $10^1$ cells. Furthermore, the median survival times for groups of mice given a 10-fold difference in cell number (ranging from $10^1$ to $10^7$) differed by an average of 39 hr. These data are consistent with an average in vivo doubling time of about 11.5 hr during the log growth phase, which terminates when tumors contain about $10^8$ cells. Results from these studies compare favorably with recent observations by Dombernowsky[19] and allow for a reasonable estimate of the number of cells present at any time during log growth.

The effectiveness of chemotherapy in tumor-bearing mice is shown in Fig. 2. Mice given $10^6$ tumor cells were treated when the tumor contained an estimated $10^8$ cells. Previous results indicated that these mice could not be cured with chemotherapy alone. Their median survival time was about 205 hr. Some mice were treated with the thioguanine—PDD combination when the tumor contained an estimated $10^8$ cells. All animals responded favorably as measured by an increase in the median survival time. None of these mice, however, were cured with this treatment. The median survival time of treated mice (315 hr) was comparable to the median survival time of untreated mice given an initial inoculum of $10^3$ tumor cells and no chemotherapy. This suggested a 5 log kill with this treatment if tumor cells surviving chemotherapy grew at the same rate as untreated cells. The same procedure was used to evaluate the effectiveness of PDD used in combination with either cyclophosphamide or cytosine arabinoside. Results are shown in Table 1. The estimated number of cells surviving after the treatment of mice bearing approximately $10^8$ tumor cells ranged from $10^2$ to $10^4$. We had previously reported that these mice could reject about $10^5$ tumor cells after immunization with $10^7$ VCN-treated cells.[14]

After chemotherapy mice were immunized with VCN-treated cultured cells, which were either drug sensitive or drug resistant. As shown in Fig. 3,

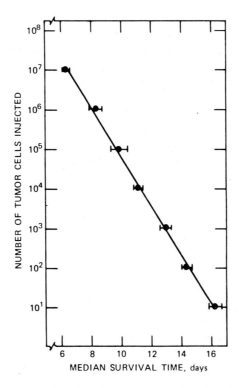

Fig. 1   The median survival time of BDF$_1$ mice as a function of the number of tumor cells injected. Bars signify range of survival times. Each point represents the results from 20 mice.

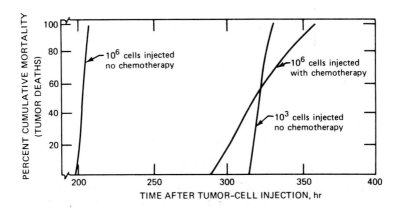

Fig. 2   Percent cumulative mortality (tumor deaths) as a function of time after tumor cell injection.

**TABLE 1**

ESTIMATED NUMBER OF TUMOR CELLS SURVIVING
AFTER CHEMOTHERAPY*

| Chemotherapeutic agents | Estimated number of surviving cells |
|---|---|
| Cyclophosphamide (100 mg/kg) + PDD (3 mg/kg) | $10^2$ |
| Thioguanine (10 mg/kg) + PDD (2 mg/kg) | $10^3$ |
| Cytosine arabinoside (10 mg/kg) + PDD (5 mg/kg) | $10^4$ |

*Tumors contained about $10^8$ cells at time of chemotherapy.

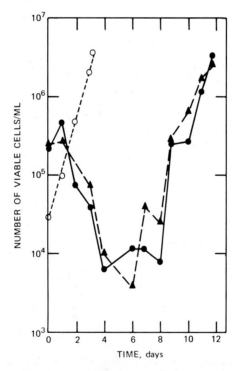

Fig. 3 The number of viable cells per milliliter as a function of time. ○, control cells without chemical agents. ● and ▲, cells grown in the presence of both thioguanine ($5.95 \times 10^{-5}$ molar) and PDD ($6.66 \times 10^{-6}$ molar). Doubling times of both drug-sensitive and drug-resistant cells were about 12 hr. ○, drug sensitive. ● and ▲, drug resistant.

drug-resistant cells emerged after about 8 days of continuous exposure to these drugs. Resistant cells had about the same doubling time as sensitive cells. Both cell types were harvested during log growth when virtually all cells were in the proliferative pool.

The time interval between termination of chemotherapy (thioguanine—PDD) and the initiation of immunotherapy ranged from 0 to 72 hr. Figure 4 shows the surviving fraction when mice were immunized with drug-sensitive VCN-treated cultured cells with or without BCG. *Bacillus Calmette-Guerin* increased the surviving fraction 10 to 20% at all intervals, except when cells and BCG were given immediately after chemotherapy. Maximum survival occurred when immunotherapy was initiated 12 hr after chemotherapy. None of the mice survived when the interval between chemotherapy and immunotherapy was 48 hr or longer.

Figure 5 shows the surviving fraction when mice were immunized with drug-resistant, VCN-treated, cultured cells with or without BCG. *Bacillus Calmette-Guerin* increased the surviving fraction 10 to 30% at all time intervals except when BCG and cells were given immediately after chemotherapy. Maximum survival occurred when the interval between chemotherapy and immunotherapy was between 12 and 36 hr. None of the mice survived when the interval was 72 hr.

Finally, surviving mice were challenged 60 days after immunotherapy to determine the extent of immunity. As shown in Fig. 6, all mice were able to reject a challenge of $10^5$ untreated cells, an inoculum which normally caused death within 11 days. An increasing number of animals died when the

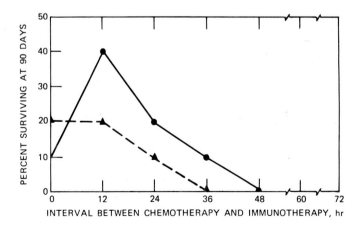

Fig. 4   The percent of mice surviving at 90 days (tumor free) as a function of the interval between chemotherapy and immunotherapy. ▲, mice given $10^7$ VCN-treated drug-sensitive cultured cells. ●, mice given $10^7$ VCN-treated drug-sensitive cultured cells plus 1 mg of BCG.

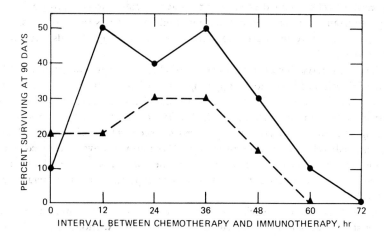

Fig. 5 The percent of mice surviving at 90 days (tumor free) as a function of the interval between chemotherapy and immunotherapy. ▲, mice given $10^7$ VCN-treated drug-resistant cultured cells. ●, mice given $10^7$ VCN-treated drug-resistant cultured cells plus 1 mg BCG.

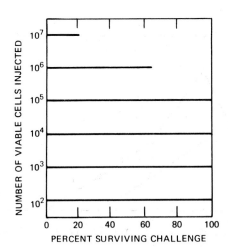

Fig. 6 The extent of immunity in tumor-free mice that had been treated with both chemotherapy and immunotherapy. These mice were challenged 60 days after immunotherapy. All mice were able to reject $10^5$ cells, but only 65 and 25% were able to reject $10^6$ and $10^7$ cells, respectively.

rechallenge dose exceeded $10^5$ cells. Sensitivity to L1578Y was not altered in mice that were immune to L1210 cells.

## DISCUSSION

Sanford[8] originally demonstrated that in vivo growth of tumors was inhibited when tumor cells were treated with neuraminidase prior to injection. More recently, Currie and Bagshawe have demonstrated increased immunogenicity of the Landschutz ascites tumor,[20] the L1210 tumor,[11] and methylcholanthrene-induced fibrosarcomas[21] that had been pretreated with VCN. Rejection of VCN-treated cells by the recipient appeared to be dependent on an immunological response from the host since these cells behaved like untreated cells when injected into immunosuppressed hosts.[11,20,21]

Simmons et al.[6] reported complete regression of firmly established methylcholanthrene-induced fibrosarcomas when tumor-bearing mice were inoculated with neuraminidase-treated tumor cells of the same antigenic type. Injection of tumor-bearing animals with VCN-treated cells with antigenic components differing from those of the original tumor did not cause remission or alter the rate of tumor growth. The probability of causing remission was dependent on the size of the primary tumor.[6] Complete remission was restricted to tumors smaller than 1 cm in diameter. The combination of VCN-treated cells and BCG was more effective than VCN-treated cells alone.[13,22] Intratumor injection of VCN caused total regression of some tumors if continued over a long period of time.[7] As noted previously, response was immunospecific and dependent on tumor size. After tumor remission the host frequently developed tumor-specific immunity.[12]

Bekesi, Arneault, and Holland[9] also reported that mice immunized with VCN-treated L1210 cells did not develop tumor but did develop tumor-specific immunity. Holland[23] demonstrated that active immunotherapy was effective in inducing tumor remission after the tumor size had been minimized with chemotherapy.

Active immunotherapy requires an effective host response, both in terms of quantity and quality. This response is at least partially dependent on the characteristics of the tumor-cell membrane. A number of reports have indicated that neuraminidase treatment alters cell membranes with respect to electrophoretic mobility,[24] immunogenicity[11] reaggregation,[25] phagocytosis,[26] and receptors for myxoviruses[27] and polyoma viruses.[28] It is not clear if these changes and/or other neuraminidase-induced alterations modify host response to treated cells. It seems entirely possible that neuraminidase-treated cells are recognized in a manner different from that in which untreated cells are recognized. Preliminary evidence from our laboratory indicates that IgM and $IgG_2$ are the principal immunoglobulins attached to the surface of tumor cells after injection of VCN-treated cells. Both are cytotoxic complement-dependent antibodies. On the other hand, untreated cells elicited primarily $IgG_1$, a noncytotoxic noncomplement binding antibody. The role of cell-mediated immunity has not yet been evaluated in this tumor—host system.

We previously reported that drug-resistant cells elicited antibodies that could not be entirely absorbed by drug-sensitive cells.[29] Other investigators have reported similar findings.[30] If chemotherapeutic agents alter antigenic determinants on surviving cells, drug-resistant cells would be expected to produce a more effective response than drug-sensitive cells.

The time of active immunotherapy with respect to termination of chemotherapy seems most important. Immunization during a period of immunosuppression apparently does not allow for maximum host response. Conversely, as the interval between chemotherapy and immunotherapy increases, the tumor burden also increases. This probably also limits the production of an adequate quantitative response from the host. Ideally, host response would attain maximum levels immediately after tumor burden had been minimized with chemotherapy. Furthermore, the optimal time for administration of active immunotherapy may depend on the type of therapy being used. Drug-resistant cultured cells treated with VCN and used with or without BCG elicited maximum host response when given from 12 to 36 hr after chemotherapy. The optimal response from VCN-treated drug-sensitive cultured cells occurred about 12 hr after termination of chemotherapy. Results are not yet available from studies in which the interval between specific and nonspecific immunotherapy was varied. Although our experiments identify an optimal interval between chemotherapy and immunotherapy, the time required by the host to produce an effective immune response after immunization with VCN-treated cells is not clear. Our previous studies have indicated that mice with growing tumors could be cured by immunizing with $10^7$ VCN-treated cells of the same antigenic type when growing tumors contained an estimated $10^5$ cells.[14] This of course does not imply that mice retain the same ability after treatment with immunosuppressive drugs. Tumor burden must be evaluated in terms of host responsiveness rather than in terms of absolute cell numbers.

The conclusion that tumor rejection after immunization with treated cells was dependent on an immunological response is supported by the following observations:

1. VCN-treated tumor cells injected into the immunosuppressed host grew as normal cells.

2. Rejection of tumors occurred only when VCN-treated cells possessed the same antigenic components as the residual tumor.

3. Animals that were cured developed tumor-specific immunity.

4. Transfer of passive immunity through the use of either serum or peritoneal exudate cells from immunized animals has been reported.[31]

The loss of cell-surface sialic acid may be indirectly involved in the enhancement of recognition and processing of cell-surface tumor antigens.

Simmons[32] has reported that tumor remission was induced in mice immunized with cells treated with concanavalin A (Con A). Both Con A and VCN alter properties of cell surface membranes especially with respect to agglutinability. Both may also alter antigenic conformation or accessibility either directly or indirectly. Regardless of the nature of these alterations, host response to treated cells must also be directed against untreated cells. This, of course, implies a block in the afferent limb of the immune system rather than in the efferent limb.

It is not yet clear if immunized mice recognize untreated cells as they recognize treated cells or if tumor rejection in these mice depends entirely on a residual-host response directed against untreated cells.

# REFERENCES

1. T. E. Starzl and C. G. Halgrimson, Immunosuppression and Malignant Neoplasma, *New Engl. J. Med.,* **283**: 934-935 (1970).
2. H. Wigzell, and J. Stjernswald, Age-Dependent Rise and Fall of Immunological Reactivity in the CBA Mouse, *J. Nat. Cancer Inst.,* **37**: 513-517 (1966).
3. J. M. Gaugas, F. C. Chesterman, M. S. Hnisch, R. J. W. Rees, J. J. Harvey, and C. Gilchrist, Unexpected High Incidence of Tumours in Thymectomized Mice Treated with Anti-Lymphocyte Globulin and Mycobacterium Leprae, *Nature (London),* **221:** 1033-1036 (1969).
4. R. A. Gatti and R. A. Good, Immunological Abnormalities and Cancer, in *Proceedings of the 10th International Cancer Congress,* Vol. 1, pp. 803-817, Houston, Tex., May 22-29, 1970, Year Book Medical Publishers, Chicago, 1971.
5. R. A. Good and J. Finstad, in *Proceedings of the International Conference on Leukemia-Lymphoma,* p. 175, C. J. D. Zarafonetis (Ed.), Ann Arbor, Mich., Oct. 9–13, 1967, Lea & Febiger, Philadelphia, 1968.
6. R. L. Simmons, A. Rios, G. Lundgren, P. K. Ray, C. F. McKhann, and G. R. Haywood, Immunospecific Regression of Methylcholanthrene Fibrosarcoma with the Use of Neuraminidase, *Surgery,* **70**(1): 38 (1971).
7. R. L. Simmons and A. Rios, Immunospecific Regression of Methylcholanthrene Fibrosarcoma with the Use of Neuraminidase. II. Intratumor Injections of Neuraminidase, *Surgery,* **71**(4): 556 (1972).
8. B. H. Sanford, An Alteration in Tumor Histocompatibility Induced by Neuraminidase, *Transplantation,* **5**(5): 1273 (1967).
9. J. G. Bekesi, G. St. Arneault, and J. F. Holland, Increase of Leukemia L1210 Immunogenicity by Vibrio Cholerae Neuraminidase Treatment, *Cancer Res.,* **31:** 2130 (1971).
10. J. G. Bekesi, G. St. Arneault, L. Walter, and J. F. Holland, Immunogenicity of Leukemia L1210 Cells After Neuraminidase Treatment, *J. Nat. Cancer Inst.,* **49:** 107 (1972).
11. K. D. Bagshawe and G. A. Currie, Immunogenicity of L1210 Murine Leukaemia Cells After Treatment with Neuraminidase, *Nature (London),* **218:** 1254 (1968).
12. R. L. Simmons, A. Rios, P. K. Ray, and G. Lundgren, Effect of Neuraminidase on Growth of a 3-Methylcholanthrene-Induced Fibrosarcoma in Normal and Immuno-suppressed Syngeneic Mice, *J. Nat. Cancer Inst.,* **47:** 1087 (1971).
13. R. L. Simmons and A. Rios, Immunotherapy of Cancer: Immunospecific Rejection of Tumors in Recipients of Neuraminidase-Treated Tumor Cells Plus BCG, *Science,* **174:** 591 (1971).

14. G. M. Kollmorgen, D. N. Erwin, J. J. Killion, and W. A. Sansing, Potential Role of Immunotherapy in Tumor Treatment, *Annals of the Oklahoma Academy of Science,* Vol. 3, p. 25, University of Oklahoma, Norman, Okla., 1973.

15. H. E. Skipper et al., Implications of Biochemical, Cytokinetic, Pharmacologic, and Toxicologic Relationships in the Design of Optimal Therapeutic Schedules, *Cancer Chemother. Rep.,* **54**(1,6): 431 (1970).

16. J. Leiter, B. J. Abbott, and S. A. Schepartz, Screening Data from the Cancer Chemotherapy National Service Center Screening Laboratories, XXI, *Cancer Res.,* **24**(2): 1093 (1964).

17. F. M. Schabel, Jr., H. E. Skipper, W. R. Laster, Jr., M. W. Trader, and S. A. Thompson, Experimental Evaluation of Potential Anticancer Agents. XX. Development of Immunity to Leukemia L1210 in $BDF_1$ Mice and Effects of Therapy, *Cancer Chemother. Rep.,* **50**(1,2): 55 (1966).

18. R. J. Speer, H. Ridgway, and J. M. Hill, Therapy of Leukemia L1210 with Cis-Platinous Diaminodichloride (PDD), *Wadley Med. Bull.,* **2**: 52 (1972).

19. P. Dombernowsky, The Proliferation Kinetics of L1210 Ascites Tumour, *Acta Pathol. Microbiol. Scand., Sect. A,* **80**: 603 (1972).

20. G. A. Currie and K. D. Bagshawe, The Role of Sialic Acid in Antigenic Expression: Further Studies of the Landschutz Ascites Tumor, *Brit. J. Cancer,* **22**: 843 (1968).

21. G. A. Currie and K. D. Bagshawe, Tumor Specific Immunogenicity of Methylcholanthrene-Induced Sarcoma Cells After Incubation in Neuraminidase, *Brit. J. Cancer,* **23**: 141 (1969).

22. R. L. Simmons and A. Rios, Immunospecific Regression of Methylcholanthrene Fibrosarcoma Using Neuraminidase: III. Synergistic Effect of BCG and Neuraminidase Treated Tumor Cells, *Ann. Surg.,* **176**(2): 188 (1972).

23. J. F. Holland, *E Pluribus Unum:* Presidential Address, *Cancer Res.,* **31**: 1319 (1971).

24. G. M. W. Cook, D. H. Heard, and G. V. F. Seaman, Sialic Acid and the Electrokinetic Charge of the Human Erythrocyte, *Nature (London),* **191**: 44 (1961).

25. R. B. Kemp, Effect of the Removal of Cell Surface Sialic Acids on Cell Aggregation *in vitro, Nature,* **218**: 1255 (1968).

26. L. Weiss, E. Mayhew, and K. Ulrich, The Effect of Neuraminidase on Phagocytic Process in Human Monocytes, *Lab. Invest.,* **15**: 1304 (1966).

27. G. K. Hirst, Agglutination of Red Cells by Allantoic Fluid of Chick Embryos Infected with Influenza Virus, *Science,* **94**: 22 (1941).

28. J. W. Hartley, W. P. Rowe, R. M. Chanock, and B. E. Andrews, Studies of Mouse Polyoma Virus Infection. IV. Evidence for Mucoprotein Erythrocyte Receptors in Polyoma Virus Hemagglutination, *J. Exp. Med.,* **110**: 81 (1959).

29. G. M. Kollmorgen, J. C. Bundren, W. A. Cain, and R. Carubelli, Antigenic Alteration of Lymphoblastic Leukemic Cells Induced by Cell Culture and Hydrocortisone, *Cancer Res.,* **32**: 1900 (1972).

30. A. Nicolin, S. Vadlamundi, and A. Goldin, Antigenicity of L1210 Leukemic Sublines Induced by Drugs, *Cancer Res.,* **32**: 653 (1972).

31. K. K. Sethi and H. Brandis, Neuraminidase Induced Loss in the Transplantability of Murine Leukemia L1210, Induction of Immunoprotection and the Transfer of Induced Immunity to Normal DBA/2 Mice by Serum and Peritoneal Cells, *Brit. J. Cancer,* **27**: 106 (1973).

32. R. L. Simmons, personal communications, Department of Surgery, University of Minnesota, 1972, 1973, 1974.

# EFFECT OF ANTITUMOR DRUGS
# ON THE KINETICS OF THE
# TUMOR CELL-BIOMARKER RELATIONSHIP

KWANG B. WOO* and KARL M. WIIG†
*Division of Cancer Treatment, National Cancer Institute, National Institutes of Health,
Bethesda, Maryland, and †Arthur D. Little, Inc., Cambridge, Massachusetts

## ABSTRACT

A mathematical model is developed to establish the quantitative relationship between tumor
cell numbers and biomarker (or potential biomarker) with reference to L1210 leukemic cells
and polyamine and their response to antileukemic agents, namely, 5-azacytidine. The
dynamics of cell-cycle kinetics was formulated by separate multicompartments for each
cell-cycle phase, including the $G_0$ phase for nonproliferating cells; and the growth patterns
of the entire cell cycle of the tumor were investigated by computer simulation using
cell-cycle kinetic data experimentally obtained for the L1210 leukemic cells. The kinetics of
polyamine syntheses based on the established metabolic pathways are represented by four
nonlinear rate equations. Various properties of the cell-cycle kinetics and corresponding
polyamine synthesis in each cell-cycle phase are integrated and characterized by kinetic
parameters that are a saturation-type nonlinear function of both tumor cell numbers and
polyamine concentrations. The model is further extended to account for the effect of
antitumor drugs on tumor growth based on equilibrium between the tumor cells and the
drugs. Inhibitory activities of the drugs on polyamine syntheses are also investigated. The
effect of 5-azacytidine on both the growth rate of L1210 leukemic cells and the synthesis
rate of polyamine is analyzed and monitored, and the results of computer simulation are
compared with experimental data.

Many types of tumor cells have identifiable metabolites, or biomarkers, whose
kinetic parameters are indicative of the presence of malignancy and reflect the
total number of neoplastic cells involved and any change occurring as a result of
treatment. An attempt to establish the quantitative relationship between tumor
cells and a biomarker is, therefore, of considerable clinical interest because it
affords the possibility of estimating the total number of tumor cells as well as
any variation in number due to therapy.

In this paper we develop and describe a mathematical model which
characterizes a quantitative relationship between L1210 leukemic cells and
polyamine and their response to an antileukemic agent, namely 5-azacytidine.

First, we formulate the dynamics of cell-cycle kinetics using multicompartments for the cell-cycle phases. The reaction kinetics of polyamine syntheses are analyzed on the basis of the established metabolic pathways. In each compartment various properties of the cell-cycle and proliferation kinetics are integrated with corresponding polyamine synthesis. The integrated tumor—biomarker model is further extended to account for the effect of antitumor drugs on tumor growth; the drug effect is formulated by equilibrium between the tumor cells and the antitumor agents. Finally, using this integrated model, we discuss the inhibitory activity of 5-azacytidine on both the growth rate of L1210 leukemic cells in mouse spleen and the synthesis rate of polyamine and compare it with experimental results.[1,2]

## THE DYNAMICS OF CELL CYCLE AND PROLIFERATION

A multicompartment model derived by treating each cell-cycle phase as a separate compartment is used to study the cell-cycle and proliferation kinetics of the L1210 leukemic population. The model consists of compartments $G_1$, $S$, $G_2$, and $M$, which constitute the proliferative pool. It also includes compartment $G_0$ for the nonproliferative pool, which has a transit time considerably longer than ones in other compartments involved. The flow of cells through the various compartments and the transfer of cells returning from $G_0$ to the proliferative pool are illustrated in Fig. 1 along with the cell loss from each compartment. With a simple conservation law for the balance of cells in each compartment, the

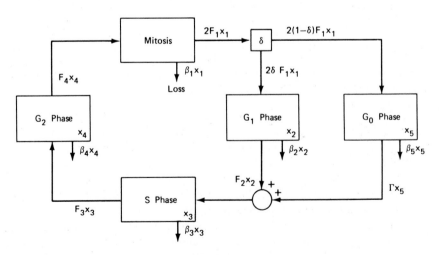

Fig. 1  Schematic diagram of the multicompartment model for the cell-cycle and proliferation kinetics.

dynamics of the entire tumor cell population is described by a set of nonlinear differential equations[3] and by a matrix form as follows:

$$\frac{dx}{dt} = Ax \tag{1}$$

where

$$x = \begin{bmatrix} x_1 \\ x_2 \\ x_3 \\ x_4 \\ x_5 \end{bmatrix} \tag{2}$$

and

$$A = \begin{bmatrix} -F_1 - \beta_1 & 0 & 0 & F_4 & 0 \\ 2\delta F_1 & -F_2 - \beta_2 & 0 & 0 & 0 \\ 0 & F_2 & -F_3 - \beta_3 & 0 & \Gamma \\ 0 & 0 & F_3 & -F_4 - \beta_4 & 0 \\ 2(1-\delta)F_1 & 0 & 0 & 0 & -\Gamma - \beta_5 \end{bmatrix} \tag{3}$$

where variable x = number of cells at time t in each compartment
   $x_1$ = number of cells in M
   $x_2$ = number of cells in $G_1$
   $x_3$ = number of cells in S
   $x_4$ = number of cells in $G_2$
   $x_5$ = number of cells in $G_0$
   $\beta$ = rate of cell loss from each compartment and is considered to be a function of cell number
   F = cell growth activity factor, which is inversely related to the mean cell transit time
   $\delta$ = fraction of dividing cells returning to daughter cells
   $1-\delta$ = fraction of cells going into $G_0$
   $\Gamma$ = function representing the mechanism of the transfer of nonproliferative cells in $G_0$ to the proliferative pool

The control in tumor growth is implemented in the cell growth activity factor for $G_1$ phase, $F_2$, which is specified as a function of both the total number of tumor cells and the concentration of a certain growth-promoting agent y. The growth-promoting agent y operates a smooth threshold mechanism that gradually shuts off growth when the concentration of the agent reaches below a certain threshold level C*. A mechanism of growth limitation is shown as a function of the total number[4] of tumor cells, $x_{tot}$. We chose the tumor growth control expressed in the form

$$F_2 = \frac{1}{\Gamma_2} \rho(y)\alpha(x_{tot}) \tag{4}$$

where

$$\rho(y) = \frac{1}{2}\left\{1 + \tanh\left[n\left(\frac{y}{C^*} - 1\right)\right]\right\} \tag{5}$$

$$\alpha(x_{tot}) = 1 - \ln\left(\frac{y_{tot}}{x_{toto}}\right) \tag{6}$$

$x_{toto}$ = initial total number of tumor cells and n = the parameter to characterize various forms of growth promoting activity. Equation 1, together with Eq. 4, can be used to describe growth patterns.

The growth rate of the total tumor cell population, $x_{tot}$, can readily be obtained from Eq. 1:

$$\frac{dx_{tot}}{dt} = F_1 x_1 - \sum_{i=1}^{5} \beta_i x_i \tag{7}$$

and for $\beta_i = \beta$,

$$\frac{dx_{tot}}{dt} = F_1 x_1 - \beta x_{tot} \tag{8}$$

When the cells in each of the proliferating cycle phases ($G_1$, S, $G_2$, and M) are proportional to their respective transit times, $\tau_i$, as shown by Okada[5] and when the proportion of cells in $G_0$ phase to the total cells in the entire cycle is in steady state, Eq. 1 can yield the following relationship:

$$x_i = \frac{\tau_i}{\tau_c}(x_{tot} - x_5) \qquad \text{(for } i = 1, 2, 3, 4) \tag{9}$$

where $\tau_c$ = the mean cell-cycle time. Equation 9 is typically nonlinear since the transit times are time and population dependent. With this relationship the growth rate of the total tumor cell population is given by

$$\frac{dx_{tot}}{dt} = \left(\frac{2\delta - 1}{\tau_c} - \beta\right)x_{tot} \tag{10}$$

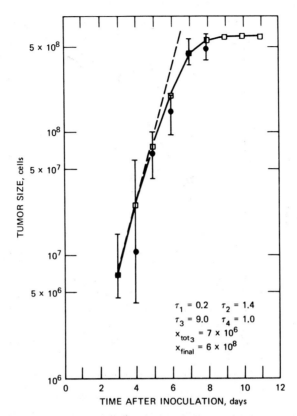

Fig. 2 Growth curves of L1210 leukemic cells. ●, experimental points from Yankee, DeVita, and Perry.[8] □, $\tau_2$ changing model. —, simulation for the $\tau_2$ changing model. - - -, simulation for the constant mean cell-cycle transit times. $x_{tot_3}$, the total number of cells at day 3. $x_{final}$, the total number of cells when they reach the plateau level.

Several growth equations similar to Eq. 10 have been used in the analysis of tumor proliferation kinetics[6,7] in which the arbitrary nonlinearities of cell loss rate and proliferation parameter are considered in order to represent experimental studies of the tumor growth characteristics.

Further analysis of the compartmental model is carried out by computer simulation, and the model result is fitted individually to a number of tumor systems with the experimentally obtained values of mean transit times and the reported or estimated values of the final tumor size. In Fig. 2 the experimental data reported by Yankee, DeVita, and Perry[8] are superimposed on the simulation results. The dotted line represents the results with constant values of cell-cycle times; and the solid line represents the results of introducing the growth-

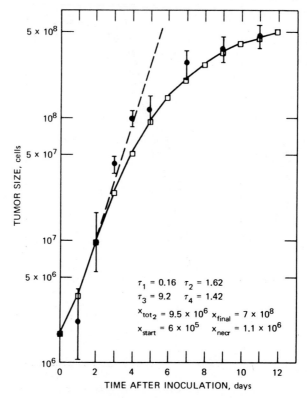

**Fig. 3  Growth curves for Ehrlich ascites tumor.** ●, experimental points from Tannock.[9] □, simulation for the $\tau_c$ changing model. - - -, simulation for the constant mean cell-cycle transit times. $x_{tot_2}$, the total number of cells at day 2. $x_{final}$, the total number of cells when they reach the plateau level.

retarding mechanism, which prolonged the transit time in $G_1$ phase. The solid line fits very well with the measured tumor growth curve.

In addition to the variation of the transit time in $G_1$ phase, two other variants of the compartmental model are introduced to provide other mechanisms for growth retardation as the tumor size increases. One variant has been to increase the cell-cycle time by unilaterally increasing the phase transit times for all four phases. This mechanism has been suggested for a number of tumor systems, especially for some Ehrlich ascites tumors[9] and DMBA-induced breast cancer.[10] Another variant is introduced by maintaining the cell-cycle time constant and increasing the cell loss as the tumor increases in size ($\beta$ changing model) as suggested by several studies for solid tumors[9] and for some Ehrlich ascites tumors.[11]

In Fig. 3 we have shown the correspondence between the $\tau_c$ changing model and the experimental results reported by Tannock[9] for an Ehrlich ascites tumor

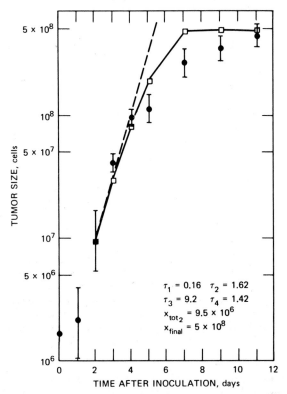

Fig. 4 Growth curves for Ehrlich ascites tumor studied by Tannock.[9] ●, experimental points. □, $\tau_2$ changing model. ——, simulation for the $\tau_2$ changing model. $x_{tot_2}$, the total number of cells at day 2. $x_{final}$, the total number of cells when they reach the plateau level.

system. The figure illustrates relatively good correspondence between the two cases. If the $\tau_2$ changing model is used for this particular Ehrlich ascites system instead of the $\tau_c$ changing model, a simulation result is not very convincing; it also indicates that the tumor system cannot be described by the $\tau_2$ changing model, as shown in Fig. 4.

A simulation result of a solid-tumor system reported by Tannock is shown in Fig. 5 in which the $\beta$ changing model is used and the experimental observations are favorably compared. It appears that the correspondence in this case is marginally good. The figure indicates that perhaps there is a change in cycle time in addition to the increased cell loss as the tumor size increases. A simulation of a DMBA-induced breast cancer system using the $\beta$ changing model is illustrated in Fig. 6. It shows an excellent correspondence between the two results and suggests that the model may be able to describe such systems very adequately.

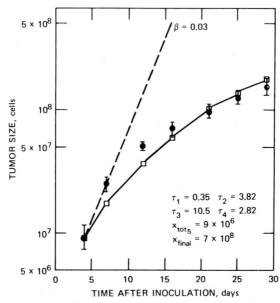

Fig. 5   Growth curves for solid tumor. ●, experimental points from Tannock.[9] □, β changing model. —, simulation for the β changing model. - - - -, simulation for constant cell loss rate. $x_{tot_5}$, the total number of cells at day 5. $x_{final}$, the total number of cells when they reach the plateau level.

## KINETICS OF BIOMARKER SYNTHESIS AND ITS RELATION TO TUMOR-CELL PROLIFERATION: THE L1210–POLYAMINE SYSTEM

Recently, a great deal of interest has been shown to the relationship between polyamines and growth in both normal and neoplastic systems. In the study of a mouse L1210 lymphoid leukemia,[12] it was shown that in the subcutaneous tumor the activity of ornithine decarboxylase, the enzyme catalyzing the formation of putrescine, was markedly elevated during the earlier phase of tumor growth and declined with the increasing size of the tumor. Anderson and Heby[13] studied the concentrations of polyamines and nucleic acids in an Ehrlich ascites carcinoma at various stages of tumor growth and found that the growth rate deceleration, which is a consequence of the increasing size of the tumor, was accompanied by a decrease in the concentration of putrescine. In AKR mice that develop spontaneous lymphoid leukemia, the cellular content of putrescine, spermidine, and spermine was measured[14] and shown to increase progressively as the cells traversed the cell cycle from $G_1$ to M.

Polyamine metabolism was studied in spleens of $BDF_1$ mice after intra-peritoneal (i.p.) inoculation of $10^6$ L1210 leukemic cells.[1] The study illustrates

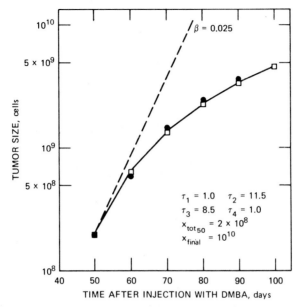

Fig. 6 Growth curves for DMBA-induced breast cancer. ●, experimental points from Skipper.[10] □, $\beta$ changing model. —, simulation for the $\beta$ changing model. - - - -, simulation for constant cell loss rate. $x_{tot_{50}}$, the total number of cells at day 50. $x_{final}$, the total number of cells when they reach the plateau level.

the changes in activities of the enzymes in the polyamine biosynthetic pathway as well as endogenous polyamine concentrations in mouse spleen after i.p. inoculation of $10^6$ L1210 leukemic cells and drug treatment. On the basis of information available on the cell-cycle kinetics and the reaction kinetics of polyamine synthesis, a quantitative model for tumor–polyamine interactions in the Ehrlich ascites carcinoma cells was developed[4] which allows for the estimation of the total number as well as the size or the proliferation rate of tumor cells by the measurement of polyamine concentrations. In our analysis of tumor–polyamine interactions, we used a multicompartment model of the cell-cycle kinetics in which the tumor system consists of three compartments: (1) S, $G_2$, and M phases, (2) $G_1$ phase, and (3) $G_0$ phase (Fig. 7).

### Reaction Kinetics of Polyamine Synthesis

The metabolic pathways of polyamine synthesis and its regulation in eukaryotic organisms have been reviewed by Williams-Ashman[15] and are summarized in Fig. 8. The reaction rates of polyamine synthesis in reference to four key enzymes may be represented by the following set of reaction-rate equations:

$$\frac{ds_1}{dt} = E_1 s_{01} - E_2 s_4 s_1 - B_1 S_1 \tag{11}$$

$$\frac{ds_2}{dt} = E_2 s_4 s_1 - E_3 s_4 s_2 - B_2 s_2 \tag{12}$$

$$\frac{ds_3}{dt} = E_3 s_4 s_2 - B_3 s_3 \tag{13}$$

$$\frac{ds_4}{dt} = E_4 s_{04} s_1 - E_2 s_4 s_1 - E_3 s_4 s_2 \tag{14}$$

where B denotes the rate constants of decay due to catabolism and mitotic loss of polyamines in each compartment. It is assumed that the substrates L-ornithine ($s_{01}$) and S-adenosyl-L-methionine ($s_{04}$) are sufficiently available. The activities of enzymes denoted by $E_1$, $E_2$, $E_3$, and $E_4$ are expressed as follows

$$E_1(s_{01}, s_1, s_2, s_3) = \frac{V_1}{s_{01} + K_1 \left(1 + \dfrac{s_1}{K_{11}}\right)\left(1 + \dfrac{s_2}{K_{12}}\right)\left(1 + \dfrac{s_3}{k_{13}}\right)} \tag{15}$$

$$E_2(s_1, s_4) = \frac{V_2}{(k_{24} + s_4)(k_{21} + s_1)} \tag{16}$$

$$E_3(s_1, s_2, s_4) = \frac{V_3}{\left[s_4 + k_{34}\left(1 + \dfrac{s_1}{k_{31}}\right)\right]\left[s_2 + k_{32}\left(1 + \dfrac{s_1}{k_{31}}\right)\right]} \tag{17}$$

$$E_4(s_{04}, s_1) = \frac{V_4}{(k_{40} + s_{04})(k_{41} + s_1)} \tag{18}$$

where $V_i$ denotes the maximum synthesis rate of polyamines: $V_1$, putrescine; $V_2$, spermidine; $V_3$, spermine; and $V_4$, decarboxylated S-adenosyl-L-methionine; and k's are the rate constants.

Since we are concerned with the total amount of polyamines present in each compartment of the cell cycle, we can convert the concentration of polyamines to the total molecular mass M in a compartment with the following relation:

$$s_i = \frac{Q_i}{M} \tag{19}$$

Thus, the synthesized quantities, in compartments each denoted by $Q_1$, $Q_2$, $Q_3$, and $Q_4$, are obtained by Eqs. 11 to 14 together with Eq. 19.

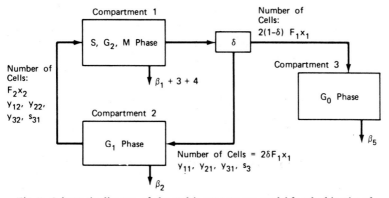

**Fig. 7  Schematic diagram of the multicompartment model for the kinetics of tumor proliferation and polyamine synthesis.**

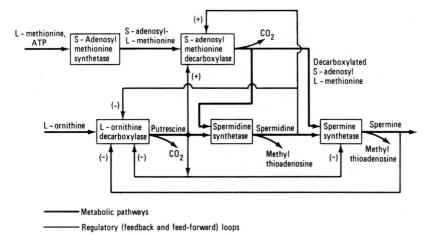

───── Metabolic pathways

───── Regulatory (feedback and feed-forward) loops

**Fig. 8  Schematic diagram representing the metabolic network of polyamine synthesis and its regulation.**

## Dynamics of Polyamine Synthesis in the Cell Cycle

Polyamine synthesis in the cell cycle is described by three compartments of the tumor system, as illustrated in Fig. 7. The total amount of polyamine $Z_j$ in a compartment j is determined by the balance of (1) polyamine transfer carried by cells across the compartment and (2) polyamine synthesis and catabolism within the compartment. For this analysis we define a set of constants for average cell sizes at various points during the cell cycle in which the relative value of $U_{1/2}$ after mitosis is 0.5 and of $U_1$ in M phase is 1.0 and all other values are between these two extremes.

The changes in quantities for polyamine i in compartments 1, 2, and 3 can then be defined by characterizing (1) the synthesis in each compartment according to Eqs. 11 to 14 and (2) the mass balances of polyamine flows into and out of each compartment as follows:

$$\frac{dZ_{i1}}{dt} = (F_2 x_2 U_{2/3})y_{i2} + Q_{i1} - [(F_1 + \beta_1)x_1 U_1 \\ + \beta_3 U_3 x_3 + \beta_4 U_4 x_4] y_{i1} \tag{20}$$

$$\frac{dZ_{i2}}{dt} = 2\delta F_1 x_1 U_{1/2} y_{i1} + Q_{i2} - (F_2 + \beta_2)x_2 U_{2/3} y_{i2} \tag{21}$$

$$\frac{dZ_{i3}}{dt} = 2(1 - \delta)F_1 x_1 U_{1/2} y_{i1} + Q_{i3} - (\Gamma + \beta_5)x_5 U_5 y_{i5} \tag{22}$$

(for i = 1, 2, 3, 4)

where $Z_{ij}$ = quantity of polyamine i in compartment j in mmoles

$F_j$ = cell growth activity factor for compartment j in hour$^{-1}$

$x_j$ = number of tumor cells in compartment j

$U_{j/j+1}$ = average size of cells when transferring to the next cell-cycle phase

$\bar{s}_{ij}$ = concentration of polyamine i in compartment j

$Q_{ij}$ = quantity of polyamine i synthesized in compartment j

$\beta_j$ = rate of cell loss from compartment j

## EFFECT OF ANTITUMOR DRUGS ON TUMOR-CELL PROLIFERATION

The antitumor agents tested inhibit specifically the synthesis of DNA and, therefore, primarily affect cells in S phase; this effect is a cell kill and prevention of the progression of cells through the S phase. The evidence also indicates that sensitivity to cycle-specific or cycle-stage-specific agents is related to the proliferative state of the cell population; tumors become less sensitive to drugs with increasing tumor mass and with decreasing growth rate. A decrease in growth rate may result from (1) an increase in cell-cycle time, (2) a decrease in growth fraction, i.e., a decrease in the ratio of proliferating cells to the total population, and (3) an increase in cell loss.

The effect of antitumor drugs on tumor-cell proliferation can be described in terms of the specific inhibition on DNA synthesis or on the formation of new cells and also in terms of the increase in cell loss from the cell cycle. First, we consider the drug effects through modification of the specific cell growth activities, $F_i$ (i = 1, 2, 3, 4), using Eq. 1 for the total tumor growth. Now $F_i$ is replaced by $F_i^*$ as follows:

$$F_i^* = F_i \cdot G_i \tag{23}$$

where $G_i$ denotes the cell-specific inhibitory effect of drug. Intuitively, one effect may be interpreted as elongation of apparent transit times when cells in the cycle-phase i are inhibited by drugs; and $G_i$ is defined to be 1.0 for no inhibition and less than 1.0 during inhibition. Quantitatively, $G_i$ may be characterized as a function of the concentration of drug as well as the duration and frequency of its application.

In relating population increase of N organisms to the rate of metabolism of sulfonamide, Garrett and Wright[16] showed that the metabolic rate in the drug-affected steady state that results in microbial growth is proportional to the number of receptor sites unreacted with, or unbound by, sulfonamide. In the study of self-control of cell-population size by a mitotic inhibitor,[17] the rate of proliferation of the cells was considered to be inversely related to the intracellular concentration of the inhibitor in which there should exist an upper limit to this proliferation rate due to the time required for wholly unrestrained cells to complete a division cycle.

In our study we assumed that the tumor cells and the antitumor drugs were equilibrated and the number of receptor sites in a single tumor cell was constant. We could then formulate the cell-specific inhibitory effect $G_i$ in terms of receptor sites reacted with drug. The fraction of receptor sites reacted with drug, $\theta$, is given by

$$\theta = \frac{k_r d}{1 + k_r d} \tag{24}$$

where $k_r$ is the equilibrium constant for the drug–site interaction and d is the concentration of drug. Since $G_i$ is related to the formation of new cells, it is expressed in terms of the fraction of receptor sites that are unreacted with drug:

$$G_i = \frac{1}{1 + k_{ri} d} \tag{25}$$

where $k_{ri}$ is the equilibrium constant for the drug–site interaction specific to cycle-phase i.

The growth rate of the total tumor cell population $x_{tot}$ under drug inhibition is now described by an equation similar to Eq. 8,

$$\frac{dx_{tot}}{dt} = F_1^* x_1 - \beta^* x_{tot} \tag{26}$$

where $\beta^*$ denotes the rate of cell loss including drug-induced cell kill. Under the assumptions that $x_i \propto (1/F_i^*)$ and $x_i = (\tau_i^*/\tau_c^*)(x_{tot} - x_5)$, Eq. 26 is reduced to

$$\frac{dx_{tot}}{dt} = \left(\frac{2\delta - 1}{\tau_c^*} - \beta^*\right) x_{tot} \qquad (27)$$

where $\tau_i^*$ and $\tau_c^*$ denote the cell-cycle time in cycle-phase i and the total cell-cycle time under drug inhibition, respectively. Since $\tau_c^*$ is given by

$$\tau_c^* = \tau_c + \sum_{i=1}^{4} \frac{1 - G_i}{F_i^*} \qquad (28)$$

Eq. 27 can be rewritten as

$$\frac{dx_{tot}}{dt} = \left(\frac{2\delta - 1}{\tau_c + \sum\limits_{i=1}^{4}[(1 - G_i)/F_i^*]} - \beta^*\right) x_{tot} \qquad (29)$$

The drug effect specific to cycle-phase j results in $G_i = 1.0$ for $i \neq j$. In this case Eq. 29 becomes

$$\frac{dx_{tot}}{dt} = \left[\frac{2\delta - 1}{\tau_c + \dfrac{(1/G_j) - 1}{F_j}} - \beta^*\right] x_{tot} \qquad (30)$$

or from Eq. 25

$$\frac{dx_{tot}}{dt} = \left(\frac{2\delta - 1}{\tau_c + k^*d} - \beta^*\right) x_{tot} \qquad (31)$$

where $k^* = k_{ri}/F_j$. For a non-cycle-stage-specific drug, $G_i = G$ for all i; and we now have

$$\frac{dx_{tot}}{dt} = \left[\frac{2\delta - 1}{\tau_c(1 + k_r d)} - \beta^*\right] x_{tot} \qquad (32)$$

We will now attempt to illustrate how these models may be used to analyze drug effects on the proliferation kinetics of L1210 leukemic mice, including the effect of 5-azacytidine on polyamine metabolism in spleen during the entire lifetime of L1210 leukemic mice.[1]

## EFFECT OF 5-AZACYTIDINE ON L1210 LEUKEMIC-CELL PROLIFERATION AND POLYAMINE SYNTHESIS

The drug 5-azacytidine has multiple effects on mammalian tissues. It is incorporated into DNA to a much smaller extent than into RNA, but it causes a

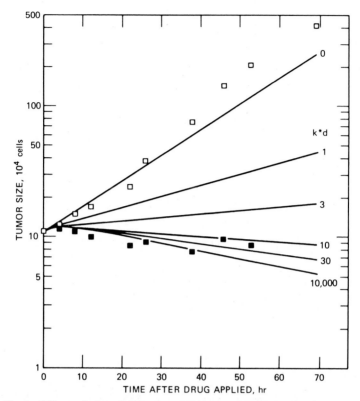

Fig. 9. Effect of 5-azacytidine at different concentration levels on the inhibition of L1210 cell growth. □, control. ■, the inhibitory effect of 5-azacytidine (5 μg/ml) as studied by Li et al.[18] The curves represent simulation results for various levels of 5-azacytidine concentration (μg/ml). The drug concentration is given with each curve.

greater inhibition of the synthesis of DNA than of RNA. The kinetics of the reduction in viability of cultured L1210 leukemic cells exposed to 5-azacytidine have been investigated;[18,19] they indicate that the agent is cell-cycle specific, and cells in the S phase are most sensitive to the agent, which results in a delay in progressing to mitosis. Cell killing is concentration dependent over a relatively wide range of concentrations (1 to 30 μg/ml), and there is no important schedule dependency.[19]

The kinetics of the regression of replicating L1210 cells exposed to lethal concentrations of 5-azacytidine deviated from first order and could be described by a Gompertz function.[19] In our study we analyzed the kinetics of proliferation and regression of L1210 cells reported by Li et al.[18] using Eqs. 10 and 31, each representing the total tumor growth and the cycle-stage-specific drug-interacted growth, respectively. The results are summarized in Fig. 9. The

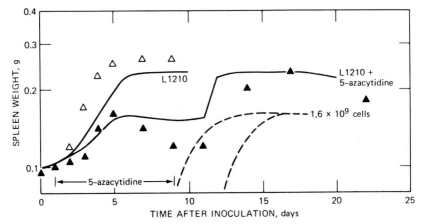

Fig. 10 Changes in mouse spleen after inoculation (i.p.) of $10^6$ L1210 leukemic cells and 5-azacytidine treatment. △, control.[2] ▲, injections (i.p.) of 5-azacytidine (3.0 μg/g body weight on days 1 through 9).[1] —, simulation for changes in mouse spleen weight. - - -, changes in total body weight.

values of $k^*$ in Eq. 31 are normalized so that the drug concentration denoted by d represents the actual amount applied. Equation 31 is not sensitive enough to accommodate extensive variation of the drug effect, and the drug effect on cell loss becomes significant. This, however, has not been studied in detail.[20]

To evaluate the polyamine metabolism in spleen during the growth period of L1210 leukemic mice, one must determine the anatomic distribution and the proliferation rate of leukemic cells. A pattern of the tumor invasion in spleen in relation to the total tumor growth in body was quantitatively formulated on the basis of information obtained earlier by Skipper et al.[21] and by Wheatley and Ambrose[22] and from a recent study by Hoelzer et al.[23] (details will be presented elsewhere). With i.p. inoculation of $10^6$ L1210 ascites leukemic cells, changes in mouse spleen were evaluated by computer simulation (Fig. 10). Although the comparison of these results is not completely satisfactory, it is considerably encouraging.

The activities of the enzymes in the polyamine-biosynthetic pathway were not inhibited directly by 5-azacytidine, even when an excess of this agent was present in the reaction mixture.[1] When the 5-azacytidine treatment was stopped, dramatic changes occurred. The wet weight and the polyamine synthesis and accumulation in spleens and livers rapidly increased. In our study of computer simulation, the effect of 5-azacytidine on the proliferation kinetics of L1210 cells is characterized by Eq. 1, which in turn influences the polyamine metabolism, which is characterized by Eqs. 20 to 22. The analysis of the ornithine decarboxylase activity in relation to putrescine synthesis illustrated in Fig. 8 is based on experimental results of reaction kinetics obtained by a number

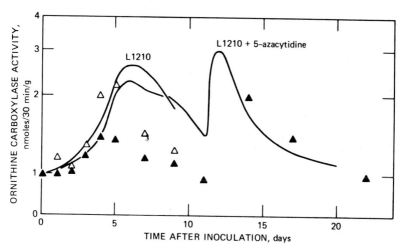

Fig. 11   Related changes in ornithine carboxylase activity with respect to changes in spleen weight as shown in Fig. 10. △, control. ▲, 5-azacytidine treatment. —, simulation.

of investigators and summarized by Williams-Ashman.[15] Changes in the ornithine decarboxylase activity as a function of tumor-cell population and drug concentration were studied by computer simulation of the model. The results are shown in Fig. 11. The simulation results reflect reasonably well the behavior of enzyme activities.

## CONCLUSION

A mathematical model was developed which characterizes the quantitative relationship between tumor cells and biomarkers on the basis of the kinetic information on tumor-cell cycle and proliferation and biomarker synthesis. The model was further expanded to cope with the effects of antitumor agents on the tumor cell—biomarker relationship. A system of L1210 leukemic cells and polyamine and the effect of 5-azacytidine on this system were investigated and quantitatively analyzed by computer simulation. Attempts are under way to deal with other potential markers, such as CEA and α-fetoproteins, and to develop analytical techniques for assaying the effectiveness of various treatments and for evaluating the disease status of cancer patients.

## ACKNOWLEDGMENTS

The authors wish to thank Seymour Perry for his encouragement and support and Olle Heby for his comments and discussion on the kinetics of tumor cell proliferation and polyamine synthesis.

# REFERENCES

1. O. Heby and D. H. Russell, Depression of Polyamine Synthesis in L1210 Leukemic Mice During Treatment with a Potent Antileukemic Agent, 5-Azacytidine, *Cancer Res.*, **33**: 159-165 (1973).

2. O. Heby and D. H. Russell, Changes in Polyamine Metabolism in Tumor Cells and Host Tissues During Tumor Growth and After Treatment with Various Anticancer Agents, in *Polyamines in Normal and Neoplastic Growth*, D. H. Russell (Ed.), pp. 221-231, Raven Press, New York, 1973.

3. K. M. Wiig and K. B. Woo, The Kinetics of L1210 Leukemic Cell Proliferation, in Digest of the 10*th* International Conference on Medical and Biological Engineering, p. 290, Aug. 13-17, 1973, Dresden, German Democratic Republic, 1973.

4. K. B. Woo and R. M. Simon, A Quantitative Model for Relating Tumor Cell Number to Polyamine Concentrations, in *Polyamines in Normal and Neoplastic Growth*, D. H. Russell (Ed.), pp. 381-393, Raven Press, New York, 1973.

5. S. Okada, A Simple Graphic Method of Computing the Parameters of the Life Cycle of Cultured Mammalian Cells in the Exponential Growth Phase, *J. Cell Biol.*, **32**: 915-916 (1967).

6. S. B. Curtis, G. W. Barendsen, and A. F. Hermens, Cell Kinetic Model of Tumor Growth and Regression for a Rhabdomyosarcoma in the Rat: Undisturbed Growth and Radiation Response to Large Single Doses, *Eur. J. Cancer*, **9**: 81-87 (1973).

7. G. G. Steel, Cell Loss from Experimental Tumors, *Cell Tissue Kinet.*, **1**: 193-207 (1968).

8. R. A. Yankee, V. T. DeVita, and S. Perry, The Cell Cycle of Leukemia L1210 Cells *in vivo*, *Cancer Res.*, **27**: 2381-2385 (1967).

9. I. F. Tannock, A Comparison of Cell Proliferation Parameters in Solid and Ascites Ehrlich Tumors, *Cancer Res.*, **29**: 1527-1534 (1969).

10. H. E. Skipper, Kinetics of Mammary Tumor Cell Growth and Implications for Therapy, *Cancer*, **28**: 1479-1499 (1971).

11. P. K. Lala, Evaluation of the Mode of Cell Death in Ehrlich Ascites Tumor, *Cancer*, **29**: 261-266 (1972).

12. D. H. Russell and C. C. Levy, Polyamine Accumulation and Biosynthesis in a Mouse L1210 Leukemia, *Cancer Res.*, **31**: 248-251 (1971).

13. G. Anderson and O. Heby, Polyamine and Nucleic Acid Concentration in Ehrlich Ascites Carcinoma Cells and Liver of Tumor-Bearing Mice at Various Stages of Tumor Growth, *J. Nat. Cancer Inst.*, **48**: 165-172 (1972).

14. O. Heby, G. P. Sarna, L. J. Marton, M. Omine, S. Perry, and D. H. Russell, Polyamine Content of AKR Leukemic Cells in Relation to the Cell Cycle, *Cancer Res.*, **33**: 2959-2964 (1973).

15. H. G. Williams-Ashman, J. Janne, G. L. Coppoc, M. E. Geroch, and A. Schenone, New Aspects of Polyamine Biosynthesis in Eukaryotic Organisms, *Advan. Enzyme Regul.*, **10**: 225-245 (1972).

16. E. R. Garrett and O. K. Wright, Kinetics and Mechanisms of Action of Drugs on Microorganisms. VII. Quantitative Adherence of Sulfonamide Action on Microbial Growth to a Receptor-Site Model, *J. Pharm. Sci.*, **56**: 1576-1585 (1967).

17. T. E. Wheldon, J. Kirk, and W. M. Gray, Mitotic Autoregulation, Growth Control and Neoplasia, *J. Theor. Biol.*, **38**: 627-639 (1973).

18. L. H. Li, E. J. Olin, H. H. Buskirk, and L. M. Reineke, Cytotoxicity and Mode of Action of 5-Azacytidine on L1210 Leukemia, *Cancer Res.*, **30**: 2760-2769 (1970).

19. H. H. Lloyd, E. A. Dulmadge, and L. J. Wilkoff, Kinetics of the Reduction in Viability of Cultured L1210 Leukemia Cells Exposed to 5-Azacytidine (NSC-102816), *Cancer Chemother. Rep.*, **56**: 585-591 (1972).

20. L. F. Lamerton, Tumor Cell Kinetics, *Brit. Med. Bull.*, **29**: 23-28 (1973).

21. H. E. Skipper, F. M. Schabel, Jr., W. S. Wilcox, W. R. Laster, Jr., M. W. Trader, and S. A. Thompson, Experimental Evaluation of Potential Anticancer Agents. XVIII. Effects of Therapy on Viability and Rate of Proliferation of Leukemic Cells in Various Anatomic Sites, *Cancer Chemother. Rep.*, **47**: 41-64 (1965).

22. D. N. Wheatley and E. J. Ambrose, Tumor Cell Invasion from Transplantable Ascites Tumours into Host Tissues, *Brit. J. Cancer*, **18**: 730-742 (1964).

23. D. Hoelzer, W. Calvo, K.-D. Meyer-Hamme, and E. B. Harriss, Cell Distribution and Proliferation Pattern of a Transferable Acute Leukemia, *J. Nat. Cancer Inst.*, **50**: 1545-1553 (1973).

# THE CELL CYCLE IN LYMPHOID TISSUES AND THE IMMUNE RESPONSE

JACOB I. FABRIKANT*

Department of Diagnostic Radiology, Royal Postgraduate Medical School, Hammersmith Hospital, London, England

## ABSTRACT

The binary structure of the immune system comprises two distinct families of lymphocytes coexisting in the body. The thymus-derived T lymphocytes mediate cellular immune phenomena, such as the homograft reaction, the destruction of tissue grafts, as effector cells. The bursa-derived B lymphocytes are concerned with humoral immunity, that is, antibody formation. The functional anatomy of the lymphoid renewal tissues in relation to immunity begins with stem cells which arise in the bone marrow and reach the thymus, a primary lymphoid organ, by way of the blood stream. Within the thymus, stem cells become differentiated to immunologically competent T lymphocytes, emigrate to the blood stream and, together with B lymphocytes, circulate between the tissues, lymphatics, and blood. T cells thus form a large proportion of the pool of recirculating small lymphocytes. They have immunological specificity and are directly involved in cell-mediated immune responses; however, they do not produce humoral antibodies. Immunoglobulins and the antibodies they produce are part of the B lymphocytes, which differentiate via the bone marrow and independently of thymic influence and which function in germinal center immune sites of secondary lymphoid effector tissues, such as the spleen and lymph nodes. However, for many antigens, B cells require the presence of appropriately reactive T cells before they can produce antibodies; the mechanism of this process of cell cooperation is poorly understood.

The interrelationships of the cytokinetics of the immune system are central to functional anatomy of the lymphoid tissues consisting of lymphocytes as mediators of cellular immunity and the regulation of lymphopoiesis in normal and perturbed states. The differential response of the thymus-dependent and bursa-dependent lymphocytes and the regulation of homeostatic controls have a significantly and fairly immediate impact on clinical immunology and health and disease in mice and men. For example, the few lymphoid cells that migrate from the thymus under normal conditions could be those with a long life-span, possibly comprising a slowly proliferating or conditional lymphoid renewal system. T cells are long lived, which explains the early finding that thymectomy in adult animals did not affect the immune response. The thymic long-lived lymphocyte may represent among the important contributions to the extra-thymic pool of small lymphocytes. This contribution may become more important when the animal is recovering from the protracted lymphopenic state produced by thymolytic agents, such as cortisone, or by the stress of irradiation. Thus, regulation of lymphocyte proliferation appears to involve complex feedback controls from outside the thymus for the production of cells required for the stress-depleted extra-thymic lymphoid pools of long-lived lymphocytes—possibly T cells capable of immune function or of cooperation with B cells.

# FUNCTIONAL ANATOMY OF THE TWO-COMPONENT LYMPHOID SYSTEM

## Central Lymphoid Tissues

It has been established that the hematopoietic system in mammals develops from pluripotential hematopoietic stem cells, which first appear in the embryonic yolk sac then ultimately reside in the bone marrow (for review, see Greaves et al.[1]). The microchemical environment in which these stem cells are proliferating provides, in large part, the inducing influence that directs their development into one committed hematopoietic line—erythropoiesis, granulo-poiesis, thrombopoiesis, or lymphopoiesis (Fig. 1). In recent years the binary structure of the cells and tissues of the immune system has been identified and comprises two distinct families of lymphocytes existing in the body. In mice, rats, chickens, and probably also in man, certain of the hematopoietic stem cells can act as precursors of one lymphoid system, the thymus system. They function as prethymic stem cells and develop into cells capable of differenti-ating, under the influence of the thymus, into a population of postthymic T cells.[2] On further maturation postthymic $T_1$ cells become postthymic $T_2$ cells directly involved in the functions of cellular immunity (Fig. 2).

The second lymphoid component develops through the bursal system by an alternate pathway not yet completely worked out for mammals (Fig. 1). It comprises lymphoid stem cells, initially of yolk-sac origin, which apparently develop through bone marrow or gut-associated lymphoid tissues into a variety of differentiating lymphoid B-cell populations. The B cells subserve the function of antibody and immunoglobulin synthesis and secretion. In birds the relatively sessile lymphoid B cells are derived from the bursa of Fabricius; the bursal lymphoid system development gives rise to the entire B-cell line. The bursa in birds, in regard to B-cell development, seems to play a major role similar to that played by the thymus for T cells. The bursal-equivalent site for mammals and man has not been identified; recent evidence suggests that it is not the gut-associated lymphoid tissues.[3] It appears for example that in mice both the bone marrow and spleen provide the milieu for differentiation of primitive lymphoid cells into immunoglobulin-producing B cells.[4] The problem remains an area of intense study.

The thymus and the bursal equivalent are central lymphoid tissues. The T-cell system develops under the direction of the inducing and differentiating environment of the thymus. A prethymic stem cell enters the thymus, where it initially undergoes intensive and apparently ineffective and wasteful prolifera-tion and eventually develops into a postthymic $T_1$ cell (Fig. 2). The $T_1$ cells are

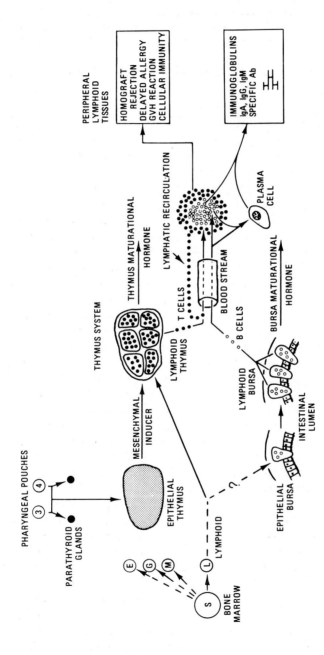

Fig. 1 The two-component lymphoid system in modern immunology. The binary structure comprises two distinct families of lymphocytes existing in the body. The thymus system produces T lymphocytes directly involved in the functions of cellular immunity. The bursal system produces B lymphocytes that subserve the function of antibody and immunoglobulin synthesis and secretion. E, erythropoiesis. G, granulopoiesis. M, megakaryocytopoiesis. L, lymphopoiesis. GVH, graft vs. host reaction.

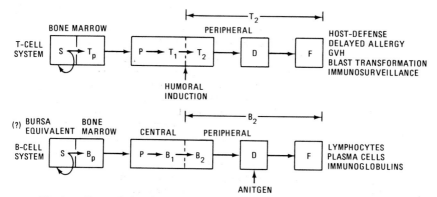

Fig. 2  Cell population kinetics in the two-component lymphoid system; the four-compartment system comprises populations of stem cells (S), proliferative cells (P), differentiating cells (D), and functional end cells (F) involved in cellular immunity or immunoglobulin secretions. The S compartment may consist of two or more subcompartments: pluripotential hematopoietic stem cells and more differentiated forms of prethymic ($T_p$) or prebursal ($B_p$) stem cells. Proliferation and differentiation occur in central lymphoid tissues, whereas immunocompetent cells differentiate and mature into functional cells in the peripheral lymphoid tissues.

capable of further proliferative and multiplicative expansion and development under the indirect and humoral-inductive influence of the epithelial thymus. During this transit life history of the T cell within the thymus, the developing and differentiating lymphoid T cells undergo chemical alterations of the cell periphery giving rise to characteristic antigenicity and surface markers, such as the TL antigen, which exists only in the thymus,[5] and the $\theta$ antigen in the mouse, which becomes apparent when the T cells leave the thymus.[6,7]

The postthymic $T_1$ cell leaves the thymus and circulates via the blood and lymph to the peripheral lymphoid tissues, such as the spleen and lymph nodes (Fig. 1). In the periphery $T_1$ cells can be further differentiated and expanded under thymic hormonal control to a second subpopulation of immunologically competent $T_2$ lymphoid cells (Fig. 2).[1,4] The $T_2$ cells are a readily mobilizable recirculating lymphoid cell pool capable of specific interaction with antigen, of proliferative expansion, of lymphoblast transformation, and of participation in the inflammatory response. The T cells are long-lived, lasting some months to a year in rodents and up to years in humans.[8] They are directly involved in cell-mediated immune responses; their major function in the body economy apparently is directed to providing a defence against certain pathogenic bacterial, fungal, and viral microorganisms, for example, tubercle bacilli. The T cells may also provide a major component of immunosurveillance against cancer cells and their destruction.

Bursal-derived B cells in birds and marrow-derived immunoglobulin-producing B cells in mammals originate as prebursal stem cells (Fig. 1). They undergo

TABLE 1

DISTRIBUTION OF SUBPOPULATIONS OF LYMPHOCYTES
IN PERIPHERAL LYMPHOID TISSUES

| Lymph node | B | Far or peripheral cortical areas, subcapsular zone, medullary cords |
|---|---|---|
| | T | Para- and infranodular deep cortical areas |
| Spleen | B | Red pulp, periarteriolar areas |
| | T | Parafollicular and perivascular regions in white pulp |
| Blood | B | Larger cells (20–30%) |
| | T | Small and medium cells (70–80%) |
| Thoracic duct | T | Most TD small lymphocytes (95%) |

migration, proliferation, and differentiation patterns that eventually give rise to subpopulations of postbursal $B_1$ cells. The exact sites for these events are not known in mammals, but this influence in birds occurs in the bursa of Fabricius. The bone marrow is extremely rich in B cells. The postbursal $B_1$ cell moves to the peripheral lymphoid tissues, and, at this early stage of differentiation, the immunoglobulin- and antibody-producing machinery is functional but still relatively immature. Fully developed B lymphocytes, in the absence of antigenic stimulation, are a much more sessile population than are the T cells. In the fully differentiated form, postbursal $B_2$ lymphocytes are secretory cells, sometimes referred to as $B_s$ cells, and many can be recognized as plasma cells (Fig. 2). They possess surface antigenic markers, such as the $PC_1$ marker in the mouse, and are capable of both production and secretion of immunoglobulin molecules into the interstitial tissues, lymph, and blood. The end stage of the development of the B-cell line is a cell that can act as a factory for the production of immunoglobulin molecules. This occurs in the peripheral lymphoid tissues, the bone marrow, lymph nodes, spleen, and in all lymphoid effector organs.

## Peripheral Lymphoid Tissues

In the peripheral lymphoid tissues, for example, the spleen and lymph nodes, the immunocompetent cells of the two lymphoid systems have overlapping distributions, but they tend to concentrate as subpopulations in certain specific regions of the peripheral lymphoid organs (Table 1). In the mammalian lymph node, postbursal $B_2$ cells are located in the far or peripheral cortical areas, in the subcapsular zone, and in the medullary cords. The T cells are concentrated in the para- and infranodular deep cortical areas of the nodes. In the spleen, $B_2$ cells are abundant in the red pulp, and $B_1$ cells are in the periarteriolar areas in which germinal centers develop into Malpighian corpuscles. The T-cell population in the spleen is concentrated in the parafollicular and perivascular accumulations in the Malpighian white matter. The T cells circulate and recirculate in blood or

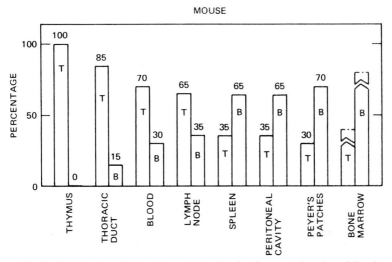

Fig. 3 Distribution of T cells and B cells in the central and peripheral lymphoid tissues in the mouse. The two lymphoid systems have overlapping distributions, but they tend to concentrate as recognizable subpopulations in certain specific regions in the peripheral lymphoid tissues. See Table 1.

lymph as small and medium-sized lymphocytes, and they percolate through all the lymphatic tissues and among them but are excluded from the thymus. Most of thoracic duct small lymphocytes are T cells. Subpopulations of postthymic $T_3$ and $T_4$ cells have now been described. The B cells are larger than the T cells and are a more sessile population. In lymph nodes and spleen germinal centers prior to antigenic stimulation, B cells do not seem to differentiate into plasma cells; but, following antigenic stimulation and a proliferative burst, secretory $B_2$ lymphocytes, and plasma cells develop and antibodies are both synthesized and secreted. The B cells contain antibody molecules of a single specificity which are attached to their surface. Following antigenic stimulation, B cells may leave the lymph nodes and enter the lymph and the blood in surprisingly large numbers.

The T cells circulate in the blood and lymph; however, the B cells with surface receptor immunoglobulin markers also represent a significant component of the peripheral blood lymphocytes, i.e., about 20 to 30% of all lymphocytes in the blood. Most are medium-sized lymphocytes, a few are small, and a few are large lymphocytes. The distribution of T cells and B cells in the various peripheral lymphoid tissues is shown in Fig. 3.

What shall we find in the lymphopoietic pot at the end of the immunological rainbow? Figure 4 shows that there will be hematopoietic stem cells, which are self-maintaining and selectively responding to regulatory induction mechanisms for proliferation and differentiation. There will be T lymphocytes and B lymphocytes and their various subpopulations undergoing proliferation and differentiation to carry out their highly specialized roles in the immune system

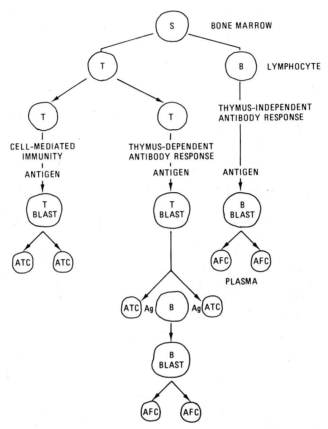

Fig. 4 Structure—function relationships of the cells and tissues of the immune system. S, stem cell; T, T lymphocyte; B, B lymphocyte; blast, lymphoblast; ATC, antigen-recognition T cells; AFC, antibody-forming cells; plasma, plasma cells; Ag, antigen.

as functional end cells. There will be a chemical wiring diagram outlining the regulation of lymphoid-cell production and molecular mechanisms involved in the signalling of cells to "turn on" or "turn off" on encounter with an antigen. There will be a map of the cooperative affairs and interactions for enhancement and suppression of the responses between T cells and B cells and macrophages, with appropriate footnotes on how these operate, and when to call the biological engineer in case regulatory control mechanisms fail to function. The wiring diagram, to a considerable extent, defines the structure—function relationships of the cells and tissues of the lymphoid system. It is these interrelationships of the cytokinetics of the immune system that are central to the functional anatomy of the lymphoid tissues consisting of lymphocytes as mediators of cellular immunity and the regulation of lymphopoiesis in normal and perturbed states.

## THE STEM CELL

The colony-forming unit (CFU) in the mouse may be morphologically indistinguishable from the small lymphocyte of the bone marrow, and it is also present in the peripheral blood but not in the thymus nor in the thoracic duct lymph (for review see Wolstenholme and O'Connor[9]). It is a limited stem cell capable of producing proliferating, differentiating, and functional myeloid, erythroid, and megakaryocytic cells.[10] It does not appear to be capable of crossing over to the immunological lymphocyte series. Since a well-recognized heterogenicity of immunologically functional small lymphocytes in peripheral lymphoid organs—T cells and B cells and their various subpopulations—exists, the evidence suggests that there is an additional morphologically similar stem cell, nonimmunological in function but central to the regulation of hematopoiesis and capable of differentiating into a granulocyte, erythrocyte, or megakaryocyte.

Little is known about the morphological or proliferative characteristics of the hematopoietic stem cell, and conclusive evidence regarding the morphological identification of a CFU cell is not yet available and probably will be difficult to obtain. However, these cells have in the past been considered as pluripotential; that is, they can produce differentiated progeny.[11] Chromosome marker experiments suggest that under certain circumstances they possibly can produce immunologically competent cells.[11-15] Van Bekkum et al.[16] have recently described a "candidate stem cell" in the mouse, selected from stem-cell concentrates prepared by repeated density separation. Under light microscopy the cell is very similar to the bone-marrow lymphocyte. Ultrastructure comparison of the candidate stem cell with the small lymphocyte from mouse thoracic duct brings out clear differences in size as well as morphological characteristics of nuclear and cytoplasmic elements.

The available evidence indicates that the rat bone-marrow CFU is a cell which is slowly proliferating, and it may be triggered into more rapid division with X-irradiation and certain cytotoxic agents, such as myleran. The "repopulating ability" functional assay system has provided evidence that the rat bone-marrow "stem cell" which differentiates into erythropoietic progeny has a cycle time of approximately 30 hr; this may be slightly faster in the mouse bone marrow.[17,18]

## THE THYMUS AND THE T-CELL SYSTEM

During fetal development in the mammal, the lymphoid tissue of the thymus becomes differentiated into cortex and medulla. Throughout growth and development after birth, in the presence of epithelial stroma, the thymus lymphocytes undergo rapid, and at times apparently wasteful, proliferation. This intense proliferative process has been recognized for some time; it is most marked in the cortical area. The developing and proliferating lymphocytes apparently migrate to the medulla from which they are ultimately discharged as educated T cells into the circulation and to peripheral lymphoid tissues (Fig. 1).

There are three cell types in the thymus cortex of the young mouse—lymphoid, reticular, and epithelial.[19,20] The epithelial cells extend as narrow septa infiltrating between the lymphocytes. Lymphopoiesis appears to be confined to the lymphoid and reticular cells. Substantial numbers of lymphocytes are born in the thymus, and substantial numbers die or leave the thymus daily (Refs. 8, 19, and 21-24). Mitotic figures are abundant in the peripheral layer of the cortex, and their frequency decreases as the corticomedullary zone is approached. This reflects the addition of new T cells in the tissue which must be balanced by the loss of cells, by both emigration and death. Most lymphocytes born within the thymus do not emigrate but die and apparently are destroyed there by phagocytic processes.

## Thymus Cell Population Kinetics

In the C57BL mouse thymus, some 20% of the lymphoid cells are primitive large and medium-size lymphocytes, and 80% are small lymphocytes.[21,22] The thymidine labelling index of the primitive thymus cells is approximately 5 to 10%, and the daily mitotic rate exceeds 1.5%; the rate of proliferation is greater than that to sustain growth. Some 2 to 3% of the small lymphocytes label, indicating that some proliferation occurs in this subcompartment.[21,22] The cell-cycle time of these proliferating T cells is relatively short—approximately 9.5 hr, with an S phase of 5.5 hr (Refs. 21, 22, 25, and 26). This is very similar to the generation time of 8.2 hr and a DNA synthesis time of 5.5 hr in the 2-month-old AKR mouse thymus (Fig. 5)[27-30] and of 9.25 hr and 7 hr, respectively, in the newborn Swiss albino mouse (Fig. 6), defined by Michalke and his colleagues.[31] The S phase difference in neonatal mice would suggest a larger growth fraction of proliferating lymphoid cells and can explain cellular growth of the thymus and lymphoid tissue development until the young mouse matures—the addition of new prethymic lymphocytic stem cells and expansion of the stem-cell pool and their lymphocyte progeny.[26] The growth fraction is greatest in the large lymphocyte compartment; it increases with growth of the thymus and decreases with involution in the mature animal.[26]

Thymidine labelling in the small lymphocyte compartment after a single injection gradually increases over the initial values of 2 to 3%; the slope of the curve changes[21,22] at about 16 hr. Apparently, although some limited cell renewal occurs, the population arises primarily from division of precursor forms, particularly the medium-size lymphocytes. From the initial slope of the curve, the half-time renewal rate is approximately 36 hr (that is, 1.4% per hour), very much the same as in the rat thymus and approaching the rapid 24-hr turnover rate of the small lymphocyte in the rat bone marrow.[8]

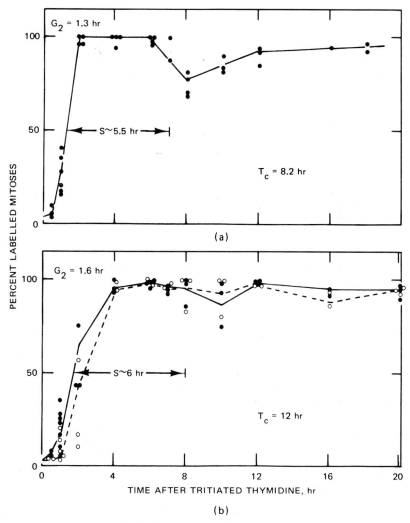

Fig. 5 Percent labelled mitoses curve for young AKR mouse thymus lymphoid cells. (a) Normal thymus, large and medium lymphocytes. (b) Thymic lymphoma, large (●) and medium (○) lymphoma cells.[30]

The cell kinetic data based on differential cell counts, pulse labelling with tritiated thymidine, labelled mitoses, repeated labelling, and grain count decrements indicate that (1) a very large fraction of lymphoid cells proliferate in the thymus; (2) the cell loss factor is high and reflects considerable ineffective or wasteful lymphopoiesis; and (3) the newly formed postthymic T cell is a small lymphocyte that emigrates or dies at the end of a 3- to 4-day intrathymic life-span (Fig. 2). The autoradiographic data are generally consistent with

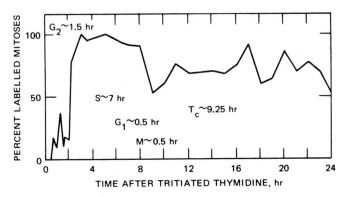

Fig. 6 Percent labelled mitoses curve for neonatal Swiss albino mouse thymus.[31]

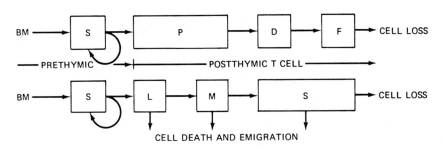

Fig. 7 Lymphopoiesis in mouse thymus. BM, bone marrow. S, prethymic stem-cell compartment. P, proliferation compartment. D, differentiation compartment. F, functional-cell compartment. L, M, S, large, medium, and small lymphocyte populations, respectively

morphological models[19,21] of thymic lymphopoiesis and suggest that T-cell proliferation may originate from a primitive blast element or stem cell[32,33] and that thymic lymphopoiesis is intensive, well controlled, and apparently regulated by symmetrical division of prethymic stem cells into progressively decreasing sizes of large and medium lymphocytes. The predominantly differentiated, nonproliferating populations of functional T-cell small lymphocytes arise from successive divisions of precursor forms. Cell maturation, emigration, and death maintain a steady state of lymphoid cell renewal (Fig. 7).

These cytokinetic observations are consistent with changes in the functional immunological anatomy of the T-cell system. During its proliferative sojourn in the thymus, the maturing $T_1$ cell develops surface isoantigens—in the mouse, TL (thymus lymphocyte)[5] and $\theta$ antigens;[6,7] the $\theta$ antigen is present in the postthymic T cell in the periphery. In the thymus the T cells become educated and capable of reacting with foreign antigens, cells, and organisms. In the periphery the immunologically competent postthymic $T_2$ lymphoid cells represent a readily mobilizable recirculating lymphoid cell pool capable of specific interaction with antigen. These cells contribute a major specific component of bodily defence against pathogenic microorganisms.

The cell kinetic data indicate that about 1.4% of all small lymphocytes in the mouse thymus are replaced each hour.[21,22] After about 3 to 4 days, that is, some seven to eight cell divisions, enough lymphocytes are produced to replace all those in the entire organ. Thus, the newly formed T cells either emigrate or die after their intrathymic life-span. From evidence of thymus-graft experiments (Refs. 20, 27, 28, and 34), it appears that the majority of the thymus lymphocytes do not emigrate and their rapid production is regulated and controlled as an effective mechanism to balance the extensive cell destruction within the thymus. This would be a regulatory processing system selective for self-recognition antigens and immunocompetence, possibly effected under a humoral inductive influence as a self-destructive autoreactive mechanism, mediated possibly by secretions of the thymus epithelial cells (Fig. 1). However, the evidence for this still remains indirect.[35]

From these observations, we conclude that, during the intrathymic process of prethymic stem-cell differentiation into a postthymic immunocompetent T cell, there is an increase in the number of immune cells due mainly to proliferation and that, during the interval between immigration and emigration, educated thymic cells are capable of dividing as many as seven or eight times. It is of interest that this estimate of proliferative potential of competent cells derived from kinetic data is comparable to that derived from histological data.[19,21] The questions that come to mind are: Why seven or eight divisions? Why not more? Why not less? What tells these cells to divide? What tells them to stop proliferating and to emigrate to the periphery? Such regulatory controls responsible for cell processing mediated possibly through an autoreactive mechanism could represent a very definite regulatory feedback control to maintain population size. This could be regulated by cell death controlling population levels in association with hormonal controls (Fig. 8). The evidence indicates that the destruction and elimination of small lymphocytes are carried out effectively, possibly in part through a macrophage—phagocytic system.[21,22,34]

It seems evident that there is some relationship between the proliferative potential of the T-cell system in the thymus and the cell-population structure of the organized lymphoid tissue. To examine this further, we chose to learn something of the properties of the T-cell system in dynamic equilibrium by perturbing it. We have used both continuous low-level irradiation and the thymolytic agent, cortisone, and have examined the cell-population characteristics of the new steady state, the patterns of recovery, and maintenance of homeostasis regulating lymphopoiesis under stress. The cell kinetic and histological studies of thymic lymphopoiesis in mice under continuous irradiation at 45 rads per day for 2 weeks indicated an increase in the proliferation rate of T cells in all lymphocyte subcompartments with little change in the median

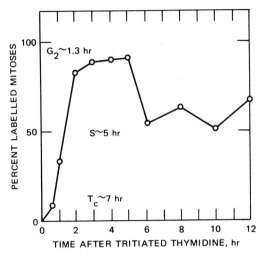

Fig. 8  **Percent labelled mitoses curve for germinal-center cells in rat spleen white pulp.**[36]

cell-cycle time and its constituent phases.[21,22] The half-time renewal of the small lymphocyte population is decreased from 36 to 30 hr owing to an increased production rate from 1.4 to 1.7% per hour.

This intense mitotic proliferative activity in T lymphocytes is associated with an early and increased appearance of cortical PAS-positive macrophage cells, and a large percentage of these cortical PAS-cells contain pyknotic lymphocyte debris (Refs. 21, 22, 26 and 37). The PAS-cell is also a primary cell component during recovery from acute cortisone injury, and our own studies (Fabrikant[21,22] and Fabrikant and Foster[26,37]), and those of Metcalf[27,29] on the preleukemic AKR mouse thymus suggest that the distribution of these macrophage cells in relation to lymphocyte destruction and proliferating lymphocytes in the regenerating populations may be involved in the regulation of lymphocyte mitotic activity. This would indicate that the proliferative stimulus may emanate from within the thymus itself. This appears to be the case in the preleukemic AKR mouse thymus (Refs. 20 and 27-29). Under normal conditions and under stress, cell division may be by physical contact with the cell periphery of these macrophage cells, or these cells may secrete a substance that stimulates mitotic activity. The PAS-macrophage described by Metcalf (Refs. 20 and 27-29) in the AKR mouse thymus does not appear to be a secretory cell. However, there is indirect evidence that the thymus may secrete a hormone under normal conditions from both the medullary and the cortical epithelial cells, but this is still to be demonstrated. Medullary epithelial cells produce a solvated acid-mucopolysaccharide. Further, in studies on myasthenia gravis, the purification of a thymic hormonelike substance, thymin, has led to the isolation of two polypeptides secreted separately by the epithelial cells of the medulla and cortex. It has been postulated that the effect of thymin on neuromuscular activity may be incidental and that the true function of these thymic polypeptides is in the proliferation and differentiation of lymphoid prethymic stem cells to immunologically competent T cells.

## THE IMMUNE RESPONSE AND THE B-CELL SYSTEM

The central lymphoid organs, the thymus and the avian bursa of Fabricius, and the bursal-equivalent in mammals do not appear to have effective antigen-trapping mechanisms. Antibody formation and cell-mediated immunity do not take place in them under normal conditions (Fig. 4). The bulk of antibody formation takes place in the peripheral lymphoid tissues: lymph nodes, spleen, germinal centers, Peyer's patches, tonsils, appendix, and other lymphoid deposits (Fig. 1). In lymphoid follicles and germinal centers, it appears that antigens become attached to specialized reticular cells, and lymphocytes that encounter antigen on the surface of reticular cells may be stimulated.[38] They turn into large rapidly dividing blast cells and create a nest of cells known as a germinal center. These germinal-center cells are B lymphocytes, and it appears that their progeny eventually develop into antibody-forming $B_2$ lymphocytes and plasma cells (Fig. 2). The B lymphocytes have the capacity to pick up antigen—antibody complexes, and antigen-carrying B cells tend to "home" to germinal centers of the spleen and lymph node.

### Germinal-Center Cell Kinetics

The unstimulated germinal center in the spleen of normal animals constitutes a steady-state compartment comprised of a relatively slowly proliferating lymphocyte mass surrounded by a relatively nonproliferating mantle zone of more densely packed small lymphocytes.[36,39] Normally, very few cells are dividing; the germinal-center cell-cycle time in the mouse is approximately 9.0 hr, and the DNA synthesis time, 5.0 hr. The growth fraction is high; about two-thirds of the cells appear capable of active proliferation. The half-time renewal rate of the small lymphocyte population is about 48 hr, about 1% per hour; this is much less than in the thymus and in the bone marrow.[21,22]

The lymphoid-cell proliferation rate in the mantle zone surrounding the germinal centers is quite low. The cell kinetic data suggest that the germinal centers of the mouse spleen may represent a major progenitor $B_1$ cell population for the early and mature secretory $B_2$ lymphoid cells and only to a lesser degree, if at all, for cells in the surrounding lymphoid mass.[36] The kinetic parameters of the germinal-center lymphocytes are quite different from those of thymus cells, indicating that two quite distinct families of lymphocytes—B cells and T cells—exist in the body with different cell kinetic characteristics. Cell migration in the spleen apparently occurs from the germinal center, possibly to the surrounding lymphoid mass and even to the red pulp, but this is still not known.

However, since the cell kinetics of the lymphoid mass in the surrounding mantle zone are independent of those of the germinal center, it appears that these two cell populations are not necessarily related directly in their patterns of cellular proliferation and differentiation. These observations were also described by Fliedner et al.[36] in the rat (Fig. 8) and by Hanna[39] in the mouse. In the rat the unstimulated germinal-center cell-cycle time is slightly shorter, some 7 hr, but with an S period similar to that found in the mouse.

Interest has been renewed in recent years in cells in the germinal centers as precursors of antibody-forming cells.[38]

1. The evidence is that cells in the germinal center are in direct contact with reticular cells which trap antigen.

2. The most dramatic histological changes in response to antigenic stimulation occur in the germinal centers, and they are correlated with serum antibody response.

3. Antibody-forming $B_2$ cells, lymphocytes, and plasma cells can be found in the germinal centers, and especially after secondary antigen stimulation.

4. Although absent in the fetus and rarely seen in the germ-free animal, germinal centers appear after antigenic stimulation.

## Antibody-Forming Cells

The profile of the typical immune response following antigenic stimulation comprises a latent period, a logarithmic rise, a plateau, and a progressive decline of antibody titer (Fig. 9). During the latent period antigens apparently stimulate nonantibody-forming progenitor cells to manufacture polyribosomal units for synthesis and secretion of specific immunoglobulins. This process requires a finite time and is a manifestation of cell differentiation in the B lymphocyte system. During the logarithmic phase the exponential rise of the antibody levels in the blood is due mainly to the increase in the number of antibody-forming cells. As many as 1000 antibody-forming cells may be present at the end of the logarithmic phase for each cell present at the beginning of the response. This occurs when antigen-stimulated progenitor B cells proliferate, then transform into proliferating antibody-forming cells, which, in turn, transform into nonproliferating antibody-forming $B_2$ cells or plasma cells (Fig. 4).

Sado and Makinodan[40] used a diffusion chamber technique to demonstrate that the majority of the functional lymphoid blast cells during the early logarithmic phase are rapidly proliferating antibody-forming cells that also have a high RNA metabolism. The cell-cycle time of these proliferating cells in the third day of the response was 8 to 9 hr, and the DNA synthesis time, 6.8 hr (Fig. 10). The majority of the functional cells during the late logarithmic phase are nonproliferating antibody-forming cells that have a very low RNA metabolism and are descendants of proliferating antibody-forming cells.[41]

The elegant studies of Gowans and his colleagues[42-44] on the transformation of small lymphocytes into large pyroninophilic cells in graft vs. host

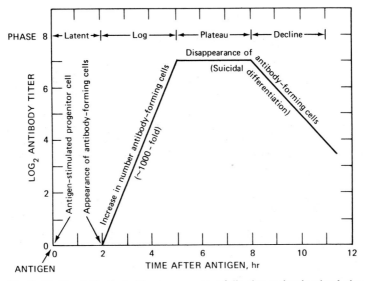

Fig. 9 Profile of the typical immune response following antigenic stimulation in the mammal. The antibody titer in the serum is plotted against the time after administration of antigen.

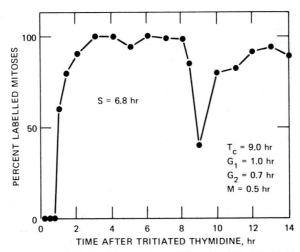

Fig. 10 Percent labelled mitoses curve of functional lymphoid blast cells grown in diffusion chambers during the early logarithmic phase of the secondary immune response. The majority of these cells are rapidly proliferating antibody-forming cells.[40]

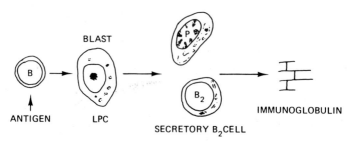

BLAST

ANTIGEN          LPC

IMMUNOGLOBULIN

SECRETORY B₂CELL

Fig. 11  The hypothesis that in the primary antibody response small lymphocytes interact with antigen and develop into antibody-forming cells (plasma cells and secretory B cells) through the intermediary of a dividing precursor [immunoblasts or lymphoblasts and large pyroninophilic cells (LPC)].

reactions have provided valuable insight to our understanding of the T-cell basis of the cell-mediated immune response. Gowans injected parental-strain labelled thoracic duct lymphocytes into $F_1$ hybrid rats and studied the early histological changes that occurred in the spleen. The main brunt of the initial attack on the host was borne by the peripheral lymphoid tissues. The most prominent early histological change occurred between 12 and 24 hr in the periarteriolar zone of small lymphocytes in the white pulp of the spleen. Initially, the normal follicular architecture of the spleen, and of the lymph nodes, to a lesser extent, became disorganized. The prominent cellular change consisted of the appearance and proliferation of a line of lymphoid cells the largest of which possessed an intensely pyroninophilic cytoplasm, a prominent pyroninophilic nucleolus, and a pale vesicular nucleus with fine chromatin structure. These large pyroninophilic cells increased in number between 24 hr and 4 days, and mitotic figures were frequent. An autoradiographic analysis of the tissues of the $F_1$ rats 24 hr after the injection of radioactively labelled thoracic duct cells led to the conclusion that some of the injected small lymphocytes had transformed within that period into large pyroninophilic cells. The spleen appeared to be a preferential site for the transformation of small lymphocytes into large pyroninophilic cells; the transformation was also detected on a small scale in the lymph nodes. In addition, large pyroninophilic cells of host origin also arose and eventually made up the majority of those cells present.

This latter observation has bearing on the early elegant experiments of Nossal and Mäkelä,[38] who presented evidence that small lymphocytes play some part in the primary antibody responses. The simplest hypothesis they presented is that these cells interact with antigen and develop into antibody-forming cells through the intermediary of a dividing precursor (Fig. 11). There is now considerable morphological and autoradiographic support, both from electron and light microscopy, in favor of this view. The following sequence appears to be one of the effector pathways in the production of the immunologically competent postbursal $B_2$ lymphocytes: small B lymphocytes → dividing large pyroninophilic cell or large blast cell $\rightarrow$ $B_2$ lymphocyte or plasma cell. The end stage of development of the B-cell line is a lymphoid cell that can act as a veritable factory for immunoglobulin molecules; for example, the $B_2$ cell secretes the relatively primitive IgM immunoglobulin, whereas the plasma cell elaborates the very efficient IgG immunoglobulin.

## Cytokinetics of the Immune Response

The autoradiographic studies in our laboratory on the cytokinetics of the immune response in the mouse have centered on the cellular kinetics of lymphocyte proliferation and transformation and the production of antibody-producing cells. Primary immunization establishes a line of dividing cells in lymphoid tissues, and the most dramatic changes are located within the germinal centers of the spleen. The arrival of a secondary response stimulates cell division in spleen germinal centers and may lead to the rapid formation of new centers. We have used the sheep erythrocyte response in mice to examine the germinal center changes in the spleen during the latent and logarithmic phases of the antibody reaction. The characteristic cellular changes include lymphocyte transformation and increased proliferation of large pyroninophilic cells, and emigration and loss of lymphocytes from the germinal center to the mantle zone of the surrounding lymphocyte mass (Hanna[39] and Fabrikant, unpublished). The germinal center undergoes hyperplastic changes within 2 hr after intravenous injection of the antigen; the dissociation event in the germinal center occurs immediately thereafter, in the subsequent 1 to 2 days. During the proliferative phase following stimulation, there is an increase in the number and in thymidine labelling of proliferating large pyroninophilic cells associated with the appearance of thymidine-labelled plasma cells. The labelled lymphocyte population remains steady. After 1 to 2 days, labelling of the plasma cells increases; thereafter, the numbers of proliferating large blast cells decrease in association with an increase in plasma-cell population size and labelling indexes.

Normally, the germinal-center cell population in the white pulp of the mouse spleen is in a steady state of cell renewal; the cell-cycle time is about 9.0 hr (Fabrikant, unpublished). Under antigenic stimulation the population may be considered a conditional cell renewal system, that is, slowly or nonproliferating cells capable of being triggered into cell cycle on a demand situation. On the second day of the primary immune response, there is a shortening of the germinal-center cell-cycle time to approximately 7.3 hr due to a decrease in the $G_1$ period, possibly as a result of rapid triggering of $G_0$ cells into cell cycle. The growth fraction decreases from 0.63 to 0.43, which suggests that the potentially proliferative resting lymphoid cells had already been committed to a differentiation pathway, prior to encounter with antigen, for the production of blast-cell and plasma-cell progeny of the B-cell system. Here, recruitment can be envisaged from an immunologically competent and responsive population of lymphoid cells, possibly from a $G_0$ resting stage (Fig. 12). The induction mechanism would

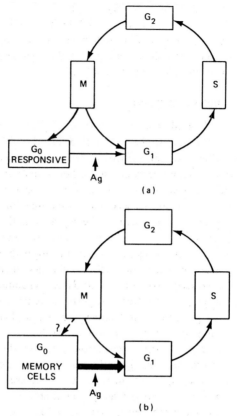

Fig. 12 Primary (a) and secondary (b) immune responses in the germinal-center cell population in the white pulp of the mouse spleen; under antigenic stimulation, the cell population responds as a conditional renewal system—responsive $G_0$ cells or $G_0$ memory cells are recruited into cell cycle to amplify the antibody-forming cell populations. Ag, antigenic stimulation.

involve the recruitment of a large number of potentially proliferative germinal-center progenitor cells that enter into cell cycle, amplify their numbers, and transform into nonproliferating antibody-forming cells. Both B- and T-cell systems are known to depend for specificity on selective combination with antigen, but in great measure their biological influence in body defense depends on their ability to use biological amplification systems. That this occurs in the B-cell population appears to be in the control of cell kinetics.

Studies on the cell types that give rise to antibody-forming cells in the secondary response in germinal centers consider the special problem in which lymphoid precursors endow the animal with the faculty of immunological memory (Fig. 12). Since antigen or any static assembly of molecules would be diluted to insignificant levels in cells that divide throughout the interval between primary and secondary responses, instruction for specific antibody synthesis may be carried genetically. The logarithmic phase of the secondary immune response involves a germinal-center cell-cycle time similar to that of the primary response—here, 7.4 hr, with an S phase of approximately 4.8 hr. These values are very close to the third-day response in the mouse blast system of cells cultured in diffusion chambers, some 8 to 9 hr (Fig. 10).[40] The evidence is that, for secondary antigenic responses effected through the B-cell system, primary immunization establishes a line of dividing cells in lymphoid tissue within the germinal center, and the memory of primary immunization may be carried by a dividing cell line. Following a second antigen stimulation, proliferation of antibody-forming cells appears to be an inextricable feature of the overall process of antibody production.

## RADIATION PERTURBATION

The interrelationships of the functional anatomy of the germinal-center lymphoid populations, their cellular microenvironment, their cellular homeostasis, and their ability to respond to stress, such as irradiation, deserve special attention. We have used continuous gamma irradiation at 45 rads per day for cellular perturbation; it can be applied without producing the general stressful response seen with many pharmacological agents.[21,22] Generally, the duration and degree of immune suppression are mediated, in large part, through radiation effects on lymphoid-cell proliferation and differentiation (Fig. 13). Mice exposed to continuous irradiation for varying periods before administration of antigen are able to produce appreciable amounts of antibody but at rather lower levels than controls produce. The patterns of response indicate a delay in the rate of production of antibody rather than a depression of peak titer of serum response. The evidence indicates that the accumulation of sufficient damage in the progenitor cell compartment before administration of antigen may suppress antibody formation by decreasing the production of antibody-forming progeny cells but not the capacity for antibody and immunoglobulin synthesis and secretion.

Here, the B-cell system immune response appears more radiosensitive than the T-cell response; indeed, a relatively radioresistant postthymic $T_4$ cell population has been identified in the periphery.[1] The ultimate effector cells in the periphery, the plasma cells and $B_2$ lymphocytes and, in certain instances, cooperating T lymphocytes, require no further DNA synthesis and little RNA synthesis for antibody and immunoglobulin production. In the proliferative phase, therefore, radiation would be expected to block immune processes by interfering with DNA synthesis and cell division, that is, by affecting the reproductive capacity of proliferating immune cells. Immune mechanisms are known to be radiosensitive, and depressed antibody production is, in large part, related to alterations of cell populations, particularly in cell-population number

of proliferating cells, except possibly at very late stages. However, reproductively
intact cells should not be similarly affected, and this appears to be the case for
both the primary and the secondary responses. Moreover, it is clear that the
progenitor cells of the germinal centers of both the primary and secondary
responses are equally radiosensitive.[45]

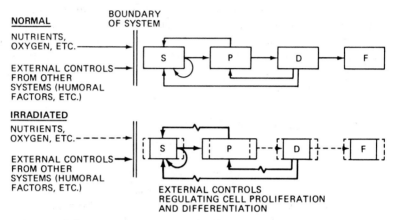

Fig. 13  Radiation perturbation of lymphopoiesis; the duration and degree of
immunosuppression is mediated, in large part, through radiation effects on
lymphoid-cell proliferation and differentiation.

It is possible to speculate on the differences in radiosensitivity between T
cells and B cells and T-cell—B-cell cooperation in this situation.[46,47] Certain
postthymic $T_4$ cells are relatively radioresistant; these are found in the
periphery—the spleen, lymph nodes, and bone marrow.[1] The B cells in the
spleen are much more radiosensitive and under continuous irradiation fail to
maintain a level of cell population compatible with function. Compensatory
thymus cell proliferation occurs under continuous irradiation in spite of a
considerable amount of cell death, and the export of immunocompetent
postthymic T cells in sufficient numbers is maintained.[21,22] Thus, provided
sufficient numbers of T cells survive and proliferate, surviving B cells can be
immunoresponsive and specialized for the production and secretion of immunoglobulins. This situation may be an expression of the T-cell function of
cooperation to help the surviving B cells get started on antibody production
(Fig. 4), and this helper function would not necessarily be impaired. Indeed,
without T-cell cooperation, many antigens would fail to produce antibody
formation in the mouse. With a sufficient number of postbursal B cells
reproducing, the function of the T cells in cooperative helping of B cells may be
preserved, albeit at lower than normal levels.

## THYMIC LEUKEMOGENESIS

It is now clear that the thymus acts both to differentiate T cells and to develop further postthymic T cells and expand the T-cell population after it has emigrated to the periphery. No molecular definition of the indirect influence of the thymus has thus far been forthcoming, even though evidence of expanding activity for thymic extracts, that is, thymosin, has been presented.[35] The observations that multiple myeloma, Hodgkin's disease, chronic lymphatic leukemia, and certain lymphoid malignancies in man are associated with abnormalities of differentiation of T cells and B cells have provided a stimulus for studies of immunodeficiency diseases and their relation to neoplastic disease.

Experimental data from a number of laboratories indicate that various oncogenic viruses transform lymphoreticular cells in mice to neoplastic behavior, and such virus-host cell specificity suggests that the same type of virus or viruses may induce either thymic lymphoma or myeloid leukemia in a number of mouse strains. Kaplan[48] has demonstrated that radiation exerts oncogenic effects on the thymus by initial damage to normal cellular target sites of the latent leukemogenic virus (RadLV), which results in release of the virus. Cellular injury to the prethymic stem cells and primitive postthymic T-cell populations in the thymus is followed by stimulation to regenerative hyperplasia, but cellular injury to the bone-marrow stem-cell population interferes with regeneration of the thymus. Impairment of thymic regeneration results in subjecting primitive and immature thymic cells—possibly prethymic stem cells or their early progeny—to prolonged maturation arrest, thereby protracting the period during which they are maximally susceptible to the leukemia virus.

The histological and autoradiographic studies in our laboratory on thymic lymphomogenesis in the C57BL mouse indicate that neoplastic transformation of T cells is associated with marked kinetic changes in the lymphoid cell cycle and cell-population characteristics—increased thymidine labelling indexes, increased duration of DNA synthesis and of the cell cycle, and increased growth fractions in the successive generations.[23,26] During the development of lymphoma, external control mechanisms involving the steady state of lymphoid cell renewal in the thymus maintaining population size and function break down after a period of induction; cellular growth exceeds certain population limits, and lymphoma develops (Refs. 20, 23, 27, and 29). Furthermore, these external controls of population size rapidly deteriorate, the tissue can no longer be contained, and dissemination occurs throughout the body. That internal controls regulating the biochemical events of the cell cycle and cell reproduction are lost is evidenced by the changes in the patterns of the kinetics of cellular proliferation (see Fig. 5), progressive aneuploidization and chromosome alterations, progressive loss of the capacity to differentiate among primitive lymphoid cells, and possibly the transformation of basically nonproliferating functional end cells to more primitive proliferative forms. Thus during leukemogenesis changes in the regulation of cell reproduction occur not only in the proliferative cell compartment but in the differentiation and mature functional end-cell compartments, and probably in the stem-cell compartment as well, thereby profoundly disturbing the rates of cell flux and transition from one compartment to another.

## SUMMARY AND CONCLUSIONS

It is difficult in this sort of review of some of our investigations on the proliferative activities of the cells of the lymphoid system and immunity to include even a few of the dynamic changes that are occurring in our general knowledge concerning the cellular aspects of immune responses, the regulation of lymphopoiesis, and structure—function relations in the lymphoid system. I have tried to discuss only some limited aspects of the binary structure of the lymphoid system in relation to immunity and the interrelationships of the cytokinetics of the immune system. These are central to the functional anatomy of the lymphoid tissues consisting of lymphocytes as mediators of cellular immunity and the regulation of lymphopoiesis in normal and perturbed states. The information that exists about lymphocyte kinetics in the two-component cell system is still somewhat meager, but certain observations are worth comment.

The functional anatomy of the lymphoid tissues in relation to the regulation of lymphopoiesis and to immunity is now becoming better understood (Fig. 14). Committed hematopoietic stem cells, the precursors of the immunologically competent T cells, arise in the bone marrow as prethymic stem cells and reach the thymus, a central lymphoid organ, via the blood stream. Within the thymus the prethymic cells, which are not immunologically competent, become differentiated into postthymic immunocompetent T cells. Postthymic $T_1$ cells migrate via the blood stream to the peripheral lymphoid tissues and are sensitive to the humoral inductive influence of the thymus. In the periphery they become fully competent long-lived recirculating postthymic $T_2$ cells, are mobile, appear in thymus-dependent areas of peripheral lymphoid tissues, and circulate between the tissues, lymphatics, and the blood stream. The T cells function as major defenses against certain pathogenic microorganisms and are directly involved in cell-mediated immune responses, such as homograft responses in the graft vs. host reaction, as effector cells.

The T cells do not produce humoral antibodies; these are synthesized and secreted by B cells derived from the bursal equivalent in mammals independently of thymic influence. Postbursal $B_1$ cells migrate to bursal-dependent areas of peripheral lymphoid tissues, then differentiate into fully competent antibody-producing immunoglobulin-secreting $B_2$ cells, and function in germinal-center immune sites of the secondary effector lymphoid tissues, such as the spleen and lymph nodes. However, for many antigens B cells require the presence of appropriate reactive T cells before they can function and produce antibodies.

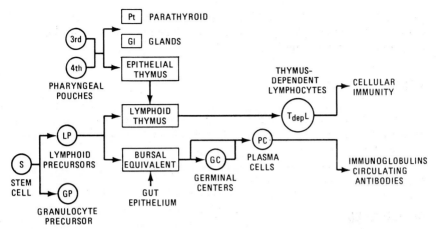

Fig. 14 Functional anatomy of lymphoid development in relation to the regulation of lymphopoiesis and to immunity. Some of the known pathways of differentiation of lymphoid stem cells to immunologically competent T-cell and B-cell systems essential to the effective development, organization, and function of a two-component lymphoid system in mammals are illustrated.

The mechanism of the process of the T-cell—B-cell cooperation is, as yet, poorly understood.[1]

The inductive influence of the thymus for the differentiation of the T-cell subpopulations may be mediated in large part by hormonal secretions of its epithelial cells. The T-cell long-lived recirculating lymphocyte may be among the important contributions to the extrathymic pool of small lymphocytes. One such contribution is the helper mechanism of cooperation with B cells in which two separate lymphoid systems can interact and amplify one another in a variety of ways. The contributions of the T-cell system may be more important when the animal is recovering from a protracted lymphopenic state produced by thymolytic agents, such as cortisone or the stress of irradiation.

Thus, regulation of lymphocyte proliferation appears to involve complex internal controls and external feedback controls from within and outside the thymus for the production of cells required for stress-depleted intrathymic lymphoid pools of long-lived lymphocytes—possibly T cells capable of immune function or of cooperation with B cells. However, little is known about the regulatory mechanisms influencing lymphocyte proliferation and modification of extrinsic factors affecting lymphopoiesis or the processing of lymphocytes under stress. For example, from our knowledge of immunological deficiency diseases, it has been postulated that abnormalities of the thymus affecting neuromuscular transmission in myasthenia gravis, or loss of homeostatic regulation of hematopoiesis leading to leukemogenesis, may reflect regulatory functions which are incidental. The structure—function relations of the thymic lymphocyte in the lymphoid system are, in part, the differentiation of lymphoid stem cells to an immunologically competent T-cell system essential to the effective development, organization, and function of a two-component lymphoid system in mammals.

## ACKNOWLEDGMENTS

I wish to express my indebtedness to all my colleagues in our laboratory and in other laboratories and, in particular, to Professor Lamerton, Dr. Foster, Mr. Hsu, Mrs. Lebert, Mrs. Kovar, and Miss Vitak.

The research reported in this paper was supported by U. S. Atomic Energy Commission contract CH AT(11-1)-3013.

## REFERENCES

1. M. F. Greaves, J. J. T. Owen, and M. C. Raff, T and B Lymphocytes: Origins, Properties and Roles in Immune Responses, *Excepta Medica*, Amsterdam, 1973.
2. M. C. Raff and H. Cantor, Subpopulations of Thymus Cells and Thymus Derived Lymphocytes, *Progress in Immunology*, B. Amos (Ed.), pp. 83-93, Academic Press, Inc., New York, 1972.
3. M. D. Cooper, A. R. Lawton, and D. E. Bockman, Agammaglobulinemia with B Lymphocytes. Specific Defect with Plasma Cell Differentiation, *Lancet*, 2: 791-794 (1971).
4. O. Stuttman and R. A. Good, Traffic of Hemopoietic Cells to the Thymus: Influence of Histocompatibility Differences, *Exp. Hematol.*, 19: 12-15 (1969).
5. E. A. Boyse, L. J. Old, and E. Stockert, An Approach to the Mapping of Antigens on the Cell Surface, *Proc. Nat. Acad. Sci. U. S. A.*, 60: 886-893 (1968).
6. M. C. Raff, Theta Isoantigen as a Marker of Thymus-Derived Lymphocytes in Mice, *Nature (London)*, 224: 378-379 (1969).
7. M. C. Raff and H. H. Wortis, Thymus Dependence of Theta-Bearing Cells in the Peripheral Lymphoid Tissues of Mice, *Immunology*, 18: 931-942 (1970).
8. N. B. Everett and R. W. Tyler, Lymphopoiesis in the Mouse and Other Tissues: Functional Implications, *Int. Rev. Cytol.*, 22: 205-237 (1967).
9. G. E. W. Wolstenholme and M. O'Connor (Eds.), *Haemopoiesis: Cell Production and Its Regulation*, J.&A. Churchill, Ltd., London, 1960.
10. J. E. Till and E. A. McCulloch, A Direct Measurement of the Radiation Sensitivity of Mouse Bone Marrow Cells, *Radiat. Res.*, 14: 213-222 (1961).
11. P. C. Nowell, B. E. Hirsch, D. H. Fox, and D. B. Wilson, Evidence for the Existence of Multipotential Lympho-Hematopoietic Stem Cells in the Adult Rat, *J. Cell. Physiol.*, 75: 151 (1970).
12. C. E. Ford and H. S. Micklem, The Thymus and Lymph-Nodes in Radiation Chimeras, *Lancet*, 1: 359 (1963).
13. C. E. Ford, H. S. Micklem, E. P. Evans, J. G. Gray, and D. A. Ogden, The Inflow of Bone Marrow Cells to the Thymus; Studies with Part-Body Irradiated Mice Injected with Chromosome-Marked Bone Marrow and Subjected to Antigenic Stimulation, *Ann. N. Y. Acad. Sci.*, 129: 283-296 (1966).
14. J. F. Loutit, Grafts of Haematopoietic Tissue: The Nature of Haematopoietic Stem Cells, *J. Clin. Pathol.*, 20: 535-539 (1967).
15. H. S. Micklem and J. F. Loutit, *Tissue Grafting and Radiation*, Academic Press, Inc., New York, 1966.

16. D. W. Van Bekkum, M. J. van Noord, B. Maat, and K. A. Dicke, Attempts at Identification of Hemopoietic Stem Cell in Mouse, *Blood J. Hematol.,* **38**: 547-558 (1971).

17. N. M. Blackett, P. J. Roylance, and K. Adams, Studies on the Capacity of Bone Marrow-Cells to Restore Erythropoiesis in Heavily Irradiated Rats, *Brit. J. Haematol.,* **10**: 453-467 (1964).

18. L. G. Lajtha, L. V. Pozzi, R. Schofield, and M. Fox, Kinetic Properties of Haemopoietic Stem Cells, *Cell Tissue Kinet.,* **2**: 39-49 (1969).

19. C. P. Leblond and G. Sainte-Marie, Models for Lymphocyte and Plasmocyte Formation, in *Haemopoiesis: Cell Production and Its Regulation,* G. E. W. Wolstenholme and M. O'Connor (Eds.), CIBA Foundation Symposium, pp. 152-172, J. & A. Churchill, Ltd., London, 1960.

20. D. Metcalf, The Thymus and Lymphopoiesis, in *The Thymus in Immunobiology,* R. A. Good and A. E. Gabrielsen (Eds.), pp. 150-179, Harper & Row, Publishers, New York, 1964.

21. J. I. Fabrikant, Cell Proliferation During Lymphopoiesis in Normal and Continuously Irradiated Mice, in *Effects of Radiation on Cellular Proliferation and Differentiation,* Symposium Proceedings, Monaco, Apr. 1-5, 1968, pp. 269-293, International Atomic Energy Agency, Vienna, 1968 (STI/PUB/186).

22. J. I. Fabrikant, Radiation Effects on Lymphopoiesis Under Continuous Low Dose Rate Exposure, *Radiology,* **93**: 887-893 (1969).

23. J. I. Fabrikant, Thymus Cell Population Studies During Radiation Leukemogenesis, *Amer. J. Roentgenol.,* **108**: 729-735 (1970).

24. J. F. A. P. Miller and D. Osoba, Current Concepts of the Immunological Function of the Thymus, *Physiol. Rev.,* **47**: 337-420 (1967).

25. J. I. Fabrikant and B. R. Foster, Cell Cycle in Lymphocytes in Mouse Thymus, *Naturwissenschaften,* **56**: 567 (1969).

26. J. I. Fabrikant and B. R. Foster, Cell Population Kinetics in Mouse and Rat Thymus, *J. Hopkins Med. J.,* **130**: 208-215 (1972).

27. D. Metcalf, The Nature and Regulation of Lymphopoiesis in the Normal and Neoplastic Thymus, in *The Thymus* (CIBA Foundation Symposium), G. E. W. Wolstenholme and M. O'Connor (Eds.), pp. 242-263, J. & A Churchill, Ltd., London, 1966.

28. D. Metcalf, Histologic and Transplantation Studies on the Preleukemic Thymus of the AKR Mouse, *J. Nat. Cancer Inst.,* **37**: 425-472 (1966).

29. D. Metcalf, The Nature and Regulation of Lymphopoiesis in the Normal and Neoplastic Thymus, in *The Thymus* (CIBA Foundation Symposium), G. E. W. Wolstenholme and R. Porter (Eds.), pp. 242-263, J. & A. Churchill, Ltd., London, 1966.

30. D. Metcalf and M. Wiadrowski, Autoradiographic Analysis of Lymphocyte Proliferation in the Thymus and Thymic Lymphoma Tissue, *Cancer Res.,* **26**: 483-491 (1966).

31. W. D. Michalke, W. W. Hess, H. Riewyl, R. D. Stoner, and H. Cottier, Thymic Lymphopoiesis and Cell Loss in Newborn Mice, *Blood,* **33**: 541-554 (1969).

32. N. B. Everett, R. W. Caffrey, and W. O. Rieke, Recirculation of Lymphocytes, *Ann. N. Y. Acad. Sci.,* **113**: 887-893 (1964).

33. R. W. Caffrey, N. B. Everett, and W. O. Ricke, Radio-Autographic Studies of Reticular and Blast Cells in the Hemopoietic Tissue of the Rat, *Anat. Rec.,* **155**: 41-55 (1966).

34. D. Metcalf and M. A. S. Moore, *Haemopoietic Cells,* North-Holland Publishing Company, Amsterdam, 1971.

35. G. Goldstein, Isolation of Bovine Thymin: A Polypeptide Hormone of the Thymus, *Nature,* **247**: 11-14 (1974).

36. T. M. Fliedner, M. Kesse, E. P. Cronkete, and J. S. Robertson, Cell Proliferation in Germinal Centers of the Rat Spleen, *Ann. N. Y. Acad. Sci.,* **113**: 578-594 (1964).

37. J. I. Fabrikant and B. R. Foster, Lymphoid Cell Renewal Under Low Level Irradiation. XI. The Cell Cycle and Growth Kinetics During Radiation Leukemogenesis in C57BL Mice, *Radiology,* **104**: 203-204 (1972).

38. G. J. V. Nossal and O. Mäkelä, Elaboration of Antibodies by Single Cells, *Annu. Rev. Microbiol.,* **16**: 53-74 (1962).

39. M. G. Hanna, An Autoradiographic Study of the Germinal Center in Spleen White Pulp During Early Intervals of the Immune Response, *Lab. Invest.,* **13**: 95-104 (1964).

40. T. Sado and T. Makinodan, The Cell Cycle of Blast Cells Involved in Secondary Antibody Response, *J. Immunol.,* **93**: 696-700 (1964).

41. J. F. Albright and T. Makinodan, Growth and Senescence of Antibody Forming Cells, *J. Cell. Physiol.,* **67** (Suppl.1): 185-206 (1966).

42. J. L. Gowans, The Fate of Parental Strain Small Lymphocytes in $F_1$ Hybrid Rats, *Ann. N. Y. Acad. Sci.,* **99**: 432-435 (1962).

43. J. L. Gowans and E. J. Knight, The Route of Recirculation of Lymphocytes in the Rat, *Proc. Roy. Soc. (London), Ser. B.,* **159**: 257-282 (1964).

44. J. L. Gowans and D. D. McGregor, The Immunological Activities of Lymphocytes, *Progr. Allergy,* **9**: 1-78 (1965).

45. J. I. Fabrikant, *Radiobiology,* Year Book Medical Publishers, Chicago, 1972.

46. H. N. Claman, E. A. Chaperon, and R. F. Triplett, Thymus—Marrow-Cell Combinations—Synergism in Antibody Production, *Proc. Soc. Exp. Biol. Med.,* **122**: 1167-1171 (1966).

47. P. Bretcher and M. Cohn, A Theory of Self—Nonself Discrimination, *Science,* **169**: 1042-1049 (1970).

48. H. S. Kaplan, On the Natural History of the Murine Leukemias: Presidential Address, *Cancer Res.,* **27**(1): 1325-1340 (1967).

# THE EFFECT OF GLUCOCORTICOIDS ON THE MITOTIC CYCLE OF MALIGNANT LYMPHOID CELLS IN CULTURE

A. D. LABRECQUE,* D. L. BERLINER, and W. STEVENS
Department of Anatomy, University of Utah, Salt Lake City, Utah

## ABSTRACT

Glucocorticoids have profound effects on normal and malignant lymphoid cells, but such cells are only partially susceptible to the cytotoxic and cytostatic action. Cell-cycle analysis can reveal if the reason for this partial effect is resistance to the steroid when the cells are in specific phases of the mitotic cycle. Continuously dividing murine lymphoblastic leukemia cells (L5178Y) were cultured with cortisol (or fluocinolone acetonide) for short or prolonged periods or were grown in control media. Population doubling times were determined and cell-cycle analysis was performed in synchronized and nonsynchronized cultures. Although the results showed a prolonged generation time in treated cultures, the effect of the steroid was not specific for any phase(s) of the mitotic cycle but was a function only of the duration of exposure to it.

In 1943 Dougherty and White[1] demonstrated the dramatic involution of lymphoid organs and disruption of lymphocytes by adrenal cortical secretions. They later suggested that steroids produced both cytotoxic effects and mitotic inhibition, or cytostasis.[2] In 1953 Trowell[3] developed a new technique for culturing intact lymph nodes to demonstrate that glucocorticoids were directly toxic to lymphocytes in vitro.

Clinical use of glucocorticoids as chemotherapeutic agents in the treatment of leukemia, inflammation, and as an immunosuppressive agent in organ transplantation has made it clear that in vivo populations of normal and malignant lymphocytes are only partially susceptible to the steroids. Since in vivo populations of such cells are randomly distributed throughout the various stages of the mitotic cycle, it is possible that the partial susceptibility, or partial

---

*Present address: T. H. Morgan School of Biological Sciences, University of Kentucky, Lexington, Kentucky.

resistance, is characteristic of specific stages of the cycle. Clarification of any stage-specific susceptibility or resistance to glucocorticoids would be of potential value for more efficient therapy. The experiments reported here characterize the standard growth parameters of an established line of continuously growing murine lymphoblastic leukemia cells in control cultures and attempt to identify variations in these parameters when cultures are treated with glucocorticoid hormones.

## MATERIALS

L5178Y cells, originated by Fischer,[4] were maintained in suspension culture in Fischer's nutrient medium containing 10% horse serum, penicillin (100 units/ml), and streptomycin (50 $\mu$g/ml). Cell concentrations were assayed by hemacytometer counts and/or counting on a Coulter counter, and viability was determined using trypan blue dye exclusion. Fluocinolone acetonide was used at a final concentration of 0.01 $\mu$g/ml, the optimal dose as determined by Berliner and Nabors,[5] who also determined the equivalent concentration of cortisol to be 440 times as much by weight, or 4.4 $\mu$g/ml (1.2 X $10^{-5}$ molar). Both steroids were solubilized using propylene glycol (1 $\mu$l/ml) as a vehicle. The effects of chronic, or long-term, exposure, and of acute, or short-term, exposure of these concentrations of steroid on the cell cycle were assayed in nonsynchronized cultures and in synchronized cultures. Experiments were planned so that the cultures were growing exponentially and the cell concentration was as near 100,000 cells/ml as possible when sampling was begun (zero time).

## METHODS AND RESULTS

### Nonsynchronized Cultures

Nonsynchronized cultures were subjected to cell-cycle analysis by the method of Howard and Pelc.[6] This technique involved pulse-labelling the population of cells for 20 min in tritiated thymidine ($^3$H−TdR 0.1 $\mu$Ci/ml, specific activity = 19.5 Ci/mmole). The cell suspension was centrifuged 10 min at 800 g, the radioactive supernatant was removed, and the cells were resuspended in medium without $^3$H−TdR. The beginning of pulse labelling was considered time zero, and the culture was sequentially sampled at semihourly intervals for a time span at least twice as long as the mean doubling time of untreated cultures. In this case the doubling time was roughly 12 hr and the sampling span was 24 hr. Samples were monitored for concentration and viability, as described previously. Smears were made for autoradiography using Kodak NTB3 emulsion, which was exposed for 4 days at 4°C and developed in Kodak D-19. Autoradiographic slides were subsequently stained with Giemsa, and at least 2000 cells per slide were scored in four categories: labelled or

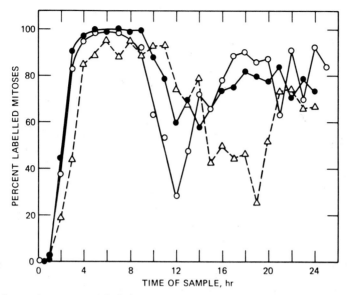

Fig. 1 The percent labelled mitoses with time of sample. o, untreated controls. •, acute steroid-treated cultures. Δ, chronic steroid-treated cultures.

nonlabelled mitoses and labelled or nonlabelled interphase. The labelling index (LI = number of labelled cells per total cells counted), the mitotic index (MI = number of mitotic cells per total cells counted), and the percent labelled mitoses were followed with time. By plotting the percent labelled mitoses of each sample time, we could follow through the cell cycle in two successive waves of mitosis that fragment of the population which was synthesizing DNA at the time the labelled thymidine precursor was added. Using the method of Howard and Pelc,[6] we measured directly or indirectly the cell-cycle time, $T_c$, and the length of time occupied by each stage of the cycle. Cell-cycle time can be measured between any point on the first wave to the corresponding point on the second wave. The usual measure from 50% labelled mitoses on the first incline to the same point on the second incline (Fig. 1) can be used to determine cell-cycle times for the control ($T_c$ = 12.0 hr) and the chronic steroid-treated culture ($T_c$ = 17.0 hr), but not for the acute steroid-treated culture in this graph. However, when the cycle times are measured from the lowest point on successive waves, the control $T_c$ = 12.0 hr, the acute treated $T_c$ = 14.0 hr, and the chronic treated $T_c$ = 19.0 hr. These results, as summarized in Table 1, suggest a graded effect depending on duration of treatment.

The mean duration of DNA synthesis ($T_s$) is measured from the point of 50% labelled mitoses on the first incline to 50% labelled mitoses on the first decline (Fig. 1). In controls, $T_s$ = 8.0 hr, and in chronic steroid-treated cultures the $T_s$ = 12.0 hr. In the acute steroid-treated cultures, $T_s$ is not directly measurable

TABLE 1

SUMMARY OF CELL-CYCLE DATA IN NONSYNCHRONIZED
L5178Y CELLS

|  | Control | Acute treated | Chronic treated |
|---|---|---|---|
| Doubling time | 12.0 hr |  | 30.0 hr |
| $T_c$ | 12.0 hr | 14.0 hr | 17.0–19.0 hr |
| $T_{G_1}$ | 1.3 hr | 1.6 hr | 3.0 hr |
| $T_s$ | 8.0 hr | (8.0–12.0 hr) | 12.0 hr |
| $T_{G_2}$ | 2.06 hr | 2.0 hr | 2.6 hr |
| $T_M$ | 0.47 hr | 0.43 hr | 0.34 hr |
| MI | 0.0256 | 0.0215 | 0.0130 |

but is between 8.0 and 12.0 hr. From time zero to 50% labelled mitoses represents $T_{G_2+(m/2)}$. For controls, this figure is 2.3 hr, for acute treated it is 2.2 hr, and for chronic treated it is 2.8 hr. The value for $T_{G_2}$ can be calculated from the latter figures if $T_m$ is known. The duration of mitosis, $T_m$, is related to the ratio of the count of mitotic cells to all cells counted, which is the mitotic index, MI. Since an exponentially growing cell population has two cells entering $G_1$ for every cell entering mitosis, the relationship between $T_m$ and MI involves the natural log of 2 (0.693) in the following way:

$$T_m = \frac{MI \times T_c}{0.693} \qquad (1)$$

For a complete explanation and derivation of Eq. 1, see Cleaver.[7]

From Eq. 1, control $T_m$ = 0.47 hr, acute treated $T_m$ = 0.43 hr, and chronic treated $T_m$ = 0.34 hr. From these figures $T_{G_2}$ was calculated as explained previously. Control $T_{G_2}$ = 2.06 hr, acute treated $T_{G_2}$ = 2.0 hr, and chronic treated $T_{G_2}$ = 2.6 hr.

Results for $T_{G_1}$ can be obtained from the known data by the subtraction $T_c - (T_s + T_{G_2} + T_m)$. This gives control $T_{G_1}$ = 1.3 hr, acute treated $T_{G_1}$ = 1.6 hr, and chronic treated $T_{G_1}$ = 3.0 hr.

## Synchronized Cultures

Cultures were synchronized by the double metabolic block method of Doida and Okada,[8] which consisted of 5-hr exposure to $2.5 \times 10^{-3}$ molar thymidine followed by 5 hr in medium containing $10^{-6}$ molar deoxycytidine (to minimize the toxicity of excess thymidine) and 0.025 μg/ml of colcemid. Each blocking agent was removed at the end of the respective 5-hr exposure by centrifuging 10 min at 800 g, decanting the supernatant, and resuspending in the appropriate medium for the following step. Time zero was the time of release from the

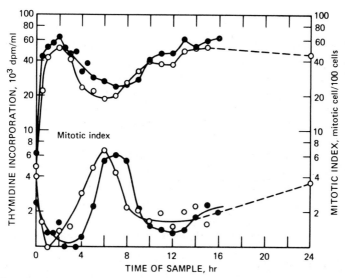

Fig. 2   Relative activity and mitotic index of samples with time. ○, untreated controls. ●, acute steroid-treated cultures.

second blocking agent. Cultures were resuspended in normal growth medium with 1 μl/ml propylene glycol for controls or in steroid-containing medium for the acute steroid-treated group. Chronic steroid treatment, beginning 72 hr before time zero, prevented cultures from being synchronized, and no data were obtained for that group. Samples were taken semihourly and monitored for cell concentration, viability, and MI, as described previously. The DNA synthesis activity for each sample was measured according to the technique described by Bosman,[9] measuring incorporation of $^3$H—TdR (5 min in 50 μCi/ml, specific activity = 19.9 Ci/mmole). Incorporation of $^3$H—TdR was arrested by the addition of cold 10% trichloracetic acid (TCA) at a volume ratio of 10:1. Samples were centrifuged (2400 rpm, 4°C) and washed three times in cold 5% TCA followed by a wash in cold ethanol—ether (3:1 by volume). Each resulting pellet was dissolved in 1 ml of solubilizer and diluted with 20 ml of scintillation fluid, and the activity was counted in a liquid scintillation spectrometer. Counts per minute (cpm) were converted to disintegrations per minute (dpm) using an external standard and correction for efficiency loss due to quenching. The duration of the cell cycle and its stages can be visualized by plotting the activity in dpm per sample against time, as in Fig. 2 and comparing the treated and control cultures. The peaks of thymidine incorporation show approximately 12 hr between successive waves of DNA synthesis. In the steroid-treated culture the wave of DNA synthesis is prolonged when compared with similar values for control cultures. The mitotic wave, in the presence of steroid, is delayed as well as prolonged. The degree of the effect is related to the duration of exposure to steroid.

An unexpected result in synchronized cultures was the remarkably accelerated time between release from the metabolic block (M phase) and peak thymidine incorporation (S phase). These results did not coincide with those reported by Doida and Okada[8] and by Bosman,[9] who developed the double-block technique for synchronizing L5178Y cells. They reported a time lag prior to the beginning of thymidine incorporation followed by a DNA-synthesis period comparable to that in nonsynchronized cultures. The data reported here show that DNA synthesis, as measured by $^3$H—TdR incorporation, begins within 15 min and ends within 6 hr after release from the colcemid block. The graph of MI included in Fig. 2 confirms that the cells, blocked in metaphase, will proceed rapidly through the entire cell cycle to a second peak of mitosis within 6 hr. However, the second wave of DNA synthesis occurs 12 hr after the first, indicating that only the first cycle following release from the blocking agent is a shortened cycle. It is apparent that the sequence of events is faster immediately following release and decelerates to the normal rate within the first cell cycle.

These results, demonstrating an accelerated cell-cycle time after release from metabolic block, are similar to those reported by Cohen and Barner[10] in synchronized cultures of bacteria; by Till, Whitmore, and Gulyas[11] in mouse L cells; by Rao and Engelberg[12] in HeLa cells; and by Zeuthen[13] in *Tetrahymena pyriformis*. Zeuthen concluded that a newly divided cell prepares for division along several relatively independent channels rather than through one chain of events in which the various synthetic and structural developments are linked in a definite sequence. According to Cohen and Barner,[10] a chemically induced metabolic block is characterized by cessation of synthesis of some cell components, which allows other components to accumulate (unbalanced growth). Reversal of this state of unbalanced growth has a synchronizing effect with a shortened duration of events immediately following the reversal.

## DISCUSSION

The results obtained by measuring cell doubling times, by autoradiographic analysis of labelled mitoses, and by monitoring the incorporation of $^3$H—TdR in synchronized cultures indicate that the cell-cycle time in glucocorticoid-treated cells is extended compared to that of controls.

Cell-cycle analyses by the method of percent labelled mitoses and by the method of relative incorporation of $^3$H—TdR in synchronized cultures measure the duration of the S phase 3 or more hours after the beginning of the glucocorticoid treatment. Both these methods indicate that the S phase is prolonged and delayed in treated cells compared to that in controls. However, the duration of other phases in steroid-treated cultures depends on the method of analysis. The method of percent labelled mitoses measures the duration of the $G_2$ phase within 2 hr after the beginning of the steroid treatment but measures the duration of $G_1$ 10 or more hours after steroid is added. Results by this method do not suggest a prolonged $G_2$ phase but do indicate that $G_1$ is prolonged. The method of relative incorporation of $^3H-TdR$ in synchronized cultures measures the $G_1$ phase within 2 hr after steroid is added but measures $G_2$ at 5 or more hours after the hormone treatment is begun. Results by this method suggest no effect on $G_1$ but indicate that $G_2$ is prolonged and delayed. Such disparate results lead these authors to the conclusion that the duration of exposure to glucocorticoid hormone is more important than the phase sequence measured.

The synchronized nature of cultures prepared in the manner described in this paper becomes random within one generation time of these cells. The chronic exposure required to attain cytostatic effects in steroid-treated leukemia suggests that synchronized preparation of the cells would not improve hormone therapy. Perhaps a cytotoxic agent causing immediate, irreparable damage to the cell would be effective in treating synchronized leukemia cells.

Under the conditions used in our laboratory, synchronizing L5178Y cells by the double-block technique results in unbalanced growth. Consequently, the synchronized cultures, when released from the metabolic blocks, proceed through the first mitotic cycle with uncharacteristically shortened $G_1$, S, and $G_2$ phases. The cultures slowly approach normal cell-cycle times in succeeding cycles.

## ACKNOWLEDGMENT

The research reported in this paper was supported by National Institutes of Health grants GM 0958 and CA 05225.

## REFERENCES

1. T. F. Dougherty and A. White, Effect of Pituitary Adrenotropic Hormone on Lymphoid Tissue, *Proc. Soc. Exp. Biol. Med.*, **53**: 132-133 (1943).
2. T. F. Dougherty and A. White, Functional Alterations in Lymphoid Tissue Induced by Adrenal Cortical Secretion, *Amer. J. Anat.*, **77**: 81-116 (1945).
3. O. A. Trowell, The Action of Cortisone on Lymphocytes *in vitro, J. Physiol. (London)*, **119**: 274-285 (1953).
4. G. A. Fischer, Studies on the Culture of Leukemia Cells *in vitro, Ann. N. Y. Acad. Sci.*, **76**: 673-680 (1958).
5. D. L. Berliner and C. J. Nabors, Jr., Effects of Corticosteroids on Fibroblast Functions, *J. Reticuloendothel. Soc.*, **4**: 284-313 (1967).
6. A. Howard and S. R. Pelc, Synthesis of Deoxyribonucleic Acid in Normal and Irradiated Cells and Its Relation to Chromosome Breakage, *Heredity* (Suppl.), **6**: 261-273 (1953).
7. J. E. Cleaver, Thymidine Metabolism and Cell Kinetics, *Frontiers of Biology,* Vol. 6, John Wiley & Sons, Inc., New York, 1967.
8. Y. Doida and S. Okada, Synchronization of L5178Y Cells by Successive Treatments with Excess Thymidine and Colcemid, *Exp. Cell Res.*, **48**: 540-548 (1967).

9. H. B. Bosman, Cellular Membranes: Membrane Marker Enzyme Activities in Synchronized Mouse Leukemic Cells L5178Y, *Biochim. Biophys. Acta,* **203**: 256-260 (1970).

10. S. S. Cohen and H. D. Barner, Studies on Unbalanced Growth in *Escherichia coli.,* *Proc. Nat. Acad. Sci. U.S.A.,* **40**: 885-893 (1954).

11. J. E. Till, G. F. Whitmore and S. Gulyas, Deoxyribonucleic Acid Synthesis in Individual L-Strain Mouse Cells. II. Effects of Thymidine Starvation, *Biochim. Biophys. Acta,* **72**: 277-289 (1963).

12. P. N. Rao and J. Engelberg, Effects of Temperature on the Mitotic Cycle of Normal and Synchronized Mammalian Cells, in *Cell Synchrony, A Study in Biosynthetic Regulation,* I. L. Cameron and G. M. Padilla (Eds.), pp. 332-352, Academic Press, Inc., New York, 1966.

13. E. Zeuthen, Artificial and Induced Periodicity in Living Cells, *Int. Rev. Cytol.,* **24**: 37-73 (1968).

# AGE DEPENDENCY OF THYMUS LYMPHOCYTE KINETICS: FUNCTIONAL CONSIDERATIONS

B. J. BRYANT, M. W. HESS, AND H. COTTIER
Pathology Institute, University of Bern, Bern, Switzerland

## ABSTRACT

The data reviewed indicate that most of the lymphocytes formed in the thymus emigrate and that the thymus behaves kinetically as if it is a responsive component of the lymphoid system. The modes of this responsiveness are discussed in relation to the thymus autonomy concept and the early development and ageing of mice.

Current opinion holds the thymus to be largely autonomous in its relations to other lymphoid organs and to the animal's antigenic experience. Antigens given peripherally to normal young adult mammals indeed elicit in the thymus few of the histological or antibody responses initiated in responding peripheral lymphoid organs. This lack of marked immune reactivity within the thymic parenchyma has been attributed both to the immaturity of its lymphocytes and to a barrier exclusion of antigens (for review see Ref. 1). There is also, in the mouse-organ grafting experiments of Metcalf,[2] evidence for strong systemic homeostatic controls governing the total tissue mass of the spleen but not the thymus. The intrinsic control of thymus lymphocyte formation implicit in these observations is obviously modified hormonally, by adrenocortical steroids in stress and by gonadal steroids in the age-involuting organ.[3]

This autonomy of the thymus conforms to its status as a central lymphoid organ wherein lymphocyte differentiation, under intrinsic and hormonal controls, yields immunocompetent cells whose antigen receptor configurations are determined by genetic rather than environmental factors. We do not wish to challenge such autonomous differentiation of lymphocytes as a major determinant of thymic activity. But we do want to point out some data that suggest the antigenic environment and a homeostatic relationship to peripheral lymphoid cells could play subtle but significant roles in thymic activities.

For example, the antigenic environment seems definitely to affect the thymus because the postnatal mouse thymus becomes progressively larger and mitotically more active under conventional than under germ-free conditions.[4] This observation is inconsistent with thymic autonomy in its uncompromised form, but it is consistent with two alternative explanations: (1) the limited antigen penetration into young thymuses perceptibly influences lymphocyte formation or (2) antigens have indirect effects on the thymus which are mediated through the peripheral system of lymphoid cells. These mutually nonexclusive explanations are evaluated in the following.

## ENVIRONMENTAL ANTIGENS AND THYMIC RESPONSES

The incidence of thymic pycnotic figures in our laboratory is 20- to 40-fold higher in conventional than in specific-pathogen-free (SPF) newborn Swiss mice.[5] This difference appears within 1 to 2 days after birth, i.e., before adrenocortical steroids are known to be secreted[6] and before significant populations of peripheral lymphoid cells have developed.[7] The earliness of this divergence therefore tends to rule out its mediation by hormones or by peripheral cells according to explanation 2; it suggests, instead, with explanation 1, that environmental antigens promote lymphocytotoxic reactions within the thymic parenchyma.

The thymus does contain potential targets for such antigens in its populations of antigen-binding and immunocompetent cells,[8] but some of these targets could be stimulated to divide rather than die; hence, the parallel changes in thymus lymphocyte formation and death rates with conventional, SPF, and germ-free conditions may both reflect corresponding variations in the intra-thymic load of environmental antigens. This idea is strengthened by other correlations indicating a primary influence of environmental antigens on the thymic medulla, namely, pycnotic figures,[5] immunocompetent cells,[8] and antigen penetration,[1] all of which are more prominent in the medulla than in the cortex. However, antigen penetration and cellular reactivity in the cortex cannot be excluded since conventional vs. SPF Swiss mice show the 20- to 40-fold augmentation of pycnosis in both cortex and medulla.[5] The low level of cortical immunocompetent cells could exclude a significant cortical blastogenesis but the plethora of cortical antigen-binding cells probably forms the source of the dying cortical lymphocytes.

The penetration of some antigen into the thymic cortex is difficult to exclude at any age. The cortical antigen barrier, which seems generally permeable in neonatal mice,[9] has been claimed in adult rodents to exclude a variety of circulating antigens by a system of perivascular structures and macrophages.[10] Other work suggests that parenchymal cortical macrophages, although sparse, can transport antigen phagocytized outside the organ. This transport was found in less than a day,[9] a few days,[11] or several weeks,[12] depending on the experimental conditions. The unresolved question provoked by these considerations is whether the small amounts of intrathymically sequestered exogenous or autoantigens play any selective role in suppression (by toxic killing) or amplification (by blastogenesis) of the diverse clones of immunocompetent cells formed under thymic genetic control.

What may be the effects of ageing on these arrangements? Does the antigen barrier in the involuting organ become progressively compromised, exaggerating the effects of circulating antigen on the residual thymic tissue? The tentative answer is "yes" if we take as an example the situation in 15-month-old Swiss mice.[13] Age-associated derangements of thymic histology of one or more of the following types were always found in these mice apart from known preneoplastic or autoimmune states: ill-defined cortico—medullary boundary, presence of lymphoid follicles and germinal centers, intra- and perithymic plasmacellular infiltrates, and distended lymph vessels packed with lymphocytes in the medulla and on the capsular surface. The deranged organ's content of mature immunocompetent cells could be explained by a compromise of the antigen barrier, by permissive extrathymic cellular infiltration, and/or by delayed release of maturing endogenous cells. Similar factors may be involved in the cellular responses that attend direct intrathymic parenchymal injection of antigens.[14]

It is interesting in this context that such thymic complexes in ageing mice show a marked, early lymphocellular and lymphoproliferative response, against a base line of reticular and endothelial cells, following primary footpad injections of tetanus toxoid (Fig. 1). The responses are maximal at 2 to 4 days posttoxoid and develop as rapidly as or more rapidly than comparable responses in draining popliteal and lumbar lymph nodes. This response was measured in smears prepared from whole deranged complexes. However, a specific cortical participation is suggested by preliminary planimetric measurements indicating a trend to increased cortex/medulla ratios within the first 24 hr. These intrathymic responses could represent an exaggeration in ageing of unrecognized responses to circulating antigens going on at a lower level in younger mice.

## LYMPHOCYTIC HOMEOSTASIS

Pycnotic thymus lymphocytes in SPF Swiss mice are constant from 2 days before birth to 6 days after birth at levels of about 0.06% in medulla and 0.02 to 0.03% in cortex (Fig. 2). Comparable pycnotic rates have been recorded in older Swiss mice. These values, which were read in our laboratory on histological sections,[5] are far lower than those observed previously in cell suspension preparations or in conventional mice.

These data call into question the idea that most of the thymic cell production dies in situ in the organ. For these data to be compatible with this idea,[5] a thymic pycnotic figure would have to have a visiblity time of no more than 60 sec. But such an "explosive" disappearance of dying cells would be without precedence in any other cellular biological system. Moreover, we have

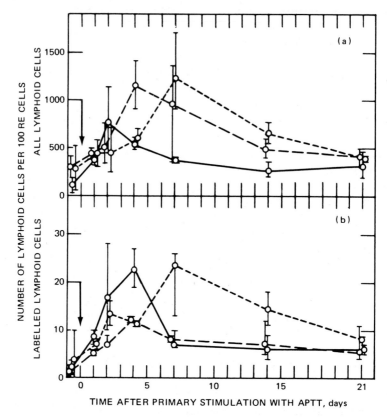

Fig. 1  Number of lymphoid cells (a) and number of labelled lymphoid cells (b) per 100 reticular or endothelial cells (RE cells) in thymic complexes (——), popliteal lymph nodes (———), and lumbar lymph nodes (- - -) of 15-month-old Swiss mice after primary stimulation with aluminum phosphate adsorbed tetanus toxoid (APTT) via both hind leg footpads. Tritiated thymidine was injected intravenously 1 hr before death. Note the intrathymic proliferative response.

calculated elsewhere that lymphocyte loss from the mouse thymus during the third postnatal day in mice equals one-third of all lymphocytes present in the organ at the end of that day.[15] The low thymic pycnotic counts (0.025%, cortex; 0.075%, medulla) also indicate that this enormous loss of lymphocytes was mainly by emigration, not in situ death.

Hence, contrary to popular belief, the young thymus probably exports nearly all the lymphocytes it produces. The massive nature of this export must be considered within its homeostatic context. And this makes it reasonable to examine those thymus data which are suggestive, with explanation 2, of influence by the peripheral system of lymphoid cells. Some such data indicate age-dependent lymphocytokinetic changes that could express the organ's

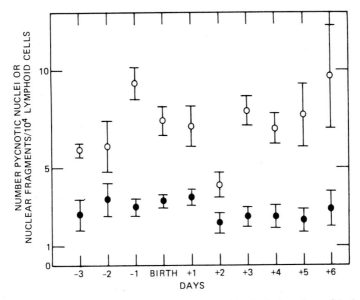

Fig. 2  Pycnotic nuclei or nuclear fragments in histological sections of Swiss mouse thymuses from 3 days before to 6 days after birth. Numbers (mean ± S.D.M.) in cortex (●) and medulla (○) per $10^4$ lymphoid cells.

responsiveness to normal changes in peripheral demand for new thymus-derived cells.

The peripheral lymphocyte deficit faced by mice at birth presents the greatest such demand during their life-span. The environmental antigens encountered in the first postnatal days, especially the enormous antigenic load of developing enteric flora, may underlie this early demand. We have accordingly found in newborn mice a massive emigration of thymus lymphocytes directed especially to gut-associated lymphoid organs.[7] This correlates with an early peak, on postnatal days 3 and 4, in the thymic $^3$H–TdR labelling index (Table 1). The emigration of thymic lymphocytes continues beyond the neonatal period[16] but the fraction of the emigrant population that survives as long-lived cells in the periphery decreases in adolescent and young adult mice to levels of 1% or less.[17,18] This decreased survival correlates not only with decreased demand, as immunocompetent cells fill peripheral compartments, but also with intrathymic lymphocytokinetic changes. Specifically, in Swiss mice between 4 days[15,19] and 6 weeks[18] of age, the thymic small lymphocyte transit time lengthens from 54 to 72 hr and the labelling index decreases from 19 to 13% (Table 1). Thymus-derived cell survival thus seems tuned to peripheral requirements, and these requirements in developing mice also seem to influence thymocytokinetics. The question is how.

The thymocytokinetic changes in developing mice do not reflect changes in proliferating cell-cycle parameters (Table 1), and they do not express variations

TABLE 1

THYMOCYTOKINETIC PARAMETERS IN SWISS MICE AT VARIOUS AGES

| Age, days | Residence time of small lymphocytes, hr | Larger lymphocytes | |
| --- | --- | --- | --- |
| | | Labelling index, % | $\dfrac{\text{Cycle time}}{\text{DNA synthesis time}}$, hr/hr |
| 0–2 | | 10 (Ref. 23) | |
| 3–4 | 54 (Ref. 19) | 19 (Refs. 15, 23) | 9/7 (Ref. 15) |
| 5–6 | | 15–16 (Ref. 23) | |
| 42–46 | 72 (Ref. 18) | 13 (Ref. 18) | 9/7 (Ref. 18) |

in intrathymic cellular death rates, as previously discussed. They do conform, however, to the hypothesis that the overall effect of lessening peripheral demand is to prolong the intrathymic residence time of small lymphocytes. Such prolongation would not only lengthen this residence time but it could also, by diluting the proliferating population with additional nonproliferating cells, account for the diminution of labelling indexes. How the developing system of peripheral lymphoid cells might influence the residence time of small thymocytes is not known, but it could relate to the fact that the small lymphocyte is the primary cell type exported by the thymus and that progressively fewer of them survive beyond a few days in the periphery.

Beyond these age-dependent lymphocytokinetic changes, certain experimental procedures also suggest that the young adult thymus in mice can be influenced by peripheral lymphoid cells.

Sublethal neonatal infestation of mice with Toxoplasma gondii has been found to markedly inhibit thymic weights up to 6 weeks of age.[20] Parasites were not found in the thymus, and the inhibition was not altered by adrenalectomy; it may therefore have been related to a chronic depletion of peripheral lymphoid cells which, like the neonatal lymphoid-cell deficit, may have favored a high rate of small thymocyte loss.

Antithymocyte IgG antiserum (ATG) injected into mice penetrates very poorly into the young-adult thymus.[21] The thymus is therefore spared the gross depletion of lymphoid cells seen elsewhere. This depletion typically lowers the peripheral organ content of graft vs. host (GVH) competent cells. But, paradoxically, ATG treatment of young-adult mice has recently been found to augment markedly the GVH reactivity of thymocyte populations.[22] This increase speaks for a delayed release of maturing immunocompetent cells from the thymus. Such delay could express a previously unrecognized conservative homeostatic mechanism activated by peripheral depletion of the type effected by ATG; it does not express any of the intrinsic or hormonal controls usually invoked in thymic lymphocyte differentiation.

## SUMMARY

Cytokinetic studies in mice indicate that the thymus has a greater overall rate of lymphocyte formation, has a shorter transit time in its small nonproliferating lymphocyte subpopulation, and exports a greater proportion of its newly formed cells to peripheral lymphoid organs in the neonatal period than in adolescence. Other studies indicate that cell death in situ accounts for only a very small fraction of the thymocytes produced in neonatal and adolescent mice and that a marked early intrathymic proliferative response follows peripheral antigen exposure of aged mice. These data challenge the idea of the autonomous thymus. The organ in young mice exports essentially all the lymphocytes it produces, and it behaves kinetically as if it were a responsive component in the lymphoid homeostasis of the body. Antigens, accordingly, could have indirect effects on the thymus by perturbing the peripheral system of lymphoid cells. The data from ageing mice indicate that peripheral antigen exposure can also have direct effects that become manifest in the deranged, involuting thymus. These direct effects may go on unrecognized at lower levels in younger mice.

## ACKNOWLEDGMENTS

The work reported here was supported by a Special Fellowship Grant from the Leukemia Society of America to B. J. Bryant and by the Swiss National Foundation for Scientific Research.

## REFERENCES

1. F. M. Burnet, *Cellular Immunology*, University of Melbourne Press, Melbourne, 1969.
2. D. Metcalf, *The Thymus, Its Role in Immune Responses, Leukaemia Development and Carcinogenesis*, Springer-Verlag, Berlin, 1966.
3. H. N. Claman, Corticosteroids and Lymphoid Cells, *New Engl. J. Med.*, **287**: 388-397 (1972).
4. R. Wilson, K. Sjodin, and M. Bealmear, Thymus Studies in Germ-Free (Axenic) Mice, in *The Thymus*, V. Defendi and D. Metcalf (Eds.), pp. 89-96, Wistar Institute Press, Philadelphia, 1964.
5. J. Schedeli et al., University of Bern, Switzerland, in preparation.
6. S. L. Clark and G. Schneider, Role of the Adrenal Cortex in Maturation of the Lymphoid System and Immunocompetence, *Amer. J. Anat.*, **137**: 231-256 (1973).
7. D. D. Joel, M. W. Hess, and H. Cottier, Magnitude and Pattern of Thymic Lymphocyte Migration in Neonatal Mice, *J. Exp. Med.*, **135**: 907-923 (1972).
8. M. C. Raff, T and B Lymphocytes and Immune Responses, *Nature*, **242**: 19-23 (1973).
9. I. Green and K. Block, Uptake of Particulate Matter Within the Thymus of Adult and Newborn Mice, *Nature*, **200**: 1099-1101 (1963).
10. E. Raviola and M. J. Karnovsky, Evidence for a Blood–Thymus Barrier Using Electron-Opaque Tracers, *J. Exp. Med.*, **136**: 466-498 (1972).
11. H. Mauss, Les modifications du thymus au cours de la tuberculose expérimentale de la souris, *Compt. Rend., Ser. D.*, **266**: 1345-1348 (1968).

12. J. M. Gaugas, S. Payne, and F. P. Wharton, Association of Macrophage Lipids with *Mycobacterium Lepraemurium* in the Mouse Thymus and Lymph Node, *Brit. J. Exp. Pathol.*, **51**: 87-91 (1970).

13. M. Kaufmann, B. J. Bryant, M. W. Hess, R. D. Stoner, and H. Cottier, University of Bern, Bern, Switzerland, in preparation.

14. A. H. E. Marshall and R. G. White, The Immunological Reactivity of the Thymus, *Brit. J. Exp. Pathol.*, **42**: 379-388 (1961).

15. W. D. Michalke, M. W. Hess, H. Riedwyl, R. D. Stoner, and H. Cottier, Thymic Lymphopoiesis and Cell Loss in Newborn Mice, *Blood*, **33**: 541-554 (1969).

16. A. D. Chanana, E. P. Cronkite, D. D. Joel, R. M. Williams, and H. Cottier, Migration of Thymic Lymphocytes: Immunofluorescence and [3]HTdR Studies, in *Morphological and Functional Aspects of Immunity*, K. Lindahl-Kiessling, G. Alm, and M. G. Hanna, Jr. (Eds.), pp. 113-121, Plenum Publishing Corporation, New York, 1971.

17. M. Matsuyama, M. Wiadrowski, and D. Metcalf, Autoradiographic Analysis of Lymphopoiesis and Lymphocyte Migration in Mice Bearing Multiple Thymus Grafts, *J. Exp. Med.*, **123**: 559-570 (1966).

18. B. J. Bryant, Renewal and Fate in the Mammalian Thymus: Mechanisms and Inferences of Thymocytokinetics, *Eur. J. Immunol.*, **2**: 38-45 (1972).

19. R. Clottu et al., University of Bern, Switzerland, in preparation.

20. G. Huldt, S. Gard, and S. G. Olovson, Effect of *Toxoplasma gondii* on the Thymus, *Nature*, **244**: 301-303 (1973).

21. E. M. Lance, The Mechanism of Action of Antilymphocyte Serum, *J. Exp. Med.*, **130**: 49-76 (1969).

22. H. Cantor and R. Asofsky, Paradoxical Effect of Antithymocyte Serum on the Thymus, *Nature*, **243**: 39-41 (1973).

23. M. W. Hess, R. D. Stoner, and H. Cottier, Growth Characteristics of Mouse Thymus in the Neonatal Period, *Nature*, **215**: 426-428 (1967).

# CELLULAR KINETICS OF EARLY AND LATE IMMUNOLOGICAL MEMORY TO SHEEP ERYTHROCYTES IN MICE

TOSHITSUGU KUROTSU and TOSHIHIKO SADO
National Institute of Radiological Science, Chiba, Japan

## ABSTRACT

The cellular basis of early and late memory to sheep erythrocytes (SRBC) was analyzed in mice by the use of cell-transfer assay. The donor spleen cells to be analyzed for early and late memory were derived from mice that had been primed with $2 \times 10^5$ SRBC for 3 days or with $2 \times 10^8$ SRBC for 3 months, respectively, before transfer to the recipient mice treated with 900 R. Numbers of direct (19 S) as well as indirect (7 S) plaque-forming cells (PFC) were assessed for each recipient spleen 6 days after transfer of the donor spleen cells ($2.5 \times 10^7$) together with an optimum dose of SRBC ($2.5 \times 10^8$). Repeated doses of vinblastine or hydroxyurea administered to the donor mice between 2 and 3 days following antigenic stimulation inhibited the development of early memory. In contrast, the pool size of virgin immunocompetent progenitor cells and long-lasting immunological memory cells was not affected by the treatment with vinblastine or hydroxyurea, indicating that these progenitor cells remain in the nonproliferative $G_0$ phase unless they are stimulated with the specific antigen. Contribution of T and B lymphocytes to the establishment of early and late memory was analyzed by limiting-dilution assay and dose–response data combined with treatment of the test spleen cells with anti-$\theta$ sera. In some experiments the test spleen cells treated with anti-$\theta$ sera were reconstituted with $10^8$ thymocytes derived from normal syngeneic mice. The results of such analysis indicated that the 19 S and 7 S early memory to SRBC was almost entirely dependent on the increase in the pool size of T lymphocytes, whereas the long-lasting 7 S late memory was due to the expansion of both T- and B-cell populations.

Immunological memory in the classical sense can be defined as the enhanced reactivity of an organism to an antigenic stimulus as a result of a prior contact with that antigen.[1-3] Cytokinetically, this enhanced reactivity is due to an increase in the pool size of immunocompetent progenitor cells that are specifically reactive to that antigen.[4-6] In other words, the size of this pool chiefly determines the magnitude of immunological memory. The X-Y-Z (or $PC_1$-$PC_2$-P) scheme of immunocyte differentiation[5-12] postulates that progenitors of antibody-forming cells can be divided into two compartments:

the cells in the first compartment are virgin progenitor cells (X or $PC_1$ cells) which have never experienced a contact with an antigen, and those in the second compartment are antigenically committed progenitor cells (Y or $PC_2$ cells) which develop from the virgin progenitor cells as a result of antigenic stimulation. The cells in the latter compartment, which are also known as immunological memory cells, are considered to undergo proliferation and maturation into antibody-forming cells (Z or P cells) on further contact with that antigen. Another view concerning the origin of immunological memory cells is that they arise from mature antibody-forming plasma cells at terminal stages of antibody response.[13-15] Furthermore, one of the more debated questions in the cytodynamics of antibody formation concerns the role of cellular proliferation in the development (Refs. 5-6, 8-9, and 12) and maintenance (Refs. 16-23) of immunological memory.

More recently, much has been added to our knowledge of the cellular basis of antibody response. Thus, it is now well established that thymus-dependent helper cells (T lymphocytes) and thymus-independent antibody-forming cell precursors (B lymphocytes) cooperate in the initiation of primary[24-27] as well as secondary[28-32] antibody responses to a variety of antigens including heterologous erythrocytes and serum proteins. It is also known that both cell lines are involved in the carriage of immunological memory.[28-32]

During the past few years we have been studying the kinetics of the development and the maintenance of immunological memory to sheep erythrocytes (SRBC) in mice. Some of the questions we have asked are:

1. Are memory cells preantibody-forming or postantibody-forming cells?

2. Does the development of immunological memory involve cellular proliferation?

3. Are memory cells constantly dividing before they meet the secondary antigenic stimulus?

4. Do both T and B lymphocytes contribute to the establishment of early as well as late immunological memory?

Results of such analyses are presented here.

## CELL TRANSFER SYSTEM

We employed a cell-transfer system (Fig. 1) to analyze these questions since it provides a condition in which the pool size of immunocompetent progenitor cells of the donor lymphoid-cell population can be measured without the pool's being interfered with by an autoregulatory mechanism as well as persistent antibodies that could affect the expression of the progenitor cells in the intact animals.[4-5] Briefly, $2.5 \times 10^7$ spleen cells from donor mice (C3Hf/HeMs, bred in our own colony under specific pathogen free conditions, and ddY/SLC, bred as a closed colony by the Shizuoka Laboratory Animal Center), which might or might not have been primed for varying lengths of time with varying doses of a

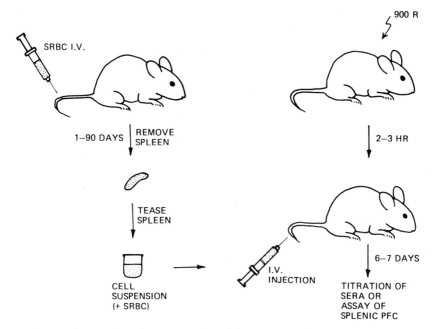

**Fig. 1** Schematic representation of the cell-transfer assay system.

test antigen, SRBC, were transferred into lethally irradiated syngeneic recipient mice together with an optimum dose of SRBC ($2.5 \times 10^8$). In some experiments the donor mice had been treated with inhibitors, such as vinblastine[33-35] or hydroxyurea,[36-37] for 24 hr before their spleen cells were transferred into the recipient mice. Six days later the spleens of the recipient mice were assessed for direct (19 S) and indirect (7 S) plaque-forming cells (PFC) according to the original method of Jerne, Nordin, and Henry[38] and the modification by Wortis, Taylor, and Dresser,[39] respectively.

For limiting-dilution analysis as well as dose—response studies, graded numbers of spleen cells ($0.8 \times 10^6$ to $102.4 \times 10^6$) derived from normal and primed donors were transplanted into lethally irradiated mice together with $2.5 \times 10^8$ SRBC, and the numbers of splenic PFC, both direct and indirect, were assessed on day 6 (Refs. 4-6 and 40-44).

# EFFECT OF ANTIGEN DOSE ON THE PRIMARY ANTIBODY RESPONSE AND ON THE DEVELOPMENT OF EARLY IMMUNOLOGICAL MEMORY

Groups of donor mice were injected intravenously (i.v.) with varying doses of SRBC, ranging from $2 \times 10^4$ to $2 \times 10^9$, and were sacrificed 3 days later.

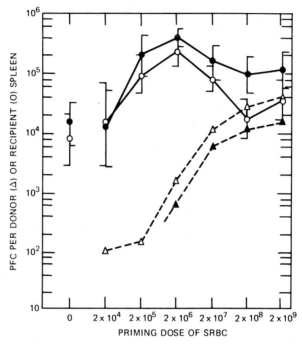

Fig. 2  Effect of priming antigen dose on the development of early immunological memory to SRBC.  ○, △: direct PFC responses.  ●, ▲: indirect PFC
responses. Geometric mean ± 2 S.E.

Aliquots of spleen-cell suspensions obtained from these donor mice were tested
for PFC. The remaining cell suspensions were then tested for the magnitude of
antibody-forming potential (AFP) by the use of cell-transfer assay. An increase
in the AFP of the donor spleen as a result of antigenic stimulation was
considered to represent the increase in the pool size of immunocompetent
progenitor cells, or the development of immunological memory. The results are
shown in Fig. 2. An increase in the priming dose of antigen resulted in an
increase in the number of PFC of the donor spleen; the AFP of the donor spleen,
expressed by the number of PFC per recipient spleen, was greatest when the
donor mice had been primed with $2 \times 10^6$ SRBC. The spleens of mice primed
with $2 \times 10^5$ SRBC contained only a near-background level of PFC 3 days after
the priming. Yet, the splenic AFP increased significantly. Thus, the data given in
Fig. 2 indicate a lack of correlation between the PFC content and the AFP of
the spleens derived from 3-day primed donors. [In the discussions that follow,
the immunological memory observed at 3 days following injection of $2 \times 10^5$
SRBC (low dose) will be referred to as "early memory." In contrast, the
immunological memory normally observed at 1 to 3 months following an
optimum dose[4-6] of antigen ($2 \times 10^8$ or $2 \times 10^9$ SRBC) will be referred to as

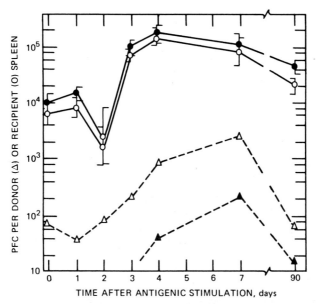

Fig. 3 Kinetics of the development of immunological memory in spleens of mice primed with suboptimum dose $(2 \times 10^5)$ of SRBC. o, △: direct PFC responses. ●, ▲: indirect PFC responses. Geometric mean ± 2 S.E.

"late memory."] This antigen dose—splenic AFP relationship confirms an earlier observation by others[8,45-46] that a greater secondary response could be elicited when mice had been immunized with a suboptimum dose of antigen than when they had been stimulated with an optimum dose of antigen, which elicits a maximum primary antibody response. Other investigators working with a protein antigen also reported a case in which pure immunological memory could be induced without detectable primary antibody response.[47] These observations suggest strongly that antibody formation is not necessarily a prerequisite for the development of immunological memory.

## KINETICS OF THE DEVELOPMENT OF EARLY IMMUNOLOGICAL MEMORY TO SRBC

A group of mice receiving a single injection of $2 \times 10^5$ SRBC were sacrificed at varying intervals after injection of the antigen and their spleens assessed for PFC as well as AFP. The results are shown in Fig. 3. The primary response to this amount of antigen was extremely low; the peak response of as low as 2936 direct PFC/spleen being observed on day 7. The number of indirect PFC never exceeded that of direct PFC at all time intervals examined. In contrast, the time course of the development of immunological memory was considerably different from that of PFC response. There was no evidence of immunological memory 1 day after priming with $2 \times 10^5$ SRBC. Then, there was a drop of splenic AFP in 2-day primed spleen cells. Similar observation was made by Radovich, Hemingsen, and Talmage[48] 1 day after priming with $10^9$ SRBC (0.2 ml of 20% SRBC). These investigators related this observation to the lymphocyte transformation, which is less effective in the cell-transfer assay because of increased mortality during transfer or reduced homing to the spleen. Between days 2 and 3, there was a logarithmic rise in the splenic AFP, and its maximum level was attained on day 4. At this time AFP of the primed spleen was as much as 20 fold higher than that of the nonprimed spleen. After day 4 there was a gradual decay of the immunological memory. However, 3 months later the splenic AFP was still 5- to 6-fold higher than that of nonprimed spleens. The data also show that there was no difference in the time course of the development of immunological memory to direct as well as indirect PFC responses. The fact that immunological memory reached the maximum level before the peak PFC response could be attained suggests that cells responsible for the immunological memory develop earlier than the antibody-forming cells.

## EFFECT OF MITOTIC OR DNA INHIBITORS ON THE DEVELOPMENT OF IMMUNOLOGICAL MEMORY

To study the role of cellular proliferation on the expansion of the pool size of immunocompetent progenitor cells, or the development of immunological memory, we gave a group of donor mice injected with $2 \times 10^5$ or $2 \times 10^8$ SRBC three injections of vinblastine (100 $\mu$g/mouse/injection) every 8 hr, beginning 12 or 48 hr after injection of the antigen. Eight hours after the last drug injection, the spleen cells obtained from the treated mice were tested for AFP by the cell-transfer assay. The results, shown in Fig. 4, indicate that the development of immunological memory was completely suppressed when the cellular proliferation was inhibited. The suppression of the splenic AFP by this drug was more dramatic when mice had been immunized with an optimum dose of antigen than when they had been stimulated with a suboptimum dose of antigen; the splenic AFP of optimally immunized mice which were treated with vinblastine between days 2 and 3 was only 8% of that of nonprimed mice which were similarly treated with the inhibitor.

In another experiment hydroxyurea, which is known to selectively kill the cells in the DNA synthetic (S) phase of the cell cycle,[36-37] was used to eliminate cells that were undergoing proliferation following antigenic stimulation. The donor mice that had been primed with varying doses of SRBC were given six injections of hydroxyurea (12 mg/mouse/injection) at 4-hr intervals (total doses, 72 mg/mouse). Four hours after the last injection of the drug, or 72 hr after injection of the test antigen, the AFP of the donor spleen was measured as in the previous experiment. The results, also shown in Fig. 4, clearly indicate

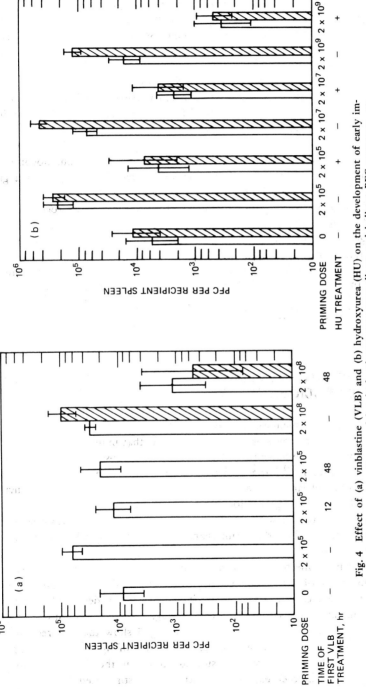

Fig. 4 Effect of (a) vinblastine (VLB) and (b) hydroxyurea (HU) on the development of early immunological memory. Open and hatched columns represent direct and indirect PFC responses, respectively. Geometric mean ±2 S.E.

that the increase in the splenic AFP was severely suppressed by treatment with hydroxyurea. The larger the antigen dose used to prime the mice, the more pronounced the effect of this drug to suppress the splenic AFP of the primed animals. This result is consistent with that observed in the preceding experiment with vinblastine.

It is evident from these two sets of data that cellular proliferation is essential for the development of immunological memory. Also, the effects of vinblastine and hydroxyurea were more pronounced for spleen cells that had been primed with optimum or supraoptimum doses of antigen. This observation suggests the following:

1. Nonprimed animals contain a fixed number of virgin immunocompetent progenitor cells (X or $PC_1$ cells) which are specifically reactive to a given antigen.[49]

2. Following antigenic stimulation, a fraction of these progenitor cells, depending on the antigen doses given to the animal, are triggered to proliferate; the higher the antigen dose, the greater the number of progenitor cells stimulated to proliferate.[11]

3. Treatment of the maximally stimulated animals with mitotic inhibitors during the time when the stimulated cells are in the active proliferation stage results in clonal elimination of the stimulated progenitor cells in addition to the depletion of virgin progenitor cells, a situation analogous to a partial tolerance due to an exhaustion of progenitor cells.[50]

## EFFECT OF MITOTIC OR DNA INHIBITORS ON THE MAINTENANCE OF IMMUNOLOGICAL MEMORY

Immunological memory lasts for many weeks in mice[51] and years in man.[52] Furthermore, many investigators favor the view that immunological memory is carried by small lymphocytes, which have a long life-span.[18-21,32] However, other investigators[16-17] reported that immunological memory was maintained by a stem line of large lymphocytes (blast cells), which were constantly dividing with a relatively short generation time before they met the secondary antigenic stimulus. We have examined, therefore, by the use of vinblastine and hydroxyurea, whether the maintenance of immunological memory indeed involves mitosis.

Donor mice injected with an optimum dose of SRBC ($2 \times 10^8$) were given three injections of vinblastine 90 days after antigenic stimulation. Dose and injection schedules were the same as in the previously described experiment. Eight hours after the last injection of the drug, the spleen cells of these treated mice were assessed for AFP. The data in Fig. 5 show that the resistance of memory cells to vinblastine was comparable to that of virgin immunocompetent progenitor cells, which were considered to be in the nonproliferative $G_0$ phase.[34-35] In another experiment antigenically stimulated ($2 \times 10^8$ SRBC)

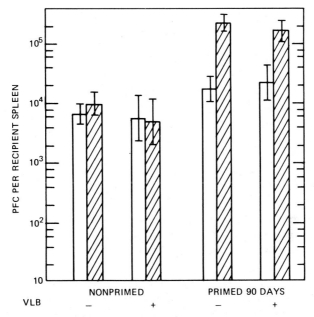

**Fig. 5  Effect of vinblastine (VLB) on the maintenance of late immunological memory. Open and hatched columns represent direct and indirect PFC responses, respectively. Geometric mean ± 2 S.E.**

donor mice were treated with hydroxyurea 3 months after injection of the test antigen, and their splenic AFP was assessed by the cell-transfer assay as in the preceding experiments. The results were similar to those observed for spleen cells treated with vinblastine except that there was a slight suppression after treatment with hydroxyurea. It is concluded that immunological memory cells, once established, remain in the nonproliferative $G_0$ phase as the virgin progenitor cells until they meet the same antigen again.

## CONTRIBUTION OF T AND B LYMPHOCYTES TO EARLY AND LATE IMMUNOLOGICAL MEMORY

### Cytokinetic Approach for Analysis of T and B Lymphocyte Interaction

In the foregoing experiments, we intentionally have not attempted to distinguish T and B lymphocytes, which are known to be involved in the initiation of primary as well as secondary antibody response to SRBC.[24–26,28–32] Thus, in the experiments that follow, we will attempt to examine the contribution of these two cell types to the establishment of early and late memory to this antigen by employing the cytokinetic approach combined with treatment of the test spleen cells with anti-$\theta$ sera and

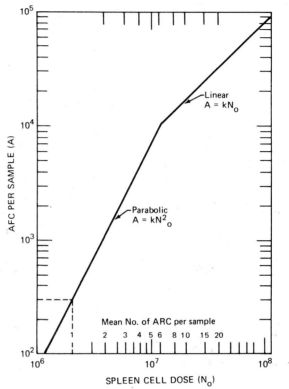

**Fig. 6** A hypothetical dose–response curve, plotted on a logarithmic scale. [From Groves, Lever, and Makinodan, *Nature*, 222: 96 (1969).]

complement.[28-31,53] The cytokinetic approach employed here uses information obtained from limiting-dilution analysis of the lymphoid cell populations and dose–response data showing the relationship between lymphoid-cell dose and the number of antibody-forming cells generated in the cell-transfer assay system.[40-44] A hypothetical logarithmic plot of the dose–response data representing the number of antibody-forming cells generated as a function of a wide dose range of spleen cells is shown in Fig. 6. The first leg of the curve is a parabolic function, and the second leg is a linear function. Such biphasic dose–response curves can be best explained by the stochastic model proposed by Groves, Lever, and Makinodan[43-44] for generating antibody-forming cells, which is based on the following assumptions:[43]

1. Two cells interact in generating antibody-forming cells (AFC).

2. One of these cells must greatly exceed the other in number.

3. The cells detected by limiting-dilution analysis are not the progenitors of antibody-forming cells. These cells are referred to as antigen-reactive cells (ARC).

4. An ARC interacts with progenitor cells (PC), which become transformed into AFC. The PC occur more frequently than the ARC.

5. Individual ARC are assumed to interact with multiple, but a finite number of, PC.

6. The mean number of divisions that a newly formed AFC undergoes is considered to be fixed.

Since most of the assumptions listed appear to be consistent with actual observations (Refs. 4-6, 24-27, 31, 40-44, 54-56), we consider that limiting-dilution as well as dose−response data are useful to analyze the relative pool size of the two cell types present in the lymphoid cell populations derived from primed animals, especially when this approach is combined with treatment of the test lymphoid cells with anti-$\theta$ sera and reconstitution of the treated cells with thymocytes.[28-31] (It is evident from what is known at present about the cellular basis of antibody response that ARC and PC described by Groves, Lever, and Makinodan[43-44] could be equated with T and B lymphocytes, respectively.)

## Analysis of Contribution of T and B Lymphocytes to Immunological Memory

Limiting-dilution data obtained for spleen-cell suspensions derived from normal as well as primed mice are shown in Fig. 7. The limiting cells (most likely T lymphocytes[43-44,56]) had indeed increased in number as a result of priming for induction of early as well as late memory, regardless of whether the antibody response was assessed for 19 S- or 7 S-antibody classes. The magnitude of the increase was 4- and 6-fold, respectively, for early and late 19 S memories and 4- and 16-fold, respectively, for early and late 7 S memories.

The dose−response data obtained with wide dose ranges of spleen cells derived from normal as well as primed animals are analyzed as follows.

### Early Memory

Spleen-cell suspensions derived from donor mice (C3H$f$/HeMs) possessing early memory to SRBC were treated with either AKR anti-C3H $\theta$ sera and complement[28-31] or AKR normal sera and complement at $37°C$ for 45 min. The dose−response data obtained for such cell suspensions are shown in Fig. 8. The dose−response curves were shifted toward minus direction for the $X$ axis as a result of antigenic stimulation of the donor mice, and the dose−response curves obtained with cell suspensions treated with AKR anti-C3H $\theta$ sera and complement almost completely overlapped those obtained with nonprimed spleen cells for both 19 S- and 7 S-antibody responses. Reconstitution of the primed spleen cells treated with anti-$\theta$ sera with $10^8$ normal thymocytes* per

---

*This number corresponds to as many as 10 ARC that are specifically reactive to SRBC.[57]

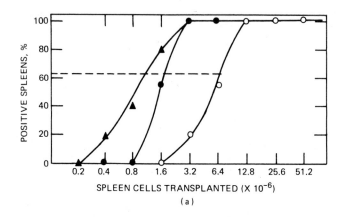

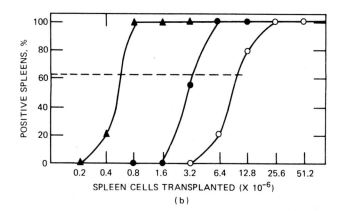

Fig. 7 Percentage of recipient spleens positive for PFC following lethal irradiation and injection of graded number of spleen cells mixed with $2.5 \times 10^8$ SRBC. (a) Direct (19 S) PFC responses. (b) Indirect (7 S) PFC responses. ○, nonprimed spleen cells. ●, primed spleen cells carrying early memory (3 days following $2 \times 10^5$ SRBC). ▲, primed spleen cells carrying late memory (90 days following $2 \times 10^8$ SRBC).

mouse restored the characteristic dose—response curve observed with primed-cell suspensions that had not been treated with the antisera. These results show that the induction of early memory to SRBC is almost entirely dependent on the increase in the pool size of T cells, the magnitude of the increase being 4 fold. In view of the parabolic nature of the dose—response curve observed with low spleen-cell doses, the 4-fold increase in the number of T cells will result in more than 16-fold increase in the number of antibody-forming cells generated, and this is what is actually observed here.

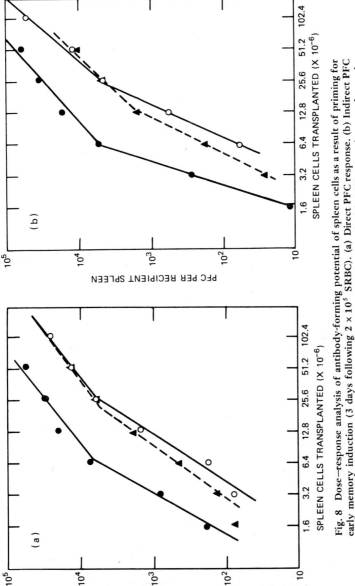

Fig. 8 Dose—response analysis of antibody-forming potential of spleen cells as a result of priming for early memory induction (3 days following $2 \times 10^5$ SRBC). (a) Direct PFC response. (b) Indirect PFC response. ○, nonprimed spleen cells. ●, primed spleen cells treated with AKR normal sera and complement. (Same as the untreated primed spleen cells.) ▲, primed spleen cells treated with AKR anti-C3H θ sera and complement.

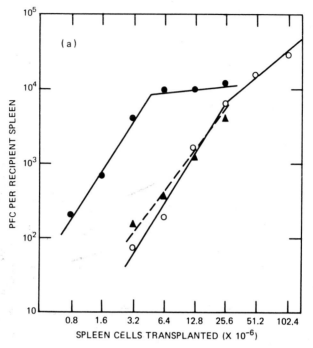

Fig. 9  Dose—response analysis of antibody-forming potential of spleen cells as a result of priming for late memory induction (90 days following $2 \times 10^8$ ṢRBC). (a) Direct PFC response. (b) Indirect PFC response. ○, nonprimed spleen cells. ●, primed spleen cells treated with AKR normal sera and complement. (Same as the untreated primed spleen cells). ▲, primed spleen cells treated with AKR anti-C3H $\theta$ sera and complement.

## Late Memory

Dose—response data obtained for spleen-cell suspensions derived from donor mice possessing late memory to SRBC and treated with either AKR anti-C3H $\theta$ sera and complement or normal AKR sera and complement are shown in Fig. 9. Figure 9 shows that 19 S late memory, which is not normally expressed in intact mice,[38,58] can be demonstrated by the cell-transfer assay when the spleen-cell dose is low. When this cell suspension was treated with AKR anti-C3H $\theta$ sera and complement, the dose—response curve overlapped almost completely that obtained with normal spleen cells, indicating that 19 S late memory was due entirely to the increase in the pool size of T lymphocytes (8-fold increase). With regard to the 7 S late memory, the situation was quite different from that observed for 19 S late memory or that for 19 S and 7 S early memories. The dose—response curve observed with spleen-cell suspensions possessing 7 S late memory (Fig. 9) indicates that the pool size of immunocompetent cells increased significantly. Treatment of this cell suspension with anti-$\theta$ sera and

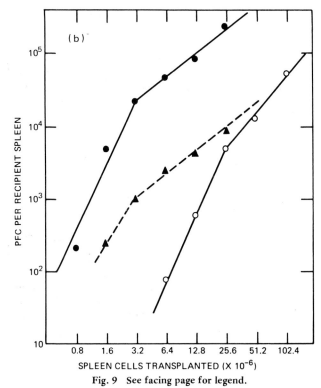

**Fig. 9** See facing page for legend.

complement did not result in the dose–response curve characteristic of the nonprimed spleen cells, suggesting that the pool size not only of T lymphocytes but also of B lymphocytes has also increased. Indeed, a dose–response curve such as this is expected to occur if B lymphocytes exceed T lymphocytes greatly in number over that normally seen in the nonprimed spleen cells. Our experiment to show conclusively that this is really so by the use of anti-B lymphocyte sera has not been completed. However, in view of current observations by others,[28-30,32] it appears safe to conclude that both T and B lymphocytes contribute to the establishment of 7 S late memory to SRBC.

In summary, analysis of the limiting-dilution and dose–response data obtained with wide dose ranges of spleen cells derived from both primed and nonprimed mice indicated that (1) 19 S and 7 S early memory is entirely dependent on the increase in the pool size of T lymphocytes reactive to the test antigen, (2) 19 S late memory, which is not expressed normally in the intact mice, could be demonstrated by the cell-transfer assay when the spleen-cell dose was low and was dependent solely on the increase in pool size of T lymphocytes, and finally (3) 7 S late memory is most likely due to the increase in the pool size of both T and B lymphocytes as shown by many investigators working in this field.[28-30,32]

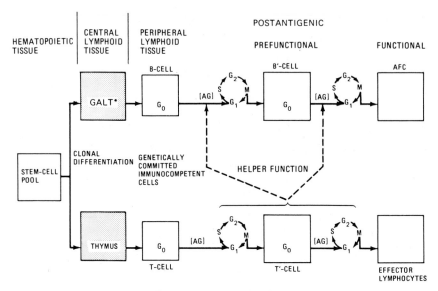

Fig. 10 Immunocyte differentiation model involving interaction of two cell types. Immunological memory cells in this model are described as B'- and T'-cells. [AG], macrophage-processed antigen. GALT*, gut-associated lymphoid tissues.

## IMMUNOCYTE DIFFERENTIATION MODEL

An immunocyte differentiation model involving the interaction of two cell types has been constructed from the data presented here and by many other investigators. It is shown in Fig. 10.

## ACKNOWLEDGMENTS

We are grateful to Dr. T. Terasima, Head of the Division of Physiology and Pathology, for constant support and encouragement and to Hitoko Kamisaku for expert technical assistance. We also thank Dr. Kazuo Moriwaki, National Institute of Genetics, Mishima, for providing the AKR/J mice used to prepare the AKR anti-C3H $\theta$ sera, and members of the Animal Facility of our institute for providing test mice.

## REFERENCES

1. F. M. Burnet, *The Clonal Selection Theory of Acquired Immunity*, Cambridge University Press, New York, 1959.

2. L. Szilard, The Molecular Basis of Antibody Formation, *Proc. Nat. Acad. Sci. U.S.A.,* **46**: 293-302 (1960).

3. J. Lederberg, Genes and Antibodies, *Stanford Med. Bull.,* **19**: 53-61 (1961).

4. E. H. Perkins, M. A. Robinson, and T. Makinodan, Agglutin Response, a Function of Cell Number, *J. Immunol.,* **86**: 533-537 (1961).

5. T. Makinodan and J. F. Albright, Cytokinetics of Antibody Response, in *Immunopathology,* Third International Symposium, pp. 99-112, P. Graber and P. A. Miescher (Eds.), Schwabe & Co., Basel, 1963.

6. J. F. Albright and T. Makinodan, Dynamics of Expression of Competence of Antibody Producing Cells, in *Molecular and Cellular Basis of Antibody Formation,* pp. 427-446, J. Sterzl (Ed.), Czechoslovak Academy of Science, Prague, 1965.

7. E. Sercarz and A. H. Coons, The Exhaustion of Specific Antibody Producing Capacity During a Secondary Response, in *Mechanisms of Immunological Tolerance,* M. Hasek, A. Lengerova, and M. Vojtiskova (Eds.), pp. 73-83, Czechoslovak Academy of Science, Prague, 1962.

8. J. Sterzl, Factors Determining the Differentiation Pathways of Immunocompetent Cells, *Cold Spring Harbor Symp. Quant. Biol.,* **32**: 493-506 (1967).

9. J. Sterzl and A. M. Silverstein, Developmental Aspects of Immunity, *Advan. Immunol.,* **6**: 337-459 (1967).

10. E. E. Sercarz and V. S. Byers, The X-Y-Z Scheme of Immunocyte Maturation. III. Early IgM Memory and Nature of the Memory Cells, *J. Immunol.,* **98**: 836-843 (1967).

11. V. S. Byers and E. E. Sercarz, The X-Y-Z Scheme of Immunocyte Maturation. IV. The Exhaustion of Memory Cells, *J. Exp. Med.,* **127**: 307-325 (1968).

12. P. Byfield and E. Sercarz, The X-Y-Z Scheme of Immunocyte Maturation. VII. Cell Division and the Establishment of Short-Term IgM Memory, *J. Exp. Med.,* **129**: 897-907 (1969).

13. M. D. Schoenberg, R. D. Moore, A. B. Stavitsky, and J. P. Gusdon, Differentiation of Antibody Forming Cells in Lymph Nodes During the Anamnestic Response, *J. Cell. Physiol.,* **71**: 133-150 (1968).

14. M. F. La Via and A. E. Vatter, A Morphological Study of the Terminal Events of Primary Antibody Response, *J. Reticuloendothel. Soc.,* **6**: 221-231 (1969).

15. M. F. La Via, Cellular Sites of Antibody Synthesis, in *Biology of the Immune Response,* P. Abramoff and M. F. La Via (Eds.), pp. 175-212, McGraw-Hill Book Company, New York, 1970.

16. G. J. V. Nossal and O. Makela, Autoradiographic Studies on the Immune Response. I. The Kinetics of Plasma Cell Proliferation, *J. Exp. Med.,* **115**: 209-230 (1962).

17. G. J. V. Nossal and O. Makela, Genetic Aspects of Antibody Formation, *Lab. Invest.,* **10**: 1094-1109 (1961).

18. J. L. Gowans and J. W. Uhr, The Carriage of Immunological Memory by Small Lymphocytes in the Rat, *J. Exp. Med.,* **124**: 1017-1030 (1966).

19. P. H. Fitzgerald, The Immunological Role and Long Life-Span of Small Lymphocytes, J. Theoret. Biol., **6**: 13-25 (1964).

20. J. J. Miller III and L. J. Cole, The Immunological Reactivity of Long-Lived Lymphocytes In Situ in Rat Popliteal Lymph Nodes, U. S. Naval Radiological Defense Laboratory Report TR-67-93, pp. 1-17, 1967.

21. E. E. Emeson and D. R. Thursh, Immunologically Specific Retention of Long-Lived Lymphoid Cells in Antigenically Stimulated Lymph Nodes, *J. Immunol.,* **106**: 635-643 (1971).

22. T. Kurotsu, T. Sado, and H. Kamisaku, Kinetics of Immunological Memory Cells, in Proceedings of the First Annual Meeting of the Japanese Society of Immunology, pp. 79-81, 1971.

23. S. Strober, Initiation of Antibody Responses by Different Classes of Lymphocytes. V. Fundamental Changes in the Physiological Characteristics of Virgin Thymus-Independent ("B") Lymphocytes and B Memory Cells, *J. Exp. Med.,* **136**: 851-871 (1972).

24. J. F. A. P. Miller and G. F. Mitchell, Thymus and Antigen Reactive Cells, *Transplant. Rev.,* **1**: 3-42 (1969).

25. A. J. S. Davies, The Thymus and the Cellular Basis of Immunity, *Transplant. Rev.,* **1**: 43-91 (1969).

26. H. N. Claman and E. A. Chaperon, Immunological Complementation Between Thymus and Marrow Cells—A Model for the Two Cell Theory of Immunocompetence, *Transplant. Rev.,* **1**: 92-113 (1969).

27. R. B. Taylor, Cellular Cooperation in the Antibody Response of Mice to Two Serum Albumins: Specific Function of Thymus Cells, *Transplant. Rev.,* **1**: 114-149 (1969).

28. J. F. A. P. Miller and J. Sprent, Cell-to-Cell Interaction in the Immune Response. VI. Contribution of Thymus-Derived Cells and Antibody-Forming Cell Precursors to Immunological Memory, *J. Exp. Med.,* **134**: 66-82 (1971).

29. G. F. Mitchell, E. L. Chan, M. S. Noble, I. L. Weissman, R. I. Mishell, and L. A. Herzenberg, Immunological Memory in Mice. III. Memory to Heterologous Erythrocytes in Both T Cell and B Cell Populations and Requirement for T Cells in Expression of B Cell Memory. Evidence Using Immunoglobulin Allotype and Mouse Allotype and Mouse Alloantigen Theta Markers with Congenic Mice, *J. Exp. Med.,* **135**: 165-184 (1972).

30. J. J. Mond, T. Takahashi, and G. J. Thorbecke, Surface Antigens of Immunocompetent Cells. III. In Vitro Studies of the Role of B and T Cells in Immunological Memory, *J. Exp. Med.,* **136**: 663-675 (1972).

31. T. Kurotsu, T. Sado, and H. Kamisaku, Kinetics of Memory Cells. II. Cell Cooperation in an Adoptive Secondary Response Studied by Limiting Dilution Assay, in Proceedings of the Second Annual Meeting of the Japanese Society of Immunology, pp. 222-224, 1972.

32. S. Strober and J. Dilley, Biological Characteristics of T and B Memory Lymphocytes in the Rat, *J. Exp. Med.,* **137**: 1275-1292 (1973).

33. F. A. Valeriote and W. R. Bruce, An *in vitro* Assay for Growth-Inhibiting Activity of Vinblastine, *J. Nat. Cancer Inst.,* **35**: 851-856 (1965).

34. D. Syeklocha, L. Siminovitch, J. E. Till, and E. A. McCulloch, The Proliferative State of Antigen-Sensitive Precursors of Hemolysin-Producing Cells, Determined by the Use of the Inhibitor, Vinblastine, *J. Immunol.,* **96**: 472-477 (1966).

35. E. H. Perkins, T. Sado, and T. Makinodan, Recruitment and Proliferation of Immunocompetent Cells During the Log Phase of the Primary Antibody Response, *J. Immunol.,* **103**: 668-679 (1969).

36. W. K. Sinclair, Hydroxyurea: Effects on Chinese Hamster Cells Grown in Culture, *Cancer Res.,* **27**: 297-308 (1967).

37. B. N. Jaroslow and L. Ortiz-Ortiz, Hydroxyurea and Cell-Cycle Kinetics of Cultured Antibody-Forming Cells, *Cell. Immunol.,* **2**: 164-170 (1971).

38. N. K. Jerne, A. A. Nordin, and C. Henry, The Agar Plaque Technique for Recognizing Antibody-Producing Cells, in *Cell-Bound Antibodies,* A. Amos and H. Koprowski (Eds.), pp. 109-125, Wistar Institute Press, Philadelphia, 1963.

39. H. H. Wortis, R. B. Taylor, and D. W. Dresser, Antibody Production Studied by Means of the LHG Assay. I. The Splenic Response of CBA Mice to Sheep Erythrocytes, *Immunology,* **11**: 603-616 (1966).

40. R. A. Brown, T. Makinodan, and J. F. Albright, Significance of a Single-Hit Event in the Initiation of Antibody Response, *Nature,* **210**: 1383-1384 (1966).

41. J. C. Kennedy, J. E. Till, L. Siminovitch, and E. A. McCulloch, The Proliferative Capacity of Antigen-Sensitive Precursors of Hemolytic Plaque-Forming Cells, *J. Immunol.*, **96**: 973-980 (1966).

42. M. J. Bosma, E. H. Perkins, and T. Makinodan, Further Characterization of the Lymphoid Cell Transfer System for the Study of Antigen Sensitive Progenitor Cells, *J. Immunol.*, **101**: 963-972 (1968).

43. D. L. Groves, W. E. Lever, and T. Makinodan, Stochastic Model for the Production of Antibody-Forming Cells, *Nature,* **222**: 95-97 (1969).

44. D. L. Groves, W. E. Lever, and T. Makinodan, A Model for the Interaction of Cell Types in the Generation of Hemolytic Plaque Forming Cells, *J. Immunol.*, **104**: 148-165 (1970).

45. M. G. Hanna, Jr., and L. C. Peters, Requirement for Continuous Antigenic Stimulation in the Development and Differentiation of Antibody-Forming Cells: Effect of Antigen Dose, *Immunology*, **20**: 707-718 (1971).

46. W. G. Grantham, The Secondary Response to High and Low Dose Priming in Mice, *J. Immunol.*, **108**: 562-565 (1972).

47. I. Jokay and E. Karczag, Development of Immunological Memory in Mice to Phosphorylase Antigen. I. The Effect of Dose and Interval of Antigenic Stimuli, *Acta Microbiol. Acad. Sci. Hung.*, **15**: 295-306 (1968).

48. J. Radovich, H. Hemingsen, and D. W. Talmage, The Immunologic Memory of LAF$_1$ Mice Following a Single Injection of Sheep Red Cells, *J. Immunol.*, **102**: 288-291 (1969).

49. G. L. Ada, Antigen Binding Cells in Tolerance and Immunity, *Transplant. Rev.*, **5**: 105-129 (1970).

50. A. C. Aisenberg, Studies on Cyclophosphamide-Induced Tolerance to Sheep Erythrocytes, *J. Exp. Med.*, **125**: 833-845 (1967).

51. T. Makinodan and W. J. Peterson, Secondary Antibody-Forming Potential of Mice in Relation to Age—Its Significance in Senescence, *Develop. Biol.*, **14**: 96-111 (1966).

52. J. V. Jones, The Production of Antibodies, in *Basic Immunology*, E R. Gold and D. B. Peacock (Eds.), pp. 125-165, John Wright & Sons Ltd., Bristol, England, 1970.

53. M. C. Raff, Role of Thymus-Derived Lymphocytes in the Secondary Humoral Immune Response in Mice, *Nature,* **226**: 1257-1258 (1970).

54. D. E. Mosier and L. W. Coppleson, A Three-Cell Interaction Required for the Induction of Primary Immune Response In Vitro, *Proc. Nat. Acad. Sci. U.S.A.*, **61**: 542-547 (1968).

55. D. C. Vann and P. A. Campbell, Plaque-Forming Cells of Two Different Origins in Single Hemolytic Foci, *J. Immunol.*, **105**: 1584-1586 (1970).

56. P. A. Campbell, T. Cells: The Limiting Cells in the Initiation of Immune Responses in Normal Mouse Spleens, *Cell. Immunol.*, **5**: 338-340 (1972).

57. G. M. Shearer, G. Cudkowicz, and R. L. Priore, Cellular Differentiation of the Immune System of Mice. IV. Lack of Class Differentiation in Thymic Antigen-Reactive Cells, *J. Exp. Med.*, **130**: 467-480 (1969).

58. J. S. Hege and L. J. Cole, Antibody Plaque-Forming Cells: Kinetics of Primary and Secondary Responses, *J. Immunol.*, **96**: 559-568 (1966).

# SUBPOPULATIONS OF T-LYMPHOCYTES IN LEUKEMIC AKR MICE

ANNA D. BARKER* and SAMUEL D. WAKSAL†

*Biomedical Sciences Section, Battelle Columbus Laboratories, Columbus, Ohio, and
†Department of Anatomy, College of Medicine, The Ohio State University, Columbus, Ohio

## ABSTRACT

AKR mice 6 to 8 weeks old were inoculated intraperitoneally with lymphoid cells derived from the thymuses, spleens, and lymph nodes of overtly leukemic AKR mice. The animals were monitored daily for death and signs of disease, and sequential changes in lymphoid organs were determined. No significant differences in mean survival times were noted in mice receiving spleen or thymus cells, but mean survival was markedly reduced in animals given lymph-node cells. Splenomegaly was manifested first in all groups of mice, followed by thymic enlargement in mice administered thymus cells and thymic atrophy in animals inoculated with spleen cells. No apparent changes were noted in the thymuses of mice receiving lymph-node cells. These data suggest that subpopulations of thymus-derived lymphocytes with distinct migration patterns exist in leukemic AKR mice.

Normal lymphocytes are classified as thymus derived (T cells) or bone-marrow derived (B cells) on the basis of differences in surface markers and function.[1-3] B cells have membrane-bound immunoglobulins and function as the precursors of antibody producing cells.[4,5]

T cells apparently exist in various stages of differentiation.[6] Less differentiated T cells (T1) predominate in the cortical regions of the thymus and in the T-dependent areas of the spleen. T1 cells undergo membrane modification and acquire new functional properties during differentiation.[6,7] More highly differentiated T cells (T2) are located in the medullary region of the thymus and in the deep cortical areas of lymph nodes.[7] T cells mediate the various cellular immune responses and are apparently required for B cells to respond to certain antigens.[2,4]

Recent studies have attempted to classify experimental and clinical neoplastic disorders of the immune system according to the lymphoid cell of origin.[8,9] One of the most promising experimental tumor models, spontaneous viral-induced leukemia in AKR mice,[10] has been classified as a thymus-derived (T-cell) disease.[8] Leukemic AKR mice have been reported to exhibit near normal humoral and cellular responses, suggesting that a functionally hetero-geneous population of T cells exists in these animals.[11-14]

The role of T-cell differentiation and/or the presence of subpopulations of T cells in leukemogenesis has not been established. This paper summarizes the effects of T cells (derived from different lymphoid tissues of leukemic AKR mice) injected intraperitoneally on the nature and course of the ensuing disease in recipient syngeneic mice.

## MATERIALS AND METHODS

Retired AKR breeders (6 to 8 months old) and 6- to 8-week-old female AKR mice obtained commercially were housed in plastic cages and allowed com-mercial food and water ad libitum.

Older AKR mice were monitored regularly for overt lymphoma by splenic palpation and peripheral blood studies. A large group of animals with palpable spleens and total white-cell counts in excess of $20,000/mm^3$ were sacrificed by cervical dislocation, and their lymphoid organs were removed, weighed, and placed in cold Hank's balanced salt solution (HBSS).

Thymuses (250 to 500 mg), spleens (400 to 700 mg), and lymph nodes (50 to 75 mg) were separately pooled, and single-cell suspensions were prepared in Eagle's minimum essential medium (E-MEM) supplemented with 10% fetal calf serum. The cells were washed twice in HBSS, and erythrocytes were removed by hypotonic lysis in cold 0.35% saline. The number of viable mononuclear cells in each of the suspensions was determined by trypan blue exclusion, the cell concentration was adjusted to $10^7$ viable cells per milliliter with E-MEM, and the cells were preserved in liquid nitrogen.

Before use cells were removed from liquid nitrogen and washed twice in HBSS; viability was again determined by trypan blue exclusion. Then AKR mice (6 to 8 weeks old) were injected intraperitoneally with $10^5$ viable thymus, spleen, or lymph-node cells from the leukemic mice and examined daily for signs of leukemia. No significant variations from the data reported here were observed when fresh cell suspensions were used.

The studies were repeated to determine the sequential changes occurring in the lymphoid tissues of recipient mice. Mice (5 mice per sample) from each of the groups were sacrificed at 3-day intervals, and their lymphoid organs were removed and weighed.

## RESULTS

The effects of lymphoid cells from thymuses, spleens, and the lymph nodes of leukemic AKR mice on the survival of recipient syngeneic animals are shown in Fig. 1. Mice given thymus cells began to die 22 days after implant, with approximately 70% of the animals dying between 22 and 28 days. The mean survival of AKR mice receiving thymus cells was 26.7 ± 1.2 days. Mice receiving spleen cells died at a more rapid rate than those given thymus cells, a 50% survival being noted 20 days after implant. The pattern of mortality in this group was similar to that observed in animals receiving thymus cells, the mean survival time being 24.7 ± 2.1 days. The disease course in AKR mice administered lymph-node cells from leukemic animals was more rapid than the courses noted in the other two groups, 100% mortality being observed at 24 days. The mean survival time was 19.0 ± 0.7 days.

Gross pathologic examination of animals receiving the three types of lymphoid cells from leukemic animals revealed differences in both the type of lymphoid tissue affected and the degree of involvement. Mice given thymus cells exhibited at death marked thymoma, moderate splenomegaly, and lymphadenopathy (multiple lymphadenocarcinomas). In animals administered splenic lymphoid cells, complete thymic atrophy, splenomegaly, and lymphadenopathy were observed at death. Splenomegaly, lymphadenopathy, and hepatomegaly were noted in mice receiving lymph-node cells, but neither thymic enlargement nor atrophy was seen in this group of mice.

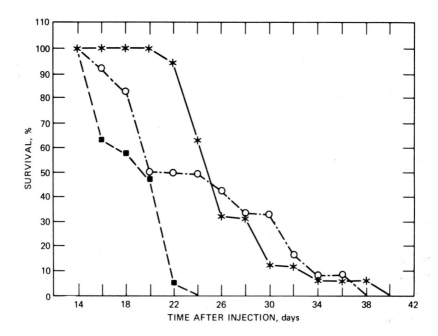

Fig. 1 Survival rate (mean) of preleukemic AKR mice implanted with 10⁵ thymus (*), spleen (○), or lymph-node (■) cells from leukemic AKR mice.

Figure 2 illustrates the sequential changes in thymus involvement (as measured by thymus weight) observed in young recipient AKR mice. In animals receiving leukemic thymus cells, mean thymus weight increased from $71.7 \pm 11.7$ mg at 3 days postimplant to $350.0 \pm 28.9$ mg at 24 days, the greatest increase occurring between 18 and 24 days. The thymus weight of mice administered splenic lymphoid cells was near normal through 18 days post-inoculation. Complete thymic atrophy was observed in these animals at the 21- and 24-day sampling intervals. The thymus weight in animals given lymph-node cells was normal at all test intervals.

Splenomegaly was noted in all three groups of mice but was most evident in mice receiving the lymph-node cells (Fig. 3). Splenomegaly was seen in these mice at the earliest sampling time (3 days postinoculation) but was delayed in mice given thymus or spleen cells, occurring at the 15- and 12-day test intervals, respectively. In mice given thymus or spleen cells, however, splenomegaly is of greater magnitude than it is in mice given lymph-node cells.

As shown in Fig. 4, a similar pattern of lymph-node enlargement was seen in animals administered the three populations of lymphoid cells. Lymph-node involvement characterized by multiple lymphadenosarcomas (inguinal, cervical, and mesenteric) was observed approximately 9 days postinoculation in animals given thymus or spleen cells and 6 days after injection of lymph-node cells.

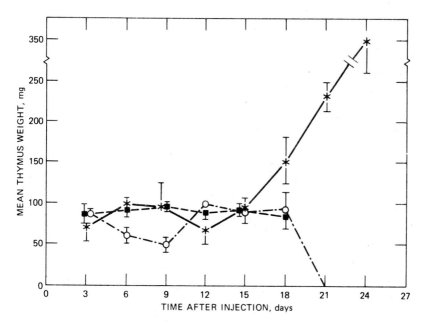

**Fig. 2** Changes in the thymus weight (mean) of preleukemic AKR mice receiving $10^5$ thymus (\*), spleen (○), or lymph-node (■) cells from leukemic donors.

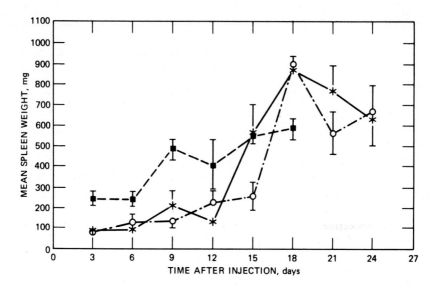

Fig. 3 Incidence of splenomegaly (mean) in preleukemic AKR mice administered $10^5$ thymus (*), spleen (○), or lymph-node (■) cells from leukemic AKR mice.

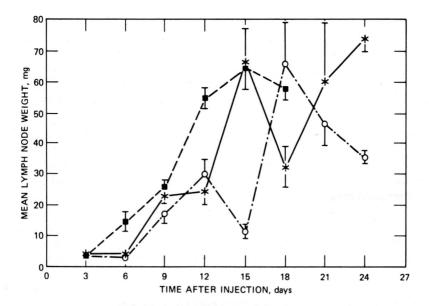

Fig. 4 Changes in mean lymph-node weights (cervical, inguinal, and mesenteric) of 6- to 8-week-old AKR mice administered thymus (*), spleen (○), or lymph-node (■) cells from leukemic AKR mice.

## DISCUSSION

T cells have been divided into subpopulations (primarily T1 and T2) on the basis of the distribution of the surface differentiation antigen theta $(\theta)$,[3,15] recirculation,[7] location in lymphoid tissues,[7,16] and functional differences.[7,16,17] T1 cells are a nonrecirculating population of cells located primarily in the thymic cortex and the periarteriolar areas of spleen, whereas more-differentiated T2 cells are a rapidly recirculating population found in the medullary regions of the thymus and the deep cortical areas of lymph nodes. T1 cells contain greater amounts of $\theta$ antigen on their surfaces than do T2 cells.[7,16]

The functional heterogeneity of T cells has been demonstrated in studies of graft vs. host (GvH) activity and differences in mitogen reactivity in mice.[7,16,17] T1 and T2 cells interact in the GvH reaction as precursors and amplifiers, respectively. Adult thymectomy results in depletion of ·the T-dependent areas of the spleen and loss of GvH activity. These findings suggest that T1 cells are under immediate thymic control.

In our study transplantation of cells from the thymuses, spleens, and lymph nodes of leukemic AKR mice into preleukemic animals produced three different disease states. The distinct differences in disease pathologies and survival noted in recipient mice suggest that subpopulations of leukemic T cells exist in these different lymphoid tissues, possibly in different stages of differentiation.

Although mice administered thymus or spleen cells from leukemic animals exhibited differences in lymphoid organ involvement, the mean survival of these two groups did not differ significantly. This could reflect the fact that the two groups received similar numbers of more-differentiated T cells or more rapid proliferation by the presumably less-differentiated thymus cells. The former explanation seems feasible because T cells represent only 35 to 40% of the lymphoid cells in the spleen, the remainder being primarily B cells. The possible effects of transplanting B cells from leukemic animals into young AKR mice are not presently known but are expected to be minimal in this T-cell disorder. Experiments are in progress to determine if the pathology observed in our study varies when pure populations of T or B cells are employed. The fulminating disease and reduced survival observed in animals receiving lymph-node cells may be due to the recirculation properties of what appear to be more highly differentiated cells.

The data reported here are in agreement with the simultaneous findings of Goldstein, Zatz, and White[18] and Zatz[19] that there are two distinct types of spontaneous leukemia in AKR mice. Mice with these two types of leukemia reportedly differ in their response to phytohemagglutin and their susceptibility to anti-$\theta$ serum, but lymphocytes from these mice exhibit similar migration patterns. Our data indicate that these distinct diseases could result from a predominance of T cells in a particular stage of differentiation.

The control mechanisms of normal T-cell differentiation are not presently understood, but it seems likely that hormonal like thymic factors may be involved. It has been postulated that hormones have an effect on receptor genes in differentiating precursor mammalian cells which results in proliferation of a new cell clone.[20]

In nonleukemic mouse strains differentiation of T cells is induced when thymic factors (thymosin) influence the pluripotential hemopoietic stem cell at certain points in the cell cycle.[21] Proliferation of clones of T cells then occurs, giving rise to a progeny of antigen reactive cells. These cells may then leave the cell cycle and enter a phase of differentiation which is characterized by changes in surface-membrane properties and function. Regulatory feedback mechanisms (possibly arising from more-differentiated peripheral cells) may control the proliferation rate of T cells in the thymus.

As discussed earlier, the diseases produced in the system described in this study may be a result of injecting cells in various stages of the cell cycle, but the breakdown of normal homeostatic feedback mechanisms involved in T-cell differentiation should also be considered. The thymic atrophy observed in mice administered spleen cells from leukemic mice could result from an overloading of the T-dependent areas of the spleen with neoplastic cells which causes increased proliferation and seeding of normal thymocytes. Thymomas may occur in mice receiving thymus cells from leukemic animals because a population of neoplastic T cells with the capacity for rapid proliferation (presumably less differentiated cells) "home" back to the thymus.

Studies to determine the kinetics of proliferation and migration patterns of transplanted T cells from the different lymphoid compartments of leukemic AKR mice are currently in progress. Additionally, the T-cell subpopulations in recipient animals are being characterized as to mitogen reactivity and sensitivity to chemotherapeutic agents.

## ACKNOWLEDGMENTS

The technical assistance of Joyce Berlo is gratefully acknowledged.

The research for this paper was supported in part by grant 1-SO1-RR05723-01 from the National Institutes of Health.

## REFERENCES

1. R. A. Good, Disorders of the Immune System, in *Immunobiology*, R. A. Good and D. W. Fisher (Eds.), Sinauer Associates, Inc., Stamford, 1971.
2. H. N. Claman and E. A. Chaperon, Immunologic Complementation Between Thymus and Marrow Cells—A Model for the Two-Cell Theory of Immunocompetence, *Transplant. Rev.*, 1: 92-113 (1969).
3. T. Aoki, U. Hammerling, E. de Harven, E. A. Boyse, and L. J. Old, Antigenic Structure of Cell Surfaces; An Immunoferritin Study of the Occurrence and Topography of H-2, $\theta$, and T2 Alloantigens on Mouse Cells, *J. Exp. Med.*, 130: 979-990 (1969).
4. J. F. A. P. Miller and G. F. Mitchell, Thymus and Antigen Reactive Cells, *Transplant. Rev.*, 1: 3-42 (1969).

5. A. J. S. Davis, The Thymus and the Cellular Basis of Immunity, *Transplant. Rev.*, **1**: 43-91 (1969).

6. M. C. Raff and H. Cantor, Subpopulations of Thymus Cells and Thymus-Derived Lymphocytes, in *Progress in Immunology*, D. B. Amos (Ed.), Academic Press, Inc., New York, 1971.

7. H. Cantor and R. Asofsky, Synergy Among Lymphoid Cells Mediating the Graft vs. Host Response. III. Evidence for Interaction Between Two Types of Thymus Derived Cells, *J. Exp. Med.*, **135**: 764-779 (1972).

8. E. M. Shevach, J. D. Stobo, and I. Green, Immunoglobulin and $\theta$-Bearing Murine Leukemias and Lymphomas, *J. Immunol.*, **108**: 1146-1151 (1972).

9. J. D. Wilson and G. J. V. Nossal, Identification of Human T and B Lymphocytes in Normal Peripheral Blood and Chronic Lymphocytic Leukemia, *Lancet*, **2**: 788-793 (1971).

10. L. Gross, Biological and Pathogenic Properties of a Mouse Leukemia Virus, *Acta Haematol.*, **23**: 259-275 (1960).

11. D. Metcalf and R. Moulds, Immune Responses in Preleukemic and Leukemic AKR Mice, *Int. J. Cancer*, **2**: 53-58 (1967).

12. M. Frey-Wettstein and E. F. Hayes, Immune Response in Preleukemic Mice, *Infec. Immunity*, **2**: 398-403 (1970).

13. A. D. Barker, M. S. Rheins, and R. L. St. Pierre, The Effect of Rabbit Antimouse Brain-Associated $\theta$ Serum on the Immunologic Responsiveness of AKR Mice, *Cell. Immunol.*, **7**: 85-91 (1973).

14. B. J. Hargis and M. Saul, The Immunocapacity of the AKR Mouse, *Cancer Res.*, **32**: 291-295 (1972).

15. M. C. Raff and H. H. Wortis, Thymus Dependence of $\theta$-Bearing Cells in the Peripheral Lymphoid Tissues of Mice, *Immunology*, **18**: 931-942 (1970).

16. R. Asofsky, H. Cantor, and R. E. Tigelaar, Cell Interactions in the Graft vs. Host Response, in *Progress in Immunology*, D. B. Amos (Ed.), Academic Press, Inc., New York, 1971.

17. J. D. Stobo and W. E. Paul, Functional Heterogeneity of Murine Lymphoid Cells. III. Differential Responsiveness of T-Cells to Phytohemagglutinin and Concanavalin A as a Probe for T-Cell Subsets, *J. Immunol.*, **110**: 362-375 (1973).

18. A. L. Goldstein, M. M. Zatz, and A. White, Effect of Leukemogenesis on Lymphocyte Recirculation, Blastogenesis, and Expression of Theta($\theta$) Antigen in AKR/J Mice, *J. Reticuloendothel. Soc.*, **13**: 369 (1973).

19. M. M. Zatz, Alterations in Lymphocyte Populations in Murine AKR/J Leukemia, *Fed. Proc.*, **3**: 4473 (1973).

20. R. S. Britten and E. H. Davidson, Gene Regulation for Higher Cells: A Theory, *Science*, **165**: 349-357 (1969).

21. A. White and A. L. Goldstein, The Role of the Thymus Gland in the Hormonal Regulation of Host Resistance, in *Control Processes in Multicellular Organisms*, G. E. W. Wolstenholme and J. Knight (Eds.), J. and A. Churchill, Ltd., London, 1970.

# TRANSFORMATION RESPONSE AND T-CELL CONTENT OF THORACIC AND BLOOD LYMPHOCYTES

DAVID L. BENNINGHOFF,* ROLAND E. GIRARDET,† and DONALD D. PORTEOUS‡
*Huntington Hospital, Huntington, New York, †Department of Surgery, University
of Louisville, Louisville, Kentucky, and ‡Radiobiology Division, State
University of New York, Downstate Medical Center, Brooklyn, New York

## ABSTRACT

Lymphocytes from nine cancer patients were obtained from the thoracic duct (TD) by cannulation and from the peripheral blood. Transformation by mitogen and T-cell content of the lymphocyte populations from these two sources were measured.

Thoracic-duct lymphocytes showed good responses to mitogens, whereas blood lymphocytes showed little response when compared to unstimulated controls. A maximal transformation response was obtained by mixing TD and blood lymphocytes in a ratio of 3 to 1. There were marked differences in rosette-forming cells, with a median value of 65% T cells for TD lymphocytes, compared to a 4% median value for the blood lymphocytes. The T-cell deficiency of the blood accounted for the absence of response to mitogens. The T-cell deficiency of the blood is suggested as the result of the cancer and not its cause.

The impact of the discovery of the transformation response of blood lymphocytes to phytohemagglutinin (PHA) by Nowell, Hungerford, and Brooks[1] has been aptly described by Yoffey and Courtice:[2] "It was not only the lymphocyte which had become transformed, but also to a remarkable extent the climate of opinion surrounding it."

Soon thereafter Billingham and Brent[3] found that a cell circulating in the peripheral blood of adult mice was capable of provoking a graft vs. host reaction in allogeneic newborn mice, and Gowans[4] identified this cell to be the small lymphocyte. Radionuclide techniques[5,6] were used to demonstrate that there were two major groups of small lymphocytes with respect to life-span, that in rats 90% of thoracic-duct (TD) lymphocytes were long-lived and recirculated through the blood, lymph nodes, spleen, and Peyer's patches, and that bone marrow contained 100% cells of short circulating life-span. Later studies[7] revealed that long-lived cells were derived from the thymus (T cells) and that short-lived cells were from bone marrow (B cells). T cells were shown[8] to carry immunologic memory and mediate cell—cell immune interactions, and B cells were shown to mediate humoral immune response. Moreover, the two lymphocytes, T and B cells, were found[9] in varying proportions in the lymph, blood, and lymphoid organs; they were shown[10] to collaborate and cooperate with other reticuloendothelial cells, particularly macrophages, in immune reactions.[11]

It was also found that T cells could be distinguished from B cells by the property of the former to form rosettes with sheep red blood cells (SRBC). Wybran and Fudenberg[12] and others,[13] using rosette-forming cells (RFC) with SRBC as a marker for T cells, found T cells depressed in a substantial fraction of patients with advanced cancer.

We will report on the lymphocyte kinetics in nine cancer patients studied with a TD side fistula, which allowed for repeated intermittent sampling of T-cell-rich TD lymph for comparison with simultaneous samples of venous blood lymphocytes. We compared the T-cell content and transformation response to mitogens of lymphocytes from these two sources. In addition, we studied the collaborative response to mitogen of a mixture of T-cell-rich TD lymphocytes and blood lymphocytes.

## METHODS

### Thoracic-Duct Side Fistula

The TD side fistula technique has been described previously.[14] The catheter diameter was less than that of the TD and was held in place by a purse string suture to allow TD lymph to flow by the catheter between samplings. Flow per minute was obtained from a 15-min collection. Cell concentration was measured in a hemacytometer, and the lymphocyte output was the product of (ml/min) X (cells/ml).

### Stimulation Response of Lymphocytes to Mitogens

Blood lymphocytes were separated from heparinized blood using the dextran sedimentation method described by Hersh and Irvin.[15] Thoracic-duct lymphocytes were collected in sterile heparinized tubes. The lymphocytes were washed twice in Hank's balanced salt solution (HBSS). Both samples of lymphocytes were diluted to a concentration of $2 \times 10^6$ cells/ml in Eagle's MEM.

The following cultures were prepared: (1) blood lymphocytes only, (2) TD lymphocytes only, and (3) "mixed" culture of 3 parts TD lymphocytes to 1 part blood lymphocytes. Fifteen percent autologous serum was added to each culture.

Following the method of Schwarz,[16] we used pokeweed mitogen (PWM), 0.01 ml/ml of culture as mitogen in eight patients, and we compared PWM and PHA, 0.01 ml/ml of culture, in duplicate samples from four of the eight patients.

Cultures were incubated for 72 hr at 37°C. Three hours before harvest $^3$H—TdR (10 Ci/mmole) was added to the appropriate cultures (10 $\mu$Ci/ml).

At harvest each culture was washed twice in HBSS. The pellet was resuspended in HBSS, and aliquots were taken for smears and liquid scintillation counting. Smears were stained with MacNeal's tetrachrome or Jenner—Giemsa. Liquid scintillation counting was performed in a counter after the cell suspension was dissolved in reagent and transferred to counting vials containing a mixture of toluene and liquifluor.

Transformation of lymphocytes was assayed by the appearance of the blast cells on stained smears and $^3$H—TdR uptake as cpm/10$^6$ lymphocytes.

## T-Cell Test

The T-cell test was that described by Stjernswärd et al.[17] Sheep red blood cells were stored at 4°C in Alsever's solution (1/1) and used within 1 week of bleeding. The SRBC were washed immediately before use and prepared as a 1% suspension in HBSS. The lymphocytes, 10$^6$ lymphocytes in 0.25 ml of HBSS, were mixed with 0.25 ml of SRBC and incubated at 37°C for 15 min. The mixed cell suspension was centrifuged at 200 G for 5 min, and the tube was incubated in chopped ice overnight. The supernatant was drawn off, and the top layer of the pellet was resuspended by tapping. A drop of cells was transferred to a glass slide and overlaid with a cover slip, which was sealed with nail polish. Under a light microscope 200 lymphocytes were counted, and a positive rosette-forming cell (RFC) was scored when more than 3 SRBC were attached to a lymphocyte. The T-cell test was performed in six cancer patients and two normal controls.

## Patients

Details regarding the patients and the studies are given in Table 1.

## Results

The TD output varied from 0.7 to 18.6 × 10$^6$ cells/min; the lymphocyte content was always in excess of 93%. The peripheral-blood lymphocyte counts in the nine patients varied from 1000 to 3300 cells/mm$^3$.

Transformation results are presented in Fig. 1. Thoracic-duct lymphocytes showed a good incorporation of $^3$H—TdR, with a median value of about 20,000 cpm/million cells, whereas the blood-lymphocyte samples showed little increase over the control samples. Maximal stimulation was seen in the mixed cultures, where the median $^3$H—TdR incorporation approached 50,000 cpm/million cells.

Autologous serum was present in all three cultures, blood lymphocytes, TD lymphocytes, and mixed lymphocytes; thus, the depressed transformation of the blood lymphocytes was not due to a serum inhibitor.

In the duplicate samples where PWM and PHA were compared, no difference in stimulation between the two mitogens was demonstrated. This has been the

**TABLE 1**

PATIENTS AND STUDIES PERFORMED

| No. | Name | Age | Sex | Diagnosis and stage | TD* | | Lymphocyte* | |
|-----|------|-----|-----|---------------------|-----|-----|-----|-----|
| | | | | | Drainage | Output | Transform | T cell |
| 1. | G.M. | 53 | M | Lung ca., resected, nodes pos. | + | + | + | + |
| 2. | W.L. | 66 | M | Lung ca., advanced | + | − | + | + |
| 3. | W.S. | 58 | M | Lung ca., resected, localized | + | − | + | + |
| 4. | L.M. | 56 | M | Esophageal ca., advanced, nodes pos. | + | + | + | + |
| 5. | B.P. | 59 | M | Lung ca., advanced | + | + | + | + |
| 6. | V.A. | 52 | M | Lung ca., advanced | + | − | + | + |
| 7. | M.F. | 44 | F | Lymphoma, stage 3 | + | + | + | + |
| 8. | J.A. | 39 | M | Hodgkin's, stage 3 | + | + | + | − |
| 9. | J.P. | 50 | M | Seminoma testis, lung mets. | + | + | − | − |

*+, measured. −, not measured.

experience of others.[18] Assay of the smears for blastoid cells agreed with the $^3$H—TdR incorporation data.

The results of T-cell tests are given in Table 2. There was a striking difference in RFC; the percentage was high in the lymph and low in the blood.

## Discussion

Although it has been hypothesized that the immune deficiency in cancer patients is related to an inherent cellular abnormality[19] or a serum inhibitor,[20] the poor blood-lymphocyte transformation in our patients was due to a lack of T cells in peripheral blood. The TD lymphocyte population was not deficient in T cells, and cultures of cells from this source transformed well; moreover, addition of T-cell-rich TD lymphocytes to the blood-lymphocyte cultures resulted in a synergistic response to the mitogens. This collaborative effect in the mixed cultures is similar to that seen in rat experiments[21] where addition of recirculating PHA-responsive TD lymphocytes to cultures of nonrecirculating PHA-unresponsive blood lymphocytes afforded maximal response to PHA. Since the T cells in the blood are part of the pool of long-lived recirculating lymphocytes, the deficiency of these cells in the blood of our patients suggests a depletion of the pool or a sequestration of these cells.

A number of investigators, Good[22] in particular, have emphasized the association of immunodeficiency and neoplasia, suggesting the former to have preceded the latter and citing as evidence immunodeficiency diseases complicated by neoplasms and the increased frequency of malignant disease in

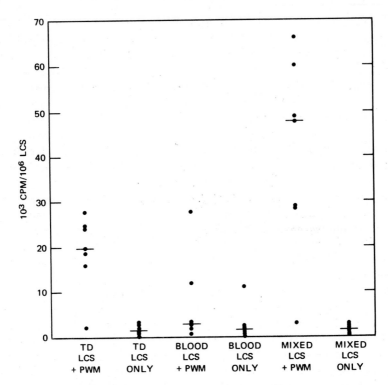

Fig. 1 Incorporation of $^3$H—TdR by lymphocytes (LCS). Horizontal bars indicate median values. [From D. L. Benninghoff, R. E. Girardet, and D. D. Porteous, Thoracic-Duct and Blood Lymphocytes in Cancer, *Lancet*, 2: 264 (1973).]

**TABLE 2**

LYMPHOCYTES FORMING ROSETTES WITH SRBC

| Patient | TD, % | Blood,* % |
|---------|-------|-----------|
| G.M. | 70 | 4 |
| W.L. | 85 | 3 |
| W.S. | 10 | 4 |
| L.M. | 65 | 7 |
| B.P. | 64 | 2 |
| V.A. | 52 | 7 |

*Values in two normal subjects were 20% and 60%.

transplant patients undergoing immunosuppressive therapy. However, there is support for a different interpretation for the decreased lymphocyte transformation and T-cell deficiency we observed in our cancer patients: that the cancer is the cause of lymphocyte dysfunction. Brown et al.[23] noted that patients with early stages of Hodgkin's disease (HD) tested immunologically normal but that immunity had failed in those with untreated late stages. Their findings suggested that HD was the cause of the immunodeficiency rather than the reverse.

More pertinent is the report of Wybran, Chantler, and Fudenberg[24] of patients with chronic lymphocytic leukemia (CLL) whose blood lymphocytes responded poorly to mitogen. When RFC were separated from the blood and tested, they responded well to mitogens, indicating that the originally observed lack of response to mitogens was the result of a relative deficiency of T cells in the blood. Piessens et al.[25] have classified patients with CLL and lymphosarcoma into two groups: a T-cell group with good mitogen response and a B-cell group with poor mitogen response. These patients would provide examples of how the neoplasm may affect the T to B cell ratio of the blood and, therefore, their apparent immune states.

The decreased response to mitogens of the blood lymphocytes in our patients was an effect of the tumor, which in some way caused a T-cell deficiency in the blood. The T cells functioned perfectly well as shown by the excellent response of TD lymphocytes to both PWM and PHA. Furthermore, the mixed cultures of T and B cells showed a synergistic boost of response, suggesting a positive collaboration of the lymphocytes. Unfortunately, since eight of nine of our patients had progressive cancer, mainly lung cancer, we could not evaluate the effect of successful treatment on the observed T-cell deficiency. However, Jackson, Garrett, and Craig[19] noted that in HD patients blood-lymphocyte transformation improved during periods of clinical remission arising from therapy. Hersh and Irvin[15] made the same observation in HD patients in a study of immune responses before and after remission induced by radiotherapy. Wybran and Fudenberg[12] found in 30 cancer patients in complete remission only one patient who had an abnormally low value of T cells in the blood. We have studied 10 breast-cancer patients in remission, and 9 of the 10 had normal response to mitogen in the peripheral blood.[26]

A distinct phenomenon that may result in T-cell depression of the blood is the response of the host lymphocytes to the antigenicity of tumor cells. In vitro lymphocyte blastogenesis induced by autochthonous tumor cells has been noted by several groups,[27-29] and increased in vitro DNA synthesis by the blood lymphocytes of cancer patients has been noted.[30] Finally, in vitro inhibition of human tumor growth by autochthonous lymphocytes has been shown.[31,32] It has been demonstrated[33] that the T cells are the lymphocytes that are cytotoxic to the tumor cells.

We have found T-cell diversion to the site of tumor activity in one breast-cancer patient with a malignant pleural effusion; the effusion lymphocytes were composed of 60% T-cell lymphocytes, whereas the blood contained only 1% T cells.[34] Cardozo and Harting[35] compared the transformation response of lymphocytes from malignant effusions and blood in 19 patients and found the effusion lymphocytes considerably more responsive. We have noted elsewhere that immune deficiency in HD is related to impaired recirculation of lymphocytes rather than to an inherent cellular defect of the lymphocytes.[36] A similar situation has been noted[37] for lepromatous leprosy in which T-cell deficiency was demonstrated and attributed to a "perturbation of lymphocyte recirculation or aberrant sequestration (or both) of these cells."

Wybran and Fudenberg[12] reported a decrease in blood T cells in a patient with osteosarcoma which preceded by several weeks the appearance of a lung metastasis, and the same workers found a transient decrease in T cells during and immediately after viral infections. T cells mediate immune responses to viruses as well as to cell-associated antigens. Finally, Borella and Green[38] observed sequestration of T cells in the bone marrow of patients with acute lymphocytic leukemia while they were undergoing intensive chemotherapy; during chemotherapy bone-marrow lymphocytes transformed well, the blood poorly; several weeks after clinical remission and cessation of chemotherapy, peripheral-blood lymphocyte transformation was on par with that of the bone marrow.

# REFERENCES

1. P. C. Nowell, D. A. Hungerford, and C. D. Brooks, Chromosomal Characteristics of Normal and Leukemic Human Leukocytes After Short-Term Tissue Culture, *Proc. Amer. Ass. Cancer Res.*, **2**: 331-332 (1958).
2. J. M. Yoffey and F. C. Courtice, *Lymphatics, Lymph, and the Lymphomyeloid Complex*, p. 6, Academic Press, Inc., New York, 1970.
3. R. E. Billingham and L. Brent, Quantitative Studies on Tissue Transplantation Immunity. IV. Induction of Tolerance in Newborn Mice and Studies on the Phenomenon of Runt Disease, *Phil. Trans. Roy. Soc. London*, **242**: 439-477 (1959).
4. J. L. Gowans, The Fate of Parental Strain Small Lymphocytes in $F_1$ Hybrid Rats, *Ann. N. Y. Acad. Sci.*, **99**: 432-455 (1962).
5. N. B. Everett, R. W. Caffrey, and W. O. Rieke, Recirculation of Lymphocytes, *Ann. N. Y. Acad. Sci.*, **113**: 887-897 (1964).
6. J. L. Gowans and E. J. Knight, The Route of Recirculation of Lymphocytes in the Rat, *Proc. Roy. Soc. (London), Ser. B*, **159**: 257-282 (1964).
7. J. F. A. P. Miller and D. Osoba, Current Concepts of the Immunological Function of the Thymus, *Physiol. Rev.*, **47**: 437-520 (1967).
8. J. F. A. P. Miller and G. F. Mitchell, Cell to Cell Interaction in the Immune Response, *J. Exp. Med.*, **128**: 801-820 (1968).
9. N. B. Everett and R. W. Tyler, Lymphopoiesis in the Thymus and Other Tissues: Functional Implications, in *International Review of Cytology*, G. H. Bourne and J. F. Danielli (Eds.), Vol. 22, pp. 205-237, Academic Press, Inc., New York, 1967.
10. H. N. Claman, E. A. Chaperon, and R. F. Triplett, Thymus—Marrow Cell Combinations—Synergism in Antibody Production, *Proc. Soc. Exp. Biol. Med.*, **122**: 1167-1171 (1966).
11. R. Evans and P. Alexander, Cooperation of Immune Lymphoid Cells with Macrophages in Tumour Immunity, *Nature*, **228**: 620-622 (1970).

12. J. Wybran and H. H. Fudenberg, Thymus-Derived Rosette-Forming Cells in Various Human Disease States: Cancer, Lymphoma, Bacterial and Viral Infections, and Other Diseases, *J. Clin. Invest.*, **52**: 1026-1032 (1973).
13. A. Brugarolas, T. Han, H. Takita, and J. Minowada, Immunologic Assays in Lung Cancer; Skin Tests, Lymphocyte Blastogenesis, Rosette-Forming Cell Count, *N. Y. State J. Med.*, **73**: 747-750 (1973).
14. R. E. Girardet and D. L. Benninghoff, Thoracic Duct Lymph and Lymphocyte Studies in Man Using a Thoracic Duct Side-Fistula, *Cancer*, **29**: 666-669 (1972).
15. E. M. Hersh and W. S. Irvin, Blastogenic Responses of Lymphocytes from Patients with Treated and Untreated Lymphomas, *Lymphology*, **2**: 150-160 (1969).
16. M. R. Schwarz, Transformation of Rat Small Lymphocytes with Pokeweed Mitogen (PWM), *Anat. Rec.*, **160**: 47-58 (1968).
17. J. Stjernswärd, M. Jondal, S. Vánky, H. Wigzell, and R. Sealy, Lymphopenia and Change in Distribution of Human B and T Lymphocytes in Peripheral Blood Induced by Irradiation for Mammary Carcinoma, *Lancet*, **1**: 1352-1356 (1972).
18. J. L. Smith and C. R. Barker, T and B Cell Separation by Sheep-Red-Cell Rosetting, *Lancet*, **1**: 558-559 (1973).
19. S. M. Jackson, J. V. Garrett, and A. W. Craig, Lymphocyte Transformation Changes During the Clinical Course of Hodgkin's Disease, *Cancer*, **25**: 843-850 (1970).
20. M. G. Whittaker, K. Ress, and C. G. Clark, Reduced Lymphocyte Transformation in Breast Cancer, *Lancet*, **1**: 892-893 (1971).
21. J. G. Iverson, Phytohemagglutinin Response of Recirculating and Nonrecirculating Rat Lymphocytes, *Exp. Cell Res.*, **56**: 219-223 (1969).
22. R. A. Good, Relations Between Immunity and Malignancy, *Proc. Nat. Acad. Sci. U.S.A.*, **69**: 1026-1032 (1972).
23. R. S. Brown, H. A. Haynes, H. T. Foley, H. A. Godwin, C. W. Berard, and P. P. Carbone, Hodgkin's Disease: Immunologic, Clinical, and Histologic Features of 50 Untreated Patients, *Ann. Intern. Med.*, **67**: 291-302 (1967).
24. J. Wybran, S. Chantler, and H. H. Fudenberg, Isolation of Normal T Cells in Chronic Lymphatic Leukemia, *Lancet*, **1**: 126-129 (1973).
25. W. F. Piessens, P. H. Schur, W. C. Moloney, and W. H. Churchill, Lymphocyte Surface Immunoglobulins, Distribution and Frequency in Lymphoproliferative Diseases, *New Engl. J. Med.*, **288**: 176-180 (1973).
26. D. D. Porteous, State University of New York, and D. L. Benninghoff, Huntington Hospital, unpublished material.
27. A. Vánky, J. Stjernswärd, G. Klein, and U. Nilsonne, Serum-Mediated Inhibition of Lymphocyte Stimulation by Autochthonous Human Tumors, *J. Nat. Cancer Inst.*, **47**: 95-103 (1971).
28. W. H. Fridman and F. M. Kourilsky, Stimulation of Lymphocytes by Autologous Leukemic Cells in Acute Leukemia, *Nature*, **224**: 277-279 (1969).
29. J. U. Gutterman et al., Immunoglobulin on Tumor Cells and Tumor-Induced Lymphocyte Blastogenesis in Human Acute Leukemia, *New Engl. J. Med.*, **288**: 169-173 (1973).
30. J. E. Harris and T. H. Stewart, Recovery of Mixed Lymphocyte Reactivity (MLR) Following Cancer Chemotherapy in Man, in *Proceedings of the 6th Leukocyte Culture Conference*, pp. 555-580, Academic Press, Inc., New York, 1972.
31. I. Hellström, K. E. Hellström, G. E. Pierce, and A. H. Bill, Demonstration of Cell-Bound and Humoral Immunity Against Neuroblastoma Cells, *Proc. Nat. Acad. Sci. U.S.A.*, **60**: 1231-1238 (1968).
32. J. Bubenik, P. Perlmann, K. Helmstein, and G. Morberger, Cellular and Humoral Immune Responses to Human Urinary Bladder Carcinomas, *Int. J. Cancer*, **5**: 310-319 (1970).

33. J. Wybran, I. Hellström, K. E. Hellström, and H. H. Fudenberg, Rosette-Forming Cells and Cytotoxicity for Malignant Cells, *J. Clin. Invest.*, **52**: 91a (1973).
34. D. D. Porteous and B. Kim, State University of New York, and D. L. Benninghoff, Huntington Hospital, unpublished data.
35. E. L. Cardozo and M. C. Harting, On the Function of Lymphocytes in Malignant Effusions, *Acta Cytol.*, **16**: 307-313 (1972).
36. D. L. Benninghoff and R. E. Girardet, Lymphocyte Function in Hodgkin's Disease, in *Progress in Lymphology, IV*, Proceedings of the 4th International Congress of Lymphology, George Thieme Verlag, Stuttgart, in press.
37. J. M. Dwyer, W. E. Bullock, and J. P. Fields, Disturbance of T : B Lymphocyte Ratio in Lepromatous Leprosy; Clinical and Immunologic Correlations, *New Engl. J. Med.*, **288**: 1036-1039 (1973).
38. L. Borella and A. A. Green, Sequestration of PHA-Responsive Cells (T Lymphocytes) in the Bone Marrow of Leukemic Children Undergoing Long-Term Immunosuppressive Therapy, *J. Immun.*, **109**: 927-932 (1972).

# INDEX

Prepared by E. Ray Bedford, Science and Technology Branch, Technical Information
Center, U. S. Energy Research and Development Administration, Oak Ridge, Tennessee.

## NOTICE

# PHYSICAL MECHANISMS IN RADIATION BIOLOGY

Raymond D. Cooper and Robert W. Wood, Editors

*Proceedings of a conference sponsored by the*
*Division of Biomedical and Environmental Research*
*U. S. Atomic Energy Commission*
*Held at Airlie, Virginia, Oct. 11-14, 1972*

This conference brought together radiation biologists, radiation chemists, and biophysicists to discuss the chain of events leading to the production by radiation of primary lesions in biological cells. The objectives of the meeting were to review understanding of physical mechanisms, to pinpoint deficiencies in present knowledge, and to recommend directions and areas of study for future emphasis. The representatives of the different sciences attempted to pool their knowledge of initial interactions in cells and to determine how theories and results in one discipline relate to those developed in another discipline. The first such compilation in 20 years, the book contains reports on the kinds of research being done, extensive discussions among the specialists, and summaries of what is known and of the problems that remain to be dealt with.

---

Available as CONF-721001
for $10.60 from
  National Technical Information
    Service
  U. S. Department of Commerce
  Springfield, Virginia 22161

Paperbound
6 by 9 in.
330 pages
Library of Congress
  catalog card number:
  74-600124

# Human Radiation Dose Studies: A Selected Bibliography

*A new volume in the U. S. Energy Research and Development Administration Technical Information Center Bibliography Series*

This bibliography covers technical reports and journal articles abstracted in *Nuclear Science Abstracts* from January 1962 to June 1973. It contains 1010 abstracts, arranged by *NSA* volume and abstract number, and a subject index.

Available as TID-3348 for $7.60 from

National Technical Information Service
Department of Commerce
Springfield, Virginia 22161

# NUCLEAR SCIENCE ABSTRACTS

*Nuclear Science Abstracts* provides the only comprehensive abstracting and indexing coverage of the international nuclear science literature. It is a semimonthly publication of the U. S. Energy Research and Development Administration and is published by the ERDA Technical Information Center. *Nuclear Science Abstracts* covers the nuclear-energy-related scientific and technical reports of ERDA and its contractors, other U. S. Government agencies, other governments, universities, and industrial and research organizations. In addition, books, conference proceedings, individual conference papers, patents, and journal literature on a worldwide basis are abstracted and indexed.

## SUBSCRIPTIONS AND PRICES

*Nuclear Science Abstracts* is available to the public on a subscription basis from the Superintendent of Documents, U. S. Government Printing Office, Washington, D. C. 20402. It is published in two volumes each calendar year, each volume containing 12 regular issues. The annual subscription rate for the two volumes is $121.05 for domestic subscribers and $151.35 for foreign subscribers. A single issue costs $5.05 domestic rates or $6.35 foreign rates. Domestic rates apply to the United States, Canada, Mexico, and Central and South American countries except Argentina, Brazil, Guyana, French Guiana, Surinam, and British Honduras.

## INDEXES

Indexes covering subject, author, corporate author, and report number are included in each issue. These indexes are cumulated for each volume, i.e., for 12 issues on a 6-month volume basis. They are sold on an annual subscription basis (24 issues in 2 volumes) at $44.40 for domestic subscribers and $55.50 for foreign subscribers. They are also sold separately by volume on the basis of pagination at the time of publication. The indexes provide a detailed and convenient key to the world's nuclear literature.

## EXCHANGES

*Nuclear Science Abstracts* is available on an exchange basis to universities, research institutions, industrial firms, and publishers of scientific information; inquiries regarding the exchange provision should be directed to the ERDA Technical Information Center, P. O. Box 62, Oak Ridge, Tennessee 37830.